PEARSON

D1404372

Bittinger • Penna

Arithmetic
FNMT 016

Third Custom Edition for Community College of Philadelphia

Taken from:
Basic Mathematics with Early Integers, Third Edition
by Marvin L. Bittinger and Judith A. Penna

Taken from:

Basic Mathematics with Early Integers, Third Edition
by Marvin L. Bittinger and Judith A. Penna
Copyright © 2015, 2011, 2007 Pearson Education, Inc
Upper Saddle River, New Jersey 07458

Copyright © 2014, by Pearson Learning Solutions
All rights reserved.

This copyright covers material written expressly for this volume by the editor/s as well as the compilation itself. It does not cover the individual selections herein that first appeared elsewhere. Permission to reprint these has been obtained by Pearson Learning Solutions for this edition only. Further reproduction by any means, electronic or mechanical, including photocopying and recording, or by any information storage or retrieval system, must be arranged with the individual copyright holders noted.

All trademarks, service marks, registered trademarks, and registered service marks are the property of their respective owners and are used herein for identification purposes only.

Pearson Learning Solutions, 501 Boylston Street, Suite 900, Boston, MA 02116
A Pearson Education Company
www.pearsoned.com

Printed in the United States of America

33   17

000200010271871430

ML

ISBN 10: 1-269-86758-X
ISBN 13: 978-1-269-86758-0

Contents

Index of Applications   vii
Preface   xiii

1 Whole Numbers   1

1.1 Standard Notation   2
1.2 Addition   9
1.3 Subtraction   14
1.4 Multiplication   19
1.5 Division   26

Mid-Chapter Review   35

1.6 Rounding and Estimating; Order   37
1.7 Solving Equations   48
1.8 Applications and Problem Solving   54

Translating for Success   62

1.9 Exponential Notation and Order of Operations   70

Summary and Review   78
Test   83

2 Integers   85

2.1 The Integers   86
2.2 Addition of Integers   92
2.3 Subtraction of Integers   98

Mid-Chapter Review   104

2.4 Multiplication of Integers   106
2.5 Division of Integers and Order of Operations   110

Translating for Success   114
Summary and Review   118
Test   123

3 Fraction Notation: Multiplication and Division   125

3.1 Factorizations   126
3.2 Divisibility   133
3.3 Fractions and Fraction Notation   139
3.4 Multiplication and Applications   149
3.5 Simplifying   155

Mid-Chapter Review   162

3.6 Multiplying, Simplifying, and Applications   164
3.7 Division and Applications   170

Translating for Success   174
Summary and Review   178
Test   183
Cumulative Review   185

4 Fraction Notation and Mixed Numerals 187

4.1 Least Common Multiples 188
4.2 Addition and Applications 195
4.3 Subtraction, Order, and Applications 202

Translating for Success 206

4.4 Mixed Numerals 210

Mid-Chapter Review 216

4.5 Addition and Subtraction Using Mixed Numerals; Applications 218
4.6 Multiplication and Division Using Mixed Numerals; Applications 228

Translating for Success 232

4.7 Order of Operations, Complex Fractions, and Estimation 238

Summary and Review 245
Test 251
Cumulative Review 253

5 Decimal Notation 255

5.1 Decimal Notation, Order, and Rounding 256
5.2 Addition and Subtraction 266
5.3 Multiplication 274
5.4 Division 282

Mid-Chapter Review 293

5.5 Converting from Fraction Notation to Decimal Notation 295
5.6 Estimating 304
5.7 Applications and Problem Solving 309

Translating for Success 314
Summary and Review 320
Test 325
Cumulative Review 327

7 Percent Notation 381

7.1 Percent Notation 382
7.2 Percent Notation and Fraction Notation 389
7.3 Solving Percent Problems Using Percent Equations 397
7.4 Solving Percent Problems Using Proportions 403

Mid-Chapter Review 409

7.5 Applications of Percent 411

Translating for Success 418

7.6 Sales Tax, Commission, and Discount 425
7.7 Simple Interest and Compound Interest; Credit Cards 434

Summary and Review 443
Test 449
Cumulative Review 451

Appendix, Chapter 6: Ratio and Proportion 329
Answers A-1
Guided Solutions A-21
Glossary G-1
Index I-1

Community
College
of Philadelphia

Welcome to Canvas

Community College of Philadelphia uses the Canvas online learning system. New Canvas users should create their Canvas password prior to the first day of the class. However, **you will not be able to access your courses in Canvas until the first day of the class**.

If you already have a Canvas account from a previous semester, you may continue to use your Canvas username and password.

If you are setting up your Canvas account for the first time, do the following:

1. Go to CCP's Canvas site: http://ccp.instructure.com There is also a link to Canvas on the MyCCP login page called "Canvas LMS".

If you are a new Canvas user, do not enter any information in the boxes labeled "MyCCP Username" and "Password". Click on the "New User/Don't know your password" link (This is found under the "MyCCP Username" box, pictured left).

2. On the **next screen**, enter your CCP email address and click **Request Password**.

In a few minutes, you will get an email from Canvas in your CCP email account with a link to set your password. Click on that link and type your new password in both boxes.

2. Go to CCP's Canvas site: http://ccp.instructure.com (Please bookmark this link.)

Enter your **MyCCP Username** (for example, **jsmith**) and the password you just set. Click on Log In.

NOTE: Your username is NOT your full email address! Do not use @ccp.edu in the username box!

If you have a problem with the sign in process, please contact the Office of Online Learning via email at onlinelearning@ccp.edu, or call the Help desk at 215-496-6000.

Community College of Philadelphia

FNMT 016 Students

To access your MyLabsPlus account:

1. Go to www.ccp.mylabsplus.com – You must use IE as your browser
2. In the Log In space, enter your J number – use upper case J
3. In the Password space, enter "password"
4. Click on Log In
5. At the Welcome Screen, find and click on MyProfile in the upper right

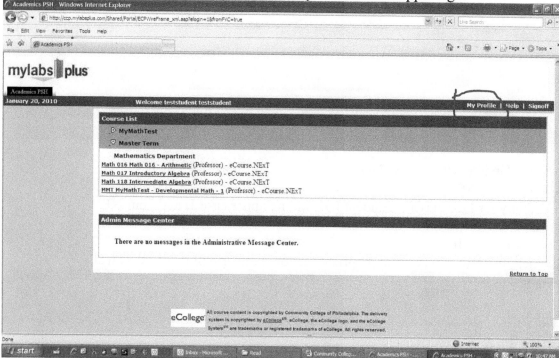

6. In the Old Password space, enter "password"
7. Create and Verify a New Password for your account

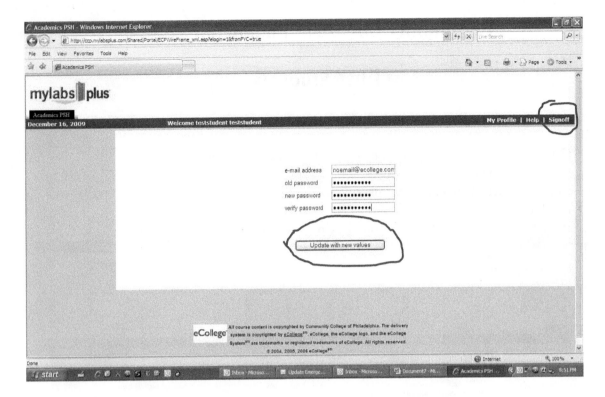

8. Click Update with new Values
9. Click Sign off
10. Enter your Log In (CCP Student ID with the upper case J) and your NEW Password
11. Click on Log In
12. Click on Math 016 (your appropriate section number will be listed as well)

13. On the left side, click on Study Plan
14. Click on the MML Study Plan link in the middle of the screen

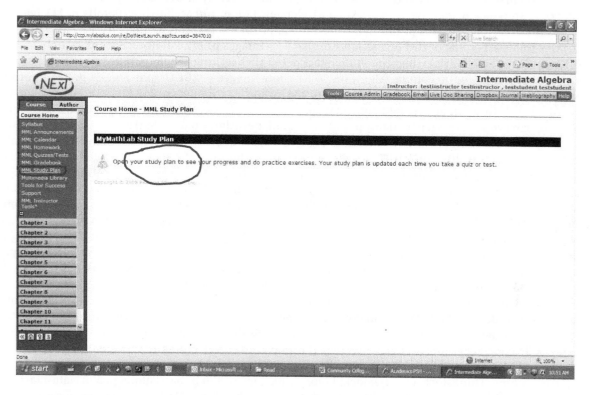

15. You will see the Licensing agreement, scroll to the bottom and click on: I Accept.
16. You will be prompted for an access code, click on Access Code and enter the access code packaged with your Textbook.
    -If you do not have an Access Code you purchase one on line, click on Buy Access Now
    -The Access code will look something like this:
    HSEMSA-QUIPU-PRAYS-ADMAN-TANIS-MOLES

Once you have entered the Access Code successfully, you will not need it again. You will have full access to all the on line materials for your course.

Once in the course materials, click on the Study Plan, Tools for Success and Multimedia Library to find tutorials, tools and practice problems that will help you understand the material covered in this class.

PHOTO CREDITS

Cover Rich Carey/Shutterstock **p. 3** Tina Manley/Alamy **p. 8** (left) Anton Balazh/Shutterstock, (right) NASA **p. 55** Courtesy of Barbara Johnson **p. 66** (left) Yevgenia Gorbulsky/Fotolia, (right) Courtesy of Geri Davis **p. 82** Sebastian Duda/Fotolia **p. 87** Ed Metz/Shutterstock **p. 90** Dave King/Dorling Kindersley, Ltd. **p. 100** Mellowbox/Fotolia **p. 111** Ivan Alvarado/ Reuters **p. 122** Brian Snyder/Reuters **p. 146** Cynoclub/Fotolia **p. 151** Petr84/Shutterstock **p. 152** Larry Roberg/Fotolia **p. 168** (left) UW Images/Fotolia, (right) Image 100/Corbis/Glow Images **p. 172** Phaitoon Sutunyawatchai/Shutterstock **p. 177** (left) Simon Greig/Fotolia, (right) Rigucci/Shutterstock **p. 182** Michael Jung/Fotolia **p. 186** Marce Clemens/Shutterstock **p. 200** (left) Christophe Fouquin/Fotolia, (right) Jim West/Glow Images **p. 201** Ursule/Fotolia **p. 221** Interfoto/Alamy **p. 222** Ruud Morijn/Fotolia **p. 230** Ruud Morijn/Fotolia **p. 234** Joshua Lott/Reuters **p. 235** Mark Duncan/AP Images **p. 236** Essam Al-Sudani/AFP/Getty Images **p. 243** Tom Sears **p. 249** Image Source/Glow Images **p. 253** I. Pilon/Shutterstock **p. 256** EPA European Pressphoto Agency/Alamy **p. 258** Daily Mail/Rex/Alamy **p. 263** (left) MSPhotographic/Fotolia, (right) Zai Aragon/Fotolia **p. 277** (left) Stockshooter/Alamy, (right) Estima/Fotolia **p. 281** (left) Michaklootwijk/Fotolia, (right) Santi Visalli/Glow Images **p. 301** (top left) Rtimages/Shutterstock, (bottom left) Scott Kane/Icon SMI, CAX/Newscom, (bottom right) ZUMA Press, Inc./Alamy **p. 310** TheFinalMiracle/Fotolia **p. 311** Iain Masterton/AGE Fotostock/SuperStock **p. 312** Comstock/Getty Images **p. 316** (left) PCN Photography/Alamy, (right) Christopher Sadowski/Splash News/Newscom **p. 322** Edward Rozzo/Corbis/Glow Images **p. 323** Jochen Tack/Glow Images **p. 332** NBAE/Getty Images **p. 335** (left) Sam72/ Shutterstock, (right) Alfred Pasieka/Science Source **p. 337** Carsten Reisinger/Fotolia **p. 338** ZUMA Press, Inc./Alamy **p. 339** Howard Shooter/Dorling Kindersley, Ltd. **p. 341** (top left) Gerard Sioen/Gamma-Rapho/Getty Images, (top right) Rudie/ Fotolia, (bottom left) Eye of Science/Science Source/Photo Researchers, Inc., (bottom right) Jose Garcia/Fotolia **p. 350** (left) RIRF Stock/Shutterstock, (right) Geri Lynn Smith/Shutterstock **p. 353** Ioannis Ioannou/Shutterstock **p. 354** M. Timothy O'Keefe/Alamy **p. 357** Antoni Murcia/Shutterstock **p. 359** (left) Pictorial Press, Ltd./Alamy, (right) Kim D. French/Fotolia **p. 360** (left) Monkey Business/Fotolia, (right) Fancy Collection/SuperStock **p. 362** (left) Stephen Meese/Fotolia, (right) mattjeppson/Fotolia **p. 363** (left) EPA European Pressphoto Agency/Alamy, (right) ZUMA Press, Inc./Alamy **p. 366** (bottom left) Courtesy of Geri Davis, (right) Courtesy of Elaine Somers **p. 369** (left and right) Courtesy of Geri Davis **p. 374** Image-broker/Alamy **p. 375** (top right) Martin Shields/Alamy, (bottom right) Mark Bonham/Shutterstock **p. 382** John Dorton/ Shutterstock **p. 383** Tina Jeans/Shutterstock **p. 386** (left) Karin Hildebrand Lau/Shutterstock, (right) Susan The/Fotolia **p. 387** (left) iStockphoto/Thinkstock, (right) iStockphoto/Thinkstock **p. 390** Bbbar/Fotolia **p. 398** Nata-Lia/Shutterstock **p. 399** (top right) Rehan Qureshi/Shutterstock, (bottom right) Studio D/Fotolia **p. 403** Gina Sanders/Fotolia **p. 413** (left to right) Uabels/Shutterstock; Winfried Wisniewski/AGE Fotostock; William Mullins/Alamy; Seitre/Nature Picture Library; Corbis/AGE Fotostock; Kevin Schafer/Alamy; Andy Rouse/Nature Picture Library **p. 415** Visions of America, LLC/Alamy **p. 416** Francis Vachon/Alamy **p. 417** David Taylor/Alamy **p. 419** Daniel Borzynski/Alamy **p. 420** (left) ZUMA Press, Inc./ Alamy, (right) Image Source Plus/Alamy **p. 421** iStockphoto/Thinkstock **p. 422** Ashley Cooper Pics/Alamy **p. 423** (left) Rob Wilson/Shutterstock, (right) Wollertz/Shutterstock **p. 428** F1online Digitale Bildagentur GmbH/Alamy **p. 429** Gmcgill/ Fotolia **p. 431** (left) Pavel L. Photo and Video/Shutterstock, (right) Brian Jackson/Fotolia **p. 432** (left) Auremar/Fotolia, (right) Christina Richards/Shutterstock **p. 437** Valua Vitaly/Shutterstock **p. 440** (left) Dmitry Vereshchagin/Fotolia, (right) Andres Rodriguez/Fotolia **p. 451** Robert F. Balazik/Shutterstock **p. 452** AP Images

Whole Numbers

1.1   Standard Notation

1.2   Addition

1.3   Subtraction

1.4   Multiplication

1.5   Division

Mid-Chapter Review

1.6   Rounding and Estimating; Order

1.7   Solving Equations

1.8   Applications and Problem Solving

Translating for Success

1.9   Exponential Notation and Order of Operations

Summary and Review

Test

STUDYING FOR SUCCESS *Getting Off to a Good Start*

- ☐ Your syllabus for this course is extremely important. Read it carefully, noting required texts and materials.
- ☐ If there is an online component for your course, register for it as soon as possible.
- ☐ At the front of the text, you will find a Student Organizer card. This pullout card will help you keep track of important dates and useful contact information.

1.1

Standard Notation

OBJECTIVES

a Give the meaning of digits in standard notation.

b Convert from standard notation to expanded notation.

c Convert between standard notation and word names.

We study mathematics in order to be able to solve problems. In this section, we study how numbers are named. We begin with the concept of place value.

a PLACE VALUE

The numbers of jobs available in 2010 for several professions are shown in the following table.

PROFESSION	NUMBER OF JOBS, 2010
Registered nurses	2,737,400
Radiologic technologists	219,900
Radiation therapists	16,900

SOURCE: U.S. Department of Labor, Bureau of Labor Statistics

A **digit** is a number 0, 1, 2, 3, 4, 5, 6, 7, 8, or 9 that names a place-value location. For large numbers, digits are separated by commas into groups of three, called **periods**. Each period has a name: *ones, thousands, millions, billions, trillions,* and so on. To understand the number of jobs for registered nurses in the table above, we can use a **place-value chart**, as shown below.

PLACE-VALUE CHART														
Periods →	Trillions			Billions			Millions			Thousands			Ones		
									2	7	3	7	4	0	0
	Hundreds	Tens	Ones	Hundreds	Tens	Ones	Hundreds	Tens	Ones	Hundreds	Tens	Ones	Hundreds	Tens	Ones

2 millions 737 thousands 400 ones

EXAMPLES   In each of the following numbers, what does the digit 8 mean?

1. 278,342   8 thousands
2. 872,342   8 hundred thousands
3. 28,343,399,223 8 billions
4. 98,413,099   8 millions
5. 6328   8 ones

Do Margin Exercises 1–6 (in the margin at right). ▶

EXAMPLE 6 *Charitable Organizations.*   Since its founding in 1881 by Clara Barton, the American Red Cross has been the nation's best-known emergency response organization. As part of a worldwide organization, the American Red Cross also aids victims of devastating natural disasters. For the fiscal year ending June 2011, the total revenue of the American Red Cross was $3,452,960,387. What digit names the number of ten millions?

Source: charitynavigator.org

Ten millions
3,452,960,387

The digit 5 is in the ten millions place, so 5 names the number of ten millions.

Do Exercise 7. ▶

b   CONVERTING FROM STANDARD NOTATION TO EXPANDED NOTATION

Heifer International is a charitable organization whose mission is to work with communities to end hunger and poverty and care for the earth by providing farm animals to impoverished families around the world. Consider the data in the following table.

GEOGRAPHICAL AREAS OF NEED	NUMBER OF FAMILIES ASSISTED DIRECTLY AND INDIRECTLY BY HEIFER INTERNATIONAL IN 2011
Africa	220,275
Americas	934,871
Asia, South Pacific	407,640
Central and Eastern Europe	344,945

SOURCE: *Heifer International 2011 Annual Report*

What does the digit 2 mean in each number?

1. 526,555   2. 265,789

3. 42,789,654   4. 24,789,654

5. 8924   6. 5,643,201

7. *Government Payroll.*   In March 2011, the total payroll for all state employees in the United States was $19,971,861,990. What digit names the number of ten billions?

Source: *2011 Annual Survey of Public Employment and Payroll*

Answers

1. 2 ten thousands   2. 2 hundred thousands
3. 2 millions   4. 2 ten millions   5. 2 tens
6. 2 hundreds   7. 1

Write expanded notation.

GS

8. 2718 mi, the length of the Congo River in Africa

$$2718 = 2\,\boxed{} + 7\,\boxed{}$$
$$+ \boxed{}\ \text{ten} + \boxed{}\ \text{ones}$$

9. 344,945, the number of families in Central and Eastern Europe assisted by Heifer International in 2011

10. 1670 ft, the height of the Taipei 101 Tower in Taiwan

11. 104,094 square miles, the area of Colorado

The number of families assisted in the Americas was 934,871. This number is expressed in **standard notation**. We write **expanded notation** for 934,871 as follows:

$$934,871 = 9 \text{ hundred thousands} + 3 \text{ ten thousands}$$
$$+ 4 \text{ thousands} + 8 \text{ hundreds}$$
$$+ 7 \text{ tens} + 1 \text{ one.}$$

EXAMPLE 7 Write expanded notation for 1815 ft, the height of the CN Tower in Toronto, Canada.

$$1815 = 1 \text{ thousand} + 8 \text{ hundreds} + 1 \text{ ten} + 5 \text{ ones}$$

EXAMPLE 8 Write expanded notation for 407,640, the number of families in Asia and the South Pacific assisted by Heifer International in 2011.

$$407,640 = 4 \text{ hundred thousands} + 0 \text{ ten thousands}$$
$$+ 7 \text{ thousands} + 6 \text{ hundreds} + 4 \text{ tens} + 0 \text{ ones}$$

or

$$4 \text{ hundred thousands} + 7 \text{ thousands} + 6 \text{ hundreds} + 4 \text{ tens}$$

◀ Do Exercises 8–11.

C CONVERTING BETWEEN STANDARD NOTATION AND WORD NAMES

We often use **word names** for numbers. When we pronounce a number, we are speaking its word name. Russia won 82 medals in the 2012 Summer Olympics in London, Great Britain. A word name for 82 is "eighty-two." Word names for some two-digit numbers like 36, 51, and 72 use hyphens. Others like that for 17 use only one word, "seventeen."

2012 Summer Olympics Medal Count

COUNTRY	GOLD	SILVER	BRONZE	TOTAL
United States of America	46	29	29	104
People's Republic of China	38	27	23	88
Russia	24	26	32	82
Great Britain	29	17	19	65
Germany	11	19	14	44

SOURCE: espn.go.com

Answers

8. 2 thousands + 7 hundreds + 1 ten + 8 ones
9. 3 hundred thousands + 4 ten thousands + 4 thousands + 9 hundreds + 4 tens + 5 ones
10. 1 thousand + 6 hundreds + 7 tens + 0 ones, or 1 thousand + 6 hundreds + 7 tens
11. 1 hundred thousand + 0 ten thousands + 4 thousands + 0 hundreds + 9 tens + 4 ones, or 1 hundred thousand + 4 thousands + 9 tens + 4 ones

Guided Solution:
8. thousands, hundreds, 1, 8

EXAMPLES Write a word name.

9. 46, the number of gold medals won by the United States

    Forty-six

10. 19, the number of silver medals won by Germany

    Nineteen

11. 104, the total number of medals won by the United States

    One hundred four

Do Exercises 12–14. ▶

For word names for larger numbers, we begin at the left with the largest period. The number named in the period is followed by the name of the period; then a comma is written and the next number and period are named. Note that the name of the ones period is not included in the word name for a whole number.

EXAMPLE 12 Write a word name for 46,605,314,732.

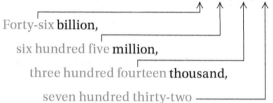

Forty-six **billion,**

    six hundred five **million,**

        three hundred fourteen **thousand,**

            seven hundred thirty-two

The word "and" *should not* appear in word names for whole numbers. Although we commonly hear such expressions as "two hundred *and* one," the use of "and" is not, strictly speaking, correct in word names for whole numbers. For decimal notation, it is appropriate to use "and" for the decimal point. For example, 317.4 is read as "three hundred seventeen *and* four tenths."

Do Exercises 15–18. ▶

EXAMPLE 13 Write standard notation.

Five hundred six **million,**

    three hundred forty-five **thousand,**

        two hundred twelve

Standard notation is 506,345,212.

Do Exercise 19. ▶

Write a word name. (Refer to the chart on the previous page.)

12. 65, the total number of medals won by Great Britain

13. 14, the number of bronze medals won by Germany

14. 38, the number of gold medals won by the People's Republic of China

Write a word name.

15. 204

16. $44,640, the average annual wage for athletic trainers in the United States in 2012
    Source: U.S. Bureau of Labor Statistics

GS **17.** 1,879,204

    One ____ , eight hundred ____ thousand, two hundred ____

18. 7,052,428,785, the world population in 2012
    Source: U.S. Census Bureau

19. Write standard notation.

    Two hundred thirteen million, one hundred five thousand, three hundred twenty-nine

---

Answers

12. Sixty-five   **13.** Fourteen
14. Thirty-eight   **15.** Two hundred four
16. Forty-four thousand, six hundred forty
17. One million, eight hundred seventy-nine thousand, two hundred four   **18.** Seven billion, fifty-two million, four hundred twenty-eight thousand, seven hundred eighty-five   **19.** 213,105,329

Guided Solution:
17. Million, seventy-nine, four

For Extra Help
MyMathLab®   MathXL® PRACTICE WATCH READ REVIEW

☑ Reading Check

Complete each statement with the correct word from the following list.

digit   expanded   period   standard

RC1. In 983, the _____ 9 represents 9 hundreds.

RC2. In 615,702, the number 615 is in the thousands _____.

RC3. The phrase "3 hundreds + 2 tens + 9 ones" is _____ notation for 329.

RC4. The number 721 is written in _____ notation.

a   What does the digit 5 mean in each number?

1. 235,888   **2.** 253,777   **3.** 1,488,526   **4.** 500,736

Movie Receipts.   The final movie of the Harry Potter series, *Harry Potter and the Deathly Hallows: Part II*, grossed $1,328,111,219 worldwide.

Source: Nash Information Services, LLC

What digit names the number of:

5. thousands?   **6.** millions?   **7.** ten millions?   **8.** hundred thousands?

b   Write expanded notation.

Stair-Climbing Races.   The figure below shows the number of stairs in four buildings in which stair-climbing races are held. In Exercises 9–12, write expanded notation for the number of stairs in each race.

Stair-Climbing Races

2058

1776

1576

1081

International Towerthon, Kuala Lumpur, Malaysia

CN Tower Stair Climb, Toronto, Ontario, Canada

Empire State Building Run-Up, New York

Skytower Vertical Challenge, Auckland, New Zealand

SOURCE: towerrunning.com

9. 2058 steps in the International Towerthon, Kuala Lumpur, Malaysia

10. 1776 steps in the CN Tower Stair Climb, Toronto, Ontario, Canada

11. 1576 steps in the Empire State Building Run-Up, New York City, New York

12. 1081 steps in the Skytower Vertical Challenge, Auckland, New Zealand

Copyright © 2015 Pearson Education, Inc.

13. 5702

14. 3097

15. 93,986

16. 38,453

Population. The table below shows the populations of four countries in 2012. In Exercises 17–20, write expanded notation for the population of the given country.

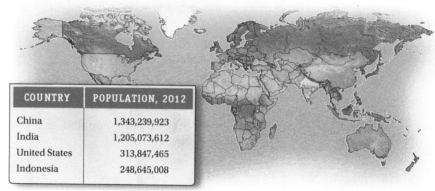

Four Most Populous Countries in the World

COUNTRY	POPULATION, 2012
China	1,343,239,923
India	1,205,073,612
United States	313,847,465
Indonesia	248,645,008

SOURCE: *CIA World Factbook*

17. 1,343,239,923 for China

18. 1,205,073,612 for India

19. 248,645,008 for Indonesia

20. 313,847,465 for the United States

C Write a word name.

21. 85

22. 48

23. 88,000

24. 45,987

25. 123,765

26. 111,013

27. 7,754,211,577

28. 43,550,651,808

29. *English Language Learners.* In the 2007–2008 academic year, there were 701,799 English language learners in Texas schools. Write a word name for 701,799.

Source: U.S. Department of Education

30. *College Football.* The 2012 Rose Bowl game was attended by 91,245 fans. Write a word name for 91,245.

Source: bizjournals.com

31. *Auto Racing.* Dario Franchitti, winner of the 2012 Indianapolis 500 auto race, won a prize of $2,474,280. Write a word name for 2,474,280.

Source: sbnation.com

32. *Busiest Airport.* In 2010, the world's busiest airport, Hartsfield-Jackson Atlanta International Airport, hosted 89,331,622 passengers. Write a word name for 89,331,622.

Source: Airports Council International

Write each number in standard notation.

33. Six hundred thirty-two thousand, eight hundred ninety-six

34. Three hundred fifty-four thousand, seven hundred two

35. Fifty thousand, three hundred twenty-four

36. Seventeen thousand, one hundred twelve

37. Two million, two hundred thirty-three thousand, eight hundred twelve

38. Nineteen million, six hundred ten thousand, four hundred thirty-nine

39. Eight billion

40. Seven hundred million

41. Forty million

42. Twenty-six billion

43. Thirty million, one hundred three

44. Two hundred thousand, seventeen

Write standard notation for the number in each sentence.

45. *Pacific Ocean.* The area of the Pacific Ocean is sixty-four million, one hundred eighty-six thousand square miles.

46. The average distance from the sun to Neptune is two billion, seven hundred ninety-three million miles.

Synthesis

To the student and the instructor: The Synthesis exercises found at the end of every exercise set challenge students to combine concepts or skills studied in the section or in preceding parts of the text. Exercises marked with a symbol are meant to be solved using a calculator.

47. How many whole numbers between 100 and 400 contain the digit 2 in their standard notation?

48. What is the largest number that you can name on your calculator? How many digits does that number have? How many periods?

Copyright © 2015 Pearson Education, Inc.

Addition

a ADDITION OF WHOLE NUMBERS

To answer questions such as "How many?", "How much?", and "How tall?", we often use whole numbers. The set, or collection, of **whole numbers** is

0, 1, 2, 3, 4, 5, 6, 7, 8, 9, 10, 11, 12, ...

The set goes on indefinitely. There is no largest whole number, and the smallest whole number is 0. Each whole number can be named using various notations. The set 1, 2, 3, 4, 5, . . . , without 0, is called the set of **natural numbers**.

Addition of whole numbers corresponds to combining things together.

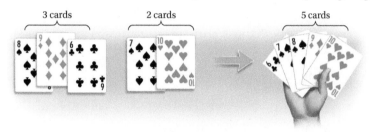

We say that the **sum** of 3 and 2 is 5. The numbers added are called **addends**. The addition that corresponds to the figure above is

$$3 + 2 = 5.$$
Addend Addend Sum

To add whole numbers, we add the ones digits first, then the tens, then the hundreds, then the thousands, and so on.

EXAMPLE 1 Add: 878 + 995.

Place values are lined up in columns.

$$\begin{array}{r} \overset{1}{} \\ 8\ 7\ 8 \\ +\ 9\ 9\ 5 \\ \hline 3 \end{array}$$
Add ones. We get 13 ones, or 1 ten + 3 ones. Write 3 in the ones column and 1 above the tens. This is called *carrying*, or *regrouping*.

$$\begin{array}{r} \overset{1}{8}\ \overset{1}{7}\ 8 \\ +\ 9\ 9\ 5 \\ \hline 7\ 3 \end{array}$$
Add tens. We get 17 tens, so we have 10 tens + 7 tens. This is also 1 hundred + 7 tens. Write 7 in the tens column and 1 above the hundreds.

$$\begin{array}{r} \overset{1}{8}\ \overset{1}{7}\ 8 \\ 9\ 9\ 5 \\ \hline 1\ 8\ 7\ 3 \end{array}$$
Add hundreds. We get 18 hundreds.

We show you these steps for explanation. You need write only this.

$$\begin{array}{r} \overset{1}{8}\ \overset{1}{7}\ 8 \\ +\ \ 9\ 9\ 5 \\ \hline 1\ 8\ 7\ 3 \end{array}$$
⟵ Addends
⟵ Sum

OBJECTIVES

a Add whole numbers.

b Use addition in finding perimeter.

SKILL TO REVIEW

Objective 1.1a: Give the meaning of digits in standard notation.

In each of the following numbers, what does the digit 4 mean?

1. 8342

2. 14,976

Answers

Skill to Review:
1. 4 tens
2. 4 thousands

How do we perform an addition of three numbers, like $2 + 3 + 6$? We could do it by adding 3 and 6, and then 2. We can show this with parentheses:

$$2 + (3 + 6) = 2 + 9 = 11.$$ Parentheses tell what to do first.

We could also add 2 and 3, and then 6:

$$(2 + 3) + 6 = 5 + 6 = 11.$$

Either way the result is 11. It does not matter how we group the numbers. This illustrates the **associative law of addition**, $a + (b + c) = (a + b) + c$. We can also add whole numbers in any order. That is, $2 + 3 = 3 + 2$. This illustrates the **commutative law of addition**, $a + b = b + a$. Together, the commutative and associative laws tell us that to add more than two numbers, we can use any order and grouping we wish. Adding 0 to a number does not change the number: $a + 0 = 0 + a = a$. That is, $6 + 0 = 0 + 6 = 6$, or $198 + 0 = 0 + 198 = 198$. We say that 0 is the **additive identity**.

EXAMPLE 2   Add: $391 + 1276 + 789 + 5498$.

Add.

1. $6203 + 3542$

2.
```
  7 9 6 8
+ 5 4 9 7
```

3.
```
  9 8 0 4
+ 6 3 7 8
```

4.
```
  1 9 3 2
  6 7 2 3
  9 8 7 8
+ 8 9 4 1
```

Answers

1. 9745   **2.** 13,465   **3.** 16,182
4. 27,474

Guided Solution:

2.
```
    1 1 1
    7 9 6 8
  + 5 4 9 7
   1 3,4 6 5
```

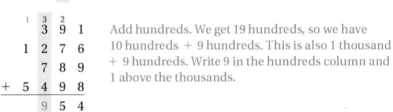

```
      2
  3   9   1      Add ones. We get 24, so we have 2 tens + 4 ones.
1 2   7   6      Write 4 in the ones column and 2 above the tens.
  7   8   9
+ 5   4   9   8
              4
```

```
    3   2
  3   9   1      Add tens. We get 35 tens, so we have 30 tens + 5 tens.
1 2   7   6      This is also 3 hundreds + 5 tens. Write 5 in the tens
  7   8   9      column and 3 above the hundreds.
+ 5   4   9   8
          5   4
```

```
  1 3   2
    3   9   1      Add hundreds. We get 19 hundreds, so we have
  1 2   7   6      10 hundreds + 9 hundreds. This is also 1 thousand
    7   8   9      + 9 hundreds. Write 9 in the hundreds column and
  + 5   4   9   8  1 above the thousands.
      9   5   4
```

```
  1 3   2
    3   9   1
  1 2   7   6      Add thousands. We get 7 thousands.
    7   8   9
  + 5   4   9   8
  7   9   5   4
```

◀ **Do Exercises 1–4.**

CALCULATOR CORNER

···

Adding Whole Numbers   This is the first of a series of *optional* discussions on using a calculator. A calculator is *not* a requirement for this textbook. Check with your instructor about whether you are allowed to use a calculator in the course.

There are many kinds of calculators and different instructions for their usage. Be sure to consult your users manual.

To add whole numbers on a calculator, we use the $\boxed{+}$ and $\boxed{=}$ keys. After we press $\boxed{=}$, the sum appears on the display.

EXERCISES   Use a calculator to find each sum.

1. $73 + 48$ **2.** $925 + 677$ **3.** $826 + 415 + 691$ **4.** $253 + 490 + 121$

b FINDING PERIMETER

Addition can be used when finding perimeter.

PERIMETER

The distance around an object is its **perimeter**.

EXAMPLE 3 Find the perimeter of the figure.

We add the lengths of the sides:

Perimeter = 29 in. + 19 in. + 37 in. + 44 in.

= 129 in.

The perimeter of the figure is 129 in. (inches).

Do Exercises 5 and 6. ▶

EXAMPLE 4 Lucas Oil Stadium in Indianapolis has a unique retractable roof. When the roof is opened (retracted) in good weather to create an open-air stadium, the opening approximates a rectangle 588 ft long and 300 ft wide. Find the perimeter of the opening.

Opposite sides of a rectangle have equal lengths, so this rectangle has two sides of length 588 ft and two sides of length 300 ft.

Perimeter = 588 ft + 300 ft + 588 ft + 300 ft

= 1776 ft

The perimeter of the opening is 1776 ft.

Do Exercise 7. ▶

Find the perimeter of each figure.

GS **5.**

Perimeter = 4 in. + 5 in. + ☐

+ 6 in. + 5 in.

= ☐ in.

6.

7. *Index Cards.* Two standard sizes for index cards are 3 in. by 5 in. and 5 in. by 8 in. Find the perimeter of each type of card.

Answers

5. 29 in.   **6.** 62 ft   **7.** 16 in.; 26 in.

Guided Solution:
5. 9 in., 29

✓ Reading Check

Complete each statement with the appropriate word or number from the following list. Not every choice will be used.

0	addends	law	product
1	factors	perimeter	sum

RC1. In the addition $5 + 2 = 7$, the numbers 5 and 2 are _____.

RC2. In the addition $5 + 2 = 7$, the number 7 is the _____.

RC3. The sum of _____ and any number a is a.

RC4. The distance around an object is its _____.

a Add.

1.
```
  3 6 4
+   2 3
```

2.
```
  1 5 2 1
+   3 4 8
```

3.
```
  8 6
+ 7 8
```

4.
```
  7 3
+ 6 9
```

5.
```
  1 7 1 6
+ 3 4 8 2
```

6.
```
  7 5 0 3
+ 2 6 8 3
```

7.
```
  9 9
+  1
```

8.
```
  9 9 9
+  1 1
```

9. $8113 + 390$

10. $271 + 3338$

11. $356 + 4910$

12. $280 + 34,902$

13. $3870 + 92 + 7 + 497$

14. $10,120 + 12,989 + 5738$

15.
```
  4 8 2 5
+ 1 7 8 3
```

16.
```
  3 6 5 4
+ 2 7 0 0
```

17.
```
  2 3,4 4 3
+ 1 0,9 8 9
```

18.
```
  4 5,8 7 9
+ 2 1,7 8 6
```

19.
```
  7 7,5 4 3
+ 2 3,7 6 7
```

20.
```
  9 9,9 9 9
+     1 1 2
```

21.
```
  4 5
  2 5
  3 6
  4 4
+ 8 0
```

22.
```
  3 8
  2 7
  3 2
  1 4
+ 7 6
```

23.
```
  1 2,0 7 0
   2,9 5 4
+  3,4 0 0
```

24.
```
  4 2,4 8 7
  8 3,1 4 1
+ 3 6,7 1 2
```

25.
```
  4 8 3 5
    7 2 9
  9 2 0 4
  8 9 8 6
+ 7 9 3 1
```

26.
```
  9 8 9
  5 6 6
  8 3 4
  9 2 0
+ 7 0 3
```

Copyright © 2015 Pearson Education, Inc.

b Find the perimeter of each figure.

27.

50 yd
23 yd
19 yd
40 yd

28.

14 mi
13 mi
8 mi
22 mi
10 mi
47 mi

29.

402 ft
298 ft
196 ft
212 ft
100 ft
453 ft

30.

62 yd
39 yd
28 yd
46 yd
54 yd

31. Find the perimeter of a standard hockey rink.

85 ft
200 ft

32. In Major League Baseball, how far does a batter travel when circling the bases after hitting a home run?

90 ft
90 ft

Skill Maintenance

The exercises that follow begin an important feature called *Skill Maintenance exercises*. These exercises provide an ongoing review of topics previously covered in the book. You will see them in virtually every exercise set. It has been found that this kind of continuing review can significantly improve your performance on a final examination.

33. What does the digit 8 mean in 486,205? [1.1a]

34. The population of the world is projected to be 9,346,399,468 in 2050. Write a word name for 9,346,399,468. [1.1c]

Source: U.S. Census Bureau

Synthesis

35. A fast way to add all the numbers from 1 to 10 inclusive is to pair 1 with 9, 2 with 8, and so on. Use a similar approach to add all numbers from 1 to 100 inclusive.

1.3 Subtraction

OBJECTIVE

a Subtract whole numbers.

SKILL TO REVIEW

Objective 1.1a: Give the meaning of digits in standard notation.

Consider the number 328,974.

1. What digit names the number of hundreds?
2. What digit names the number of ones?

a SUBTRACTION OF WHOLE NUMBERS

Subtraction is finding the difference of two numbers. Suppose you purchase 6 tickets for a concert and give 2 to a friend.

6 tickets

Give 2 away   Keep 4

The subtraction that represents this situation is

$$6 \quad - \quad 2 \quad = \quad 4.$$

Minuend   Subtrahend   Difference

The **minuend** is the number from which another number is being subtracted. The **subtrahend** is the number being subtracted. The **difference** is the result of subtracting the subtrahend from the minuend.

In the subtraction above, note that the difference, 4, is the number we add to 2 to get 6. This illustrates the relationship between addition and subtraction and leads us to the following definition of subtraction.

SUBTRACTION

The difference $a - b$ is that unique whole number c for which $a = c + b$.

We see that $6 - 2 = 4$ because $4 + 2 = 6$.

To subtract whole numbers, we subtract the ones digits first, then the tens digits, then the hundreds, then the thousands, and so on.

EXAMPLE 1 Subtract: $9768 - 4320$.

$$
\begin{array}{r}
9\ 7\ 6\ \mathbf{8} \\
-\ 4\ 3\ 2\ \mathbf{0} \\
\hline
8
\end{array}
$$
Subtract ones.

$$
\begin{array}{r}
9\ 7\ \mathbf{6}\ 8 \\
-\ 4\ 3\ \mathbf{2}\ 0 \\
\hline
4\ 8
\end{array}
$$
Subtract tens.

$$
\begin{array}{r}
9\ \mathbf{7}\ 6\ 8 \\
-\ 4\ \mathbf{3}\ 2\ 0 \\
\hline
4\ 4\ 8
\end{array}
$$
Subtract hundreds.

$$
\begin{array}{r}
\mathbf{9}\ 7\ 6\ 8 \\
-\ \mathbf{4}\ 3\ 2\ 0 \\
\hline
5\ 4\ 4\ 8
\end{array}
$$
Subtract thousands.

We show these steps for explanation. You need write only this.

$$
\begin{array}{r}
9\ 7\ 6\ 8 \\
-\ 4\ 3\ 2\ 0 \\
\hline
5\ 4\ 4\ 8
\end{array}
$$

Answers

Skill to Review:
1. 9   2. 4

Because subtraction is defined in terms of addition, we can use addition to *check* subtraction.

Subtraction:

```
  9 7 6 8
- 4 3 2 0
  5 4 4 8
```

Check by Addition:

```
  5 4 4 8
+ 4 3 2 0
  9 7 6 8
```

Do Exercise 1. ▶

EXAMPLE 2 Subtract: 348 − 165.
We have

$$3\text{ hundreds} + 4\text{ tens} + 8\text{ ones} = 2\text{ hundreds} + 14\text{ tens} + 8\text{ ones}$$
$$\underline{-\ 1\text{ hundred} - 6\text{ tens} - 5\text{ ones}} = \underline{-1\text{ hundred} - 6\text{ tens} - 5\text{ ones}}$$
$$= 1\text{ hundred} + 8\text{ tens} + 3\text{ ones}$$
$$= 183.$$

First, we subtract the ones.

```
  3 4 8
- 1 6 5
      3
```
Subtract ones.

We cannot subtract the tens because there is no whole number that when added to 6 gives 4. To complete the subtraction, we must *borrow* 1 hundred from 3 hundreds and regroup it with the 4 tens. Then we can do the subtraction 14 tens − 6 tens = 8 tens.

```
  2 14
  3 4̸ 8
- 1 6 5
      3
```
Borrow one hundred. That is, 1 hundred = 10 tens, and 10 tens + 4 tens = 14 tens. Write 2 above the hundreds column and 14 above the tens.

```
  2 14
  3̸ 4̸ 8
- 1 6 5
  1 8 3
```
Subtract tens; subtract hundreds.

This is what you should write. → ```
  2 14
  3̸ 4̸ 8
- 1 6 5
  1 8 3
``` *Check:* → ```
    1
  1 8 3
+ 1 6 5
  3 4 8
```  ← The answer checks because this is the top number in the subtraction.

**GS**   **1.** Subtract. Check by adding.

```
  7 8 9 3
- 4 0 9 2
```

```
  7 8 9 3
- 4 0 9 2
      8   1
```

Check:

```

+ 4 0 9 2

```

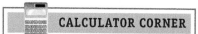 **CALCULATOR CORNER**

Subtracting Whole Numbers
To subtract whole numbers on a calculator, we use the [−] and [=] keys.

EXERCISES Use a calculator to perform each subtraction. Check by adding.

1. 57 − 29
2. 81 − 34
3. 145 − 78
4. 612 − 493
5.  ```
      4 9 7 6
    - 2 8 4 8
    ```
6.  ```
    1 2,4 0 6
    -  9 8 1 3
    ```

Answer
1. 3801
Guided Solution:
1. 3, 0; 3801, 7893

EXAMPLE 3   Subtract: $6246 - 1879$.

$$
\begin{array}{r}
\overset{3\ 16}{6\,2\,\cancel{4}\,\cancel{6}} \\
-\,1\,8\,7\,9 \\
\hline
7
\end{array}
$$

We cannot subtract 9 ones from 6 ones, but we can subtract 9 ones from 16 ones. We borrow 1 ten to get 16 ones.

$$
\begin{array}{r}
\overset{\ \ \ \ \ 13}{\overset{1\ 3\ 16}{6\,\cancel{2}\,\cancel{4}\,\cancel{6}}} \\
-\,1\,8\,7\,9 \\
\hline
6\ 7
\end{array}
$$

We cannot subtract 7 tens from 3 tens, but we can subtract 7 tens from 13 tens. We borrow 1 hundred to get 13 tens.

$$
\begin{array}{r}
\overset{\ \ \ 11\ 13}{\overset{5\ 1\ 3\ 16}{\cancel{6}\,\cancel{2}\,\cancel{4}\,\cancel{6}}} \\
-\,1\,8\,7\,9 \\
\hline
4\ 3\ 6\ 7
\end{array}
$$

We cannot subtract 8 hundreds from 1 hundred, but we can subtract 8 hundreds from 11 hundreds. We borrow 1 thousand to get 11 hundreds. Finally, we subtract the thousands.

This is what you should write. →

$$
\begin{array}{r}
\overset{\ \ \ 11\ 13}{\overset{5\ 1\ 3\ 16}{\cancel{6}\,\cancel{2}\,\cancel{4}\,\cancel{6}}} \\
-\,1\,8\,7\,9 \\
\hline
4\ 3\ 6\ 7
\end{array}
$$

Check: →

$$
\begin{array}{r}
\overset{1\ 1\ 1}{\ \ } \\
4\,3\,6\,7 \\
+\,1\,8\,7\,9 \\
\hline
6\,2\,4\,6
\end{array}
$$

← The answer checks because this is the top number in the subtraction.

Subtract. Check by adding.

2.
$$
\begin{array}{r}
8\,6\,8\,6 \\
-\,2\,3\,5\,8 \\
\hline
\end{array}
$$

3.
$$
\begin{array}{r}
7\,1\,4\,5 \\
-\,2\,3\,9\,8 \\
\hline
\end{array}
$$

◀ Do Exercises 2 and 3.

EXAMPLE 4   Subtract: $902 - 477$.

$$
\begin{array}{r}
\overset{8\ 9\ 12}{\cancel{9}\,\cancel{0}\,2} \\
-\,4\,7\,7 \\
\hline
4\,2\,5
\end{array}
$$

We cannot subtract 7 ones from 2 ones. We have 9 hundreds, or 90 tens. We borrow 1 ten to get 12 ones. We then have 89 tens.

◀ Do Exercises 4 and 5.

EXAMPLE 5   Subtract: $8003 - 3667$.

$$
\begin{array}{r}
\overset{7\ 9\ 9\ 13}{\cancel{8}\,\cancel{0}\,\cancel{0}\,3} \\
-\,3\,6\,6\,7 \\
\hline
4\,3\,3\,6
\end{array}
$$

We have 8 thousands, or 800 tens. We borrow 1 ten to get 13 ones. We then have 799 tens.

Subtract.

4.
$$
\begin{array}{r}
7\,0 \\
-\,1\,4 \\
\hline
\end{array}
$$

5.
$$
\begin{array}{r}
5\,0\,3 \\
-\,2\,9\,8 \\
\hline
\end{array}
$$
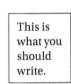

$$
\begin{array}{r}
\overset{\ \ \ \ \ \ \ 13}{5\,\cancel{0}\,\cancel{3}} \\
-\,2\,9\,8 \\
\hline
\square\ 0\ \square
\end{array}
$$

Subtract.

6.
$$
\begin{array}{r}
7\,0\,0\,7 \\
-\,6\,3\,4\,9 \\
\hline
\end{array}
$$

7.
$$
\begin{array}{r}
6\,0\,0\,0 \\
-\,3\,1\,4\,9 \\
\hline
\end{array}
$$

8.
$$
\begin{array}{r}
9\,0\,3\,5 \\
-\,7\,4\,8\,9 \\
\hline
\end{array}
$$

9.
$$
\begin{array}{r}
2\,0\,0\,1 \\
-\,\ \ 1\,2\,4 \\
\hline
\end{array}
$$

EXAMPLES

6. Subtract: $6000 - 3762$.

$$
\begin{array}{r}
\overset{5\ 9\ 9\ 10}{\cancel{6}\,\cancel{0}\,\cancel{0}\,\cancel{0}} \\
-\,3\,7\,6\,2 \\
\hline
2\,2\,3\,8
\end{array}
$$

7. Subtract: $6024 - 2968$.

$$
\begin{array}{r}
\overset{\ \ \ \ \ \ 11}{\overset{5\ 9\ 1\ 14}{\cancel{6}\,\cancel{0}\,\cancel{2}\,\cancel{4}}} \\
-\,2\,9\,6\,8 \\
\hline
3\,0\,5\,6
\end{array}
$$

◀ Do Exercises 6–9.

Answers

2. 6328   **3.** 4747   **4.** 56   **5.** 205
6. 658   **7.** 2851   **8.** 1546   **9.** 1877

Guided Solution:

5.
$$
\begin{array}{r}
\overset{4\ 9\ 13}{\cancel{5}\,\cancel{0}\,\cancel{3}} \\
-\,2\,9\,8 \\
\hline
2\,0\,5
\end{array}
$$

☑ Reading Check

Match each word or phrase from the following list with the indicated part of the subtraction sentence.

difference   minuend   subtraction symbol   subtrahend

RC1. A _____

RC2. B _____

RC3. C _____

RC4. D _____

Ⓐ   Ⓑ   Ⓒ   Ⓓ
↓   ↓   ↓   ↓
97   −   51 = 26

a   Subtract. Check by adding.

1.   6 5
       − 2 1

2.   8 7
       − 3 4

3.   8 6 6
       − 3 3 3

4.   5 2 6
       − 3 2 3

5. 86 − 47

6. 73 − 28

7. 51 − 37

8. 64 − 19

9.   5 6 3
       − 1 9 4

10.   7 9 5
        − 3 9 8

11.   3 9 1
        − 3 6 5

12.   3 1 6
        − 2 4 7

13. 981 − 747

14. 887 − 698

15. 683 − 266

16. 342 − 217

17.   7 7 6 9
        − 2 3 8 7

18.   6 4 3 1
        − 2 8 9 6

19.   4 5 1 2
        − 1 7 3 4

20.   8 3 6 4
        − 5 3 7 5

21. 5318 − 2249

22. 9241 − 5643

23. 3947 − 2858

24. 7583 − 3641

25. $\begin{array}{r} 12{,}647 \\ -\ \ 4{,}899 \end{array}$

26. $\begin{array}{r} 16{,}222 \\ -\ \ 5{,}888 \end{array}$

27. $\begin{array}{r} 51{,}342 \\ -\ 47{,}198 \end{array}$

28. $\begin{array}{r} 32{,}194 \\ -\ 29{,}236 \end{array}$

29. $\begin{array}{r} 80 \\ -\ 24 \end{array}$

30. $\begin{array}{r} 90 \\ -\ 78 \end{array}$

31. $\begin{array}{r} 690 \\ -\ 236 \end{array}$

32. $\begin{array}{r} 803 \\ -\ 418 \end{array}$

33. $\begin{array}{r} 6808 \\ -\ 3059 \end{array}$

34. $\begin{array}{r} 9405 \\ -\ \ 258 \end{array}$

35. $\begin{array}{r} 2300 \\ -\ \ 109 \end{array}$

36. $\begin{array}{r} 7500 \\ -\ 3604 \end{array}$

37. $90{,}237 - 47{,}209$

38. $84{,}703 - 298$

39. $101{,}734 - 5760$

40. $15{,}017 - 7809$

41. $\begin{array}{r} 6007 \\ -\ 1589 \end{array}$

42. $\begin{array}{r} 8003 \\ -\ \ 599 \end{array}$

43. $\begin{array}{r} 39{,}000 \\ -\ 37{,}695 \end{array}$

44. $\begin{array}{r} 17{,}000 \\ -\ 11{,}598 \end{array}$

45. $10{,}008 - 19$

46. $40{,}006 - 147$

47. $50{,}001 - 1984$

48. $30{,}004 - 6749$

Skill Maintenance

Add. [1.2a]

49. $567 + 778$

50. $901 + 23$

51. $12{,}885 + 9807$

52. $9909 + 1011$

53. Write a word name for 6,375,602. [1.1c]

54. Write expanded notation for 9103. [1.1b]

Synthesis

55. Fill in the missing digits to make the subtraction true:

$$9{,}\square 48{,}621 - 2{,}097{,}\square 81 = 7{,}251{,}140.$$

56. ▦ Subtract: $3{,}928{,}124 - 1{,}098{,}947.$

Copyright © 2015 Pearson Education, Inc.

Multiplication

a MULTIPLICATION OF WHOLE NUMBERS

Repeated Addition

The multiplication 3×5 corresponds to this repeated addition.

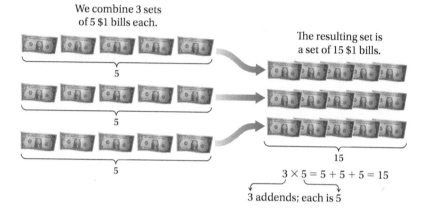

We combine 3 sets of 5 $1 bills each.

The resulting set is a set of 15 $1 bills.

$$3 \times 5 = 5 + 5 + 5 = 15$$

3 addends; each is 5

OBJECTIVES

a Multiply whole numbers.

b Use multiplication in finding area.

SKILL TO REVIEW

Objective 1.2a: Add whole numbers.

Add.

1.
$$\begin{array}{r} 3\ 4\ 7 \\ +\ 5\ 5\ 6 \end{array}$$

2.
$$\begin{array}{r} 1\ 8\ 3\ 5 \\ +\ 4\ 6\ 1\ 9 \end{array}$$

The numbers that we multiply are called **factors**. The result of the multiplication is called a **product**.

$$\begin{array}{ccccc} 3 & \times & 5 & = & 15 \\ \downarrow & & \downarrow & & \downarrow \\ \text{Factor} & & \text{Factor} & & \text{Product} \end{array}$$

Rectangular Arrays

Multiplications can also be thought of as rectangular arrays. Each of the following corresponds to the multiplication 3×5.

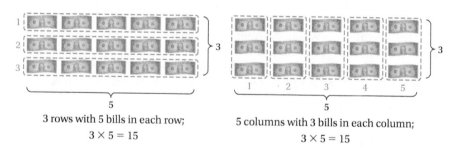

3 rows with 5 bills in each row;
$3 \times 5 = 15$

5 columns with 3 bills in each column;
$3 \times 5 = 15$

When you write a multiplication corresponding to a real-world situation, you should think of either a rectangular array or repeated addition. In some cases, it may help to think both ways.

We have used an "$\times$" to denote multiplication. A dot "$\cdot$" is also commonly used. (Use of the dot is attributed to the German mathematician Gottfried Wilhelm von Leibniz over three centuries ago.) Parentheses are also used to denote multiplication. For example,

$$3 \times 5 = 3 \cdot 5 = (3)(5) = 3(5) = 15.$$

Answers

Skill to Review:
1. 903 **2.** 6454

The product of 0 and any whole number is 0: $0 \cdot a = a \cdot 0 = 0$. For example, $0 \cdot 3 = 3 \cdot 0 = 0$. Multiplying a number by 1 does not change the number: $1 \cdot a = a \cdot 1 = a$. For example, $1 \cdot 3 = 3 \cdot 1 = 3$. We say that 1 is the **multiplicative identity**.

EXAMPLE 1 Multiply: 5×734.

We have

$$
\begin{array}{r}
7\ 3\ 4 \\
\times \quad\ \ 5 \\
\hline
2\ 0 \\
1\ 5\ 0 \\
3\ 5\ 0\ 0 \\
\hline
3\ 6\ 7\ 0 \\
\end{array}
$$

← Multiply the 4 ones by 5: $5 \times 4 = 20$.
← Multiply the 3 tens by 5: $5 \times 30 = 150$.
← Multiply the 7 hundreds by 5: $5 \times 700 = 3500$.
← Add.

Instead of writing each product on a separate line, we can use a shorter form.

$$
\begin{array}{r}
\overset{2}{7}\ 3\ 4 \\
\times \quad\ \ 5 \\
\hline
0 \\
\end{array}
$$

Multiply the 4 ones by 5: $5 \cdot (4\,\text{ones}) = 20\,\text{ones} = 2\,\text{tens} + 0\,\text{ones}$. Write 0 in the ones column and 2 above the tens.

$$
\begin{array}{r}
\overset{1}{7}\ \overset{2}{3}\ 4 \\
\times \quad\ \ 5 \\
\hline
7\ 0 \\
\end{array}
$$

Multiply the 3 tens by 5 and add 2 tens: $5 \cdot (3\,\text{tens}) = 15\,\text{tens}$, $15\,\text{tens} + 2\,\text{tens} = 17\,\text{tens} = 1\,\text{hundred} + 7\,\text{tens}$. Write 7 in the tens column and 1 above the hundreds.

$$
\begin{array}{r}
\overset{1}{7}\ \overset{2}{3}\ 4 \\
\times \quad\ \ 5 \\
\hline
3\ 6\ 7\ 0 \\
\end{array}
$$

Multiply the 7 hundreds by 5 and add 1 hundred: $5 \cdot (7\,\text{hundreds}) = 35\,\text{hundreds}$, $35\,\text{hundreds} + 1\,\text{hundred} = 36\,\text{hundreds}$.

$$
\left.\begin{array}{r}
\overset{1}{7}\ \overset{2}{3}\ 4 \\
\times \quad\ \ 5 \\
\hline
3\ 6\ 7\ 0 \\
\end{array}\right\}
$$

You should write only this.

◀ **Do Exercises 1–4.**

Multiplication of whole numbers is based on a property called the **distributive law**. It says that to multiply a number by a sum, $a \cdot (b + c)$, we can multiply each addend by a and then add like this: $(a \cdot b) + (a \cdot c)$. Thus, $a \cdot (b + c) = (a \cdot b) + (a \cdot c)$. For example, consider the following.

$$4 \cdot (2 + 3) = 4 \cdot 5 = 20$$

Adding first; then multiplying

$$4 \cdot (2 + 3) = (4 \cdot 2) + (4 \cdot 3) = 8 + 12 = 20$$

Multiplying first; then adding

The results are the same, so $4 \cdot (2 + 3) = (4 \cdot 2) + (4 \cdot 3)$.

Let's find the product 51×32. Since $32 = 2 + 30$, we can think of this product as

$$51 \times 32 = 51 \times (2 + 30) = (51 \times 2) + (51 \times 30).$$

That is, we multiply 51 by 2, then we multiply 51 by 30, and finally we add. We can write our work in columns.

Multiply.

1.
$$
\begin{array}{r}
5\ 8 \\
\times\ \ 2 \\
\hline
\end{array}
$$

2.
$$
\begin{array}{r}
3\ 7 \\
\times\ \ 4 \\
\hline
\end{array}
$$

3.
$$
\begin{array}{r}
8\ 2\ 3 \\
\times\quad 6 \\
\hline
\end{array}
$$

4.
$$
\begin{array}{r}
1\ 3\ 4\ 8 \\
\times\qquad 5 \\
\hline
\end{array}
$$

GS

$$
\begin{array}{r}
\ \ \square\ \ \overset{2}{\ }\ \square\ \ \\
1\ \ 3\ \ 4\ \ 8 \\
\times\qquad\quad 5 \\
\hline
\square\ \ 7\ \ \square\ \ 0 \\
\end{array}
$$

Answers

1. 116   2. 148   3. 4938   4. 6740

Guided Solution:

4.
$$
\begin{array}{r}
\overset{1\ 2\ 4}{\ } \\
1\ 3\ 4\ 8 \\
\times\qquad 5 \\
\hline
6\ 7\ 4\ 0 \\
\end{array}
$$

```
    5 1
  × 3 2
  1 0 2        Multiplying by 2
1 5 3 0        Multiplying by 30. (We write a 0 and then multiply 51 by 3.)
```

> You may have learned that such a 0 need not be written. You may omit it if you wish. If you do omit it, remember, when multiplying by tens, to start writing the answer in the tens place.

We add to obtain the product.

```
      5 1
    × 3 2
    1 0 2
  1 5 3 0
  1 6 3 2        Adding to obtain the product
```

EXAMPLE 2   Multiply: 457 × 683.

```
        5 2
      6 8 3
    × 4 5 7
    4 7 8 1        Multiplying 683 by 7
```

```
      4 1
      5 2
      6 8 3
    × 4 5 7
    4 7 8 1
  3 4 1 5 0        Multiplying 683 by 50
```

```
        3 1
        4 1
        5 2
      6 8 3
    × 4 5 7
      4 7 8 1
    3 4 1 5 0
  2 7 3 2 0 0        Multiplying 683 by 400. (We write
  3 1 2 , 1 3 1      00 and then multiply 683 by 4.)
                     Adding
```

Do Exercises 5–8. ▶

EXAMPLE 3   Multiply: 306 × 274.

Note that 306 = 3 hundreds + 6 ones.

```
      2 7 4
    × 3 0 6
    1 6 4 4        Multiplying by 6
  8 2 2 0 0        Multiplying by 3 hundreds. (We write 00
  8 3 , 8 4 4      and then multiply 274 by 3.)
                   Adding
```

Do Exercises 9–12. ▶

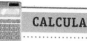

CALCULATOR CORNER

Multiplying Whole Numbers   To multiply whole numbers on a calculator, we use the ☒ and ▭ keys.

EXERCISES   Use a calculator to find each product.

1. 56 × 8
2. 845 × 26
3. 5 · 1276
4. 126(314)
5.   3 7 6 0
     ×   4 8
6.   5 2 1 8
     ×   4 5 3

Multiply.

5.   4 5   6. 48 × 63
  × 2 3

7.   7 4 6   8. 245 × 837
  × 6 2

Multiply.

9.   4 7 2   10. 408 × 704
  × 3 0 6

11.   2 3 4 4   12.   1 0 0 6
   × 6 0 0 5   × 7 0 3

Answers

5. 1035   6. 3024   7. 46,252   8. 205,065
9. 144,432   10. 287,232   11. 14,075,720
12. 707,218

Multiply.

13. $4\,7\,2$
       $\underline{\times\,8\,3\,0}$

14. $2\,3\,4\,4$
       $\underline{\times\,7\,4\,0\,0}$

15. 100×562

16. 1000×562

17. a) Find $23 \cdot 47$.

  b) Find $47 \cdot 23$.

  c) Compare your answers to parts (a) and (b).

Multiply.

18. $5 \cdot 2 \cdot 4$

19. $4 \cdot 2 \cdot 6$

EXAMPLE 4   Multiply: 360×274.

Note that $360 = 3$ hundreds $+ 6$ tens.

$$
\begin{array}{r}
274 \\
\times\ 360 \\
\hline
16440 \\
82200 \\
\hline
98{,}640
\end{array}
$$

— Multiplying by 6 tens. (We write 0 and then multiply 274 by 6.)

— Multiplying by 3 hundreds. (We write 00 and then multiply 274 by 3.)

Adding

◀ **Do Exercises 13–16.**

When we multiply two numbers, we can change the order of the numbers without changing their product. For example, $3 \cdot 6 = 18$ and $6 \cdot 3 = 18$. This illustrates the **commutative law of multiplication:** $a \cdot b = b \cdot a$.

◀ **Do Exercise 17.**

To multiply three or more numbers, we group them so that we multiply two at a time. Consider $2 \cdot 3 \cdot 4$. We can group these numbers as $2 \cdot (3 \cdot 4)$ or as $(2 \cdot 3) \cdot 4$. The parentheses tell what to do first:

$$2 \cdot (3 \cdot 4) = 2 \cdot (12) = 24.$$ We multiply 3 and 4 and then that product by 2.

We can also multiply 2 and 3 and then that product by 4:

$$(2 \cdot 3) \cdot 4 = (6) \cdot 4 = 24.$$

Either way we get 24. It does not matter how we group the numbers. This illustrates the **associative law of multiplication:** $a \cdot (b \cdot c) = (a \cdot b) \cdot c$.

◀ **Do Exercises 18 and 19.**

b FINDING AREA

We can think of the area of a rectangular region as the number of square units needed to fill it. Here is a rectangle 4 cm (centimeters) long and 3 cm wide. It takes 12 square centimeters (sq cm) to fill it.

This is a square centimeter (a square unit).

In this case, we have a rectangular array of 3 rows, each of which contains 4 squares. The number of square units is given by $3 \cdot 4$, or 12. That is, $A = l \cdot w = 3 \text{ cm} \cdot 4 \text{ cm} = 12 \text{ sq cm}$.

Answers

13. 391,760   **14.** 17,345,600
15. 56,200   **16.** 562,000
17. (a) 1081; **(b)** 1081; **(c)** same
18. 40   **19.** 48

EXAMPLE 5 *Professional Pool Table.* The playing area of a pool table used in professional tournaments is 50 in. by 100 in. (There are 6-in. wide rails on the outside that are not included in the playing area.) Determine the playing area.

GS **20. Painting a Room.** Ben and Elizabeth plan to paint one wall of a bedroom in a dark accent color. The wall is a rectangle 12 ft long and 8 ft high. Determine the area of the wall.

$$A = l \cdot w$$
$$= 12\ \text{ft} \cdot \boxed{}$$
$$= \boxed{}\ \text{sq ft}$$

If we think of filling the rectangle with square inches, we have a rectangular array. The length $l = 100$ in. and the width $w = 50$ in. Thus the area A is given by the formula

$$A = l \cdot w = 100\ \text{in.} \cdot 50\ \text{in.} = 5000\ \text{sq in.}$$

Do Exercise 20. ▶

Answer
20. 96 sq ft
Guided Solution:
20. 8 ft, 96

1.4 Exercise Set

For Extra Help
MyMathLab® MathXL® PRACTICE WATCH READ REVIEW

✓ Reading Check

Complete each statement with the appropriate word or number from the following list. Not every choice will be used.

0	addends	product
1	factors	sum

RC1. In the multiplication $4 \times 3 = 12$, 4 and 3 are _____.

RC2. In the multiplication $4 \times 3 = 12$, 12 is the _____.

RC3. The product of _____ and any number a is 0.

RC4. The product of _____ and any number a is a.

a Multiply.

1. 65
    × 8

2. 87
    × 4

3. 94
    × 6

4. 76
    × 9

5. 3 · 509

6. 7 · 806

7. 7(9229)

8. 4(7867)

9. 90(53)

10. 60(78)

11. (47)(85)

12. (34)(87)

13. 87
    × 10

14. 2 3 4 0
    × 1 0 0 0

15. 96
    × 20

16. 8 0 0
    × 7 0 0

17. 6 4 3
    × 7 2

18. 7 7 7
    × 7 7

19. 4 4 4
    × 3 3

20. 5 4 9
    × 8 8

21. 5 6 4
    × 4 5 8

22. 4 3 2
    × 3 7 5

23. 8 5 3
    × 9 3 6

24. 3 4 6
    × 6 5 9

25. 6 4 2 8
    × 3 2 2 4

26. 8 9 2 8
    × 3 1 7 2

27. 3 4 8 2
    × 1 0 4

28. 6 4 0 8
    × 6 0 6 4

29. 8 7 6
    × 3 4 5

30. 3 5 5
    × 2 9 9

31. 7 8 8 9
    × 6 2 2 4

32. 6 5 2 1
    × 3 4 4 9

Copyright © 2015 Pearson Education, Inc.

33.   5 6 0 8
        × 4 5 0 0

34.   4 5 0 6
        × 7 8 0 0

35.   5 0 0 6
        × 4 0 0 8

36.   6 0 0 9
        × 2 0 0 3

b Find the area of each region.

37.

728 mi

728 mi

38.   129 yd

65 yd

39. Find the area of the region formed by the base lines on a Major League Baseball diamond.

90 ft

90 ft

40. Find the area of a standard-sized hockey rink.

85 ft

200 ft

Skill Maintenance

Add. [1.2a]

41.   4 9 0 8
        5 6 6 7
      + 2 1 1 0

42.   9 8 7 6
          8 7 6
           7 6
      +   6

Subtract. [1.3a]

43.   9 8 7 6
      −   9 8 7

44.   3 4 0, 7 9 8
      −   8 6, 6 7 9

45. What does the digit 4 mean in 9,482,157? [1.1a]

46. What digit in 38,026 names the number of hundreds? [1.1a]

47. Write expanded notation for 12,847. [1.1b]

48. Write a word name for 7,432,000. [1.1c]

Synthesis

49. ⊞ An 18-story office building is box-shaped. Each floor measures 172 ft by 84 ft with a 20-ft by 35-ft rectangular area lost to an elevator and a stairwell. How much area is available as office space?

1.5 Division

OBJECTIVE

....

a Divide whole numbers.

....

SKILL TO REVIEW

....

Objective 1.3a:
Subtract whole numbers.

Subtract.

1. 5 6 4 2. 7 0 3 5
   − 3 9 7   − 2 9 4 4

a DIVISION OF WHOLE NUMBERS

Repeated Subtraction

Division of whole numbers applies to two kinds of situations. The first is repeated subtraction. Suppose we have 20 doughnuts, and we want to find out how many sets of 5 there are. One way to do this is to repeatedly subtract sets of 5 as follows.

20 doughnuts

How many sets of 5 doughnuts each?

Since there are 4 sets of 5 doughnuts each, we have

$$20 \div 5 = 4.$$

Dividend Divisor Quotient

The division $20 \div 5$ is read "20 divided by 5." The **dividend** is 20, the **divisor** is 5, and the **quotient** is 4. We divide the *dividend* by the *divisor* to get the *quotient*. We can also express the division $20 \div 5 = 4$ as

$$\frac{20}{5} = 4 \quad \text{or} \quad 5\overline{)20}.$$

Rectangular Arrays

We can also think of division in terms of rectangular arrays. Consider again the 20 doughnuts and division by 5. We can arrange the doughnuts in a rectangular array with 5 rows and ask, "How many are in each row?"

We can also consider a rectangular array with 5 doughnuts in each column and ask, "How many columns are there?" The answer is still 4.

In each case, we are asking, "What do we multiply 5 by in order to get 20?"

Missing factor   Quotient

$5 \cdot \square = 20 \qquad 20 \div 5 = \square$

This leads us to the following definition of division.

Answers

Skill to Review:
1. 167 **2.** 4091

DIVISION

The quotient $a \div b$, where b is not 0, is that unique number c for which $a = b \cdot c$.

This definition shows the relation between division and multiplication. We see, for instance, that

$$20 \div 5 = 4 \text{ because } 20 = 5 \cdot 4.$$

This relation allows us to use multiplication to check division.

EXAMPLE 1   Divide. Check by multiplying.

a) $16 \div 8$ **b)** $\dfrac{36}{4}$ **c)** $7\overline{)56}$

We do so as follows.

a) $16 \div 8 = 2$ *Check*: $8 \cdot 2 = 16.$

b) $\dfrac{36}{4} = 9$ *Check*: $4 \cdot 9 = 36.$

c) $7\overline{)56}^{\,8}$ *Check*: $7 \cdot 8 = 56.$

Do Exercises 1–3.

Divide. Check by multiplying.
1. $9\overline{)45}$

2. $27 \div 3$

3. $\dfrac{48}{6}$

Let's consider some basic properties of division.

DIVIDING BY 1

Any number divided by 1 is that same number: $a \div 1 = \dfrac{a}{1} = a.$

For example, $6 \div 1 = 6$ and $\dfrac{15}{1} = 15.$

DIVIDING A NUMBER BY ITSELF

Any nonzero number divided by itself is 1: $a \div a = \dfrac{a}{a} = 1, \quad a \neq 0.$

For example, $7 \div 7 = 1$ and $\dfrac{22}{22} = 1.$

Divide.
4. $\dfrac{9}{9}$ 5. $\dfrac{8}{1}$

DIVIDENDS OF 0

Zero divided by any nonzero number is 0: $0 \div a = \dfrac{0}{a} = 0, \quad a \neq 0.$

For example, $0 \div 14 = 0$ and $\dfrac{0}{3} = 0.$

6. $\dfrac{0}{12}$ 7. $\dfrac{28}{28}$

Do Exercises 4–7.

Answers

1. 5 2. 9 3. 8 4. 1 5. 8 6. 0 7. 1

EXCLUDING DIVISION BY 0

Division by 0 is not defined: $a \div 0$, or $\dfrac{a}{0}$, is **not defined**.

For example, $16 \div 0$, or $\dfrac{16}{0}$, is not defined.

8. Divide if possible: $0 \div 2$. If not possible, write "not defined."

$0 \div 2$ means ☐ divided by ☐.

Since zero divided by any nonzero number is 0, $0 \div 2 =$ ☐.

9. Divide if possible: $7 \div 0$. If not possible, write "not defined."

$7 \div 0$ means ☐ divided by ☐.

Since division by 0 is not defined, $7 \div 0$ is ☐.

Why can't we divide by 0? Suppose the number 4 could be divided by 0. Then if ☐ were the answer, we would have

$$4 \div 0 = \square,$$

and since 0 times any number is 0, we would have

$$4 = \square \cdot 0 = 0. \quad \text{False!}$$

Thus, the only possible number that could be divided by 0 would be 0 itself. But such a division would give us any number we wish. For instance,

$$\left.\begin{array}{l} 0 \div 0 = 8 \quad \text{because} \quad 0 = 8 \cdot 0; \\ 0 \div 0 = 3 \quad \text{because} \quad 0 = 3 \cdot 0; \\ 0 \div 0 = 7 \quad \text{because} \quad 0 = 7 \cdot 0. \end{array}\right\} \quad \text{All true!}$$

We avoid the preceding difficulties by agreeing to exclude division by 0.

◀ **Do Exercises 8–9.**

Division with a Remainder

Suppose everyone in a group of 22 people wants to ride a roller coaster. If each car on the ride holds 6 people, the group will fill 3 cars and there will be 4 people left over.

We can think of this situation as the following division. The people left over are the **remainder**.

$$\begin{array}{r} 3 \leftarrow \text{Quotient} \\ 6\,)\overline{2\,2} \\ \underline{1\,8} \\ 4 \leftarrow \text{Remainder} \end{array}$$

Answers

8. 0 **9.** Not defined

Guided Solutions:
8. 0, 2, 0
9. 7, 0, not defined

We express the result as

$$22 \div 6 = 3 \text{ R } 4.$$

Dividend　Divisor　Quotient　Remainder

Note that

Quotient · Divisor + Remainder = Dividend.

Thus we have

$3 \cdot 6 = 18$　　　Quotient · Divisor

and　$18 + 4 = 22.$　　Adding the remainder. The result is the dividend.

We now show a procedure for dividing whole numbers.

EXAMPLE 2　Divide and check: $4 \overline{)3457}$.

First, we try to divide the first digit of the dividend, 3, by the divisor, 4. Since $3 \div 4$ is not a whole number, we consider the first *two* digits of the dividend.

```
        8
   4) 3 4 5 7
      3 2
      ———
        2
```

Since $4 \cdot 8 = 32$ and 32 is smaller than 34, we write an 8 in the quotient above the 4. We also write 32 below 34 and subtract.

What if we had chosen a number other than 8 for the first digit of the quotient? Suppose we had used 7 instead of 8 and subtracted $4 \cdot 7$, or 28, from 34. The result would have been $34 - 28$, or 6. Because 6 is larger than the divisor, 4, we know that there is at least one more factor of 4 in 34, and thus 7 is too small. If we had used 9 instead of 8, then we would have tried to subtract $4 \cdot 9$, or 36, from 34. That difference is not a whole number, so we know 9 is too large. When we subtract, the difference must be smaller than the divisor.

Let's continue dividing.

```
        8 6
   4) 3 4 5 7
      3 2
      ———
        2 5
        2 4
        ———
          1
```

Now we bring down the 5 in the dividend and consider $25 \div 4$. Since $4 \cdot 6 = 24$ and 24 is smaller than 25, we write 6 in the quotient above the 5. We also write 24 below 25 and subtract. The difference, 1, is smaller than the divisor, so we know that 6 is the correct choice.

```
        8 6 4
   4) 3 4 5 7
      3 2
      ———
        2 5
        2 4
        ———
          1 7
          1 6
          ———
            1   ← The remainder is 1.
```

We bring down the 7 and consider $17 \div 4$. Since $4 \cdot 4 = 16$ and 16 is smaller than 17, we write 4 in the quotient above the 7. We also write 16 below 17 and subtract.

Check:　$864 \cdot 4 = 3456$ and $3456 + 1 = 3457$.

The answer is 864 R 1.

Do Exercises 10–12. ▶

Divide and check.

10. $3 \overline{)239}$

11. $5 \overline{)5864}$

12. $6 \overline{)3855}$

Answers

10. 79 R 2　**11.** 1172 R 4
12. 642 R 3

EXAMPLE 3 Divide: 8904 ÷ 42.

Because 42 is close to 40, we think of the divisor as 40 when we make our choices of digits in the quotient.

$$
\begin{array}{r}
2 \\
42\overline{\smash{)}8904} \\
\underline{84}\downarrow \\
50
\end{array}
$$
← *Think:* 89 ÷ 40. We try 2. Multiply 42 · 2 and subtract. Then bring down the 0.

$$
\begin{array}{r}
21 \\
42\overline{\smash{)}8904} \\
\underline{84} \\
50 \\
\underline{42}\downarrow \\
84
\end{array}
$$
← *Think:* 50 ÷ 40. We try 1. Multiply 42 · 1 and subtract. Then bring down the 4.

$$
\begin{array}{r}
212 \\
42\overline{\smash{)}8904} \\
\underline{84} \\
50 \\
\underline{42} \\
84 \\
\underline{84} \\
0
\end{array}
$$
← *Think:* 84 ÷ 40. We try 2. Multiply 2 · 42 and subtract.

The remainder is 0, so the answer is 212.

◀ **Do Exercises 13 and 14.**

Divide.

13. $45\overline{\smash{)}6030}$

14. $52\overline{\smash{)}3288}$

.... **Caution!** ....

Be careful to keep the digits lined up correctly when you divide.
....

CALCULATOR CORNER

Dividing Whole Numbers To divide whole numbers on a calculator, we use the $\boxed{\div}$ and $\boxed{=}$ keys.

When we enter 453 ÷ 15, the display reads $\boxed{30.2}$. Note that the result is not a whole number. This tells us that there is a remainder. The number 30.2 is expressed in decimal notation. The symbol "." is called a decimal point. Although it is possible to use the number to the right of the decimal point to find the remainder, we will not do so here.

EXERCISES Use a calculator to perform each division.

1. $19\overline{\smash{)}532}$
2. $7\overline{\smash{)}861}$
3. $9367 \div 29$
4. $12{,}276 \div 341$

Zeros in Quotients

EXAMPLE 4   Divide: $6341 \div 7$.

```
      9
  7 )6 3 4 1
    6 3
        4
```
← *Think:* $63 \div 7 = 9$. The first digit in the quotient is 9. We do not write the 0 when we find $63 - 63$. Bring down the 4.

```
      9 0
  7 )6 3 4 1
    6 3
        4 1
```
← *Think:* $4 \div 7$. If we subtract a group of 7's, such as 7, 14, 21, etc., from 4, we do not get a whole number, so the next digit in the quotient is 0. Bring down the 1.

```
      9 0 5
  7 )6 3 4 1
    6 3
        4 1
        3 5
          6
```
← *Think:* $41 \div 7$. We try 5. Multiply $7 \cdot 5$ and subtract.

← The remainder is 6.

The answer is 905 R 6.

Do Exercises 15 and 16. ▶

Divide.

15. $6)\overline{4\ 8\ 4\ 6}$

16. $7)\overline{7\ 6\ 1\ 6}$

EXAMPLE 5   Divide: $8169 \div 34$.

Because 34 is close to 30, we think of the divisor as 30 when we make our choices of digits in the quotient.

```
       2
  3 4 )8 1 6 9
      6 8
      1 3 6
```
← *Think:* $81 \div 30$. We try 2. Multiply $34 \cdot 2$ and subtract. Then bring down the 6.

```
       2 4
  3 4 )8 1 6 9
      6 8
      1 3 6
      1 3 6
            9
```
← *Think:* $136 \div 30$. We try 4. Multiply $34 \cdot 4$ and subtract. The difference is 0, so we do not write it. Bring down the 9.

```
       2 4 0
  3 4 )8 1 6 9
      6 8
      1 3 6
      1 3 6
            9
            0
            9
```
← *Think:* $9 \div 34$. If we subtract a group of 34's, such as 34 or 68, from 9, we do not get a whole number, so the last digit in the quotient is 0.

← The remainder is 9.

The answer is 240 R 9.

Do Exercises 17 and 18. ▶

Divide.

17. $2 7)\overline{9\ 7\ 2\ 4}$

18. $5 6)\overline{4\ 4,\ 8\ 4\ 7}$

Answers

15. 807 R 4   **16.** 1088
17. 360 R 4   **18.** 800 R 47

✓ Reading Check

Match each word from the following list with the indicated part of the division.

dividend   divisor   quotient   remainder

RC1. A _____

RC2. B _____

RC3. C _____

RC4. D _____

$$\begin{array}{r} 2\ 9 \leftarrow Ⓐ \\ Ⓓ \rightarrow 8\overline{)2\ 3\ 5} \leftarrow Ⓑ \\ 1\ 6 \\ \overline{7\ 5} \\ 7\ 2 \\ \overline{3} \leftarrow Ⓒ \end{array}$$

a   Divide, if possible. If not possible, write "not defined."

1. $72 \div 6$

2. $54 \div 9$

3. $\dfrac{23}{23}$

4. $\dfrac{37}{37}$

5. $22 \div 1$

6. $\dfrac{56}{1}$

7. $\dfrac{0}{7}$

8. $\dfrac{0}{32}$

9. $\dfrac{16}{0}$

10. $74 \div 0$

11. $\dfrac{48}{8}$

12. $\dfrac{20}{4}$

Divide.

13. $277 \div 5$

14. $699 \div 3$

15. $864 \div 8$

16. $869 \div 8$

17. $4\overline{)1\ 2\ 2\ 8}$

18. $3\overline{)2\ 1\ 2\ 4}$

19. $6\overline{)4\ 5\ 2\ 1}$

20. $9\overline{)9\ 1\ 1\ 0}$

21. $297 \div 4$

22. $389 \div 2$

23. $738 \div 8$

24. $881 \div 6$

Copyright © 2015 Pearson Education, Inc.

25. $5 \overline{)8515}$

26. $3 \overline{)6027}$

27. $9 \overline{)8888}$

28. $8 \overline{)4139}$

29. $127{,}000 \div 10$

30. $127{,}000 \div 100$

31. $127{,}000 \div 1000$

32. $4260 \div 10$

33. $70 \overline{)3692}$

34. $20 \overline{)5798}$

35. $30 \overline{)875}$

36. $40 \overline{)987}$

37. $852 \div 21$

38. $942 \div 23$

39. $85 \overline{)7672}$

40. $54 \overline{)2729}$

41. $111 \overline{)3219}$

42. $102 \overline{)5612}$

43. $8 \overline{)843}$

44. $7 \overline{)749}$

45. $5 \overline{)8047}$

46. $9 \overline{)7273}$

47. $5 \overline{)5036}$

48. $7 \overline{)7074}$

49. $1058 \div 46$

50. $7242 \div 24$

51. $3425 \div 32$

52. $48 \overline{)4899}$

53. $24 \overline{)8880}$

54. $36 \overline{)7563}$

55. $28 \overline{)17,067}$

56. $36 \overline{)28,929}$

57. $80 \overline{)24,320}$

58. $90 \overline{)88,560}$

59. $285 \overline{)999,999}$

60. $306 \overline{)888,888}$

61. $456 \overline{)3,679,920}$

62. $803 \overline{)5,622,606}$

Skill Maintenance

Subtract. [1.3a]

63. $\begin{array}{r} 4\,9\,0\,8 \\ -\ 3\,6\,6\,7 \end{array}$

64. $\begin{array}{r} 8\,8,7\,7\,7 \\ -\ 2\,2,3\,3\,3 \end{array}$

Multiply. [1.4a]

65. $\begin{array}{r} 1\,9\,8 \\ \times\ 1\,0\,0 \end{array}$

66. $\begin{array}{r} 2\,6\,8 \\ \times\ 3\,5 \end{array}$

Use the following figure for Exercises 67 and 68.

11 ft

9 ft

67. Find the perimeter of the figure. [1.2b]

68. Find the area of the figure. [1.4b]

Synthesis

69. Complete the following table.

a	b	$a \cdot b$	$a + b$
	68	3672	
84			117
		32	12

70. Find a pair of factors whose product is 36 and:
   a) whose sum is 13.
   b) whose difference is 0.
   c) whose sum is 20.
   d) whose difference is 9.

71. A group of 1231 college students is going to use buses to take a field trip. Each bus can hold 42 students. How many buses are needed?

72. ▦ Fill in the missing digits to make the equation true:

$$34,584,132 \div 76\square = 4\square,386.$$

Copyright © 2015 Pearson Education, Inc.

Concept Reinforcement

Determine whether each statement is true or false.

_____ 1. If $a - b = c$, then $b = a + c$. [1.3a]

_____ 2. We can think of the multiplication 4×3 as a rectangular array containing 4 rows with 3 items in each row. [1.4a]

_____ 3. We can think of the multiplication 4×3 as a rectangular array containing 3 columns with 4 items in each column. [1.4a].

_____ 4. The product of two whole numbers is always greater than either of the factors. [1.4a]

_____ 5. Zero divided by any nonzero number is 0. [1.5a]

_____ 6. Any number divided by 1 is the number 1. [1.5a]

Guided Solutions

GS Fill in each blank with the number that creates a correct statement or solution.

7. Write a word name for 95,406,237. [1.1c]

Ninety-five ☐ ,

☐ thousand,

☐

8. Subtract: $604 - 497$. [1.3a]

$$\begin{array}{r} \square\ \square\ \square \\ 6\ 0\ 4 \\ -\ 4\ 9\ 7 \\ \hline \square\ \square\ \square \end{array}$$

Mixed Review

In each of the following numbers what does the digit 6 mean? [1.1a]

9. 2698   **10.** 61,204   **11.** 146,237   **12.** 586

Consider the number 306,458,129. What digit names the number of: [1.1a]

13. tens?   **14.** millions?   **15.** ten thousands?   **16.** hundreds?

Write expanded notation. [1.1b]   Write a word name. [1.1c]

17. 5602   **18.** 69,345   **19.** 136   **20.** 64,325

Write standard notation. [1.1c]

21. Three hundred eight thousand, seven hundred sixteen

22. Four million, five hundred sixty-seven thousand, two hundred sixteen

Add. [1.2a]

23.
```
  316
+ 482
```

24.
```
  593
+ 437
```

25.
```
  2638
+ 5284
```

26.
```
  4617
  2436
+  481
```

Subtract. [1.3a]

27.
```
  786
- 321
```

28.
```
  624
- 285
```

29.
```
  3602
- 1748
```

30.
```
  5004
-  676
```

Multiply. [1.4a]

31.
```
   36
×   6
```

32.
```
  567
×  28
```

33.
```
  407
× 325
```

34.
```
  9435
×  602
```

Divide. [1.5a]

35. 4) 1 0 1 2

36. 38) 4 2 6 1

37. 60) 1 3 9 9

38. 56) 8 0 9 5

39. Find the perimeter of the figure (m stands for "meters"). [1.2b]

40. Find the area of the region. [1.4b]

Understanding Through Discussion and Writing

To the student and the instructor: The Discussion and Writing exercises are meant to be answered with one or more sentences. They can be discussed and answered collaboratively by the entire class or by small groups.

41. Explain in your own words what the associative law of addition means. [1.2a]

42. Is subtraction commutative? That is, is there a commutative law of subtraction? Why or why not? [1.3a]

43. Describe a situation that corresponds to each multiplication: 4 · $150; $4 · 150. [1.4a]

44. Suppose a student asserts that "0 ÷ 0 = 0 because nothing divided by nothing is nothing." Devise an explanation to persuade the student that the assertion is false. [1.5a]

Copyright © 2015 Pearson Education, Inc.

STUDYING FOR SUCCESS   *Using the Textbook*

☐ Study the step-by-step solutions to the examples, paying attention to the extra explanations shown in red.

☐ Stop and do the margin exercises when directed to do so. Answers are at the bottom of the margin, so you can check your work right away.

☐ The objective symbols ⓐ, ⓑ, ⓒ, and so on, allow you to refer to the appropriate place in the text whenever you need to review a topic.

Rounding and Estimating; Order

1.6

ⓐ ROUNDING

We round numbers in various situations when we do not need an exact answer. For example, we might round to see if we are being charged the correct amount in a store. We might also round to check if an answer to a problem is reasonable or to check a calculation done by hand or on a calculator.

To understand how to round, we first look at some examples using the number line. The number line displays numbers at equally spaced intervals.

EXAMPLE 1   Round 47 to the nearest ten.

47 is between 40 and 50. Since 47 is closer to 50, we round up to 50.

EXAMPLE 2   Round 42 to the nearest ten.

42 is between 40 and 50. Since 42 is closer to 40, we round down to 40.

EXAMPLE 3   Round 45 to the nearest ten.

45 is halfway between 40 and 50. We could round 45 down to 40 or up to 50. We agree to round up to 50.

> When a number is halfway between rounding numbers, round up.

Do Margin Exercises 1–7. ▶

Based on these examples, we can state a rule for rounding whole numbers.

OBJECTIVES

ⓐ Round to the nearest ten, hundred, or thousand.

ⓑ Estimate sums, differences, products, and quotients by rounding.

ⓒ Use < or > for ☐ to write a true sentence in a situation like 6 ☐ 10.

SKILL TO REVIEW

Objective 1.1a: Give the meaning of digits in standard notation.

In the number 145,627, what digit names the number of:
1. Tens?
2. Thousands?

Round to the nearest ten.
1. 37

2. 52   3. 35

4. 73   5. 75

6. 88   7. 64

Answers

Skill to Review:
1. 2   **2.** 5

Margin Exercises:
1. 40   **2.** 50   **3.** 40   **4.** 70
5. 80   **6.** 90   **7.** 60

ROUNDING WHOLE NUMBERS

To round to a certain place:

a) Locate the digit in that place.

b) Consider the next digit to the right.

c) If the digit to the right is 5 or higher, round up. If the digit to the right is 4 or lower, round down.

d) Change all digits to the right of the rounding location to zeros.

EXAMPLE 4 Round 6485 to the nearest ten.

a) Locate the digit in the tens place, 8.

> 6 4 8 5
>   ↑

b) Consider the next digit to the right, 5.

> 6 4 8 5

c) Since that digit, 5, is 5 or higher, round 8 tens up to 9 tens.

d) Change all digits to the right of the tens digit to zeros.

> 6 4 9 0 ← This is the answer.

Round to the nearest ten.

8. 137   **9.** 473

10. 235   **11.** 285

◀ Do Exercises 8–11.

EXAMPLE 5 Round 6485 to the nearest hundred.

a) Locate the digit in the hundreds place, 4.

> 6 4 8 5
>   ↑

b) Consider the next digit to the right, 8.

> 6 4 8 5

c) Since that digit, 8, is 5 or higher, round 4 hundreds up to 5 hundreds.

d) Change all digits to the right of hundreds to zeros.

> 6 5 0 0 ← This is the answer.

Round to the nearest hundred.

12. 641   **13.** 759

14. 1871   **15.** 9325

·············· Caution! ··············

It is incorrect in Example 6 to round from the ones digit over, as follows:

> 6485 → 6490 → 6500 → 7000.

Note that 6485 is closer to 6000 than it is to 7000.

◀ Do Exercises 12–15.

EXAMPLE 6 Round 6485 to the nearest thousand.

a) Locate the digit in the thousands place, 6.

> 6 4 8 5
> ↑

b) Consider the next digit to the right, 4.

> 6 4 8 5

c) Since that digit, 4, is 4 or lower, round down, meaning that 6 thousands stays as 6 thousands.

d) Change all digits to the right of thousands to zeros.

> 6 0 0 0 ← This is the answer.

Round to the nearest thousand.

16. 7896   **17.** 8459

18. 19,343   **19.** 68,500

◀ Do Exercises 16–19.

Answers

8. 140   **9.** 470   **10.** 240   **11.** 290
12. 600   **13.** 800   **14.** 1900   **15.** 9300
16. 8000   **17.** 8000   **18.** 19,000   **19.** 69,000

Sometimes rounding involves changing more than one digit in a number.

EXAMPLE 7 Round 78,595 to the nearest ten.

a) Locate the digit in the tens place, 9.

$$7\ 8\ ,5\ \underset{\uparrow}{9}\ 5$$

b) Consider the next digit to the right, 5.

$$7\ 8\ ,5\ 9\ 5$$

c) Since that digit, 5, is 5 or higher, round 9 tens to 10 tens. We think of 10 tens as 1 hundred + 0 tens and increase the hundreds digit by 1, to get 6 hundreds + 0 tens. We then write 6 in the hundreds place and 0 in the tens place.

d) Change the digit to the right of the tens digit to zero.

$$7\ 8\ ,6\ 0\ 0 \leftarrow \text{This is the answer.}$$

Note that if we round this number to the nearest hundred, we get the same answer.

Do Exercises 20 and 21. ▶

b ESTIMATING

Estimating can be done in many ways. In general, an estimate rounded to the nearest ten is more accurate than one rounded to the nearest hundred, and an estimate rounded to the nearest hundred is more accurate than one rounded to the nearest thousand, and so on.

EXAMPLE 8 Estimate this sum by first rounding to the nearest ten:

$$78 + 49 + 31 + 85.$$

We round each number to the nearest ten. Then we add.

```
  7 8        8 0
  4 9        5 0
  3 1        3 0
+ 8 5      + 9 0
           ─────
           2 5 0  ← Estimated answer
```

Do Exercises 22 and 23. ▶

EXAMPLE 9 Estimate the difference by first rounding to the nearest thousand: 9324 − 2849.

We have

```
  9 3 2 4       9 0 0 0
− 2 8 4 9     − 3 0 0 0
              ─────────
              6 0 0 0  ← Estimated answer
```

Do Exercises 24 and 25. ▶

---

20. Round 48,968 to the nearest ten, hundred, and thousand.

21. Round 269,582 to the nearest ten, hundred, and thousand.

22. Estimate the sum by first rounding to the nearest ten. Show your work.

```
  7 4
  2 3
  3 5
+ 6 6
```

23. Estimate the sum by first rounding to the nearest hundred. Show your work.

```
  6 5 0
  6 8 5
  2 3 8
+ 1 6 8
```

24. Estimate the difference by first rounding to the nearest hundred. Show your work.

```
  9 2 8 5
− 6 7 3 9
```

25. Estimate the difference by first rounding to the nearest thousand. Show your work.

```
  2 3,2 7 8
− 1 1,6 9 8
```

Answers

20. 48,970; 49,000; 49,000
21. 269,580; 269,600; 270,000
22. 70 + 20 + 40 + 70 = 200
23. 700 + 700 + 200 + 200 = 1800
24. 9300 − 6700 = 2600
25. 23,000 − 12,000 = 11,000

In the sentence $7 - 5 = 2$, the equals sign indicates that $7 - 5$ is the *same* as 2. When we round to make an estimate, the outcome is rarely the same as the exact result. Thus we cannot use an equals sign when we round. Instead, we use the symbol $\approx$. This symbol means "**is approximately equal to**." In Example 9, for instance, we could have written

$$9324 - 2849 \approx 6000.$$

EXAMPLE 10 Estimate the following product by first rounding to the nearest ten and then to the nearest hundred: 683×457.

Nearest ten:

$$
\begin{array}{r}
6\ 8\ 0 \\
\times\quad 4\ 6\ 0 \\
\hline
4\ 0\ 8\ 0\ 0 \\
2\ 7\ 2\ 0\ 0\ 0 \\
\hline
3\ 1\ 2{,}8\ 0\ 0
\end{array}
\qquad
\begin{array}{l}
683 \approx 680 \\
457 \approx 460
\end{array}
$$

Nearest hundred:

$$
\begin{array}{r}
7\ 0\ 0 \\
\times\quad 5\ 0\ 0 \\
\hline
3\ 5\ 0{,}0\ 0\ 0
\end{array}
\qquad
\begin{array}{l}
683 \approx 700 \\
457 \approx 500
\end{array}
$$

Exact:

$$
\begin{array}{r}
6\ 8\ 3 \\
\times\quad 4\ 5\ 7 \\
\hline
4\ 7\ 8\ 1 \\
3\ 4\ 1\ 5\ 0 \\
2\ 7\ 3\ 2\ 0\ 0 \\
\hline
3\ 1\ 2{,}1\ 3\ 1
\end{array}
$$

We see that rounding to the nearest ten gives a better estimate than rounding to the nearest hundred.

◀ **Do Exercise 26.**

EXAMPLE 11 Estimate the following quotient by first rounding to the nearest ten and then to the nearest hundred: $12{,}238 \div 175$.

Nearest ten: *Nearest hundred:*

$$
\begin{array}{r}
6\ 8 \\
1\ 8\ 0\overline{)1\ 2{,}2\ 4\ 0} \\
\underline{1\ 0\ 8\ 0} \\
1\ 4\ 4\ 0 \\
\underline{1\ 4\ 4\ 0} \\
0
\end{array}
\qquad
\begin{array}{r}
6\ 1 \\
2\ 0\ 0\overline{)1\ 2{,}2\ 0\ 0} \\
\underline{1\ 2\ 0\ 0} \\
2\ 0\ 0 \\
\underline{2\ 0\ 0} \\
0
\end{array}
$$

The exact answer is 69 R 163. Again we see that rounding to the nearest ten gives a better estimate than rounding to the nearest hundred.

◀ **Do Exercise 27.**

---

26. Estimate the product by first rounding to the nearest ten and then to the nearest hundred. Show your work. **GS**

$$
\begin{array}{r}
8\ 3\ 7 \\
\times\ 2\ 4\ 5
\end{array}
$$

Nearest ten:

$$
\begin{array}{r}
8\ 4\ 0 \\
\times\quad \boxed{} \\
\hline
4\ 2\ 0\ 0\ 0 \\
\boxed{}\ 0\ 0\ 0 \\
\hline
\boxed{}{,}0\ 0\ 0
\end{array}
$$

Nearest hundred:

$$
\begin{array}{r}
8\ 0\ 0 \\
\times\quad \boxed{} \\
\hline
\boxed{}\ 0{,}0\ 0\ 0
\end{array}
$$

27. Estimate the quotient by first rounding to the nearest hundred. Show your work.

$$64{,}534 \div 349$$

Answers

26. $840 \times 250 = 210{,}000;$
$800 \times 200 = 160{,}000$
27. $64{,}500 \div 300 = 215$

Guided Solution:
26. Nearest ten: 250, 1, 6, 8, 2, 1, 0;
Nearest hundred: 200, 1, 6

The next two examples show how estimating can be used in making financial decisions.

EXAMPLE 12 *Tuition.* Ellen plans to take 12 credit hours of classes next semester. If she takes the courses on campus, the cost per credit hour is $248. Estimate, by rounding to the nearest ten, the total cost of tuition.

We have

$$\begin{array}{r} 2\ 5\ 0 \\ \times\quad 1\ 0 \\ \hline 2\ 5\ 0\ 0. \end{array}$$

The tuition will cost about $2500.

Do Exercise 28.

EXAMPLE 13 *Purchasing a New Car.* Jon and Joanna are shopping for a new car. They are considering buying a Ford Focus S sedan. The base price of the car is $16,200. A 6-speed automatic transmission package can be added to this, as well as several other options, as shown in the chart below. Jon and Joanna want to stay within a budget of $18,000.

Estimate, by rounding to the nearest hundred, the cost of the Focus with the automatic transmission package and all other options and determine whether this will fit within their budget.

FORD FOCUS S SEDAN	PRICE
Basic price	$16,200
6-speed automatic transmission	$1,095
Remote start system (requires purchase of automatic transmission)	$445
SYNC basic (includes Bluetooth and USB input jacks)	$295
Cargo management	$115
Graphics package	$375
Exterior protection package	$245

SOURCE: motortrend.com

First, we list the base price of the car and then the cost of each of the options. We then round each number to the nearest hundred and add.

$$\begin{array}{r} 1\ 6{,}2\ 0\ 0 \\ 1{,}0\ 9\ 5 \\ 4\ 4\ 5 \\ 2\ 9\ 5 \\ 1\ 1\ 5 \\ 3\ 7\ 5 \\ +\quad 2\ 4\ 5 \\ \end{array} \qquad \begin{array}{r} 1\ 6{,}2\ 0\ 0 \\ 1{,}1\ 0\ 0 \\ 4\ 0\ 0 \\ 3\ 0\ 0 \\ 1\ 0\ 0 \\ 4\ 0\ 0 \\ +\quad 2\ 0\ 0 \\ \hline 1\ 8{,}7\ 0\ 0 \end{array} \leftarrow \text{Estimated cost}$$

The estimated cost is $18,700. This exceeds Jon and Joanna's budget of $18,000, so they will have to forgo at least one option.

Do Exercises 29 and 30.

28. *Tuition.* If Ellen takes courses online, the cost per credit hour is $198. Estimate, by rounding to the nearest ten, the total cost of 12 credit hours of classes.

Refer to the chart in Example 13 to do Margin Exercises 29 and 30.

29. By eliminating at least one option, determine how Jon and Joanna can buy a Focus S sedan and stay within their budget. Keep in mind that purchasing the remote-start system requires purchasing the automatic transmission.

30. Elizabeth and C.J. are also considering buying a Focus S sedan. Estimate, by rounding to the nearest hundred, the cost of this car with automatic transmission, SYNC basic, and exterior protection package.

Answers

28. $2000   **29.** Eliminate either the automatic transmission and the remote-start system or the remote-start system and the graphics package. There are other correct answers as well.   **30.** $17,800

c ORDER

A sentence like $8 + 5 = 13$ is called an **equation**. It is a *true* equation. The equation $4 + 8 = 11$ is a *false* equation.

A sentence like $7 < 11$ is called an **inequality**. The sentence $7 < 11$ is a *true* inequality. The sentence $23 > 69$ is a *false* inequality.

Some common **inequality symbols** follow.

INEQUALITY SYMBOLS

$<$ means   "is less than"

$>$ means   "is greater than"

$\neq$ means   "is not equal to"

We know that 2 is not the same as 5. We express this by the sentence $2 \neq 5$. We also know that 2 is less than 5. We symbolize this by the expression $2 < 5$. We can see this order on the number line: 2 is to the left of 5. The number 0 is the smallest whole number.

ORDER OF WHOLE NUMBERS

For any whole numbers a and b:

1. $a < b$ (read "a is less than b") is true when a is to the left of b on the number line.

2. $a > b$ (read "a is greater than b") is true when a is to the right of b on the number line.

Use $<$ or $>$ for ☐ to write a true sentence. Draw the number line if necessary.

31. 8 ☐ 12   GS

Since 8 is to the ___ of 12 on the number line, 8 ___ 12.

32. 12 ☐ 8

33. 76 ☐ 64

34. 64 ☐ 76

35. 217 ☐ 345

36. 345 ☐ 217

EXAMPLE 14   Use $<$ or $>$ for ☐ to write a true sentence: 7 ☐ 11.

Since 7 is to the left of 11 on the number line, $7 < 11$.

EXAMPLE 15   Use $<$ or $>$ for ☐ to write a true sentence: 92 ☐ 87.

Since 92 is to the right of 87 on the number line, $92 > 87$.

◀ Do Exercises 31–36.

Answers

31. $<$ **32.** $>$ **33.** $>$ **34.** $<$
35. $<$ **36.** $>$

Guided Solution:
31. left, $<$

✓ Reading Check

Determine whether each statement is true or false.

_____ **RC1.** When rounding to the nearest hundred, if the digit in the tens place is 5 or higher, we round up.

_____ **RC2.** When rounding 3500 to the nearest thousand, we should round down.

_____ **RC3.** An estimate made by rounding to the nearest thousand is more accurate than an estimate made by rounding to the nearest ten.

_____ **RC4.** Since 78 rounded to the nearest ten is 80, we can write $78 \approx 80$.

a   Round to the nearest ten.

1. 48

2. 532

3. 463

4. 8945

5. 731

6. 54

7. 895

8. 798

Round to the nearest hundred.

9. 146

10. 874

11. 957

12. 650

13. 9079

14. 4645

15. 32,839

16. 198,402

Round to the nearest thousand.

17. 5876

18. 4500

19. 7500

20. 2001

21. 45,340

22. 735,562

23. 373,405

24. 6,713,255

b   Estimate each sum or difference by first rounding to the nearest ten. Show your work.

25.
```
    7 8
  + 9 2
```

26.
```
    6 2
    9 7
    4 6
  + 8 1
```

27.
```
  8 0 7 4
− 2 3 4 7
```

28.
```
    6 7 3
  −   2 8
```

Estimate each sum by first rounding to the nearest ten. State if the given sum seems to be incorrect when compared to the estimate.

29.
```
    4 5
    7 7
    2 5
  + 5 6
    3 4 3
```

30.
```
    4 1
    2 1
    5 5
  + 6 0
    1 7 7
```

31.
```
    6 2 2
      7 8
      8 1
  + 1 1 1
    9 3 2
```

32.
```
    8 3 6
    3 7 4
    7 9 4
  + 9 3 8
    3 9 4 7
```

Estimate each sum or difference by first rounding to the nearest hundred. Show your work.

33. $\begin{array}{r} 7348 \\ +9247 \\ \hline \end{array}$

34. $\begin{array}{r} 568 \\ 472 \\ 938 \\ +402 \\ \hline \end{array}$

35. $\begin{array}{r} 6852 \\ -1748 \\ \hline \end{array}$

36. $\begin{array}{r} 9438 \\ -2787 \\ \hline \end{array}$

Estimate each sum by first rounding to the nearest hundred. State if the given sum seems to be incorrect when compared to the estimate.

37. $\begin{array}{r} 216 \\ 84 \\ 745 \\ +595 \\ \hline 1640 \end{array}$

38. $\begin{array}{r} 481 \\ 702 \\ 623 \\ +1043 \\ \hline 1849 \end{array}$

39. $\begin{array}{r} 750 \\ 428 \\ 63 \\ +205 \\ \hline 1446 \end{array}$

40. $\begin{array}{r} 326 \\ 275 \\ 758 \\ +943 \\ \hline 2302 \end{array}$

Estimate each sum or difference by first rounding to the nearest thousand. Show your work.

41. $\begin{array}{r} 9643 \\ 4821 \\ 8943 \\ +7004 \\ \hline \end{array}$

42. $\begin{array}{r} 7648 \\ 9348 \\ 7842 \\ +2222 \\ \hline \end{array}$

43. $\begin{array}{r} 92,149 \\ -22,555 \\ \hline \end{array}$

44. $\begin{array}{r} 84,890 \\ -11,110 \\ \hline \end{array}$

Estimate each product by first rounding to the nearest ten. Show your work.

45. $\begin{array}{r} 45 \\ \times 67 \\ \hline \end{array}$

46. $\begin{array}{r} 51 \\ \times 78 \\ \hline \end{array}$

47. $\begin{array}{r} 34 \\ \times 29 \\ \hline \end{array}$

48. $\begin{array}{r} 63 \\ \times 54 \\ \hline \end{array}$

Estimate each product by first rounding to the nearest hundred. Show your work.

49. $\begin{array}{r} 876 \\ \times 345 \\ \hline \end{array}$

50. $\begin{array}{r} 355 \\ \times 299 \\ \hline \end{array}$

51. $\begin{array}{r} 432 \\ \times 199 \\ \hline \end{array}$

52. $\begin{array}{r} 789 \\ \times 434 \\ \hline \end{array}$

Estimate each quotient by first rounding to the nearest ten. Show your work.

53. $347 \div 73$

54. $454 \div 87$

55. $8452 \div 46$

56. $1263 \div 29$

Copyright © 2015 Pearson Education, Inc.

Estimate each quotient by first rounding to the nearest hundred. Show your work.

57. $1165 \div 236$ **58.** $3641 \div 571$ **59.** $8358 \div 295$ **60.** $32{,}854 \div 748$

Planning a Vacation.   Most cruise ships offer a choice of rooms at varying prices, as well as additional packages and shore excursions at each port. The table below lists room prices for a seven-day Mediterranean cruise, as well as prices for several additional packages and excursions.

ROOMS	PRICE
Suite	$856
Balcony	$686
Ocean View	$586
Interior	$536

ADDITIONAL PACKAGES	PRICE
Spa	$115
Specialty Dining	$129
Beverage	$79

EXCURSIONS	PRICE
Athens, Greece; Private Tour	$289
Venice, Italy	$95
Istanbul, Turkey	$130
Pisa, Italy; Biking Tour	$199

61. Estimate the total price of a cruise with an ocean view room, a spa package, and an Istanbul excursion. Round each price to the nearest hundred dollars.

62. Estimate the total price of a cruise with a balcony room, no additional packages, a Venice excursion, and a biking tour in Pisa. Round each price to the nearest hundred dollars.

63. Antonio has a budget of $1000 for a Mediterranean cruise. He would like a balcony room, a specialty dining package, a private tour of Athens, and a tour of Venice. Estimate the total price of this cruise by rounding each price to the nearest hundred dollars. Can he afford his choices?

64. Alyssa has a budget of $1400 for a Mediterranean cruise. She is planning to book an interior room and would like to go on all the excursions listed. Estimate the total price of this cruise by rounding each price to the nearest hundred dollars. Does her budget cover her choices?

65. If you were going on a Mediterranean cruise and had a budget of $1500, what options would you choose? Decide on the options you would like and estimate the total price by rounding each price to the nearest hundred dollars. Could you afford all your chosen options?

66. If you were going on a Mediterranean cruise and had a budget of $1200, what options would you choose? Decide on the options you would like and estimate the total price by rounding each price to the nearest hundred dollars. Could you afford all your chosen options?

67. Mortgage Payments. To pay for their new home, Tim and Meribeth will make 360 payments of $751.55 each. In addition, they must add an escrow amount of $112.67 to each payment for insurance and taxes.

a) Estimate the total amount they will pay by rounding the number of payments, the amount of each payment, and the escrow amount to the nearest ten.

b) Estimate the total amount they will pay by rounding the number of payments, the amount of each payment, and the escrow amount to the nearest hundred.

68. Conference Expenses. The cost to attend a three-day teachers' conference is $245, and a hotel room costs $169 a night. One year, 489 teachers attended the conference, and 315 rooms were rented for two nights each.

a) Estimate the total amount spent by the teachers by rounding the cost of attending the conference, the cost of a hotel room, the number of teachers, and the number of rooms to the nearest ten.

b) Estimate the total amount spent by the teachers by rounding the cost of attending the conference, the cost of a hotel room, the number of teachers, and the number of rooms to the nearest hundred.

69. Banquet Attendance. Tickets to the annual awards banquet for the Riviera Swim Club cost $28 each. Ticket sales for the banquet totaled $2716. Estimate the number of people who attended the banquet by rounding the cost of a ticket to the nearest ten and the total sales to the nearest hundred.

70. School Fundraiser. For a school fundraiser, Charlotte sells trash bags at a price of $11 per roll. If her sales totaled $2211, estimate the number of rolls she sold by rounding the price per roll to the nearest ten and the total sales to the nearest hundred.

C Use < or > for ☐ to write a true sentence. Draw the number line if necessary.

71. 0 ☐ 17

72. 32 ☐ 0

73. 34 ☐ 12

74. 28 ☐ 18

75. 1000 ☐ 1001

76. 77 ☐ 117

77. 133 ☐ 132

78. 999 ☐ 997

79. 460 ☐ 17

80. 345 ☐ 456

81. 37 ☐ 11

82. 12 ☐ 32

Copyright © 2015 Pearson Education, Inc.

New Book Titles. The number of new book titles published in the United States in each of three recent years is shown in the table below. Use this table to do Exercises 83 and 84.

YEAR	NEW BOOK TITLES
2009	1,335,475
2010	4,134,519
2011	1,532,623*

SOURCE: R. R. Bowker
*Projected

83. Write an inequality to compare the numbers of new titles published in 2009 and in 2010.

84. Write an inequality to compare the numbers of new titles published in 2010 and in 2011.

85. *Public Schools.* The number of public schools in the United States increased from 97,382 in 2006 to 98,817 in 2010. Write an inequality to compare these numbers of schools.

86. *Life Expectancy.* The life expectancy of a female in the United States in 2020 is predicted to be about 82 years and that of a male about 77 years. Write an inequality to compare these life expectancies.

Public Schools

SOURCE: National Center for Education Statistics

Life Expectancy in the United States

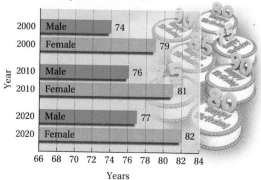

SOURCE: U.S. Census Bureau

Skill Maintenance

Add. [1.2a]

87.
$$\begin{array}{r} 6\,7,7\,8\,9 \\ +\ 1\,8,9\,6\,5 \\ \hline \end{array}$$

88.
$$\begin{array}{r} 9\,0\,0\,2 \\ +\ 4\,5\,8\,7 \\ \hline \end{array}$$

Subtract. [1.3a]

89.
$$\begin{array}{r} 6\,7,7\,8\,9 \\ -\ 1\,8,9\,6\,5 \\ \hline \end{array}$$

90.
$$\begin{array}{r} 9\,0\,0\,2 \\ -\ 4\,5\,8\,7 \\ \hline \end{array}$$

Multiply. [1.4a]

91.
$$\begin{array}{r} 4\,6 \\ \times\ 3\,7 \\ \hline \end{array}$$

92.
$$\begin{array}{r} 3\,0\,6 \\ \times\ \ 5\,8 \\ \hline \end{array}$$

Divide. [1.5a]

93. $328 \div 6$

94. $4784 \div 23$

Synthesis

95.–98. 🖩 Use a calculator to find the sums and the differences in each of Exercises 41–44. Then compare your answers with those found using estimation. Even when using a calculator it is possible to make an error if you press the wrong buttons, so it is a good idea to check by estimating.

OBJECTIVES

a   Solve simple equations by trial.

b   Solve equations like $t + 28 = 54$, $28 \cdot x = 168$, and $98 \cdot 2 = y$.

SKILL TO REVIEW

Objective 1.5a: Divide whole numbers.

Divide.

1. $1008 \div 36$
2. $675 \div 15$

Find a number that makes each sentence true.

1. $8 = 1 + \square$

2. $\square + 2 = 7$

3. Determine whether 7 is a solution of $\square + 5 = 9$.

4. Determine whether 4 is a solution of $\square + 5 = 9$.

Solve by trial.

5. $n + 3 = 8$

6. $x - 2 = 8$

7. $45 \div 9 = y$

8. $10 + t = 32$

Answers

Skill to Review:
1. 28   2. 45

Margin Exercises:
1. 7   2. 5   3. No   4. Yes   5. 5
6. 10   7. 5   8. 22

a   SOLUTIONS BY TRIAL

Let's find a number that we can put in the blank to make this sentence true:

$$9 = 3 + \square.$$

We are asking "9 is 3 plus what number?" The answer is 6.

$$9 = 3 + 6$$

◄ Do Margin Exercises 1 and 2.

A sentence with = is called an **equation**. A **solution** of an equation is a number that makes the sentence true. Thus, 6 is a solution of

$$9 = 3 + \square \quad \text{because} \quad 9 = 3 + 6 \text{ is true.}$$

However, 7 is not a solution of

$$9 = 3 + \square \quad \text{because} \quad 9 = 3 + 7 \text{ is false.}$$

◄ Do Exercises 3 and 4.

We can use a letter in an equation instead of a blank:

$$9 = 3 + n.$$

We call n a **variable** because it can represent any number. If a replacement for a variable makes an equation true, the replacement is a solution of the equation.

SOLUTIONS OF AN EQUATION

A **solution of an equation** is a replacement for the variable that makes the equation true. When we find all the solutions, we say that we have **solved** the equation.

EXAMPLE 1   Solve $y + 12 = 27$ by trial.

We replace y with several numbers.

If we replace y with 13, we get a false equation: $13 + 12 = 27$.
If we replace y with 14, we get a false equation: $14 + 12 = 27$.
If we replace y with 15, we get a true equation: $15 + 12 = 27$.

No other replacement makes the equation true, so the solution is 15.

EXAMPLES   Solve.

2. $7 + n = 22$
(7 plus what number is 22?)
The solution is 15.

3. $63 = 3 \cdot x$
(63 is 3 times what number?)
The solution is 21.

◄ Do Exercises 5–8.

b SOLVING EQUATIONS

We now begin to develop more efficient ways to solve certain equations. When an equation has a variable alone on one side and a calculation on the other side, we can find the solution by carrying out the calculation.

EXAMPLE 4 Solve: $x = 245 \times 34$.

To solve the equation, we carry out the calculation.

$$
\begin{array}{r}
2\ 4\ 5 \\
\times\ 3\ 4 \\
\hline
9\ 8\ 0 \\
7\ 3\ 5\ 0 \\
\hline
8\ 3\ 3\ 0
\end{array}
$$

$x = 245 \times 34$

$x = 8330$

The solution is 8330.

Do Exercises 9–12.

Look at the equation

$x + 12 = 27.$

We can get x alone by subtracting 12 *on both sides*. Thus,

$$x + 12 - 12 = 27 - 12 \qquad \text{Subtracting 12 on both sides}$$
$$x + 0 = 15 \qquad \text{Carrying out the subtraction}$$
$$x = 15.$$

SOLVING $x + a = b$

To solve $x + a = b$, subtract a on both sides.

If we can get an equation in a form with the variable alone on one side, we can "see" the solution.

EXAMPLE 5 Solve: $t + 28 = 54$.

We have

$$t + 28 = 54$$
$$t + 28 - 28 = 54 - 28 \qquad \text{Subtracting 28 on both sides}$$
$$t + 0 = 26$$
$$t = 26.$$

To check the answer, we substitute 26 for t in the original equation.

Check: $\dfrac{t + 28 = 54}{26 + 28\ ?\ 54}$
$54\ |$ TRUE   Since $54 = 54$ is true, 26 checks.

The solution is 26.

Do Exercises 13 and 14.

Solve.

9. $346 \times 65 = y$

10. $x = 2347 + 6675$

11. $4560 \div 8 = t$

12. $x = 6007 - 2346$

Solve. Be sure to check.

GS 13. $x + 9 = 17$

$x + 9 - \boxed{} = 17 - 9$

$x = \boxed{}$

Check: $\dfrac{x + 9 = 17}{\boxed{} + 9\ ?\ 17}$

$\boxed{}\ |$

Since $17 = 17$ is $\boxed{}$, the answer checks. The solution is $\boxed{}$.

14. $77 = m + 32$

Answers

9. 22,490   **10.** 9022   **11.** 570   **12.** 3661
13. 8   **14.** 45

Guided Solution:
13. 9, 8, 8, 17; true; 8

EXAMPLE 6 Solve: $182 = 65 + n$.

We have

$$182 = 65 + n$$
$$182 - 65 = 65 + n - 65 \qquad \text{Subtracting 65 on both sides}$$
$$117 = 0 + n \qquad \text{65 plus } n \text{ minus 65 is } 0 + n.$$
$$117 = n.$$

Check: $\dfrac{182 = 65 + n}{182 \ ? \ 65 + 117}$
$$\quad | \ 182 \qquad \text{TRUE}$$

The solution is 117.

◀ **Do Exercise 15.**

15. Solve: $155 = t + 78$. Be sure to check.

EXAMPLE 7 Solve: $7381 + x = 8067$.

We have

$$7381 + x = 8067$$
$$7381 + x - 7381 = 8067 - 7381 \qquad \text{Subtracting 7381 on both sides}$$
$$x = 686.$$

Check: $\dfrac{7381 + x = 8067}{7381 + 686 \ ? \ 8067}$
$$\qquad 8067 \ | \qquad \text{TRUE}$$

The solution is 686.

◀ **Do Exercises 16 and 17.**

Solve. Be sure to check.

16. $4566 + x = 7877$

17. $8172 = h + 2058$

We now learn to solve equations like $8 \cdot n = 96$. Look at

$$8 \cdot n = 96.$$

We can get n alone by dividing by 8 *on both sides.* Thus,

$$\frac{8 \cdot n}{8} = \frac{96}{8} \qquad \text{Dividing by 8 on both sides}$$
$$n = 12. \qquad \text{8 times } n \text{ divided by 8 is } n.$$

To check the answer, we substitute 12 for n in the original equation.

Check: $\dfrac{8 \cdot n = 96}{8 \cdot 12 \ ? \ 96}$
$$\qquad 96 \ | \qquad \text{TRUE}$$

Since $96 = 96$ is a true equation, 12 is the solution of the equation.

SOLVING $a \cdot x = b$

To solve $a \cdot x = b$, divide by a on both sides.

Answers

15. 77 **16.** 3311 **17.** 6114

EXAMPLE 8 Solve: $10 \cdot x = 240$.

We have

$$10 \cdot x = 240$$
$$\frac{10 \cdot x}{10} = \frac{240}{10} \qquad \text{Dividing by 10 on both sides}$$
$$x = 24.$$

Check: $$\begin{array}{c|c} 10 \cdot x = 240 \\ \hline 10 \cdot 24 \; ? \; 240 \\ 240 & \text{TRUE} \end{array}$$

The solution is 24.

EXAMPLE 9 Solve: $5202 = 9 \cdot t$.

We have

$$5202 = 9 \cdot t$$
$$\frac{5202}{9} = \frac{9 \cdot t}{9} \qquad \text{Dividing by 9 on both sides}$$
$$578 = t.$$

Check: $$\begin{array}{c|c} 5202 = 9 \cdot t \\ \hline 5202 \; ? \; 9 \cdot 578 \\ 5202 & \text{TRUE} \end{array}$$

The solution is 578.

Do Exercises 18–20.

EXAMPLE 10 Solve: $14 \cdot y = 1092$.

We have

$$14 \cdot y = 1092$$
$$\frac{14 \cdot y}{14} = \frac{1092}{14} \qquad \text{Dividing by 14 on both sides}$$
$$y = 78.$$

The check is left to the student. The solution is 78.

EXAMPLE 11 Solve: $n \cdot 56 = 4648$.

We have

$$n \cdot 56 = 4648$$
$$\frac{n \cdot 56}{56} = \frac{4648}{56} \qquad \text{Dividing by 56 on both sides}$$
$$n = 83.$$

The check is left to the student. The solution is 83.

Do Exercises 21 and 22.

Solve. Be sure to check.

18. $8 \cdot x = 64$

GS **19.** $144 = 9 \cdot n$

$$\frac{144}{9} = \frac{9 \cdot n}{\square}$$
$$\square = n$$

Check: $$\begin{array}{c|c} 144 = 9 \cdot n \\ \hline 144 \; ? \; 9 \cdot \square \\ \square \end{array}$$

Since $144 = 144$ is $\square$, the answer checks. The solution is $\square$.

20. $5152 = 8 \cdot t$

Solve. Be sure to check.

21. $18 \cdot y = 1728$

22. $n \cdot 48 = 4512$

Answers

18. 8   **19.** 16   **20.** 644   **21.** 96   **22.** 94

Guided Solution:
19. 9, 16, 16, 144; true; 16

✓ Reading Check

Match each word with its definition from the list on the right.

RC1. Equation _____

RC2. Solution _____

RC3. Solved _____

RC4. Variable _____

a) A replacement for the variable that makes an equation true

b) A letter that can represent any number

c) A sentence containing $=$

d) An equation for which we have found all solutions

a Solve by trial.

1. $x + 0 = 14$

2. $x - 7 = 18$

3. $y \cdot 17 = 0$

4. $56 \div m = 7$

b Solve. Be sure to check.

5. $x = 12{,}345 + 78{,}555$

6. $t = 5678 + 9034$

7. $908 - 458 = p$

8. $9007 - 5667 = m$

9. $16 \cdot 22 = y$

10. $34 \cdot 15 = z$

11. $t = 125 \div 5$

12. $w = 256 \div 16$

13. $13 + x = 42$

14. $15 + t = 22$

15. $12 = 12 + m$

16. $16 = t + 16$

17. $10 + x = 89$

18. $20 + x = 57$

19. $61 = 16 + y$

20. $53 = 17 + w$

21. $3 \cdot x = 24$

22. $6 \cdot x = 42$

23. $112 = n \cdot 8$

24. $162 = 9 \cdot m$

25. $3 \cdot m = 96$

26. $4 \cdot y = 96$

27. $715 = 5 \cdot z$

28. $741 = 3 \cdot t$

Copyright © 2015 Pearson Education, Inc.

29. $8322 + 9281 = x$

30. $9281 - 8322 = y$

31. $47 + n = 84$

32. $56 + p = 92$

33. $45 \cdot 23 = x$

34. $23 \cdot 78 = y$

35. $x + 78 = 144$

36. $z + 67 = 133$

37. $6 \cdot p = 1944$

38. $4 \cdot w = 3404$

39. $567 + x = 902$

40. $438 + x = 807$

41. $234 \cdot 78 = y$

42. $10{,}534 \div 458 = q$

43. $18 \cdot x = 1872$

44. $19 \cdot x = 6080$

45. $40 \cdot x = 1800$

46. $20 \cdot x = 1500$

47. $2344 + y = 6400$

48. $9281 = 8322 + t$

49. $m = 7006 - 4159$

50. $n = 3004 - 1745$

51. $165 = 11 \cdot n$

52. $660 = 12 \cdot n$

53. $58 \cdot m = 11{,}890$

54. $233 \cdot x = 22{,}135$

55. $491 - 34 = y$

56. $512 - 63 = z$

Skill Maintenance

Divide. [1.5a]

57. $1283 \div 9$

58. $1278 \div 9$

59. $1\,7\,\overline{)\,5\,6\,7\,8}$

60. $1\,7\,\overline{)\,5\,6\,8\,9}$

Use $>$ or $<$ for $\square$ to write a true sentence. [1.6c]

61. $123 \;\square\; 789$

62. $342 \;\square\; 339$

63. $688 \;\square\; 0$

64. $0 \;\square\; 11$

65. Round 6,375,602 to the nearest thousand. [1.6a]

66. Round 6,375,602 to the nearest ten. [1.6a]

Synthesis

Solve.

67. 🖩 $23{,}465 \cdot x = 8{,}142{,}355$

68. 🖩 $48{,}916 \cdot x = 14{,}332{,}388$

1.8

Applications and Problem Solving

OBJECTIVE

a Solve applied problems involving addition, subtraction, multiplication, or division of whole numbers.

SKILL TO REVIEW

Objective 1.6b: Estimate sums, differences, products, and quotients by rounding.

Estimate each sum or difference by first rounding to the nearest thousand. Show your work.

1.
$$
\begin{array}{r}
3\,6\,7{,}9\,8\,2 \\
+\quad 4\,3{,}4\,9\,5 \\
\end{array}
$$

2.
$$
\begin{array}{r}
9\,2\,8\,7 \\
-\,3\,5\,0\,2 \\
\end{array}
$$

a A PROBLEM-SOLVING STRATEGY

One of the most important ways in which we use mathematics is as a tool in solving problems. To solve a problem, we use the following five-step strategy.

FIVE STEPS FOR PROBLEM SOLVING

1. **Familiarize** yourself with the problem situation.
2. **Translate** the problem to an equation using a variable.
3. **Solve** the equation.
4. **Check** to see whether your possible solution actually fits the problem situation and is thus really a solution of the problem.
5. **State** the answer clearly using a complete sentence and appropriate units.

The first of these five steps, becoming familiar with the problem, is probably the most important.

THE FAMILIARIZE STEP

- If the problem is presented in words, read and reread it carefully until you understand what you are being asked to find.
- Make a drawing, if it makes sense to do so.
- Write a list of the known facts and a list of what you wish to find out.
- Assign a letter, or *variable*, to the unknown.
- Organize the information in a chart or a table.
- Find further information. Look up a formula, consult a reference book or an expert in the field, or do research on the Internet.
- Guess or estimate the answer and check your guess or estimate.

Answers

Skill to Review:
1. $368{,}000 + 43{,}000 = 411{,}000$
2. $9000 - 4000 = 5000$

EXAMPLE 1 *Video Game Platforms.* The following table shows the total number of units of eight popular video game platforms sold worldwide, as of December 8, 2012. Three of these are made by PlayStation®. Find the total number of PlayStation units sold.

PLATFORM	GLOBAL SALES
Nintendo 3DS	682,396
Xbox 360	614,353
Nintendo Wii U	610,384
PlayStation® 3	576,565
Nintendo Wii	252,484
Nintendo DS	178,209
PlayStation® Vita	152,049
PlayStation® Portable	54,677

Source: www.vgchartz.com

1. **Familiarize.** First, we assign a letter, or variable, to the number we wish to find. We let p = the total number of video game units sold by PlayStation. Since we are combining numbers, we will add.

2. **Translate.** We translate to an equation:

Number of PlayStation 3 units	plus	Number of PlayStation Vita units	plus	Number of PlayStation Portable units	is	Total number of PlayStation units
576,565	+	152,049	+	54,677	=	p

3. **Solve.** We solve the equation by carrying out the addition.

$$576{,}565 + 152{,}049 + 54{,}677 = p$$
$$783{,}291 = p$$

$$\begin{array}{r} 576{,}565 \\ 152{,}049 \\ +\ \ 54{,}677 \\ \hline 783{,}291 \end{array}$$

4. **Check.** We check our result by rereading the original problem and seeing if 783,291 answers the question. Since we are looking for a total, we could repeat the addition calculation. We could also check whether the answer is reasonable. In this case, since the total is greater than any of the three separate sales numbers, the result seems reasonable. Another way to check is to estimate the expected result and compare the estimate with the calculated result. If we round each PlayStation sales number to the nearest ten thousand and add, we have

$$580{,}000 + 150{,}000 + 50{,}000 = 780{,}000.$$

Since $780{,}000 \approx 783{,}291$, our result again seems reasonable.

5. **State.** The total number of the three PlayStation units sold worldwide as of December 8, 2012, is 783,291.

Do Exercises 1–3. ▶

Refer to the table in Example 1 to do Margin Exercises 1–3.

1. Find the total number of Nintendo units sold.

2. Find the total number of units sold for the four most popular game platforms listed in the table.

3. Find the total number of units sold for all the game platforms listed in the table.

Answers

1. 1,723,473 units 2. 2,483,698 units
3. 3,121,117 units

EXAMPLE 2 *Travel Distance.* Abigail is driving from Indianapolis to Salt Lake City to attend a family reunion. The distance from Indianapolis to Salt Lake City is 1634 mi. In the first two days, she travels 1154 mi to Denver. How much farther must she travel?

1. **Familiarize.** We first make a drawing or at least visualize the situation. We let d = the remaining distance to Salt Lake City.

2. **Translate.** We want to determine how many more miles Abigail must travel. We translate to an equation:

Distance already traveled	plus	Distance to go	is	Total distance of trip
↓	↓	↓	↓	↓
1154	+	d	=	1634.

3. **Solve.** To solve the equation, we subtract 1154 on both sides.

$$1154 + d = 1634$$
$$1154 + d - 1154 = 1634 - 1154$$
$$d = 480$$

$$\begin{array}{r} {\scriptstyle 5\ 13} \\ 1\ 6\ 3\ 4 \\ -\ 1\ 1\ 5\ 4 \\ \hline 4\ \cdot 8\ 0 \end{array}$$

4. **Check.** We check our answer of 480 mi in the original problem. This number should be less than the total distance, 1634 mi, and it is. We can add the distance traveled, 1154, and the distance left to go, 480: $1154 + 480 = 1634$. We can also estimate:

$$1634 - 1154 \approx 1600 - 1200$$
$$= 400 \approx 480.$$

The answer, 480 mi, checks.

5. **State.** Abigail must travel 480 mi farther to Salt Lake City.

◀ Do Exercise 4.

---

4. **Reading Assignment.** William **GS** has been assigned 234 pages of reading for his history class. He has read 86 pages. How many more pages does he have to read?

1. **Familiarize.** Let p = the number of pages William still has to read.

2. **Translate.**

Pages already read	plus	Number of pages to read	is	Total number of pages
↓	↓	↓	↓	↓
86	+	☐	=	☐

3. **Solve.**

$$86 + p = 234$$
$$86 + p - \boxed{} = 234 - 86$$
$$p = \boxed{}$$

4. **Check.** If William reads 148 more pages, he will have read a total of $86 + 148$ pages, or ☐ pages.

5. **State.** William has ☐ more pages to read.

Answer

4. 148 pages

Guided Solution:

4. p, 234; 86, 148; 234; 148

EXAMPLE 3 *Total Cost of Chairs.* What is the total cost of 6 Adirondack chairs if each one costs $169?

1. Familiarize. We make a drawing and let $C =$ the cost of 6 chairs.

$169 $169 $169 $169 $169 $169

2. Translate. We translate to an equation:

Number of chairs	times	Cost of each chair	is	Total cost
6	×	169	=	C.

3. Solve. This sentence tells us what to do. We multiply.

$$6 \times 169 = C$$
$$1014 = C$$

```
    1 6 9
  ×     6
  1 0 1 4
```

4. Check. We have an answer, 1014, that is greater than the cost of any one chair, which is reasonable. We can also check by estimating:

$$6 \times 169 \approx 6 \times 170 = 1020 \approx 1014.$$

The answer checks.

5. State. The total cost of 6 chairs is $1014.

Do Exercise 5. ▶

5. *Total Cost of Gas Grills.* What is the total cost of 14 gas grills, each with 520 sq in. of total cooking surface, if each one costs $398?

EXAMPLE 4 *Area of an Oriental Rug.* The dimensions of the oriental rug in the Fosters' front hallway are 42 in. by 66 in. What is the area of the rug?

1. Familiarize. We let $A =$ the area of the rug and use the formula for the area of a rectangle, $A = $ length $\cdot$ width $= l \cdot w$. Since we usually consider length to be larger than width, we will let $l = 66$ in. and $w = 42$ in.

42 in.

← 66 in. →

2. Translate. We substitute in the formula:

$$A = l \cdot w = 66 \cdot 42.$$

Answer

5. $5572

3. Solve. We carry out the multiplication.

$$A = 66 \cdot 42$$
$$A = 2772$$

$$
\begin{array}{r}
6\ 6 \\
\times\ 4\ 2 \\
\hline
1\ 3\ 2 \\
2\ 6\ 4\ 0 \\
\hline
2\ 7\ 7\ 2
\end{array}
$$

4. Check. We can repeat the calculation. We can also round and estimate:

$$66 \times 42 \approx 70 \times 40 = 2800 \approx 2772.$$

The answer checks.

5. State. The area of the rug is 2772 sq in.

◀ Do Exercise 6.

6. *Bed Sheets.* The dimensions of a flat sheet for a queen-size bed are 90 in. by 102 in. What is the area of the sheet?

EXAMPLE 5 *Packages of Gum.* A candy company produces 3304 sticks of gum. How many 12-stick packages can be filled? How many sticks will be left over?

1. Familiarize. We make a drawing to visualize the situation and let $n =$ the number of 12-stick packages that can be filled. The problem can be considered as repeated subtraction, taking successive sets of 12 sticks and putting them into n packages.

12-stick packages

How many packages?   How many sticks are left over?

2. Translate. We translate to an equation:

Number of sticks divided by Number in each package is Number of packages

$$3304 \quad \div \quad 12 \quad = \quad n.$$

3. Solve. We solve the equation by carrying out the division.

$$3304 \div 12 = n$$
$$275\,\text{R}\,4 = n$$

$$
\begin{array}{r}
2\ 7\ 5 \\
12\overline{)3\ 3\ 0\ 4} \\
\underline{2\ 4} \\
9\ 0 \\
\underline{8\ 4} \\
6\ 4 \\
\underline{6\ 0} \\
4
\end{array}
$$

Answer

6. 9180 sq in.

4. Check. We can check by multiplying the number of packages by 12 and adding the remainder, 4:

$$12 \cdot 275 = 3300,$$
$$3300 + 4 = 3304.$$

5. State. Thus, 275 twelve-stick packages of gum can be filled. There will be 4 sticks left over.

Do Exercise 7. ▶

EXAMPLE 6 *Automobile Mileage.* A 2013 Toyota Matrix gets 26 miles per gallon (mpg) in city driving. How many gallons will it use in 4758 mi of city driving?
Source: Toyota

1. Familiarize. We make a drawing and let g = the number of gallons of gasoline used in 4758 mi of city driving.

← 26 mi → ← 26 mi → ← 26 mi → • • • ← 26 mi →
4758 mi to drive

2. Translate. Repeated addition or multiplication applies here.

Number of miles per gallon	times	Number of gallons used	is	Number of miles driven
26	·	g	=	4758

3. Solve. To solve the equation, we divide by 26 on both sides.

$$26 \cdot g = 4758$$
$$\frac{26 \cdot g}{26} = \frac{4758}{26}$$
$$g = 183$$

```
      1 8 3
2 6 ) 4 7 5 8
      2 6
      2 1 5
      2 0 8
          7 8
          7 8
           0
```

4. Check. To check, we multiply 183 by 26.

```
    1 8 3
  ×   2 6
  1 0 9 8
  3 6 6 0
  4 7 5 8
```

The answer checks.

5. State. The Toyota Matrix will use 183 gal of gasoline.

Do Exercise 8. ▶

7. *Packages of Gum.* The candy company in Example 5 also produces 6-stick packages. How many 6-stick packages can be filled with 2269 sticks of gum? How many sticks will be left over?

8. *Automobile Mileage.* A 2013 Toyota Matrix gets 32 miles per gallon (mpg) in highway driving. How many gallons will it use in 2528 mi of highway driving?

Source: Toyota

Answers

7. 378 packages with 1 stick left over
8. 79 gal

Multistep Problems

Sometimes we must use more than one operation to solve a problem, as in the following example.

EXAMPLE 7 *Weight Loss.* To lose one pound, you must burn about 3500 calories in excess of what you already burn doing your regular daily activities. The following chart shows how long a person must engage in several types of exercise in order to burn 100 calories. For how long would a person have to run at a brisk pace in order to lose one pound?

To burn 100 calories, you must:

• Run for 8 minutes at a brisk pace, or
• Swim for 2 minutes at a brisk pace, or
• Bicycle for 15 minutes at 9 mph, or
• Do aerobic exercises for 15 minutes, or
• Golf, walking, for 20 minutes, or
• Play tennis, singles, for 11 minutes

1. **Familiarize.** This is a multistep problem. We will first find how many hundreds are in 3500. This will tell us how many times a person must run for 8 min in order to lose one pound. Then we will find the total number of minutes required for the weight loss.

   We let $x =$ the number of hundreds in 3500 and $t =$ the time it takes to lose one pound.

2. **Translate.** We translate to two equations.

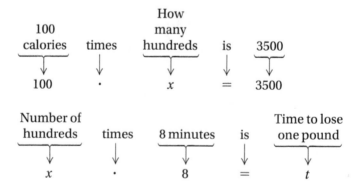

$$100 \cdot x = 3500$$

$$x \cdot 8 = t$$

3. Solve. We divide by 100 on both sides of the first equation to find x.

$$100 \cdot x = 3500$$

$$\frac{100 \cdot x}{100} = \frac{3500}{100}$$

$$x = 35$$

$$
\begin{array}{r}
3\,5 \\
100\,\overline{)\,3\,5\,0\,0} \\
3\,0\,0 \\
\hline
5\,0\,0 \\
5\,0\,0 \\
\hline
0
\end{array}
$$

Then we use the fact that $x = 35$ to find t.

$$x \cdot 8 = t$$
$$35 \cdot 8 = t$$
$$280 = t$$

$$
\begin{array}{r}
3\,5 \\
\times\ \ 8 \\
\hline
2\,8\,0
\end{array}
$$

4. Check. Suppose you run for 280 min. For every 8 min of running, you burn 100 calories. Since $280 \div 8 = 35$, there are 35 groups of 8 min in 280 min, so you will burn $35 \times 100 = 3500$ calories.

5. State. You must run for 280 min, or 4 hr 40 min, at a brisk pace in order to lose one pound.

Do Exercise 9. ▶

The key words, phrases, and concepts in the following table are useful when translating the problems to equations.

Key Words, Phrases, and Concepts

ADDITION (+)	SUBTRACTION (−)	MULTIPLICATION (×)	DIVISION (÷)
add	subtract	multiply	divide
added to	subtracted from	multiplied by	divided by
sum	difference	product	quotient
total	minus	times	repeated subtraction
plus	less than	of	missing factor
more than	decreased by	repeated addition	finding equal quantities
increased by	take away	rectangular arrays	
	how much more		

The following tips are also helpful in problem solving.

> **PROBLEM-SOLVING TIPS**
>
> 1. Look for patterns when solving problems.
> 2. When translating in mathematics, consider the dimensions of the variables and constants in the equation. The variables that represent length should all be in the same unit, those that represent money should all be in dollars or all in cents, and so on.
> 3. Make sure that units appear in the answer whenever appropriate and that you completely answer the original problem.

 9. Weight Loss. Use the information in Example 7 to determine how long an individual must swim at a brisk pace in order to lose one pound.

1. **Familiarize.** Let $x =$ the number of hundreds in 3500. Let $t =$ the time it takes to lose one pound.

2. **Translate.**

$$100 \cdot x = \boxed{}$$
$$x \cdot \boxed{} = t$$

3. **Solve.** From Example 7, we know that $x = \boxed{}$.

$$x \cdot 2 = t$$
$$\boxed{} \cdot 2 = t$$
$$\boxed{} = t$$

4. **Check.** Since $70 \div 2 = 35$, there are $\boxed{}$ groups of 2 min in 70 min. Thus, you will burn $35 \times 100 = \boxed{}$ calories.

5. **State.** You must swim for $\boxed{}$ min, or 1 hr $\boxed{}$ min, in order to lose one pound.

Answer

9. 70 min, or 1 hr 10 min

Guided Solution:

9. 3500, 2; 35, 35, 70, 35, 3500, 70, 10

Translating for Success

1. **Brick-Mason Expense.** A commercial contractor is building 30 two-unit condominiums in a retirement community. The brick-mason expense for each building is $10,860. What is the total cost of bricking the buildings?

2. **Heights.** Dean's sons are on the high school basketball team. Their heights are 73 in., 69 in., and 76 in. How much taller is the tallest son than the shortest son?

3. **Account Balance.** James has $423 in his checking account. Then he deposits $73 and uses his debit card for purchases of $76 and $69. How much is left in the account?

4. **Purchasing a Computer.** A computer is on sale for $423. Jenny has only $69. How much more does she need to buy the computer?

5. **Purchasing Coffee Makers.** Sara purchases 8 coffee makers for the newly remodeled bed-and-breakfast that she manages. If she pays $52 for each coffee maker, what is the total cost of her purchase?

The goal of these matching questions is to practice step (2), Translate, of the five-step problem-solving process. Translate each word problem to an equation and select a correct translation from equations A–O.

A. $8 \cdot 52 = n$

B. $69 \cdot n = 76$

C. $73 - 76 - 69 = n$

D. $423 + 73 - 76 - 69 = n$

E. $30 \cdot 10{,}860 = n$

F. $15 \cdot n = 195$

G. $69 + n = 423$

H. $n = 10{,}860 - 300$

I. $n = 423 \div 69$

J. $30 \cdot n = 10{,}860$

K. $15 \cdot 195 = n$

L. $n = 52 - 8$

M. $69 + n = 76$

N. $15 \div 195 = n$

O. $52 + n = 60$

Answers on page A-2

6. **Hourly Rate.** Miller Auto Repair charges $52 per hour for labor. Jackson Auto Care charges $60 per hour. How much more does Jackson charge than Miller?

7. **College Band.** A college band with 195 members marches in a 15-row formation in the home-coming halftime performance. How many members are in each row?

8. **Shoe Purchase.** A college football team purchases 15 pairs of shoes at $195 a pair. What is the total cost of this purchase?

9. **Loan Payment.** Kendra's uncle loans her $10,860, interest free, to buy a car. The loan is to be paid off in 30 payments. How much is each payment?

10. **College Enrollment.** At the beginning of the fall term, the total enrollment in Lakeview Community College was 10,860. By the end of the first two weeks, 300 students had withdrawn. How many students were then enrolled?

✓ Reading Check

List the steps of the problem-solving strategy in order, using the choices given below. The last step is already listed.

Check   Familiarize   Solve   Translate

RC1. 1. _____ .

RC2. 2. _____ .

RC3. 3. _____ .

RC4. 4. _____ .

5. State.

Towers Never Built.   The buildings shown in the figure below were designed but never completed. Use the information to do Exercises 1–4.

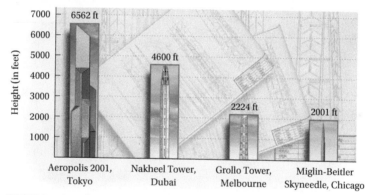

Towers Never Built

SOURCE: http://en.wikipedia.org/wiki/Proposed_tall_buildings_and_structures

1. How much taller would the Aeropolis 2001 have been than the Nakheel Tower?

2. How much taller would the Grollo Tower have been than the Miglin-Beitler Skyneedle?

3. The Willis Tower (formerly the Sears Tower) is the tallest building in Chicago. If the Miglin-Beitler Skyneedle had been built, it would have been 551 ft higher than the Willis Tower. What is the height of the Willis Tower?

4. The Burj Khalifa is the tallest building in Dubai. If the Nakheel Tower had been built, it would have been 1883 ft higher than the Burj Khalifa. What is the height of the Burj Khalifa?

5. *Caffeine Content.*   An 8-oz serving of Red Bull energy drink contains 76 milligrams of caffeine. An 8-oz serving of brewed coffee contains 19 more milligrams of caffeine than the energy drink. How many milligrams of caffeine does the 8-oz serving of coffee contain?

Source: The Mayo Clinic

6. *Caffeine Content.*   Hershey's 6-oz milk chocolate almond bar contains 25 milligrams of caffeine. A 20-oz bottle of Coca-Cola has 32 more milligrams of caffeine than the Hershey bar. How many milligrams of caffeine does the 20-oz bottle of Coca-Cola have?

Source: *National Geographic*, "Caffeine," by T. R. Reid, January 2005

7. A carpenter drills 216 holes in a rectangular array to construct a pegboard. There are 12 holes in each row. How many rows are there?

8. Lou arranges 504 entries on a spreadsheet in a rectangular array that has 36 rows. How many entries are in each row?

9. *Olympics.* There were 302 events in the 2012 Summer Olympics in London, England. This was 259 more events than there were in the first modern Olympic games in Athens, Greece, in 1896. How many events were there in 1896?

Sources: *USA Today* research; infoplease.com

10. *Drilling Activity.* In 2011, there were 984 rotary rigs drilling for crude oil in the United States. This was 687 more rigs than were active in 2007. Find the number of active rotary oil rigs in 2007.

Source: Energy Information Administration

11. *Boundaries between Countries.* The boundary between mainland United States and Canada including the Great Lakes is 3987 mi long. The length of the boundary between the United States and Mexico is 1933 mi. How much longer is the Canadian border?

Source: U.S. Geological Survey

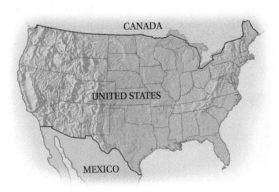

12. *Longest Rivers.* The longest river in the world is the Nile in Africa at about 4135 mi. The longest river in the United States is the Missouri–Mississippi at about 3860 mi. How much longer is the Nile?

13. *Pixels.* A high-definition television (HDTV) screen consists of small rectangular dots called *pixels*. How many pixels are there on a screen that has 1080 rows with 1920 pixels in each row?

Pixel

14. *Crossword Puzzle.* The *USA Today* crossword puzzle is a rectangle containing 15 rows with 15 squares in each row. How many squares does the puzzle have altogether?

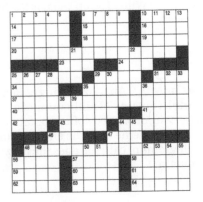

Copyright © 2015 Pearson Education, Inc.

15. There are 24 hr in a day and 7 days in a week. How many hours are there in a week?

16. There are 60 min in an hour and 24 hr in a day. How many minutes are there in a day?

Housing Costs. The graph below shows the average monthly rent for a one-bedroom apartment in several cities in November 2012. Use this graph to do Exercises 17–22.

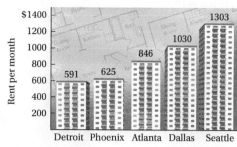

Average Rent for a One-Bedroom Apartment

Rent per month

$1400
1200
1000
800
600
400
200

591 625 846 1030 1303

Detroit Phoenix Atlanta Dallas Seattle

SOURCE: rentjungle.com

17. How much higher is the average monthly rent in Seattle than in Dallas?

18. How much lower is the average monthly rent in Phoenix than in Atlanta?

19. Phil, Scott, and Julio plan to rent a one-bedroom apartment in Detroit immediately after graduation, sharing the rent equally. What average monthly rent can each of them expect to pay?

20. Maria and her sister Theresa plan to share a one-bedroom apartment in Dallas, dividing the monthly rent equally between them. About how much can each of them expect to pay?

21. On average, how much rent would a tenant pay for a one-bedroom apartment in Detroit during a 12-month period?

22. On average, how much rent would a tenant pay for a one-bedroom apartment in Seattle during a 6-month period?

23. *Colonial Population.* Before the establishment of the U.S. Census in 1790, it was estimated that the colonial population in 1780 was 2,780,400. This was an increase of 2,628,900 from the population in 1680. What was the colonial population in 1680?

Source: *Time Almanac*

24. *Interstate Speed Limits.* The speed limit for passenger cars on interstate highways in rural areas in Montana is 75 mph. This is 10 mph faster than the speed limit for trucks on the same roads. What is the speed limit for trucks?

25. Yard-Sale Profit. Ruth made $312 at her yard sale and divided the money equally among her four grandchildren. How much did each child receive?

26. Paper Measures. A quire of paper consists of 25 sheets, and a ream of paper consists of 500 sheets. How many quires are in a ream?

27. Parking Rates. The most expensive parking in the United States is found in midtown New York City, where the average rate is $585 per month. This is $545 per month more than in the city with the least expensive rate, Bakersfield, California. What is the average monthly parking rate in Bakersfield?

Source: Colliers International

28. Trade Balance. In 2011, international visitors spent $153,000,000,000 traveling in the United States, while Americans spent $110,200,000,000 traveling abroad. How much more was spent by visitors to the United States than by Americans traveling abroad?

Source: U.S. Office of Travel and Tourism Industries

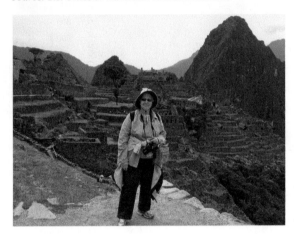

29. Refrigerator Purchase. Gourmet Deli has a chain of 24 restaurants. It buys a commercial refrigerator for each store at a cost of $1019 each. Determine the total cost of the purchase.

30. Microwave Purchase. Each room in the new dorm at Bridgeway College has a small kitchen. To furnish the kitchens, the college buys 96 microwave ovens at $88 each. Determine the total cost of the purchase.

31. "Seinfeld." A local television station plans to air the 177 episodes of the long-running comedy series "Seinfeld." If the station airs 5 episodes per week, how many full weeks will pass before it must begin re-airing previously shown episodes? How many unaired episodes will be shown the following week before the previously aired episodes are rerun?

32. "Everybody Loves Raymond." The popular television comedy series "Everybody Loves Raymond" had 208 scripted episodes and 2 additional episodes consisting of clips from previous shows. A local television station plans to air the 208 scripted episodes, showing 5 episodes per week. How many full weeks will pass before it must begin re-airing episodes? How many unaired episodes will be shown the following week before the previously aired episodes are rerun?

33. Crossword Puzzle. The *Los Angeles Times* crossword puzzle is a rectangle containing 441 squares arranged in 21 rows. How many columns does the puzzle have?

34. Mailing Labels. A box of mailing labels contains 750 labels on 25 sheets. How many labels are on each sheet?

Copyright © 2015 Pearson Education, Inc.

35. *Automobile Mileage.* The 2013 Hyundai Tucson GLS gets 30 miles per gallon (mpg) in highway driving. How many gallons will it use in 7080 mi of highway driving?

Source: Hyundai

36. *Automobile Mileage.* The 2013 Volkswagen Jetta (5 cylinder) gets 24 miles per gallon (mpg) in city driving. How many gallons will it use in 3960 mi of city driving?

Source: Volkswagen of America, Inc.

37. *High School Court.* The standard basketball court used by high school players has dimensions of 50 ft by 84 ft.
   a) What is its area?
   b) What is its perimeter?

38. *College Court.* The standard basketball court used by college players has dimensions of 50 ft by 94 ft.
   a) What is its area?
   b) What is its perimeter?
   c) How much greater is the area of a college court than a high school court? (See Exercise 37.)

39. Copies of this book are usually shipped from the warehouse in cartons containing 24 books each. How many cartons are needed to ship 1344 books?

40. The H. J. Heinz Company ships 16-oz bottles of ketchup in cartons containing 12 bottles each. How many cartons are needed to ship 528 bottles of ketchup?

41. *Map Drawing.* A map has a scale of 215 mi to the inch. How far apart *in reality* are two cities that are 3 in. apart on the map? How far apart *on the map* are two cities that, in reality, are 1075 mi apart?

42. *Map Drawing.* A map has a scale of 288 mi to the inch. How far apart *on the map* are two cities that, in reality, are 2016 mi apart? How far apart *in reality* are two cities that are 8 in. apart on the map?

43. *Loan Payments.* Dana borrows $5928 for a used car. The loan is to be paid off in 24 equal monthly payments. How much is each payment (excluding interest)?

44. *Home Improvement Loan.* The Van Reken family borrows $7824 to build a detached garage next to their home. The loan is to be paid off in equal monthly payments of $163 (excluding interest). How many months will it take to pay off the loan?

Refer to the information in Example 7 to do Exercises 45 and 46.

45. For how long must you do aerobic exercises in order to lose one pound?

46. For how long must you bicycle at 9 mph in order to lose one pound?

New Jobs. Many of the fastest-growing occupations in the United States require education beyond a high school diploma. The following table lists some of these and gives the projected numbers of new jobs expected to be created between 2010 and 2020. Use the information in the table for Exercises 47 and 48.

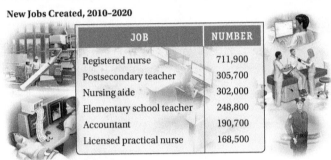

New Jobs Created, 2010–2020

JOB	NUMBER
Registered nurse	711,900
Postsecondary teacher	305,700
Nursing aide	302,000
Elementary school teacher	248,800
Accountant	190,700
Licensed practical nurse	168,500

SOURCE: U.S. Bureau of Labor Statistics

47. The U.S. Bureau of Labor Statistics predicts that between 2010 and 2020, there will be 1,014,100 more new jobs created for registered nurses, nursing aides, and licensed practical nurses than there will be for physicians. How many new jobs will be created for physicians between 2010 and 2020?

48. The U.S. Bureau of Labor Statistics predicts that between 2010 and 2020, there will be 484,600 more new jobs created for postsecondary teachers and elementary teachers than there will be for secondary teachers. How many new jobs will be created for secondary teachers between 2010 and 2020?

49. *Seating Configuration.* The seats in the Boeing 737-500 airplanes in United Airlines' North American fleet are configured with 2 rows of 4 seats across in first class and 16 rows of 6 seats across in economy class. Determine the total seating capacity of one of these planes.

Source: United Airlines

Economy class: 16 rows of 6 seats

First class: 2 rows of 4 seats

50. *Seating Configuration.* The seats in the Airbus 320 airplanes in United Airlines' North American fleet are configured with 3 rows of 4 seats across in first class and 21 rows of 6 seats across in economy class. Determine the total seating capacity of one of these planes.

Source: United Airlines

Economy class: 21 rows of 6 seats

First class: 3 rows of 4 seats

Copyright © 2015 Pearson Education, Inc.

51. Elena buys 5 video games at $64 each and pays for them with $10 bills. How many $10 bills does it take?

52. Pedro buys 5 video games at $64 each and pays for them with $20 bills. How many $20 bills does it take?

53. The balance in Meg's bank account is $568. She uses her debit card for purchases of $46, $87, and $129. Then she deposits $94 in the account after returning a textbook. How much is left in her account?

54. The balance in Dylan's bank account is $749. He uses his debit card for purchases of $34 and $65. Then he makes a deposit of $123 from his paycheck. What is the new balance?

55. *Bones in the Hands and Feet.* There are 27 bones in each human hand and 26 bones in each human foot. How many bones are there in all in the hands and feet?

56. An office for adjunct instructors at a community college has 6 bookshelves, each of which is 3 ft wide. The office is moved to a new location that has dimensions of 16 ft by 21 ft. Is it possible for the bookshelves to be put side by side on the 16-ft wall?

Skill Maintenance

57. Add: [1.2a]

$$\begin{array}{r} 6254 \\ 1537 \\ + 482 \\ \hline \end{array}$$

58. Subtract: [1.3a]

$$\begin{array}{r} 9602 \\ -1843 \\ \hline \end{array}$$

59. Multiply: [1.4a]

$$\begin{array}{r} 3405 \\ \times 237 \\ \hline \end{array}$$

60. Divide: [1.5a]

$$32\overline{)4708}$$

61. Find the perimeter of the figure. [1.2b]

6 m, 9 m, 4 m, 7 m, 8 m

62. Find the area of the region. [1.4b]

211 ft, 46 ft

63. Estimate 238×596 by rounding to the nearest hundred. [1.6b]

64. Solve: $x + 15 = 81$. [1.7b]

Synthesis

65. *Speed of Light.* Light travels about 186,000 miles per second (mi/sec) in a vacuum such as in outer space. In ice it travels about 142,000 mi/sec, and in glass it travels about 109,000 mi/sec. In 18 sec, how many more miles will light travel in a vacuum than in ice? than in glass?

66. Carney Community College has 1200 students. Each instructor teaches 4 classes, and each student takes 5 classes. There are 30 students and 1 instructor in each classroom. How many instructors are there at Carney Community College?

Exponential Notation and Order of Operations

OBJECTIVES

a Write exponential notation for products such as 4 · 4 · 4.

b Evaluate exponential notation.

c Simplify expressions using the rules for order of operations.

d Remove parentheses within parentheses.

SKILL TO REVIEW

Objective 1.4a: Multiply whole numbers.

Multiply.

1. 5 × 5 × 5

2. 2 × 2 × 2 × 2 × 2

a WRITING EXPONENTIAL NOTATION

Consider the product 3 · 3 · 3 · 3. Such products occur often enough that mathematicians have found it convenient to create a shorter notation, called **exponential notation**, for them. For example,

$\underbrace{3 \cdot 3 \cdot 3 \cdot 3}_{4 \text{ factors}}$ is shortened to 3^4. ← exponent
                                            ↑ base

We read exponential notation as follows.

NOTATION	WORD DESCRIPTION
3^4	"three to the fourth power," or "the fourth power of three"
5^3	"five-cubed," or "the cube of five," or "five to the third power," or "the third power of five"
7^2	"seven squared," or "the square of seven," or "seven to the second power," or "the second power of seven"

The wording "seven squared" for 7^2 is derived from the fact that a square with side s has area A given by $A = s^2$.

$$A = s^2$$

An expression like $3 \cdot 5^2$ is read "three times five squared," or "three times the square of five."

EXAMPLE 1 Write exponential notation for 10 · 10 · 10 · 10 · 10.

Exponential notation is 10^5.   5 is the *exponent*. 10 is the *base*.

EXAMPLE 2 Write exponential notation for 2 · 2 · 2.

Exponential notation is 2^3.

◀ Do Margin Exercises 1–4.

Write exponential notation.

1. 5 · 5 · 5 · 5

2. 5 · 5 · 5 · 5 · 5 · 5

3. 10 · 10

4. 10 · 10 · 10 · 10

Answers

Skill to Review:
1. 125 **2.** 32

Margin Exercises:
1. 5^4 **2.** 5^6 **3.** 10^2 **4.** 10^4

b EVALUATING EXPONENTIAL NOTATION

We evaluate exponential notation by rewriting it as a product and then computing the product.

EXAMPLE 3 Evaluate: 10^3.

$$10^3 = 10 \cdot 10 \cdot 10 = 1000$$

·········· **Caution!** ··········

10^3 does not mean $10 \cdot 3$.

EXAMPLE 4 Evaluate: 5^4.

$$5^4 = 5 \cdot 5 \cdot 5 \cdot 5 = 625$$

Do Exercises 5–8.

GS 5. Evaluate: 10^4.

$$10^4 = \boxed{} \cdot \boxed{} \cdot \boxed{} \cdot \boxed{} = \boxed{}$$

Evaluate.

6. 10^2 **7.** 8^3

8. 2^5

c SIMPLIFYING EXPRESSIONS

Suppose we have a calculation like the following:

$$3 + 4 \cdot 8.$$

How do we find the answer? Do we add 3 to 4 and then multiply by 8, or do we multiply 4 by 8 and then add 3? In the first case, the answer is 56. In the second, the answer is 35. We agree to compute as in the second case:

$$3 + 4 \cdot 8 = 3 + 32 = 35.$$

The following rules are an agreement regarding the order in which we perform operations. These are the rules that computers and most scientific calculators use to do computations.

CALCULATOR CORNER

Exponential Notation
Many calculators have a $\boxed{y^x}$ or $\boxed{\wedge}$ key for raising a base to a power. To find 16^3, for example, we press $\boxed{1}$ $\boxed{6}$ $\boxed{y^x}$ $\boxed{3}$ $\boxed{=}$ or $\boxed{1}$ $\boxed{6}$ $\boxed{\wedge}$ $\boxed{3}$ $\boxed{=}$. The result is 4096.

EXERCISES Use a calculator to find each of the following.

1. 3^5

2. 5^6

3. 12^4

4. 2^{11}

RULES FOR ORDER OF OPERATIONS

1. Do all calculations within parentheses ( ), brackets [ ], or braces { } before operations outside.

2. Evaluate all exponential expressions.

3. Do all multiplications and divisions in order from left to right.

4. Do all additions and subtractions in order from left to right.

EXAMPLE 5 Simplify: $16 \div 8 \cdot 2$.

There are no parentheses or exponents, so we begin with the third step.

$$\begin{aligned} 16 \div 8 \cdot 2 &= 2 \cdot 2 \\ &= 4 \end{aligned} \Bigg\}$$ Doing all multiplications and divisions in order from left to right

EXAMPLE 6 Simplify: $7 \cdot 14 - (12 + 18)$.

$$\begin{aligned} 7 \cdot 14 - (12 + 18) &= 7 \cdot 14 - 30 \qquad \text{Carrying out operations inside parentheses} \\ &= 98 - 30 \qquad \text{Doing all multiplications and divisions} \\ &= 68 \qquad \text{Doing all additions and subtractions} \end{aligned}$$

Do Exercises 9–12.

Simplify.

9. $93 - 14 \cdot 3$

10. $104 \div 4 + 4$

11. $25 \cdot 26 - (56 + 10)$

12. $75 \div 5 + (83 - 14)$

Answers

5. 10,000   **6.** 100   **7.** 512   **8.** 32   **9.** 51
10. 30   **11.** 584   **12.** 84

Guided Solution:
5. 10, 10, 10, 10, 10,000

Simplify and compare.

13. $64 \div (32 \div 2)$ and $(64 \div 32) \div 2$

14. $(28 + 13) + 11$ and $28 + (13 + 11)$

15. Simplify:

$9 \times 4 - (20 + 4) \div 8 - (6 - 2)$.

$9 \times 4 - (20 + 4) \div 8 - (6 - 2)$

$= 9 \times 4 - \boxed{} \div 8 - \boxed{}$

$= \boxed{} - 24 \div 8 - 4$

$= 36 - \boxed{} - 4$

$= \boxed{} - 4$

$= \boxed{}$

Simplify.

16. $5 \cdot 5 \cdot 5 + 26 \cdot 71 - (16 + 25 \cdot 3)$

17. $30 \div 5 \cdot 2 + 10 \cdot 20 + 8 \cdot 8 - 23$

18. $95 - 2 \cdot 2 \cdot 2 \cdot 5 \div (24 - 4)$

Simplify.

19. $5^3 + 26 \cdot 71 - (16 + 25 \cdot 3)$

20. $(1 + 3)^3 + 10 \cdot 20 + 8^2 - 23$

21. $81 - 3^2 \cdot 2 \div (12 - 9)$

EXAMPLE 7 Simplify and compare: $23 - (10 - 9)$ and $(23 - 10) - 9$.

We have

$23 - (10 - 9) = 23 - 1 = 22;$

$(23 - 10) - 9 = 13 - 9 = 4.$

We can see that $23 - (10 - 9)$ and $(23 - 10) - 9$ represent different numbers. Thus subtraction is not associative.

◀ Do Exercises 13 and 14.

EXAMPLE 8 Simplify: $7 \cdot 2 - (12 + 0) \div 3 - (5 - 2)$.

$7 \cdot 2 - (12 + 0) \div 3 - (5 - 2)$

$= 7 \cdot 2 - 12 \div 3 - 3$ Carrying out operations inside parentheses

$= 14 - 4 - 3$ Doing all multiplications and divisions in order from left to right

$\left. \begin{array}{l} = 10 - 3 \\ = 7 \end{array} \right\}$ Doing all additions and subtractions in order from left to right

◀ Do Exercise 15.

EXAMPLE 9 Simplify: $15 \div 3 \cdot 2 \div (10 - 8)$.

$15 \div 3 \cdot 2 \div (10 - 8)$

$= 15 \div 3 \cdot 2 \div 2$ Carrying out operations inside parentheses

$\left. \begin{array}{l} = 5 \cdot 2 \div 2 \\ = 10 \div 2 \\ = 5 \end{array} \right\}$ Doing all multiplications and divisions in order from left to right

◀ Do Exercises 16–18.

EXAMPLE 10 Simplify: $4^2 \div (10 - 9 + 1)^3 \cdot 3 - 5$.

$4^2 \div (10 - 9 + 1)^3 \cdot 3 - 5$

$= 4^2 \div (1 + 1)^3 \cdot 3 - 5$ Subtracting inside parentheses

$= 4^2 \div 2^3 \cdot 3 - 5$ Adding inside parentheses

$= 16 \div 8 \cdot 3 - 5$ Evaluating exponential expressions

$\left. \begin{array}{l} = 2 \cdot 3 - 5 \\ = 6 - 5 \end{array} \right\}$ Doing all multiplications and divisions in order from left to right

$= 1$ Subtracting

◀ Do Exercises 19–21.

Answers

13. 4; 1   **14.** 52; 52   **15.** 29   **16.** 1880
17. 253   **18.** 93   **19.** 1880   **20.** 305
21. 75

Guided Solution:
15. 24, 4, 36, 3, 33, 29

EXAMPLE 11 Simplify: $2^9 \div 2^6 \cdot 2^3$.

$2^9 \div 2^6 \cdot 2^3 = 512 \div 64 \cdot 8$ Since there are no parentheses, we evaluate the exponential expressions.

$\left.\begin{array}{l} = 8 \cdot 8 \\ = 64 \end{array}\right\}$ Doing all multiplications and divisions in order from left to right

Do Exercise 22. ▶

22. Simplify: $2^3 \cdot 2^8 \div 2^9$.

Averages

In order to find the average of a set of numbers, we use addition and then division. For example, the average of 2, 3, 6, and 9 is found as follows.

The number of addends is 4.

$$\text{Average} = \frac{2 + 3 + 6 + 9}{4} = \frac{20}{4} = 5$$

Divide by 4.

The fraction bar acts as a grouping symbol, so

$$\frac{2 + 3 + 6 + 9}{4} \text{ is equivalent to } (2 + 3 + 6 + 9) \div 4.$$

Thus we are using order of operations when we compute an average.

> **AVERAGE**
>
> The **average** of a set of numbers is the sum of the numbers divided by the number of addends.

EXAMPLE 12 *National Parks.* Since 1995, four national parks have been established in the United States. The sizes of these parks are shown in the figure below. Determine the average size of the four parks.

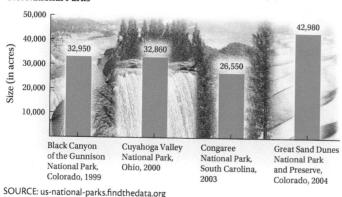

U.S. National Parks

Size (in acres): 32,950 — Black Canyon of the Gunnison National Park, Colorado, 1999; 32,860 — Cuyahoga Valley National Park, Ohio, 2000; 26,550 — Congaree National Park, South Carolina, 2003; 42,980 — Great Sand Dunes National Park and Preserve, Colorado, 2004

SOURCE: us-national-parks.findthedata.org

CALCULATOR CORNER

Order of Operations
We can test whether a calculator is programmed to follow the rules for order of operations by entering a calculation such as $3 + 4 \cdot 2$. Using the rules for order of operations, the value of this expression is 11. If a calculator returns the result 14 instead of 11, that calculator performs operations as they are entered rather than following the rules for order of operations. When using such a calculator, we have to enter the operations in the order in which we want them performed.

EXERCISES Simplify.
1. $84 - 5 \cdot 7$
2. $80 + 50 \div 10$
3. $3^2 + 9^2 \div 3$
4. $4^4 \div 64 - 4$
5. $15 \cdot 7 - (23 + 9)$
6. $(4 + 3)^2$

Answer

22. 4

23. *Average Number of Career Hits.* The numbers of career hits of five Hall of Fame baseball players are given in the graph below. Find the average number of career hits of all five.

Career Hits

2876 2930 3110 3255 3419

Mel Ott Jake Beckley Dave Winfield Eddie Murray Carl Yastrzemski

SOURCES: Associated Press; Major League Baseball

Simplify.

24. $9 \times 5 + \{6 \div [14 - (5 + 3)]\}$

25. $[18 - (2 + 7) \div 3]$ $- (31 - 10 \times 2)$ **GS**

$= [18 - \boxed{} \div 3] - (31 - 10 \times 2)$

$= [18 - \boxed{}] - (31 - \boxed{})$

$= \boxed{} - \boxed{}$

$= \boxed{}$

The average is given by

$$\frac{32{,}950 + 32{,}860 + 26{,}550 + 42{,}980}{4} = \frac{135{,}340}{4} = 33{,}835.$$

The average size of the four national parks is 33,835 acres.

◀ Do Exercise 23.

d REMOVING PARENTHESES WITHIN PARENTHESES

When parentheses occur within parentheses, we can make them different shapes, such as [ ] (called "brackets") and { } (called "braces"). All of these have the same meaning. When parentheses occur within parentheses, computations in the innermost ones are to be done first.

EXAMPLE 13 Simplify: $[25 - (4 + 3) \cdot 3] \div (11 - 7)$.

$[25 - (4 + 3) \cdot 3] \div (11 - 7)$

$= [25 - 7 \cdot 3] \div (11 - 7)$ Doing the calculations in the innermost parentheses first

$= [25 - 21] \div (11 - 7)$ Doing the multiplication in the brackets

$= 4 \div 4$ Subtracting

$= 1$ Dividing

EXAMPLE 14 Simplify: $16 \div 2 + \{40 - [13 - (4 + 2)]\}$.

$16 \div 2 + \{40 - [13 - (4 + 2)]\}$

$= 16 \div 2 + \{40 - [13 - 6]\}$ Doing the calculations in the innermost parentheses first

$= 16 \div 2 + \{40 - 7\}$ Again, doing the calculations in the innermost brackets

$= 16 \div 2 + 33$ Subtracting inside the braces

$= 8 + 33$ Dividing

$= 41$ Adding

◀ Do Exercises 24 and 25.

Answers

23. 3118 hits **24.** 46 **25.** 4

Guided Solution:
25. 9, 3, 20, 15, 11, 4

✓ Reading Check

Complete each statement by choosing the correct word or number from below the blank.

RC1. In the expression 5^3, the number 3 is the _____.
base/exponent

RC2. The expression 9^2 can be read "nine _____."
cubed/squared

RC3. To calculate $10 - 4 \cdot 2$, we perform the _____ first.
multiplication/subtraction

RC4. To find the average of 7, 8, and 9, we add the numbers and divide the sum by _____.
2/3

a Write exponential notation.

1. $3 \cdot 3 \cdot 3 \cdot 3$

2. $2 \cdot 2 \cdot 2 \cdot 2 \cdot 2$

3. $5 \cdot 5$

4. $13 \cdot 13 \cdot 13$

5. $7 \cdot 7 \cdot 7 \cdot 7 \cdot 7$

6. $9 \cdot 9$

7. $10 \cdot 10 \cdot 10$

8. $1 \cdot 1 \cdot 1 \cdot 1$

b Evaluate.

9. 7^2

10. 5^3

11. 9^3

12. 8^2

13. 12^4

14. 10^5

15. 3^5

16. 2^6

c Simplify.

17. $12 + (6 + 4)$

18. $(12 + 6) + 18$

19. $52 - (40 - 8)$

20. $(52 - 40) - 8$

21. $1000 \div (100 \div 10)$

22. $(1000 \div 100) \div 10$

23. $(256 \div 64) \div 4$

24. $256 \div (64 \div 4)$

25. $(2 + 5)^2$

26. $2^2 + 5^2$

27. $(11 - 8)^2 - (18 - 16)^2$

28. $(32 - 27)^3 + (19 + 1)^3$

29. $16 \cdot 24 + 50$

30. $23 + 18 \cdot 20$

31. $83 - 7 \cdot 6$

32. $10 \cdot 7 - 4$

33. $10 \cdot 10 - 3 \cdot 4$

34. $90 - 5 \cdot 5 \cdot 2$

35. $4^3 \div 8 - 4$

36. $8^2 - 8 \cdot 2$

37. $17 \cdot 20 - (17 + 20)$

38. $1000 \div 25 - (15 + 5)$

39. $6 \cdot 10 - 4 \cdot 10$

40. $3 \cdot 8 + 5 \cdot 8$

41. $300 \div 5 + 10$

42. $144 \div 4 - 2$

43. $3 \cdot (2 + 8)^2 - 5 \cdot (4 - 3)^2$

44. $7 \cdot (10 - 3)^2 - 2 \cdot (3 + 1)^2$

45. $4^2 + 8^2 \div 2^2$

46. $6^2 - 3^4 \div 3^3$

47. $10^3 - 10 \cdot 6 - (4 + 5 \cdot 6)$

48. $7^2 + 20 \cdot 4 - (28 + 9 \cdot 2)$

49. $6 \cdot 11 - (7 + 3) \div 5 - (6 - 4)$

50. $8 \times 9 - (12 - 8) \div 4 - (10 - 7)$

51. $120 - 3^3 \cdot 4 \div (5 \cdot 6 - 6 \cdot 4)$

52. $80 - 2^4 \cdot 15 \div (7 \cdot 5 - 45 \div 3)$

53. $2^3 \cdot 2^8 \div 2^6$

54. $2^7 \div 2^5 \cdot 2^4 \div 2^2$

55. Find the average of $64, $97, and $121.

56. Find the average of four test grades of 86, 92, 80, and 78.

57. Find the average of 320, 128, 276, and 880.

58. Find the average of $1025, $775, $2062, $942, and $3721.

Copyright © 2015 Pearson Education, Inc.

d Simplify.

59. $8 \times 13 + \{42 \div [18 - (6 + 5)]\}$

60. $72 \div 6 - \{2 \times [9 - (4 \times 2)]\}$

61. $[14 - (3 + 5) \div 2] - [18 \div (8 - 2)]$

62. $[92 \times (6 - 4) \div 8] + [7 \times (8 - 3)]$

63. $(82 - 14) \times [(10 + 45 \div 5) - (6 \cdot 6 - 5 \cdot 5)]$

64. $(18 \div 2) \cdot \{[(9 \cdot 9 - 1) \div 2] - [5 \cdot 20 - (7 \cdot 9 - 2)]\}$

65. $4 \times \{(200 - 50 \div 5) - [(35 \div 7) \cdot (35 \div 7) - 4 \times 3]\}$

66. $15(23 - 4 \cdot 2)^3 \div (3 \cdot 25)$

67. $\{[18 - 2 \cdot 6] - [40 \div (17 - 9)]\} + \{48 - 13 \times 3 + [(50 - 7 \cdot 5) + 2]\}$

68. $(19 - 2^4)^5 - (141 \div 47)^2$

Skill Maintenance

Solve. [1.7b]

69. $x + 341 = 793$

70. $4197 + x = 5032$

71. $7 \cdot x = 91$

72. $1554 = 42 \cdot y$

73. $6000 = 1102 + t$

74. $10{,}000 = 100 \cdot t$

Solve. [1.8a]

75. *Colorado.* The state of Colorado is roughly the shape of a rectangle that is 273 mi by 382 mi. What is its area?

76. On a long four-day trip, a family bought the following amounts of gasoline for their motor home: 23 gal, 24 gal, 26 gal, and 25 gal. How much gasoline did they buy in all?

Synthesis

Each of the answers in Exercises 77–79 is incorrect. First find the correct answer. Then place as many parentheses as needed in the expression in order to make the incorrect answer correct.

77. $1 + 5 \cdot 4 + 3 = 36$

78. $12 \div 4 + 2 \cdot 3 - 2 = 2$

79. $12 \div 4 + 2 \cdot 3 - 2 = 4$

80. Use one occurrence each of 1, 2, 3, 4, 5, 6, 7, 8, and 9, in order, and any of the symbols $+$, $-$, $\cdot$, $\div$, and ( ) to represent 100.

Vocabulary Reinforcement

In each of Exercises 1–8, fill in the blank with the correct term from the given list. Some of the choices may not be used and some may be used more than once.

1. The distance around an object is its _____. [1.2b]

2. The _____ is the number from which another number is being subtracted. [1.3a]

3. For large numbers, _____ are separated by commas into groups of three, called _____. [1.1a]

4. In the sentence 28 ÷ 7 = 4, the _____ is 28. [1.5a]

5. In the sentence 10 × 1000 = 10,000, 10 and 1000 are called _____ and 10,000 is called the _____. [1.4a]

6. The number 0 is called the _____ identity. [1.2a]

7. The sentence 3 × (6 × 2) = (3 × 6) × 2 illustrates the _____ law of multiplication. [1.4a]

8. We can use the following statement to check division:
   quotient · _____ + _____ = _____. [1.5a]

associative

commutative

addends

factors

area

perimeter

minuend

subtrahend

product

digits

periods

additive

multiplicative

dividend

quotient

remainder

divisor

Concept Reinforcement

Determine whether each statement is true or false.

_____ 1. $a > b$ is true when a is to the right of b on the number line. [1.6c]

_____ 2. Any nonzero number divided by itself is 1. [1.5a]

_____ 3. For any whole number a, $a \div 0 = 0$. [1.5a]

_____ 4. Every equation is true. [1.7a]

_____ 5. The rules for order of operations tell us to multiply and divide before adding and subtracting. [1.9c]

_____ 6. The average of three numbers is the middle number. [1.9c]

Study Guide

Objective 1.1a   Give the meaning of digits in standard notation.

Example   What does the digit 7 mean in 2,379,465?

2,3 7 9,4 6 5

7 means 7 ten thousands.

Practice Exercise

1. What does the digit 2 mean in 432,079?

Objective 1.2a   Add whole numbers.

Example   Add: 7368 + 3547.

```
  1 1
  7 3 6 8
+ 3 5 4 7
1 0,9 1 5
```

Practice Exercise

2. Add: 36,047 + 29,255.

Objective 1.3a   Subtract whole numbers.

Example   Subtract: 8045 − 2897.

```
        13
    7 9 3 15
    8 0 4 5
  − 2 8 9 7
    5 1 4 8
```

Practice Exercise

3. Subtract: 4805 − 1568.

Objective 1.4a   Multiply whole numbers.

Example   Multiply: 57 × 315.

```
      2
    1 3
    3 1 5
  ×   5 7
    2 2 0 5  ← 315 × 7
  1 5 7 5 0  ← 315 × 50
  1 7,9 5 5
```

Practice Exercise

4. Multiply: 329 × 684.

Objective 1.5a   Divide whole numbers.

Example   Divide: 6463 ÷ 26.

```
        2 4 8
   26)6 4 6 3
      5 2
      1 2 6
      1 0 4
        2 2 3
        2 0 8
          1 5
```

The answer is 248 R 15.

Practice Exercise

5. Divide: 8519 ÷ 27.

Objective 1.6a Round to the nearest ten, hundred, or thousand.

Example Round to the nearest thousand.

6 [4] 7 1
↑

  The digit 6 is in the thousands place. We consider the next digit to the right. Since the digit, 4, is 4 or lower, we round down, meaning that 6 thousands stays as 6 thousands. Change all digits to the right of the thousands digit to zeros. The answer is 6000.

Practice Exercise

6. Round 36,468 to the nearest thousand.

Objective 1.6c Use < or > for ☐ to write a true sentence in a situation like 6 ☐ 10.

Example Use < or > for ☐ to write a true sentence:

34 ☐ 29.

Since 34 is to the right of 29 on the number line,

  34 > 29.

Practice Exercise

7. Use < or > for ☐ to write a true sentence:
78 ☐ 81.

Objective 1.7b Solve equations like $t + 28 = 54$, $28 \cdot x = 168$, and $98 \cdot 2 = y$.

Example Solve: $y + 12 = 27$.
$$y + 12 = 27$$
$$y + 12 - 12 = 27 - 12$$
$$y + 0 = 15$$
$$y = 15$$
The solution is 15.

Practice Exercise

8. Solve: $24 \cdot x = 864$.

Objective 1.9b Evaluate exponential notation.

Example Evaluate: 5^4.
$$5^4 = 5 \cdot 5 \cdot 5 \cdot 5 = 625$$

Practice Exercise

9. Evaluate: 6^3.

Review Exercises

The review exercises that follow are for practice. Answers are given at the back of the book. If you miss an exercise, restudy the objective indicated in red next to the exercise or on the direction line that precedes it.

1. What does the digit 8 mean in 4,678,952? [1.1a]

2. In 13,768,940, what digit tells the number of millions? [1.1a]

Write expanded notation. [1.1b]

3. 2793

4. 56,078

5. 4,007,101

Write a word name. [1.1c]

6. 67,819

7. 2,781,427

Write standard notation. [1.1c]

8. Four hundred seventy-six thousand, five hundred eighty-eight

9. *Subway Ridership.* Ridership on the New York City Subway system totaled one billion, six hundred forty million in 2011.

Source: Metropolitan Transit Authority

Copyright © 2015 Pearson Education, Inc.

Add. [1.2a]

10. 7304 + 6968

11. 27,609 + 38,415

12. 2703 + 4125 + 6004 + 8956

13. 9 1,4 2 6
    + 7,4 9 5

Subtract. [1.3a]

14. 8045 − 2897

15. 9001 − 7312

16. 6003 − 3729

17. 3 7,4 0 5
    − 1 9,6 4 8

Multiply. [1.4a]

18. 17,000 · 300

19. 7846 · 800

20. 726 · 698

21. 587 · 47

22. 8 3 0 5
    × 6 4 2

Divide. [1.5a]

23. 63 ÷ 5

24. 80 ÷ 16

25. 7) 6 3 9 4

26. 3073 ÷ 8

27. 6 0) 2 8 6

28. 4266 ÷ 79

29. 3 8) 1 7,1 7 6

30. 1 4) 7 0,1 1 2

31. 52,668 ÷ 12

Round 345,759 to the nearest: [1.6a]

32. Hundred.

33. Ten.

34. Thousand.

35. Hundred thousand.

Use < or > for ☐ to write a true sentence. [1.6c]

36. 67 ☐ 56

37. 1 ☐ 23

Estimate each sum, difference, or product by first rounding to the nearest hundred. Show your work. [1.6b]

38. 41,348 + 19,749

39. 38,652 − 24,549

40. 396 · 748

Solve. [1.7b]

41. $46 \cdot n = 368$

42. $47 + x = 92$

43. $1 \cdot y = 58$

44. $24 = x + 24$

45. Write exponential notation: 4 · 4 · 4. [1.9a]

Evaluate. [1.9b]

46. 10^4

47. 6^2

Simplify. [1.9c, d]

48. 8 · 6 + 17

49. $10 \cdot 24 - (18 + 2) \div 4 - (9 - 7)$

50. $(80 \div 16) \times [(20 - 56 \div 8) + (8 \cdot 8 - 5 \cdot 5)]$

51. Find the average of 157, 170, and 168. [1.9c]

Solve. [1.8a]

52. *Computer Purchase.* Natasha has $196 and wants to buy a computer for $698. How much more does she need?

53. Toni has $406 in her checking account. She is paid $78 for a part-time job and deposits that in her checking account. How much is then in her account?

54. *Lincoln-Head Pennies.* In 1909, the first Lincoln-head pennies were minted. Seventy-three years later, these pennies were first minted with a decreased copper content. In what year was the copper content reduced?

55. A beverage company packed 228 cans of soda into 12-can cartons. How many cartons were filled?

56. An apartment builder bought 13 gas stoves at $425 each and 13 refrigerators at $620 each. What was the total cost?

57. An apple farmer keeps bees in her orchard to help pollinate the apple blossoms. The bees from an average beehive can pollinate 30 surrounding trees during one growing season. A farmer has 420 trees. How many beehives does she need to pollinate all of them?

Source: Jordan Orchards, Westminster, PA

58. *Olympic Trampoline.* Shown below is an Olympic trampoline. Determine the area and the perimeter of the trampoline. [1.2b], [1.4b]

Source: International Trampoline Industry Association, Inc.

59. A chemist has 2753 mL of alcohol. How many 20-mL beakers can be filled? How much will be left over?

60. A family budgeted $7825 a year for food and clothing and $2860 for entertainment. The yearly income of the family was $38,283. How much of this income remained after these two allotments?

61. Simplify: $7 + (4 + 3)^2$. [1.9c]
A. 32   B. 56
C. 151   D. 196

62. Simplify: $7 + 4^2 + 3^2$. [1.9c]
A. 32   B. 56
C. 130   D. 196

63. $[46 - (4 - 2) \cdot 5] \div 2 + 4$ [1.9d]
A. 6   B. 20
C. 114   D. 22

Synthesis

64. 🖩 Determine the missing digit d. [1.4a]

$$\begin{array}{r} 9\ d \\ \times \quad d\ 2 \\ \hline 8\ 0\ 3\ 6 \end{array}$$

65. 🖩 Determine the missing digits a and b. [1.5a]

$$\begin{array}{r} 9\ a\ 1 \\ 2\ b\ 1\ \overline{)\ 2\ 3\ 6{,}4\ 2\ 1} \end{array}$$

66. A mining company estimates that a crew must tunnel 2000 ft into a mountain to reach a deposit of copper ore. Each day, the crew tunnels about 500 ft. Each night, about 200 ft of loose rocks roll back into the tunnel. How many days will it take the mining company to reach the copper deposit? [1.8a]

Understanding Through Discussion and Writing

1. Is subtraction associative? Why or why not? [1.3a]

2. Explain how estimating and rounding can be useful when shopping for groceries. [1.6b]

3. Write a problem for a classmate to solve. Design the problem so that the solution is "The driver still has 329 mi to travel." [1.8a]

4. Consider the expressions $9 - (4 \cdot 2)$ and $(3 \cdot 4)^2$. Are the parentheses necessary in each case? Explain. [1.9c]

Copyright © 2015 Pearson Education, Inc.

CHAPTER

1 **Test**

For Extra Help For step-by-step test solutions, access the Chapter Test Prep Videos in
MyMathLab® or on You Tube (search "BittingerBasicEI" and click on "Channels").

1. In the number 546,789, which digit tells the number of hundred thousands?

2. Write expanded notation: 8843.

3. Write a word name: 38,403,277.

Add.

4.   6 8 1 1
     + 3 1 7 8

5.   4 5,8 8 9
     + 1 7,9 0 2

6.   1 2 3 9
        8 4 3
        3 0 1
     +   7 8 2

7.   6 2 0 3
     + 4 3 1 2

Subtract.

8.   7 9 8 3
     − 4 3 5 3

9.   2 9 7 4
     − 1 9 3 5

10.   8 9 0 7
     − 2 0 5 9

11.   2 3,0 6 7
     − 1 7,8 9 2

Multiply.

12.   4 5 6 8
     ×   9

13.   8 8 7 6
     ×   6 0 0

14.   6 5
     × 3 7

15.   6 7 8
     × 7 8 8

Divide.

16. $15 \div 4$

17. $420 \div 6$

18. $8\,9\,\overline{)\,8\,6\,3\,3}$

19. $4\,4\,\overline{)\,3\,5,4\,2\,8}$

Round 34,528 to the nearest:

20. Thousand.

21. Ten.

22. Hundred.

Estimate each sum, difference, or product by first rounding to the nearest hundred. Show your work.

23.   2 3,6 4 9
     + 5 4,7 4 6

24.   5 4,7 5 1
     − 2 3,6 4 9

25.   8 2 4
     × 4 8 9

Use < or > for ☐ to write a true sentence.

26. 34 ☐ 17

27. 117 ☐ 157

Solve.

28. $28 + x = 74$

29. $169 \div 13 = n$

30. $38 \cdot y = 532$

31. $381 = 0 + a$

Solve.

32. *Calorie Content.* An 8-oz serving of whole milk contains 146 calories. This is 63 calories more than the number of calories in an 8-oz serving of skim milk. How many calories are in an 8-oz serving of skim milk?

Source: *American Journal of Clinical Nutrition*

33. A box contains 5000 staples. How many staplers can be filled from the box if each stapler holds 250 staples?

34. *Largest States.* The following table lists the five largest states in terms of their land area. Find the total land area of these states.

STATE	AREA (in square miles)
Alaska	571,951
Texas	261,797
California	155,959
Montana	145,552
New Mexico	121,356

Sources: U.S. Department of Commerce; U.S. Census Bureau

35. *Pool Tables.* The Bradford™ pool table made by Brunswick Billiards comes in three sizes of playing area, 50 in. by 100 in., 44 in. by 88 in., and 38 in. by 76 in.

Source: Brunswick Billiards

a) Determine the perimeter and the playing area of each table.
b) By how much does the area of the largest table exceed the area of the smallest table?

36. *Hostess Ding Dongs®.* Hostess packages its Ding Dong snack cakes in 12-packs. How many 12-packs can it fill with 22,231 cakes? How many will be left over?

37. *Office Supplies.* Morgan manages the office of a small graphics firm. He buys 3 black inkjet cartridges at $15 each and 2 photo inkjet cartridges at $25 each. How much does the purchase cost?

38. Write exponential notation: $12 \cdot 12 \cdot 12 \cdot 12$.

Evaluate.

39. 7^3

40. 10^5

Simplify.

41. $35 - 1 \cdot 28 \div 4 + 3$

42. $10^2 - 2^2 \div 2$

43. $(25 - 15) \div 5$

44. $2^4 + 24 \div 12$

45. $8 \times \{(20 - 11) \cdot [(12 + 48) \div 6 - (9 - 2)]\}$

46. Find the average of 97, 99, 87, and 89.

A. 93   **B.** 124   **C.** 186   **D.** 372

Synthesis

47. An open cardboard container is 8 in. wide, 12 in. long, and 6 in. high. How many square inches of cardboard are used?

48. Use trials to find the single-digit number a for which

$$359 - 46 + a \div 3 \times 25 - 7^2 = 339.$$

49. Cara spends $229 a month to repay her student loan. If she has already paid $9160 on the 10-year loan, how many payments remain?

Copyright © 2015 Pearson Education, Inc.

CHAPTER
2

Integers

2.1 The Integers

2.2 Addition of Integers

2.3 Subtraction of Integers

Mid-Chapter Review

2.4 Multiplication of Integers

2.5 Division of Integers and Order of Operations

Translating for Success

Summary and Review

Test

85

STUDYING FOR SUCCESS   *Make the Most of Your Homework*

☐ Double-check that you have copied an exercise correctly.
☐ Check that your answer is reasonable.
☐ Include correct units with answers.

2.1   The Integers

OBJECTIVES

a State the integer that corresponds to a real-world situation.

b Graph integers on the number line.

c Determine which of two integers is greater and indicate which, using < or >.

d Find the absolute value of an integer.

SKILL TO REVIEW

Objective 1.6c: Use < or > for ☐ to write a true sentence in a situation like 6 ☐ 10.

Use < or > to write a true sentence.

1. 101 ☐ 99   **2.** 29 ☐ 32

In this section, we introduce the *integers*. To describe integers, we start with the whole numbers, 0, 1, 2, 3, and so on. For each number 1, 2, 3, and so on, we obtain a new number to the left of zero on the number line:

For the number 1, there will be an *opposite* number -1 (negative 1).

For the number 2, there will be an *opposite* number -2 (negative 2).

For the number 3, there will be an *opposite* number -3 (negative 3), and so on.

The **integers** consist of the whole numbers and these new numbers. We picture them on the number line as follows.

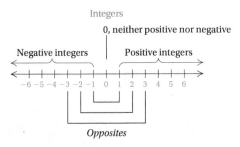

Opposites

We call the integers to the left of zero **negative integers**. The natural numbers are called **positive integers**. Zero is neither positive nor negative. We call -1 and 1 **opposites** of each other. Similarly, -2 and 2 are opposites, -3 and 3 are opposites, -100 and 100 are opposites, and 0 is its own opposite. Opposite pairs of numbers like -3 and 3 are the same distance from 0. The integers extend infinitely on the number line to the left and right of zero.

> **INTEGERS**
>
> The **integers:** . . . , $-5, -4, -3, -2, -1, 0, 1, 2, 3, 4, 5,$ . . .

a INTEGERS AND THE REAL WORLD

Integers correspond to many real-world problems and situations. The following examples will help you get ready to translate problem situations that involve integers to mathematical language.

Answers

Skill to Review:
1. >   2. <

EXAMPLE 1 Tell which integer corresponds to this situation: The temperature is 4 degrees below zero.

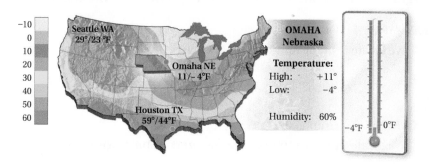

The integer −4 corresponds to the situation. The temperature is −4°.

EXAMPLE 2 *Water Level.* Tell which integer corresponds to this situation: As the water level of the Mississippi River fell during the drought of 2012, barge traffic was restricted, causing a severe decline in shipping volumes. On August 24, the river level at Greenville, Mississippi, was 10 ft below normal.

Source: Rick Jervis, *USA TODAY*, August 24, 2012

The integer −10 corresponds to the drop in water level.

EXAMPLE 3 *Stock Price Change.* Tell which integers correspond to this situation: Hal owns a stock whose price decreased from $27 per share to $11 per share over a recent time period. He owns another stock whose price increased from $20 per share to $22 per share over the same time period.

The integer −16 corresponds to the decrease in the value of the first stock. The integer 2 represents the increase in the value of the second stock.

Do Exercises 1–5. ▶

Tell which integers correspond to each situation.

1. *High and Low Temperatures.* As of 2010, the highest recorded temperature in Illinois was 117°F on July 14, 1954, in East St. Louis. The lowest recorded temperature in Illinois was 36°F below zero on January 5, 1999, in Congerville.

   Source: National Climate Data Center, NESDIS, NOAA, U.S. Dept. of Commerce

2. *Stock Price Decrease.* The price of a stock decreased from $41 per share to $38 per share over a recent period.

3. At 10 sec before liftoff, ignition occurs. At 148 sec after liftoff, the first stage is detached from the rocket.

4. The halfback gained 8 yd on first down. The quarterback was sacked for a 5-yd loss on second down.

5. A submarine dove 120 ft, rose 50 ft, and then dove 80 ft.

Answers
1. 117; −36   2. −3   3. −10; 148
4. 8; −5   5. −120; 50; −80

b GRAPH OF INTEGERS

To **graph** a number means to find and mark its point on the number line.

EXAMPLE 4 Graph: 5.

We locate 5 on the number line and mark its point with a dot.

EXAMPLE 5 Graph: 0.

We locate 0 on the number line and mark its point with a dot.

EXAMPLE 6 Graph: −3.

We locate −3 on the number line and mark its point with a dot.

◀ Do Exercises 6–8.

c THE INTEGERS AND ORDER

The integers are named in order on the number line. (See Section 1.6.) For any two numbers on the line, the one to the left is less than the one to the right.

We use the symbol **<** to mean "**is less than**." The sentence $-8 < 6$ means "-8 is less than 6." The symbol **>** means "**is greater than**." The sentence $-3 > -7$ means "-3 is greater than -7."

EXAMPLES Use either $<$ or $>$ for ☐ to write a true sentence.

7. -7 ☐ 3 Since -7 is to the left of 3, we have $-7 < 3$.

8. 6 ☐ -12 Since 6 is to the right of -12, we have $6 > -12$.

9. -18 ☐ -5 Since -18 is to the left of -5, we have $-18 < -5$.

10. 25 ☐ 23 Since 25 is to the right of 23, we have $25 > 23$.

11. -8 ☐ 0 Since -8 is to the left of 0, we have $-8 < 0$.

12. -11 ☐ -13 Since -11 is to the right of -13, we have $-11 > -13$.

◀ Do Exercises 9–14.

Graph on the number line.

6. −4

7. 1

8. 4

Use either $<$ or $>$ for ☐ to write a true sentence.

9. -3 ☐ 7 **10.** -8 ☐ -5

11. 7 ☐ -10 **12.** 0 ☐ -15

13. 79 ☐ 63 **14.** -9 ☐ -8

Answers

9. < **10.** < **11.** > **12.** >

13. > **14.** <

d ABSOLUTE VALUE

From the number line, we see that numbers like 4 and −4 are the same distance from zero. Distance is always a nonnegative number. We call the distance of a number from zero the **absolute value** of the number.

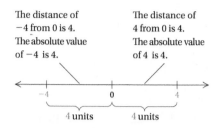

The distance of −4 from 0 is 4.
The absolute value of −4 is 4.

The distance of 4 from 0 is 4.
The absolute value of 4 is 4.

4 units   4 units

ABSOLUTE VALUE

The **absolute value** of a number is its distance from zero on the number line. We use the symbol $|x|$ to represent the absolute value of a number x.

EXAMPLES   Find the absolute value.

13. $|-7|$ The distance of −7 from 0 is 7, so $|-7| = 7$.
14. $|12|$ The distance of 12 from 0 is 12, so $|12| = 12$.
15. $|0|$ The distance of 0 from 0 is 0, so $|0| = 0$.
16. $|45| = 45$
17. $|-101| = 101$

Do Exercises 15–20. ▶

Find the absolute value.

15. $|8|$ **16.** $|0|$

17. $|-9|$ **18.** $|-84|$

19. $|157|$ **20.** $|-225|$

To find the absolute value of a number:

a) If a number is negative, its absolute value is its opposite.

b) If a number is positive or zero, its absolute value is the same as the number.

⋯⋯⋯⋯⋯⋯⋯⋯⋯⋯⋯⋯⋯⋯ Caution! ⋯⋯⋯⋯⋯⋯⋯⋯⋯⋯⋯⋯⋯⋯

Absolute value is a distance, so the absolute value of a number is always positive or zero. Absolute value cannot be negative.

⋯⋯⋯⋯⋯⋯⋯⋯⋯⋯⋯⋯⋯⋯⋯⋯⋯⋯⋯⋯⋯⋯⋯⋯⋯⋯⋯⋯⋯⋯⋯⋯⋯⋯⋯⋯⋯⋯

Answers

15. 8   **16.** 0   **17.** 9   **18.** 84
19. 157   **20.** 225

Reading Check

Use the number line below, on which the letters name numbers, for Exercises RC1–RC8.

Match each number with its graph.

RC1. -2 _____   **RC2.** $|0|$ _____   **RC3.** $|-5|$ _____   **RC4.** 3 _____

Determine whether each statement is true or false.

RC5. $H < J$ _____   **RC6.** $F > E$ _____   **RC7.** $G < D$ _____   **RC8.** $A > B$ _____

a   State which integers correspond to each situation.

1. On Wednesday, the temperature was 24° above zero. On Thursday, it was 2° below zero.

2. A student deposited her tax refund of $750 in a savings account. Two weeks later, she withdrew $125 to pay technology fees.

3. *Temperature Extremes.* The highest temperature ever created on Earth was 950,000,000°F. The lowest temperature ever created was approximately 460°F below zero.

Source: *The Guinness Book of Records*

4. *Extreme Climate.* Verkhoyansk, a river port in northeast Siberia, has the most extreme climate on the planet. Its average monthly winter temperature is 58.5°F below zero, and its average monthly summer temperature is 56.5°F.

Source: *The Guinness Book of Records*

5. *Empire State Building.* The Empire State Building has a total height, including the lightning rod at the top, of 1454 ft. The foundation depth is 55 ft below ground level.

Source: www.empirestatebuildingfacts.com

6. *Shipwreck.* There are numerous shipwrecks to explore near Bermuda. One of the most frequently visited wrecks is *L'Herminie*, a French warship that sank in 1837. This wreck is 35 ft below the surface.

Source: www./10best.com/interests/adventure/scuba-diving-in-pirate-territory/

b   Graph each number on the number line.

7. -5

8. 3

9. 2

10. -1

Copyright © 2015 Pearson Education, Inc.

c   Use either $<$ or $>$ for ☐ to write a true sentence.

11. 8 ☐ 0   **12.** 3 ☐ 0   **13.** -8 ☐ 3   **14.** 6 ☐ -6

15. 8 ☐ -8 **16.** 0 ☐ -9 **17.** -10 ☐ -5 **18.** -4 ☐ -3

19. -5 ☐ -11 **20.** -3 ☐ -4 **21.** -6 ☐ -5 **22.** -10 ☐ -14

23. -7 ☐ 0   **24.** -3 ☐ -2 **25.** 1 ☐ -15 **26.** 2 ☐ -12

d   Find the absolute value.

27. $|-3|$ **28.** $|-6|$ **29.** $|18|$ **30.** $|0|$

31. $|325|$ **32.** $|-4|$ **33.** $|-29|$ **34.** $|217|$

35. $|-300|$ **36.** $|-47|$ **37.** $|53|$ **38.** $|-76|$

Skill Maintenance

Add.   [1.2a]

39.   9 1 8 2
     $+4\ 3\ 6\ 7$

40.   2 7 8
     $+8\ 2\ 9$

41.   3 2,0 4 7
     $+1\ 8,5\ 6\ 2$

Subtract.   [1.3a]

42.   6 5 1
     $-\ 4\ 3\ 2$

43.   1 2 0 7
     $-\ \ 9\ 4\ 8$

44.   4 3,0 0 4
     $-3\ 4,2\ 2\ 6$

Synthesis

Use either $<$, $>$, or $=$ for ☐ to write a true sentence.

45. $|-5|$ ☐ $|-2|$ **46.** $|4|$ ☐ $|-7|$ **47.** $|-8|$ ☐ $|8|$

48. List in order from the least to the greatest: $-6, 7, -10, |-6|, 2^2, |3|, 1^6, -5, 0.$

2.2 Addition of Integers

OBJECTIVES

a Add integers without using the number line.

b Find the opposite, or additive inverse, of an integer.

SKILL TO REVIEW

Objective 1.3a: Subtract whole numbers.

Subtract.

1. 14 − 6   **2.** 5 − 3

We now consider addition of integers. First, to gain an understanding, we add using the number line. Then we consider rules for addition.

Addition on the Number Line

To find $a + b$, we start at 0, move to a, and then move according to b.

a) If b is positive, we move from a to the right.

b) If b is negative, we move from a to the left.

c) If b is 0, we stay at a.

EXAMPLE 1 Add: $3 + (-5)$.

We start at 0 and move to 3. Then we move 5 units left since -5 is negative.

$3 + (-5) = -2$

EXAMPLE 2 Add: $-4 + (-3)$.

We start at 0 and move to -4. Then we move 3 units left since -3 is negative.

$-4 + (-3) = -7$

EXAMPLE 3 Add: $-4 + 9$.

$-4 + 9 = 5$

EXAMPLE 4 Add: $-6 + 0$.

$-6 + 0 = -6$

◀ **Do Margin Exercises 1–6.**

Add using the number line.

1. $0 + (-3)$

2. $1 + (-4)$

3. $-3 + (-2)$

4. $-3 + 7$

5. $-2 + 2$

6. $-1 + (-3)$

Answers

Skill to Review:
1. 8   2. 2

Margin Exercises:
1. −3   2. −3   3. −5   4. 4   5. 0
6. −4

a ADDITION WITHOUT THE NUMBER LINE

You may have noticed some patterns in the preceding examples. These lead us to rules for adding without using the number line that are more efficient for adding larger or more complicated numbers.

RULES FOR ADDITION OF INTEGERS

1. *Positive numbers*: Add the same way you do whole numbers. The answer is positive.

2. *Negative numbers*: Add absolute values. The answer is negative.

3. *A positive number and a negative number*:
   - If the numbers have the same absolute value, the answer is 0.
   - If the numbers have different absolute values, subtract the smaller absolute value from the larger. Then:
     a) If the positive number has the greater absolute value, the answer is positive.
     b) If the negative number has the greater absolute value, the answer is negative.

4. *One number is zero*: The sum is the other number.

Rule 4 is known as the **identity property of 0**. It says that for any number a, $a + 0 = a$.

EXAMPLES Add without using the number line.

5. $-12 + (-7) = -19$ Add the absolute values, 12 and 7, getting 19. Make the answer *negative*, -19.

6. $-1 + 8 = 7$ The absolute values are 1 and 8. The difference is 7. The positive number has the larger absolute value, so the answer is *positive*, 7.

7. $-36 + 21 = -15$ The absolute values are 36 and 21. The difference is 15. The negative number has the larger absolute value, so the answer is *negative*, -15.

8. $5 + (-5) = 0$ The numbers have the same absolute value. The sum is 0.

9. $-7 + 0 = -7$ One number is zero. The sum is the other number, -7.

10. $-9 + 3 = -6$

11. $15 + (-4) = 11$

12. $-13 + (-27) = -40$

Do Exercises 7–20. ▶

Suppose we wish to add several numbers, some positive and some negative, such as $15 + (-2) + 7 + 14 + (-5) + (-12)$. How can we proceed?

Add without using the number line.

7. $-5 + (-6)$

8. $-9 + (-3)$

9. $-4 + 6$

10. $-7 + 3$

11. $5 + (-7)$

12. $-20 + 20$

13. $-11 + (-11)$

14. $10 + (-7)$

15. $0 + (-26)$

16. $-6 + 8$

17. $-4 + (-5)$

18. $-8 + 2$

19. $9 + (-7)$

20. $-19 + (-11)$

Answers

7. -11 8. -12 9. 2   10. -4
12. 0   13. -22 14. 3   15. -26
17. -9 18. -6 19. 2   20. -

94

The commutative and associative laws hold for integers. Thus we can change grouping and order as we please when adding. For instance, we can group the positive numbers together and the negative numbers together and add them separately. Then we add the two results.

EXAMPLE 13 Add: $15 + (-2) + 7 + 14 + (-5) + (-12)$.

a) $15 + 7 + 14 = 36$ Adding the positive numbers
b) $-2 + (-5) + (-12) = -19$ Adding the negative numbers
c) $36 + (-19) = 17$ Adding the results of (a) and (b)

We can also add the numbers in any other order we wish, say, from left to right as follows:

$$
\begin{aligned}
15 + (-2) + 7 + 14 + (-5) + (-12) &= 13 + 7 + 14 + (-5) + (-12) \\
&= 20 + 14 + (-5) + (-12) \\
&= 34 + (-5) + (-12) \\
&= 29 + (-12) \\
&= 17
\end{aligned}
$$

Add.

21. $(-15) + (-37) + 25 + 42 + (-59) + (-14)$

22. $42 + (-81) + (-28) + 24 + 18 + (-31)$

23. $-2 + (-10) + 6 + (-7)$

24. $-35 + 17 + 14 + (-27) + 31 + (-12)$

◀ Do Exercises 21–24.

b OPPOSITES, OR ADDITIVE INVERSES

Suppose we add two numbers that are **opposites**, such as 6 and -6. The result is 0. When opposites are added, the result is always 0. Opposites are also called **additive inverses**. Every integer has an opposite, or additive inverse.

> **OPPOSITES, OR ADDITIVE INVERSES**
>
> Two numbers whose sum is 0 are called **opposites**, or **additive inverses**, of each other.

Find the opposite, or additive inverse.

25. -4 **26.** 8

27. -7 **28.** -34

29. 0   **30.** 12

EXAMPLES Find the opposite, or additive inverse, of each number.

14. 34   The opposite of 34 is -34 because $34 + (-34) = 0$.
15. -8 The opposite of -8 is 8 because $-8 + 8 = 0$.
16. 0   The opposite of 0 is 0 because $0 + 0 = 0$.

◀ Do Exercises 25–30.

To name an opposite, we use the symbol $-$, as follows.

> **SYMBOLIZING OPPOSITES**
>
> The opposite, or additive inverse, of a number a can be named $-a$ (read "the opposite of a," or "the additive inverse of a").

Note that if we take a number, say 8, and find its opposite, -8, and then find the opposite of the result, we will have the original number, 8, again.

Answers

'. -58 **22.** -56 **23.** -13 **24.** -12
4   **26.** -8 **27.** 7   **28.** 34   **29.** 0
-12

THE OPPOSITE OF THE OPPOSITE

The opposite of the opposite of a number is the number itself. (The additive inverse of the additive inverse of a number is the number itself.) That is, for any number a,

$$-(-a) = a.$$

EXAMPLE 17 Evaluate $-x$ and $-(-x)$ when $x = 16$.

We replace x in each case with 16.

a) If $x = 16$, then $-x = -16 = -16$.   The opposite of 16 is -16.

b) If $x = 16$, then $-(-x) = -(-16) = 16$.   The opposite of the opposite of 16 is 16.

EXAMPLE 18 Evaluate $-x$ and $-(-x)$ when $x = -3$.

We replace x in each case with -3.

a) If $x = -3$, then $-x = -(-3) = 3$.

b) If $x = -3$, then $-(-x) = -(-(-3)) = -(3) = -3$.

Note that in Example 18 we used an extra set of parentheses to show that we are substituting the negative number -3 for x. Symbolism like $--x$ is not considered meaningful.

Do Exercises 31–34. ▶

A symbol such as -8 is usually read "negative 8." It could be read "the additive inverse of 8," because the additive inverse of 8 is negative 8. It could also be read "the opposite of 8," because the opposite of 8 is -8. Thus a symbol like -8 can be read in more than one way. A symbol like $-x$, which has a variable, should be read "the opposite of x" or "the additive inverse of x" and *not* "negative x," because we do not know whether x represents a positive number, a negative number, or 0.

We can use the symbolism $-a$ to restate the definition of opposite, or additive inverse.

OPPOSITES, OR ADDITIVE INVERSES

For any integer a, the opposite, or additive inverse, of a, denoted $-a$, is such that

$$a + (-a) = (-a) + a = 0.$$

Signs of Numbers

A negative number is sometimes said to have a "negative sign." A positive number is said to have a "positive sign." When we replace a number with its opposite, we can say that we have "changed its sign."

EXAMPLES Change the sign. (Find the opposite.)

19. -3 $-(-3) = 3$

21. 0 $-(0) = 0$

20. -13 $-(-13) = 13$

22. 14 $-(14) = -14$

Do Exercises 35–38. ▶

Evaluate $-x$ and $-(-x)$ when:

31. $x = 14$.

GS **32.** $x = -5$.
$$-x = -(\boxed{}) = 5$$
and $-(-x) = -(-(\boxed{}))$
$$= -(\boxed{}) = -5$$

33. $x = -9$.   **34.** $x = 2$.

CALCULATOR CORNER

Negative Numbers   On many calculators, we can enter negative numbers using the $\boxed{+/-}$ key. This allows us to perform calculations with integers. On some calculators, this key is labeled $\boxed{(-)}$. To enter -8, for example, we press $\boxed{8}$ $\boxed{+/-}$. To find the sum $-14 + (-9)$, we press $\boxed{1}\boxed{4}\boxed{+/-}\boxed{+}$ $\boxed{9}\boxed{+/-}\boxed{=}$. The result is -23. Note that it is not necessary to use parentheses when entering this expression.

EXERCISES   Add.

1. $-4 + 17$

2. $3 + (-11)$

3. $-2 + (-10)$

Find the opposite. (Change the sign.)

35. -4 **36.** -21

37. 0 **38.** 46

Answers

31. $-14; 14$ **32.** $5; -5$ **33.** $9; -9$ 3

35. 4 **36.** 21 **37.** 0 **38.** -46

Guided Solution:
32. $-5; -5, 5$

☑ **Reading Check**

Fill in each blank with either "left" or "right" so that the statement describes the steps for adding the given numbers on the number line.

RC1. To add 7 + 2, start at 0, move _____ to 7, and then move 2 units _____. The sum is 9.

RC2. To add −3 + (−5), start at 0, move _____ to −3, and then move 5 units _____. The sum is −8.

RC3. To add 4 + (−6), start at 0, move _____ to 4, and then move 6 units _____. The sum is −2.

RC4. To add −8 + 3, start at 0, move _____ to −8, and then move 3 units _____. The sum is −5.

a   Add. Do not use the number line except as a check.

1. $-9 + 2$

2. $-5 + 2$

3. $-10 + 6$

4. $4 + (-3)$

5. $-8 + 8$

6. $4 + (-4)$

7. $-3 + (-5)$

8. $-6 + (-8)$

9. $-7 + 0$

10. $-10 + 0$

11. $0 + (-27)$

12. $0 + (-36)$

13. $17 + (-17)$

14. $-20 + 20$

15. $-17 + (-25)$

16. $-23 + (-14)$

17. $18 + (-18)$

18. $-13 + 13$

19. $-18 + 18$

20. $11 + (-11)$

21. $8 + (-5)$

22. $-7 + 8$

23. $-4 + (-5)$

24. $10 + (-12)$

25. $13 + (-6)$

26. $-3 + 14$

27. $-25 + 25$

28. $40 + (-40)$

29. $63 + (-18)$

30. $85 + (-65)$

31. $-6 + 4$

32. $-3 + 2$

33. $-2 + (-5)$

34. $-7 + (-6)$

35. $-22 + 3$

36. $35 + (-19)$

37. $\_ + 6$

38. $-10 + (-8) + 3$

39. $-4 + 7 + (-4)$

40. $-1 + 20 + (-1)$

Integers

Copyright © 2015 Pearson Education, Inc.

41. $75 + (-14) + (-17) + (-5)$

42. $28 + (-44) + 17 + 31 + (-94)$

43. $-44 + (-3) + 95 + (-5)$

44. $24 + 3 + (-44) + (-8) + 63$

45. $98 + (-54) + 113 + (-998) + 44 + (-612) + (-18) + 334$

46. $-455 + (-123) + 1026 + (-919) + 213 + 111 + (-874)$

b　Find the opposite, or additive inverse.

47. 24

48. -84

49. -26

50. 36

Find $-x$ when:

51. $x = 9.$

52. $x = -26.$

53. $x = -14.$

54. $x = 52.$

Find $-(-x)$ when:

55. $x = -65.$

56. $x = 31.$

57. $x = 5.$

58. $x = -18.$

Change the sign. (Find the opposite.)

59. -14

60. 33

61. 10

62. -17

Skill Maintenance

Multiply.　[1.4a]

63.　$\begin{array}{r} 1\ 9\ 2 \\ \times\ \ 1\ 8 \\ \hline \end{array}$

64.　$\begin{array}{r} 2\ 6\ 4 \\ \times\ 5\ 1\ 9 \\ \hline \end{array}$

65.　$\begin{array}{r} 6\ 4\ 0\ 3 \\ \times\ \ 7\ 0\ 8 \\ \hline \end{array}$

Divide.　[1.5a]

66. $6\overline{)2\ 4\ 5\ 1}$

67. $54\overline{)6\ 9\ 0\ 4}$

68. $404\overline{)8\ 9,6\ 1\ 5}$

Round 641,539 to the nearest:　[1.6a]

69. Ten.

70. Hundred.

71. Thousand.

Synthesis

72. For what integers x is $-x$ positive?

73. For what integers x is $-x$ negative?

Tell whether each sum is positive, negative, or zero.

74. If $n = m$ and n is negative, then $-n + (-m)$ is _____.

75. If n is positive and m is negative, then $-n + m$ _____.

Subtraction of Integers

OBJECTIVES

a Subtract integers and simplify combinations of additions and subtractions.

b Solve applied problems involving addition and subtraction of integers.

a SUBTRACTION

We now consider subtraction of integers.

> **SUBTRACTION**
>
> The difference $a - b$ is the number c for which $a = b + c$.

Consider, for example, $45 - 17$. *Think*: What number can we add to 17 to get 45? Since $45 = 17 + 28$, we know that $45 - 17 = 28$. Let's consider an example whose answer is a negative number.

EXAMPLE 1 Subtract: $3 - 7$.

Think: What number can we add to 7 to get 3? The number must be negative. Since $7 + (-4) = 3$, we know the number is -4: $3 - 7 = -4$. That is, $3 - 7 = -4$ because $7 + (-4) = 3$.

◀ **Do Exercises 1–3.**

The definition above does not provide the most efficient way to do subtraction. We can develop a faster way to subtract. As a rationale for the faster way, let's compare $3 + 7$ and $3 - 7$ on the number line.

To find $3 + 7$ on the number line, we start at 0, move to 3, and then move 7 units to the *right* since 7 is positive.

To find $3 - 7$ we do the "opposite" of adding 7: From 3, we move 7 units to the *left* to subtract 7. This is the same as *adding* the opposite of 7, -7, to 3.

$3 - 7 = 3 + (-7) = -4$

◀ **Do Exercises 4–6.**

Look for a pattern in the following examples.

SUBTRACTING	ADDING AN OPPOSITE
$5 - 8 = -3$	$5 + (-8) = -3$
$-6 - 4 = -10$	$-6 + (-4) = -10$
$-7 - (-10) = 3$	$-7 + 10 = 3$
$-7 - (-2) = -5$	$-7 + 2 = -5$

Subtract.

1. $-6 - 4$

Think: What number can be added to 4 to get -6:

$$\square + 4 = -6?$$

2. $-7 - (-10)$

Think: What number can be added to -10 to get -7:

$$\square + (-10) = -7?$$

3. $-7 - (-2)$

Think: What number can be added to -2 to get -7:

$$\square + (-2) = -7?$$

Subtract. Use the number line, doing the "opposite" of addition.

4. $-4 - (-3)$

5. $-4 - (-6)$

6. $5 - 9$

98 4. −1

Integers

Do Exercises 7–10. ▶

Perhaps you have noticed that we can subtract by adding the opposite of the number being subtracted. This can always be done.

SUBTRACTING BY ADDING THE OPPOSITE

For any numbers a and b,

$$a - b = a + (-b).$$

(To subtract, add the opposite, or additive inverse, of the number being subtracted.)

This is the method generally used for quick subtraction of integers.

EXAMPLES Subtract.

2. $2 - 6 = 2 + (-6) = -4$

The opposite of 6 is -6. We change the subtraction to addition and add the opposite. *Check:* $-4 + 6 = 2$.

3. $4 - (-9) = 4 + 9 = 13$

The opposite of -9 is 9. We change the subtraction to addition and add the opposite. *Check:* $13 + (-9) = 4$.

4. $-4 - (-3) = -4 + 3 = -1$

Adding the opposite. *Check:* $-1 + (-3) = -4$.

5. $-10 - (-13) = -10 + 13 = 3$

Adding the opposite. *Check:* $3 + (-13) = -10$.

Do Exercises 11–16. ▶

EXAMPLES Subtract by adding the opposite of the number being subtracted.

6. $3 - 5$ *Think:* "Three minus five is three plus the opposite of five."

$3 - 5 = 3 + (-5) = -2$

7. $-16 - 7$ *Think:* "Negative sixteen minus seven is negative sixteen plus the opposite of seven."

$-16 - 7 = -16 + (-7) = -23$

8. $8 - (-9)$ *Think:* "Eight minus negative nine is eight plus the opposite of negative nine."

$8 - (-9) = 8 + 9 = 17$

9. $-11 - (-6)$ *Think:* "Negative eleven minus negative six is negative eleven plus the opposite of negative six."

$-11 - (-6) = -11 + 6 = -5$

Do Exercises 17–21. ▶

Complete the addition and compare with the subtraction.

7. $4 - 6 = -2$;
$4 + (-6) =$ _____

8. $-3 - 8 = -11$;
$-3 + (-8) =$ _____

9. $-5 - (-9) = 4$;
$-5 + 9 =$ _____

10. $-5 - (-3) = -2$;
$-5 + 3 =$ _____

Subtract.

GS 11. $2 - 8$
$= 2 + ($ ___ $) =$ ___

12. $-6 - 10$

13. $2 - 8$

14. $-8 - (-11)$

15. $-8 - (-8)$

16. $2 - (-5)$

Subtract by adding the opposite of the number being subtracted.

17. $3 - 11$

18. $12 - 5$

GS 19. $-12 - (-9)$
$= -12 +$ ___ $=$ ___

20. $-7 - 10$

21. $-4 - (-4)$

Answers

7. -2 **8.** -11 **9.** 4   **10.** -2 **11.** -6
12. -16 **13.** -6 **14.** 3   **15.** 0   **16.** 7
17. -8 **18.** 7   **19.** -3 **20.** -17
21. 0

Guided Solutions:
11. $-8, -6$ **19.** $9, -3$

Simplify.

22. $-6 - (-2) - (-4) - 12 + 3$

23. $20 - 16 - (-22) + 21 - 45$

24. $-10 + 7 - (-4) - (-11)$

When several additions and subtractions occur together, we can make them all additions.

EXAMPLES Simplify.

10. $8 - (-4) - 2 - (-4) + 2 = 8 + 4 + (-2) + 4 + 2$ Adding the opposites

$$= 16$$

11. $3 - (-6) + 2 - (-4) = 3 + 6 + 2 + 4 = 15$

12. $9 - (-1) - 7 - 11 = 9 + 1 + (-7) + (-11) = -8$

◀ Do Exercises 22–24.

b   APPLICATIONS AND PROBLEM SOLVING

Let's now see how we can use addition and subtraction of integers to solve applied problems.

EXAMPLE 13 *Surface Temperatures on Mars.* Surface temperatures on Mars vary from $-128°C$ during the polar night to $27°C$ at the equator at mid-day when Mars is at the point in its orbit closest to the sun. Find the difference between the highest value and the lowest value in this temperature range.

Source: Mars Institute

We let $D =$ the difference in the temperatures. Then the problem translates to the following subtraction:

Difference in temperature	is	Highest temperature	minus	Lowest temperature
D	$=$	27	$-$	(-128).

We then solve the equation: $D = 27 - (-128) = 27 + 128 = 155$.

The difference in the temperatures is $155°C$.

◀ Do Exercise 25.

25. *Temperature Extremes.* The highest temperature ever recorded in the United States was $134°F$ in Greenland Ranch, California, on July 10, 1913. The lowest temperature ever recorded was $-80°F$ in Prospect Creek, Alaska, on January 23, 1971. How much higher was the temperature in Greenland Ranch than the temperature in Prospect Creek?

Source: National Oceanographic and Atmospheric Administration

Answers

22. -9 **23.** 2 **24.** 12 **25.** $214°F$

✓ Reading Check

Match each expression with the expression from the list at the right that names the same number.

RC1. $18 - 6$ _____

RC2. $-18 - (-6)$ _____

RC3. $-18 - 6$ _____

RC4. $18 - (-6)$ _____

a) $18 + 6$

b) $-18 + 6$

c) $18 + (-6)$

d) $-18 + (-6)$

a Subtract.

1. $3 - 7$

2. $5 - 10$

3. $0 - 7$

4. $0 - 8$

5. $-8 - (-2)$

6. $-6 - (-8)$

7. $-10 - (-10)$

8. $-8 - (-8)$

9. $12 - 16$

10. $14 - 19$

11. $20 - 27$

12. $26 - 7$

13. $-9 - (-3)$

14. $-6 - (-9)$

15. $-11 - (-11)$

16. $-14 - (-14)$

17. $8 - (-3)$

18. $-7 - 4$

19. $-6 - 8$

20. $6 - (-10)$

21. $-4 - (-9)$

22. $-14 - 2$

23. $2 - 9$

24. $2 - 8$

25. $0 - 5$

26. $0 - 10$

27. $-5 - (-2)$

28. $-3 - (-1)$

29. $2 - 25$

30. $18 - 63$

31. $-42 - 26$

32. $-18 - 63$

33. $-71 - 2$

34. $-49 - 3$

35. $24 - (-92)$

36. $48 - (-73)$

37. $-2 - 0$

38. $-6 - 1$

39. $3 - 8$

40. $5 - 9$

41. $2 - 3$

42. $4 - 12$

43. $-3 - 2$

44. $-8 - 5$

45. $13 - (-9)$

46. $15 - (-7)$

47. $6 - (-13)$

48. $2 - (-4)$

49. $-14 - 6$ **50.** $-7 - 9$ **51.** $1 - 9$ **52.** $1 - 7$

53. $11 - 21$ **54.** $30 - 51$ **55.** $7 - 10$ **56.** $8 - (-9)$

57. $16 - 23$ **58.** $-38 - (-12)$ **59.** $-47 - (-17)$ **60.** $-12 + 12$

61. $-9 - (-9)$ **62.** $8 - (-16)$ **63.** $122 - 123$ **64.** $20 - (-21)$

Simplify.

65. $18 - (-15) - 3 - (-5) + 2$ **66.** $22 - (-18) + 7 + (-42) - 27$

67. $-31 + (-28) - (-14) - 17$ **68.** $-43 - (-19) - (-21) + 25$

69. $-93 - (-84) - 41 - (-56)$ **70.** $84 + (-99) + 44 - (-18) - 43$

71. $-5 - (-30) + 30 + 40 - (-12)$ **72.** $14 - (-50) + 20 - (-32)$

73. $132 - (-21) + 45 - (-21)$ **74.** $81 - (-20) - 14 - (-50) + 53$

b   Solve.

75. *"Flipping" Houses.*   Buying run-down houses, fixing them up, and reselling them is referred to as "flipping." Charlie and Sophia flipped four houses in a recent year. The profits and losses are shown in the following bar graph. Find the sum of the profits and losses.

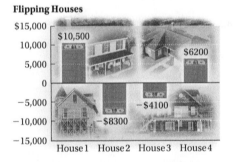

76. *Elevations in Asia.*   The elevation of the highest point in Asia, Mt. Everest, on the border between Nepal and Tibet, is 29,035 ft. The lowest elevation, at the Dead Sea, between Israel and Jordan, is -1348 ft. What is the difference in the elevations of the two locations?

Copyright © 2015 Pearson Education, Inc.

77. *Difference in Elevation.* The highest elevation in Japan is 3776 m above sea level at Fujiyama. The lowest elevation in Japan is 4 m below sea level at Hachirogata. Find the difference in the elevations.

Source: *The CIA World Factbook 2012*

78. *Copy-Center Account.* Rachel's copy-center bill for July was $327. She made a payment of $200 and then made $48 worth of copies in August. How much did she then owe on her account?

79. *Temperature Changes.* One day the temperature in Lawrence, Kansas, is 32° at 6:00 A.M. It rises 15° by noon, but falls 50° by midnight when a cold front moves in. What is the final temperature?

80. *Stock Price Changes.* On a recent day, the price of a stock opened at a value of $61. It rose $5, dropped $7, and then rose $3. Find the value of the stock at the end of the day.

81. Francisca has charged a total of $476 on her credit card, but she then returns a sweater that cost $128. How much does she now owe on her credit card?

82. Jacob has $825 in a checking account. What is the balance in his account after he writes a check for $920 to pay for a laptop?

83. *Tallest Mountain.* The tallest mountain in the world, when measured from base to peak, is Mauna Kea (White Mountain) in Hawaii. From its base 19,684 ft below sea level in the Hawaiian Trough, it rises 33,480 ft. What is the elevation of the peak?

Source: *The Guinness Book of Records*

84. *Low Points on Continents.* The lowest point in Africa is Lake Assal, which is 512 ft below sea level. The lowest point in South America is the Valdes Peninsula, which is 131 ft below sea level. How much lower is Lake Assal than the Valdes Peninsula?

Source: National Geographic Society

Skill Maintenance

Evaluate.   [1.9b]

85. 4^3

86. 5^3

Simplify.   [1.9c]

87. $5 \cdot 4 + 9$

88. $3 \cdot 16 - (7 - 1) \div 6 - (10 - 4)$

89. $2 + (5 + 3)^2$

90. $27 - 2^3 \cdot 3$

Solve.   [1.8a]

91. How many 12-oz cans of soda can be filled with 96 oz of soda?

92. A case of soda contains 24 bottles. If each bottle contains 12 oz, how many ounces of soda are in the case?

Synthesis

Tell whether each statement is true or false for all integers m and n. If false, give an example to show why.

93. $-n = 0 - n$

94. $n - 0 = 0 - n$

95. If $m \neq n$, then $m - n \neq 0$.

96. If $m = -n$, then $m + n = 0$.

97. If $m + n = 0$, then m and n are opposites.

98. If $m - n = 0$, then $m = -n$.

99. $m = -n$ if m and n are opposites.

100. If $m = -m$, then $m = 0$.

Mid-Chapter Review

Concept Reinforcement

Determine whether each statement is true or false.

_____ **1.** All of the natural numbers are integers. [2.1a]

_____ **2.** If $a > b$, then a lies to the left of b on the number line. [2.1c]

_____ **3.** The absolute value of a number is always nonnegative. [2.1d]

Guided Solutions

 Fill in each blank with the number that creates a correct statement or solution.

4. Evaluate $-x$ and $-(-x)$ when $x = -4$. [2.2b]

$$-x = -(\boxed{}) = \boxed{};$$

$$-(-x) = -(-(\boxed{})) = -(\boxed{}) = \boxed{}$$

Subtract. [2.3a]

5. $5 - 13 = 5 + (\boxed{}) = \boxed{}$

6. $-6 - (-7) = -6 + \boxed{} = \boxed{}$

Mixed Review

State the integers that correspond to the situation. [2.1a]

7. Jerilyn deposited $450 in her checking account. Later that week she wrote a check for $79.

8. The temperature in Coatsville rose $20°$ in the morning. It fell $23°$ overnight.

Graph the number on the number line. [2.1b]

9. -3

10. 0

Use either $<$ or $>$ for ☐ to write a true sentence. [2.1c]

11. $-6 \,\square\, 6$

12. $-5 \,\square\, -3$

13. $-9 \,\square\, -10$

14. $5 \,\square\, 0$

Find the absolute value. [2.1d]

15. $|15|$

16. $|-18|$

17. $|0|$

18. $|-12|$

Copyright © 2015 Pearson Education, Inc.

Find the opposite, or additive inverse, of the number.   [2.2b]

19. -5 **20.** 7 **21.** 0 **22.** -49

23. Evaluate $-x$ when x is -19.   [2.2b]

24. Evaluate $-(-x)$ when x is 2.   [2.2b]

Compute and simplify.   [2.2a], [2.3a]

25. $7 + (-9)$ **26.** $-3 + 1$ **27.** $3 + (-3)$ **28.** $-8 + (-9)$

29. $2 + (-12)$ **30.** $-4 + (-3)$ **31.** $-14 + 5$ **32.** $19 + (-21)$

33. $-4 - 6$ **34.** $5 - (-11)$ **35.** $-1 - (-3)$ **36.** $12 - 24$

37. $-8 - (-4)$ **38.** $-1 - 5$ **39.** $12 - 14$ **40.** $6 - (-7)$

41. $16 - (-9) - 20 - (-4)$ **42.** $-4 + (-10) - (-3) - 12$

43. $17 - (-25) + 15 - (-18)$ **44.** $-9 + (-3) + 16 - (-10)$

Solve.   [2.3b]

45. *Temperature Change.*   In a chemistry lab, Ben works with a substance whose initial temperature is 25°C. During an experiment, the temperature falls to -8°C. Find the difference between the two temperatures.

46. *Stock Price Change.*   The price of a stock opened at $56. During the day it dropped $3, then rose $1, and dropped $6. Find the price of the stock at the end of the day.

Understanding Through Discussion and Writing

47. Find an example of a real-world situation that can be represented by a negative integer.   [2.1a]

48. Explain why the absolute value of a number cannot be negative.   [2.1d]

49. Explain in your own words why the sum of two negative numbers is always negative.   [2.2a]

50. If a negative number is subtracted from a positive number, will the result always be positive? Why or why not?   [2.3a]

STUDYING FOR SUCCESS   *Your Textbook as a Resource*

☐   Study any drawings. Observe details in any sketches or graphs that accompany the explanations.
☐   Note the careful use of color to indicate substitutions and highlight steps in a multi-step solution.

2.4   Multiplication of Integers

OBJECTIVE

a   Multiply integers.

a   MULTIPLICATION

Multiplication of integers is very much like multiplication of whole numbers. The only difference is that we must determine whether the answer is positive or negative.

Multiplication of a Positive Number and a Negative Number

This number decreases
by 1 each time.

$$4 \cdot 5 = 20$$
$$3 \cdot 5 = 15$$
$$2 \cdot 5 = 10$$
$$1 \cdot 5 = 5$$
$$0 \cdot 5 = 0$$
$$-1 \cdot 5 = -5$$
$$-2 \cdot 5 = -10$$
$$-3 \cdot 5 = -15$$

This number decreases
by 5 each time.

To see how to multiply a positive number and a negative number, consider the pattern shown at the left.

According to this pattern, it looks as though the product of a negative number and a positive number is negative. That is the case, and we have the first part of the rule for multiplying integers.

> **THE PRODUCT OF A POSITIVE NUMBER AND A NEGATIVE NUMBER**
>
> To multiply a positive number and a negative number, multiply their absolute values. The answer is negative.

EXAMPLES   Multiply.

1. $8(-5) = -40$ **2.** $-3 \cdot 7 = -21$ **3.** $(-8)6 = -48$

◀ Do Exercises 1–6.

Multiply.

1. $-3 \cdot 6$ 2. $20 \cdot (-5)$

3. $4 \cdot (-20)$ 4. $-7 \cdot 8$

5. $4(-7)$ 6. $8\,(-4)$

Multiplication of Two Negative Numbers

How do we multiply two negative numbers? Again we look for a pattern.

This number decreases
by 1 each time.

$$4 \cdot (-5) = -20$$
$$3 \cdot (-5) = -15$$
$$2 \cdot (-5) = -10$$
$$1 \cdot (-5) = -5$$
$$0 \cdot (-5) = 0$$
$$-1 \cdot (-5) = 5$$
$$-2 \cdot (-5) = 10$$
$$-3 \cdot (-5) = 15$$

This number increases
by 5 each time.

Answers

1. -18 2. -100 3. -80
4. -56 5. -28 6. -32

According to the pattern, it looks as though the product of two negative numbers is positive. That is actually so, and we have the second part of the rule for multiplying real numbers.

THE PRODUCT OF TWO NEGATIVE NUMBERS

To multiply two negative numbers, multiply their absolute values. The answer is positive.

Do Exercises 7–12. ▶

To multiply two nonzero numbers:

a) Multiply the absolute values.

b) If the signs are the same, the answer is positive.

c) If the signs are different, the answer is negative.

EXAMPLES Multiply.

4. $(-3)(-4) = 12$ **5.** $-6(2) = -12$ **6.** $-5(-9) = 45$

Do Exercises 13–16. ▶

Multiplying More Than Two Numbers

When multiplying more than two integers, we can choose order and grouping as we please, using the commutative and associative laws.

EXAMPLES Multiply.

7. $-8 \cdot 2(-3) = -16(-3)$ Multiplying the first two numbers
$\qquad\qquad\quad = 48$ Multiplying the results

8. $-8 \cdot 2(-3) = 24 \cdot 2$ Multiplying the negative numbers. Every pair
$\qquad\qquad\quad = 48$ of negative numbers gives a positive product.

9. $-3(-2)(-5)(4) = 6(-5)(4)$ Multiplying the first two numbers
$\qquad\qquad\qquad = (-30)4 = -120$

10. $-2 \cdot 2(-3)(-4) = -4 \cdot 12$ Multiplying the first two numbers and
$\qquad\qquad\qquad\; = -48$ the last two numbers

11. $-5 \cdot (-2) \cdot (-3) \cdot (-6) = 10 \cdot 18 = 180$

12. $(-3)(-5)(-2)(-3)(-6) = (-30)(18) = -540$

Considering that the product of a pair of negative numbers is positive, we can see the following pattern in the results of Examples 11 and 12.

The product of an even number of negative numbers is positive.
The product of an odd number of negative numbers is negative.

Do Exercises 17–22. ▶

Multiply.

7. $-3 \cdot (-4)$

8. $-16 \cdot (-2)$

9. $-7 \cdot (-5)$

10. $-7(-9)$

11. $-3(-12)$

12. $-6(-4)$

Multiply.

13. $5(-6)$

14. $(-5)(-6)$

15. $(-3) \cdot 10$

16. $(-4)(15)$

Multiply.

17. $5 \cdot (-3) \cdot 2$

18. $-3 \times (-4) \times (-2)$

19. $-2 \cdot (-10) \cdot (-5)$

GS **20.** $-2 \cdot (-5) \cdot (-4) \cdot (-3)$
$= \boxed{} \cdot (-4) \cdot (-3)$
$= \boxed{} \cdot (-3)$
$= \boxed{}$

21. $(-4)(-5)(-2)(-3)(-1)$

22. $(-1)(-1)(-2)(-3)(-1)(-1)$

Answers

7. 12   **8.** 32   **9.** 35   **10.** 63   **11.** 36
12. 24   **13.** −30   **14.** 30   **15.** −30
16. −60   **17.** −30   **18.** −24   **19.** −100
20. 120   **21.** −120   **22.** 6

Guided Solution:
20. 10, −40, 120

✓ Reading Check

Fill in each blank with either "positive" or "negative."

RC1. To multiply a positive number and a negative number, we multiply their absolute values. The answer is _____.

RC2. To multiply two negative numbers, we multiply their absolute values. The answer is _____.

RC3. The product of an even number of negative numbers is _____.

RC4. The product of an odd number of negative numbers is _____.

a Multiply.

1. $-8 \cdot 2$

2. $-3 \cdot 5$

3. $8 \cdot (-3)$

4. $5 \cdot (-2)$

5. $-9 \cdot 8$

6. $-20 \cdot 3$

7. $-8 \cdot (-2)$

8. $-4 \cdot (-5)$

9. $-7 \cdot (-6)$

10. $-9 \cdot (-2)$

11. $15 \cdot (-8)$

12. $-11 \cdot (-10)$

13. $-14 \cdot 17$

14. $-13 \cdot (-15)$

15. $-25 \cdot (-48)$

16. $39 \cdot (-43)$

17. $-3 \cdot (-28)$

18. $97 \cdot (-2)$

19. $4 \cdot (-3)$

20. $3 \cdot (-22)$

21. $-6 \cdot (-4)$

22. $-5 \cdot (-6)$

23. $-7 \cdot (-3)$

24. $-4 \cdot (-32)$

25. $23 \cdot (-3)$

26. $7 \cdot (-9)$

27. $-3 \cdot (-9)$

28. $-25 \cdot (-8)$

29. -6×3

30. -8×6

31. $-9 \cdot 5$

32. $-8 \cdot 9$

33. $7 \cdot (-4) \cdot (-3) \cdot 5$

34. $9 \cdot (-2) \cdot (-6) \cdot 7$

35. $-3 \cdot 2 \cdot (-6)$

36. $-8 \cdot (-4) \cdot (-3)$

Copyright © 2015 Pearson Education, Inc.

37. $-3 \cdot (-4) \cdot (-5)$

38. $-2 \cdot (-5) \cdot (-7)$

39. $-2 \cdot (-5) \cdot (-3) \cdot (-5)$

40. $-3 \cdot (-5) \cdot (-2) \cdot (-1)$

41. $5(-18)$

42. $-35(-2)$

43. $-7 \cdot (-21) \cdot 13$

44. $-14 \cdot 34 \cdot 12$

45. $-4 \cdot (-2) \cdot 7$

46. $-8 \cdot (-3) \cdot (-5)$

47. $-3(-2)(5)$

48. $-7(-5)(-2)$

49. $4 \cdot (-4) \cdot (-5) \cdot (-12)$

50. $-2 \cdot (-3) \cdot (-4) \cdot (-5)$

51. $7 \cdot (-7) \cdot 6 \cdot (-6)$

52. $8 \cdot (-8) \cdot (-9) \cdot (-9)$

53. $(-5)(8)(-3)(-2)$

54. $(4)(-2)(-3)(2)$

55. $(-6)(-7)(-8)(-9)(-10)$

56. $7 \cdot (-6) \cdot 5 \cdot (-4) \cdot 3 \cdot (-2) \cdot 1 \cdot (-1)$

Skill Maintenance

Round 237,456 to the nearest: [1.6a]

57. Ten.

58. Hundred.

59. Thousand.

Solve. [1.7b]

60. $16 + x = 29$

61. $14 \cdot y = 42$

62. Simplify: $3 + 6[18 - (12 + 3)]$. [1.9d]

Synthesis

63. What must be true of a and b if $-ab$ is to be **(a)** positive? **(b)** zero? **(c)** negative?

OBJECTIVES

a Divide integers.

b Solve applied problems involving multiplication and division of integers.

c Simplify expressions using rules for order of operations.

SKILL TO REVIEW

Objective 1.9c: Simplify expressions using the rules for order of operations.

Simplify.

1. $100 \div 4 - 6$

2. $3 \cdot 8 - 2 \cdot 9$

We now consider division of integers. The definition of division results in rules for division that are the same as those for multiplication.

a DIVISION OF INTEGERS

> **DIVISION**
>
> The quotient $a \div b$, or $\dfrac{a}{b}$, where $b \neq 0$, is that unique number c for which $a = b \cdot c$.

EXAMPLES   Divide, if possible. Check each answer.

1. $14 \div (-7) = -2$ *Think*: What number multiplied by -7 gives 14? That number is -2. *Check*: $(-2)(-7) = 14$.

2. $-32 \div (-4) = 8$ *Think*: What number multiplied by -4 gives -32? That number is 8. *Check*: $8(-4) = -32$.

3. $-20 \div 5 = -4$ *Think*: What number multiplied by 5 gives -20? That number is -4. *Check*: $-4 \cdot 5 = -20$.

4. $\dfrac{-17}{0}$ is **not defined**.   *Think*: What number multiplied by 0 gives -17? There is no such number because the product of 0 and *any* number is 0.

◀ Do Margin Exercises 1–3.

The rules for division are the same as those for multiplication.

> To multiply or divide two numbers (where the divisor is nonzero):
>
> **a)** Multiply or divide the absolute values.
> **b)** If the signs are the same, the answer is positive.
> **c)** If the signs are different, the answer is negative.

◀ Do Exercises 4–6.

Excluding Division by 0

Example 4 shows why we cannot divide -17 by 0. We can use the same argument to show why we cannot divide any nonzero number b by 0. Consider $b \div 0$. We look for a number that when multiplied by 0 gives b. There is no such number because the product of 0 and any number is 0. Thus we cannot divide a nonzero number b by 0.

On the other hand, if we divide 0 by 0, we look for a number c such that $0 \cdot c = 0$. But $0 \cdot c = 0$ for any number c. Thus it appears that $0 \div 0$ could be any number we choose. Getting any answer we want when we divide 0 by 0 would be very confusing. Thus we agree that division by 0 is not defined.

Divide.

1. $6 \div (-3)$ *Think*: What number multiplied by -3 gives 6?

2. $\dfrac{-15}{-3}$ *Think*: What number multiplied by -3 gives -15?

3. $-24 \div 8$ *Think*: What number multiplied by 8 gives -24?

Divide.

4. $\dfrac{-72}{-8}$ 5. $\dfrac{30}{-5}$ 6. $\dfrac{56}{-7}$

Answers

Skill to Review:
1. 19   2. 6

Margin Exercises:
1. -2 2. 5   3. -3 4. 9   5. -6
6. -8

EXCLUDING DIVISION BY 0

Division by 0 is not defined:

$a \div 0$ is not defined for all integers a.

Dividing 0 by Other Numbers

Note that $0 \div 8 = 0$ because $0 = 0 \cdot 8$.

DIVIDENDS OF 0

Zero divided by any nonzero number is 0:

$$0 \div a = 0, \quad a \neq 0.$$

EXAMPLES   Divide.

5. $0 \div (-6) = 0$ **6.** $0 \div 12 = 0$ **7.** $-3 \div 0$ is not defined.

Do Exercises 7 and 8. ▶

Divide, if possible.

7. $-5 \div 0$ **8.** $0 \div (-3)$

APPLICATIONS AND PROBLEM SOLVING

We can use multiplication and division of integers to solve applied problems.

EXAMPLE 8   *Mine Rescue.*   The San Jose copper and gold mine near Copiapó, Chile, caved in on August 5, 2010, trapping 33 miners. Each miner was safely brought out in a specially designed capsule that could be lowered into the mine at -137 feet per minute. It took approximately 15 min to lower the capsule to the miners' location. Determine how far below the surface of the earth the miners were trapped.

Source: Reuters News

Since the capsule moved -137 feet per minute and it took 15 min to reach the miners, we have the depth d given by

$$d = 15 \cdot (-137) = -2055.$$

Thus the miners were trapped at -2055 ft.

EXAMPLE 9   *Chemical Reaction.*   During a chemical reaction, the temperature in a beaker decreased every minute by the same number of degrees. The temperature was $56°F$ at 10:10 A.M. By 10:42 A.M., the temperature had dropped to $-8°F$. By how many degrees did it change each minute?

We first determine by how many degrees d the temperature changed altogether. We subtract -8 from 56:

$$d = 56 - (-8) = 56 + 8 = 64.$$

Answers

7. Not defined   **8.** 0

9. *Chemical Reaction.* During a chemical reaction, the temperature in a beaker increased by 3°C every minute. If the temperature was −17°C at 1:10 P.M., when the reaction began, what was the temperature at 1:34 P.M.?

10. *Chemical Reaction.* During a chemical reaction, the temperature in a beaker decreased every minute by the same number of degrees. The temperature was 71°F at 2:12 P.M. By 2:29 P.M., the temperature had changed to −14°F. By how many degrees did it change each minute?

The temperature changed a total of 64°. We can express this as −64° since the temperature dropped.

The amount of time *t* that passed was 42 − 10, or 32 min. Thus the number of degrees *T* that the temperature dropped each minute is given by

$$T = d \div t = -64 \div 32 = -2.$$

The change was −2°F per minute.

◄ **Do Exercises 9 and 10.**

C **ORDER OF OPERATIONS**

When several operations are to be done in a calculation or a problem involving integers, we apply the same rules that we did in Section 1.9. We repeat them here for review. If you did not study that section before, you should do so before continuing.

> **RULES FOR ORDER OF OPERATIONS**
> ....
>
> **1.** Do all operations within grouping symbols before operations outside.
> **2.** Evaluate all exponential expressions.
> **3.** Do all multiplications and divisions in order from left to right.
> **4.** Do all additions and subtractions in order from left to right.

EXAMPLE 10 Simplify: $-34 \cdot 56 - 17$.

There are no parentheses or exponents so we start with the third step.

$$-34 \cdot 56 - 17 = -1904 - 17 \qquad \text{Carrying out all multiplications and divisions in order from left to right}$$

$$= -1921 \qquad \text{Carrying out all additions and subtractions in order from left to right}$$

EXAMPLE 11 Simplify: $256 \div 2^4 \cdot (-5)$.

There are no calculations within grouping symbols so we start with the second step.

$$256 \div 2^4 \cdot (-5) = 256 \div 16 \cdot (-5) \qquad \text{Evaluating the exponential expression}$$

$$= 16 \cdot (-5) \qquad \text{Doing all multiplications and divisions in order from left to right}$$

$$= -80$$

Answers

9. 55°C   **10.** −5°F per minute

EXAMPLE 12   Simplify: $2^4 + 51 \cdot 4 - (37 + 23 \cdot 2)$.

$2^4 + 51 \cdot 4 - (37 + 23 \cdot 2)$

$= 2^4 + 51 \cdot 4 - (37 + 46)$ Carrying out all operations inside parentheses, first multiplying 23 by 2, following the rules for order of operations within the parentheses

$= 2^4 + 51 \cdot 4 - 83$ Completing the addition inside parentheses

$= 16 + 51 \cdot 4 - 83$ Evaluating exponential expressions

$= 16 + 204 - 83$ Doing all multiplications

$= 220 - 83$ Doing all additions and subtractions in order from left to right

$= 137$

EXAMPLE 13   Simplify: $[-64 \div (-16) \div (-2)] \div [2^3 - 3^2]$.

$[-64 \div (-16) \div (-2)] \div [2^3 - 3^2] = [4 \div (-2)] \div [8 - 9]$

$= -2 \div (-1)$

$= 2$

Do Exercises 11–14. ▶

Simplify.

11. $23 - 42 \cdot 30$

GS **12.** $32 \div 8 \cdot 2 \div 4$

$= \boxed{} \cdot 2 \div 4$

$= \boxed{} \div 4$

$= \boxed{}$

13. $52 \cdot 5 + 5^3 - (4^2 - 48 \div 4)$

14. $[5 - 10 - 5 \cdot 23] \div (2^3 + 3^2 - 7)$

Answers

11. -1237 **12.** 2 **13.** 381 **14.** -12

Guided Solution:

12. 4, 8, 2

Translating for Success

1. **Gas Mileage.** After driving his compact car for 759 mi on the first day of a trip, Nathan noticed that it took 23 gal of gasoline to fill the tank. How many miles per gallon did the compact car get?

2. **Apartment Rent.** Cecilia needs $4500 for tuition. This is two times as much as she needs for apartment rent. How much does she need for the rent?

3. **Purchase Price.** The price of an office copier is $4500 and the sales tax is $150. Find the total purchase price.

4. **Change in Elevation.** The lowest elevation in Australia, Lake Eyre, is 52 ft below sea level. The highest elevation in Australia, Mt. Kosciusko, is 7310 ft. Find the difference in elevation between the highest point and the lowest point.

5. **Cell-Phone Bill.** Jeff's cell-phone bill for September was $73. He made a payment of $52. How much did he then owe on his cell-phone bill?

The goal of these matching questions is to practice step (2), Translate, of the five-step problem-solving process. Translate each problem to an equation and select a correct translation from equations A–O.

A. $7 \cdot x = 588$

B. $52 + x = 73$

C. $2 \cdot x = 4500$

D. $150 \cdot x = 4500$

E. $23(759) = x$

F. $4500 = 150 + x$

G. $4500 + 150 = x$

H. $x = 150 \cdot 4500$

I. $23 \cdot x = 759$

J. $7 \div 588 = x$

K. $x = 23 + 759$

L. $x = 7310 - (-52)$

M. $x = 588 \cdot 7$

N. $2(4500) = x$

O. $52 \cdot x = 7310$

Answers on page A-3

6. **Camp Sponsorships.** Donations of $52 per camper are needed for camp sponsorships at Lazy Day Summer Camp. Two weeks prior to camp, $7310 had been collected for sponsorships. How many campers can be enrolled?

7. **Drain Pipe.** A construction engineer has 588 ft of flexible drain pipe. How many 7-ft lengths can be cut from the total amount of pipe available?

8. **Savings-Account Balance.** After $150 interest has been added to Kelly's savings account, the new balance is $4500. Find the previous balance.

9. **Loan Payments.** Matt's student loan totals $4500. If he repays $150 each month, how many months will it take him to repay the loan?

10. **Drain Pipe.** A subcontractor needs 588 pieces of pipe for a large irrigation project. If each piece must be 7 ft long, how many feet of pipe have to be purchased?

☑ Reading Check

Determine whether each statement is true or false.

_____ **RC1.** The quotient $a \div b$, where $b \neq 0$, is that unique number c for which $a = b \cdot c$.

_____ **RC2.** When a positive number is divided by a negative number, the answer is negative.

_____ **RC3.** $0 \div (-5)$ is not defined.

_____ **RC4.** $0 \div 0 = 1$.

a   Divide, if possible. Check each answer.

1. $36 \div (-6)$

2. $42 \div (-7)$

3. $26 \div (-2)$

4. $24 \div (-12)$

5. $-16 \div 8$

6. $-18 \div (-2)$

7. $-48 \div (-12)$

8. $-72 \div (-9)$

9. $-72 \div 9$

10. $-50 \div 25$

11. $-100 \div (-50)$

12. $-200 \div 8$

13. $-108 \div 9$

14. $-64 \div (-8)$

15. $200 \div (-25)$

16. $-390 \div (-13)$

17. $75 \div 0$

18. $0 \div (-5)$

19. $81 \div (-9)$

20. $-145 \div (-5)$

b   Solve.

21. *Drop in Temperature.*   The temperature in Osgood was 62°F at 2:00 P.M. It dropped 6°F per hour for the next 4 hr. What was the temperature at the end of the 4-hr period?

22. *Juice Consumption.*   Oliver bought a 64-oz container of cranberry juice and drank 8 oz per day for a week. How much juice was left in the container at the end of the week?

23. *Stock Price.*   The price of a stock began the day at $32 per share and dropped $2 per hour for 3 hr. What was the price of the stock after 3 hr?

24. *Population Decrease.*   The population of a rural town was 12,500. It decreased 380 each year for 4 years. What was the population of the town after 4 years?

25. *Diver's Position.* After diving 95 m below sea level, a diver rises at a rate of 7 meters per minute for 9 min. At that point, where is the diver in relation to the surface?

26. *Bank Account Balance.* Karen had $234 in her bank account. After she used her debit card to make seven purchases at $39 each, what was the balance in her bank account?

C   Simplify.

27. $8 - 2 \cdot 3 - 9$

28. $8 - (2 \cdot 3 - 9)$

29. $(8 - 2 \cdot 3) - 9$

30. $(8 - 2)(3 - 9)$

31. $16 \cdot (-24) + 50$

32. $10 \cdot 20 - 15 \cdot 24$

33. $2^4 + 2^3 - 10$

34. $40 - 3^2 - 2^3$

35. $5^3 + 26 \cdot 71 - (16 + 25 \cdot 3)$

36. $4^3 + 10 \cdot 20 + 8^2 - 23$

37. $4 \cdot 5 - 2 \cdot 6 + 4$

38. $4 \cdot (6 + 8)(4 + 3)$

39. $4^3 \div 8$

40. $5^3 - 7^2$

41. $8(-7) + 6(-5)$

42. $10(-5) + 1(-1)$

43. $19 - 5(-3) + 3$

44. $14 - 2(-6) + 7$

45. $9 \div (-3) + 16 \div 8$

46. $-32 - 8 \div 4 - (-2)$

47. $-4^2 + 6$

48. $-5^2 + 7$

49. $-8^2 - 3$

50. $-9^2 - 11$

51. $12 - 20^3$

52. $20 + 4^3 \div (-8)$

53. $2 \times 10^3 - 5000$

54. $-7(3^4) + 18$

Copyright © 2015 Pearson Education, Inc.

55. $6[9 - (3 - 4)]$

56. $8[(6 - 13) - 11]$

57. $-1000 \div (-100) \div 10$

58. $256 \div (-32) \div (-4)$

59. $8 - (7 - 9)$

60. $(8 - 7) - 9$

61. $(10 - 6^2) \div (3^2 + 2^2)$

62. $(-3 - 5^3 - 4^3) \div (6^2 - 10^2)$

63. $[20(8 - 3) - 4(10 - 3)] \div [10(2 - 6) + 2(7 + 4)]$

64. $[(3 - 5)^2 - 4(5 - 13)] \div [(12 - 9)^2 + (11 - 14)^2]$

Skill Maintenance

What does the digit 8 mean in each number?   [1.1a]

65. 4,678,952

66. 8,473,901

67. 7148

68. 23,803

Subtract.   [1.3a]

69. $9001 - 6798$

70. $2037 - 1189$

71. $67,113 - 29,874$

72. $12,327 - 476$

Solve.   [1.8a]

73. A playing field is 78 ft long and 64 ft wide. What is its area? its perimeter?

74. A painter buys three 5-gal pails of exterior paint at \$112 each and eight 1-gal cans of interior paint at \$28 each. How much is spent altogether for the paint?

Synthesis

Simplify.

75. 🖩 $[195 + (-15)^3] \div [195 - 7 \cdot 5^2]$

76. 🖩 $[19 - 17^2] \div [13^2 - 34]$

Determine the sign of each expression if m is negative and n is positive.

77. $-n \div (-m)$

78. $-n \div m$

79. $-[n \div (-m)]$

80. $-(-n \div m)$

81. $-[-n \div (-m)]$

Vocabulary Reinforcement

In Exercises 1–6, fill in each blank with the correct term from the given list. Some of the choices may not be used.

1. The _____ are . . . , −3, −2, −1, 0, 1, 2, 3, ...   [2.1a]

2. The _____ value of a number is its distance from zero on the number line.   [2.1d]

3. Numbers such as −3 and 3 are called _____, or _____ inverses.   [2.2b]

4. The _____ $a - b$ is the number c for which $a = b + c$.   [2.3a]

5. The product of two negative numbers is _____.   [2.4a]

6. The quotient of a positive number and a negative number is _____.   [2.5a]

| sum |
| difference |
| product |
| quotient |
| integers |
| whole numbers |
| additive |
| multiplicative |
| opposites |
| absolute |
| positive |
| negative |

Concept Reinforcement

Determine whether each statement is true or false.

_____ 1. The sum of two negative numbers is positive.   [2.2a]

_____ 2. The sum of a number and its opposite is 0.   [2.2b]

_____ 3. The product of an even number of negative numbers is negative.   [2.4a]

_____ 4. The opposite of the opposite of a number is the number itself.   [2.2b]

Study Guide

Objective 2.1b   Graph integers on the number line.

Example   Graph −3 on the number line.

We locate −3 on the number line and mark its point with a dot.

Practice Exercise

1. Graph 4 on the number line.

Objective 2.1c   Determine which of two real numbers is greater and indicate which, using < or >.

Example   Use either < or < for ☐ to write a true sentence.

$$-5 \,\square\, -8$$

Since −5 is to the right of −8 on the number line, we have −5 > −8.

Practice Exercise

2. Use either < or > for ☐ to write a true sentence.

$$-7 \,\square\, 1$$

Objective 2.1d   Find the absolute value of an integer.

Example   Find.   **a)** $|-9|$ **b)** $|35|$

a) The number is negative, so we make it positive.

$$|-9| = 9$$

b) The number is positive, so the absolute value is the same as the number.

$$|35| = 35$$

Practice Exercise

3. Find.

   a) $|-17|$ **b)** $|14|$

Objective 2.2a   Add integers without using the number line.

Example   Add without using the number line: $-15 + 9$.

We have a negative number and a positive number. The absolute values are 15 and 9. Their difference is 6. The negative number has the larger absolute value, so the answer is negative.

$$-15 + 9 = -6$$

Example   Add without using the number line: $-8 + (-9)$.

We have two negative numbers. We add the absolute values, 8 and 9. The answer is negative.

$$-8 + (-9) = -17$$

Practice Exercises

Add without using the number line.

4. $6 + (-9)$

5. $-5 + (-3)$

Objective 2.3a   Subtract integers.

Example   Subtract: $8 - 12$.

We add the opposite of the number being subtracted.

$$8 - 12 = 8 + (-12)$$
$$= -4$$

Practice Exercise

6. Subtract: $6 - (-8)$.

Objective 2.4a   Multiply integers.

Example   Multiply: $-6(-4)$.

The signs are the same, so the answer is positive.

$$-6(-4) = 24$$

Example   Multiply: $-5(7)$.

The signs are different, so the answer is negative.

$$-5(7) = -35$$

Practice Exercises

Multiply.

7. $-9(-8)$

8. $6(-15)$

Objective 2.5a   Divide integers.

Example   Divide: $-36 \div (-4)$.
  The signs are the same, so the answer is positive.
$$-36 \div (-4) = 9$$

Example   Divide: $-21 \div 7$.
  The signs are different, so the answer is negative.
$$-21 \div 7 = -3$$

Practice Exercises
Divide.
  9. $-32 \div (-8)$
  10. $48 \div (-12)$

Objective 2.5c   Simplify expressions using rules for order of operations.

Example   Simplify: $3^2 - 24 \div 2 - (4 + 2 \cdot 8)$.

$$3^2 - 24 \div 2 - (4 + 2 \cdot 8)$$
$$= 3^2 - 24 \div 2 - (4 + 16)$$
$$= 3^2 - 24 \div 2 - 20$$
$$= 9 - 24 \div 2 - 20$$
$$= 9 - 12 - 20 = -3 - 20 = -23$$

Practice Exercise
  11. Simplify: $4 - 8^2 \div (10 - 6)$.

Review Exercises

1. State the integers that correspond to this situation: Josh earned $620 for one week's work. While driving to work one day, he received a speeding ticket for $125.   [2.1a]

Simplify.   [2.1d]

  2. $|-38|$

  3. $|7|$

  4. $|0|$

  5. $-|-2|$

Use either $<$ or $>$ for $\square$ to write a true sentence.   [2.1c]
  6. $-3 \,\square\, 10$

  7. $-1 \,\square\, -6$

  8. $11 \,\square\, -12$

  9. $-2 \,\square\, -1$

Graph the number on the number line.   [2.1b]
  10. 6

  11. -2

Find the opposite, or additive inverse, of each number.   [2.2b]

  12. 8

  13. -14

  14. 0

  15. -23

Copyright © 2015 Pearson Education, Inc.

16. Evaluate $-x$ when x is -34. [2.2b]

17. Evaluate $-(-x)$ when x is 5. [2.2b]

Compute and simplify.

18. $4 + (-7)$ [2.2a]

19. $-8 + 1$ [2.2a]

20. $6 + (-9) + (-8) + 7$ [2.2a]

21. $-4 + 5 + (-12) + (-4) + 10$ [2.2a]

22. $-3 - (-7)$ [2.3a]

23. $-9 - 5$ [2.3a]

24. $-4 - 4$ [2.3a]

25. $-9 \cdot (-6)$ [2.4a]

26. $-3(13)$ [2.4a]

27. $7 \cdot (-8)$ [2.4a]

28. $3 \cdot (-7) \cdot (-2) \cdot (-5)$ [2.4a]

29. $35 \div (-5)$ [2.5a]

30. $-51 \div 17$ [2.5a]

31. $-42 \div (-7)$ [2.5a]

Simplify. [2.5c]

32. $-12(-3) - 2^3 - (-9)(-10)$

33. $2(-3 - 12) - 8(-7)$

34. $625 \div (-25) \div 5$

35. $-16 \div 4 - 30 \div (-5)$

36. $9[(7 - 14) - 13]$

Solve.

37. Chang's total assets are $2140. Then he borrows $2500. What are his total assets now? [2.3b]

38. *Stock Price.* The price of a stock opened at $78 per share and dropped by $2 per hour for 8 hr. What was the price of the stock after 8 hr? [2.5b]

39. On the first, second, and third downs, a football team had these gains and losses: 5-yd gain, 12-yd loss, and 15-yd gain, respectively. Find the total gain or loss. [2.3b]

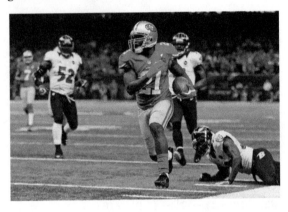

40. *Bank Account Balance.* Yuri had $68 in his bank account. After using his debit card to buy seven equally priced tee shirts, the balance in his account was −$65. What was the price of each shirt? [2.5b]

41. Compute and simplify: $8 - (-5) - 7 - (-9)$. [2.3a]

  A. −13   **B.** −3
  C. 15   **D.** 29

42. Simplify: $-3 \cdot 4 - 12 \div 4$. [2.5c]

  A. −16   **B.** −15
  C. 0   **D.** 6

Synthesis

43. The following are examples of consecutive integers: 4, 5, 6, 7, 8; −13, −12, −11, −10. [2.3b], [2.5b]

  a) Express the number 8 as the sum of 16 consecutive integers.
  b) Find the product of the 16 consecutive integers in part (a).

44. Insert one pair of parentheses to make the following a true statement: [2.5c]
$$9 - 3 - 4 + 5 = 15.$$

Simplify.

45. $-|8 - (-4 \div 2) - 3 \cdot 5|$ [2.1d], [2.5c]

46. $(|-6 - 3| + 3^2 - |-3|) \div (-3)$ [2.1d], [2.5c]

Understanding Through Discussion and Writing

  1. What rule have we developed that would tell you the sign of $(-7)^8$ and $(-7)^{11}$ without doing the computations? Explain. [2.4a]

  2. Under what circumstances will the sum of a positive integer and a negative integer be negative? [2.2a]

  3. Jake enters $18 \div 2 \cdot 3$ on his calculator and expects the result to be 3. What mistake is he making? [2.5c]

  4. Write a problem for a classmate to solve. Design the problem so that the solution is "The temperature dropped to −9°F." [2.3b], [2.5b]

Copyright © 2015 Pearson Education, Inc.

For Extra Help For step-by-step test solutions, access the Chapter Test Prep Videos in MyMathLab® or on YouTube (search "BittingerBasicEl" and click on "Channels").

Use either $<$ or $>$ for ☐ to write a true sentence.

1. -4 ☐ 0

2. -3 ☐ -8

3. -7 ☐ -8

4. -1 ☐ 1

Simplify.

5. $|-7|$

6. $|94|$

7. $-|-27|$

Find the opposite, or additive inverse.

8. 23

9. -14

10. Evaluate $-x$ when x is -8.

11. Graph -6 on the number line.

Compute and simplify.

12. $31 - (-47)$

13. $-8 + 4 + (-7) + 3$

14. $-13 + 15$

15. $2 - (-8)$

16. $32 - 57$

17. $18 + (-3)$

18. $4 \cdot (-12)$

19. $-8 \cdot (-3)$

20. $-45 \div 5$

21. $-63 \div (-7)$

22. $64 \div (-16)$

23. $-2(16) - [2(-8) - 5^3]$

24. *Difference in Elevation.* The lowest elevation in Australia, Lake Eyre, is 15 m below sea level. The highest elevation in Australia, Mount Kosciuszko, is 2229 m. Find the difference in elevation between the highest point and the lowest point.
Source: *The CIA World Factbook 2012*

Lake Eyre
−15 m

Sydney

Mt. Kosciuszko
2229 m

25. Isabella kept track of the changes in the stock market over a period of 5 weeks. By how many points had the market risen or fallen over this time?

WEEK 1	WEEK 2	WEEK 3	WEEK 4	WEEK 5
Down 13 pts	Down 16 pts	Up 36 pts	Down 11 pts	Up 19 pts

26. *Population Decrease.* The population of Stone City was 18,600. It decreased by 420 each year for 6 years. What was the population of the city after 6 years?

27. *Chemical Reaction.* During a chemical reaction, the temperature in a beaker decreased every minute by the same number of degrees. The temperature was 17°C at 11:08 A.M. By 11:25 A.M., the temperature had dropped to −17°C. By how many degrees did it change each minute?

28. Evaluate $-(-x)$ when x is 14.

  A. −14   **B.** 196
  C. 0   **D.** 14

Synthesis

29. Simplify: $|-27 - 3(4)| - |-36| + |-12|$.

30. The deepest point in the Pacific Ocean is the Marianas Trench with a depth of 11,033 m. The deepest point in the Atlantic Ocean is the Puerto Rico Trench with a depth of 8648 m. How much higher is the Puerto Rico Trench than the Marianas Trench?
Source: Defense Mapping Agency, Hydrographic/Topographic Center

31. Find the next three numbers in each sequence.

  a) 6, 5, 3, 0, ____, ____, ____
  b) 14, 10, 6, 2, ____, ____, ____
  c) −4, −6, −9, −13, ____, ____, ____
  d) 64, −32, 16, −8, ____, ____, ____

Copyright © 2015 Pearson Education, Inc.

Fraction Notation: Multiplication and Division

3.1 Factorizations

3.2 Divisibility

3.3 Fractions and Fraction Notation

3.4 Multiplication and Applications

3.5 Simplifying

Mid-Chapter Review

3.6 Multiplying, Simplifying, and Applications

3.7 Division and Applications

Translating for Success

Summary and Review

Test

Cumulative Review

STUDYING FOR SUCCESS   *Learning Resources on Campus*

☐ There may be a learning lab or a tutoring center for drop-in tutoring.

☐ There may be group tutoring sessions for this specific course.

☐ The math department may have a bulletin board or network that provides contact information for private tutors.

3.1   Factorizations

OBJECTIVES

a Determine whether one number is a factor of another, and find the factors of a number.

b Find some multiples of a number, and determine whether a number is divisible by another.

c Given a number from 1 to 100, tell whether it is prime, composite, or neither.

d Find the prime factorization of a composite number.

SKILL TO REVIEW

Objective 1.5a: Divide whole numbers.

Divide.

1. $329 \div 8$

2. $23 \overline{)1\,0\,8\,1}$

In this chapter, we begin our work with fractions and fraction notation. *Factoring* is an important skill in working with fractions. For example, in order to simplify $\frac{12}{32}$, it is important that we be able to factor 12 and 32, as follows:

$$\frac{12}{32} = \frac{4 \cdot 3}{4 \cdot 8}.$$

Then we "remove" a factor of 1:

$$\frac{4 \cdot 3}{4 \cdot 8} = \frac{4}{4} \cdot \frac{3}{8} = 1 \cdot \frac{3}{8} = \frac{3}{8}.$$

a   FACTORS AND FACTORIZATIONS

Here we consider only the **natural numbers** 1, 2, 3, and so on.

Let's look at the product $3 \cdot 4 = 12$. We say that 3 and 4 are **factors** of 12. When we divide 12 by 3, we get a remainder of 0. We say that the divisor 3 is a **factor** of the dividend 12.

> **FACTOR**
>
> • In the product $a \cdot b$, a and b are called **factors**.
> • If we divide Q by d and get a remainder of 0, then the divisor d is a **factor** of the dividend Q.

EXAMPLE 1 Determine by long division **(a)** whether 6 is a factor of 198 and **(b)** whether 15 is a factor of 198.

Determine whether the second number is a factor of the first.

1. 72; 8   **2.** 2384; 28

a)
```
       33
   6)198
     18
     ──
     18
     18
     ──
      0  ← Remainder is 0.
```

b)
```
       13
  15)198
     15
     ──
     48
     45
     ──
      3  ← Not 0
```

The remainder is 0, so 6 is a factor of 198.

The remainder is not 0, so 15 is not a factor of 198.

◀ **Do Margin Exercises 1 and 2.**

Answers

Skill to Review:
1. 41 R 1   **2.** 47

Margin Exercises:
1. Yes   **2.** No

Consider $12 = 3 \cdot 4$. We say that $3 \cdot 4$ is a **factorization** of 12. Similarly, $6 \cdot 2, 12 \cdot 1, 2 \cdot 2 \cdot 3,$ and $1 \cdot 3 \cdot 4$ are also factorizations of 12. Since $a = a \cdot 1$, every number has a factorization, and every number has factors. For some numbers, the factors consist of only the number itself and 1. For example, the only factorization of 17 is $17 \cdot 1$, so the only factors of 17 are 17 and 1.

EXAMPLE 2   List all the factors of 70.

We list as many "two-factor" factorizations as we can. We check sequentially the numbers 1, 2, 3, and so on, to see if we can form any factorizations:

70
$1 \cdot 70$
$2 \cdot 35$
$5 \cdot 14$ 3 and 4 are not factors of 70.
$7 \cdot 10$ 6 is not a factor of 70.
       8 and 9 are not factors of 70.
       10 is already listed.

Note that all of the factors of a natural number are *less than or equal to* the number.

The factors of 70 are 1, 2, 5, 7, 10, 14, 35, and 70.

Do Exercises 3–6. ▶

b MULTIPLES AND DIVISIBILITY

A **multiple** of a natural number is a product of that number and some natural number. For example, some multiples of 2 are

2   (because $2 = 1 \cdot 2$);
4   (because $4 = 2 \cdot 2$);
6   (because $6 = 3 \cdot 2$);
8   (because $8 = 4 \cdot 2$).

Note that all of the multiples of a number are *greater than or equal to* the number.

We find multiples of 2 by counting by twos: 2, 4, 6, 8, and so on. We can find multiples of 3 by counting by threes: 3, 6, 9, 12, and so on.

EXAMPLE 3   Show that each of the numbers 8, 12, 20, and 36 is a multiple of 4.

$8 = 2 \cdot 4$ $12 = 3 \cdot 4$ $20 = 5 \cdot 4$ $36 = 9 \cdot 4$

Do Exercises 7 and 8. ▶

EXAMPLE 4   Multiply by 1, 2, 3, and so on, to find ten multiples of 7.

$1 \cdot 7 = 7$ $3 \cdot 7 = 21$ $5 \cdot 7 = 35$ $7 \cdot 7 = 49$ $9 \cdot 7 = 63$
$2 \cdot 7 = 14$ $4 \cdot 7 = 28$ $6 \cdot 7 = 42$ $8 \cdot 7 = 56$ $10 \cdot 7 = 70$

Do Exercise 9. ▶

List all the factors of each number.

3. 10

 4. 45

$1 \cdot \boxed{}$
   2 is not a factor of 45.
$3 \cdot \boxed{}$
   4 is not a factor of 45.
$5 \cdot \boxed{}$
   6, 7, and 8 are not factors of 45.
   9 is already listed.

The factors of 45 are 1, $\boxed{}$, 5, $\boxed{}$, 15, and $\boxed{}$.

5. 62   **6.** 24

7. Show that each of the numbers 5, 45, and 100 is a multiple of 5.

8. Show that each of the numbers 10, 60, and 110 is a multiple of 10.

9. Multiply by 1, 2, 3, and so on, to find ten multiples of 5.

Answers

3. 1, 2, 5, 10   **4.** 1, 3, 5, 9, 15, 45
5. 1, 2, 31, 62   **6.** 1, 2, 3, 4, 6, 8, 12, 24
7. $5 = 1 \cdot 5$; $45 = 9 \cdot 5$; $100 = 20 \cdot 5$
8. $10 = 1 \cdot 10$; $60 = 6 \cdot 10$; $110 = 11 \cdot 10$
9. 5, 10, 15, 20, 25, 30, 35, 40, 45, 50

Guided Solution:
4. 45, 15, 9; 3, 9, 45

DIVISIBILITY

The number *a* is **divisible** by another number *b* if there exists a number *c* such that $a = b \cdot c$. The statements "*a* is **divisible** by *b*," "*a* is a **multiple** of *b*," and "*b* is a **factor** of *a*" all have the same meaning.

---

10. Determine whether 16 is divisible by 2.

$$\begin{array}{r} 8 \\ \boxed{}\overline{)16} \\ \underline{16} \\ \boxed{} \end{array}$$

Since the remainder is ⬚ , 16 ⬚ divisible by 2.
  is/is not

Thus, 27 is *divisible* by 3 because $27 = 3 \cdot 9$. We can also say that 27 is a *multiple* of 3, and 3 is a *factor* of 27.

EXAMPLE 5 Determine **(a)** whether 45 is divisible by 9 and **(b)** whether 45 is divisible by 4.

a) We divide 45 by 9.

$$\begin{array}{r} 5 \\ 9\overline{)45} \\ \underline{45} \\ 0 \end{array} \leftarrow \text{Remainder is 0.}$$

Because the remainder is 0, 45 is divisible by 9.

b) We divide 45 by 4.

$$\begin{array}{r} 11 \\ 4\overline{)45} \\ \underline{4} \\ 5 \\ \underline{4} \\ 1 \end{array} \leftarrow \text{Not 0}$$

Since the remainder is not 0, 45 is not divisible by 4.

11. Determine whether 125 is divisible by 5.

12. Determine whether 125 is divisible by 6.

◀ Do Exercises 10–12.

c PRIME AND COMPOSITE NUMBERS

PRIME AND COMPOSITE NUMBERS

- A natural number that has exactly two *different* factors, only itself and 1, is called a **prime number**.
- The number 1 is *not* prime.
- A natural number, other than 1, that is not prime is **composite**.

EXAMPLE 6 Determine whether the numbers 1, 2, 7, 8, 9, 11, 18, 39, and 59 are prime, composite, or neither.

The number 1 is not prime. It does not have two different factors.

The number 2 is prime. It has only the factors 2 and 1.

The numbers 7, 11, and 59 are prime. Each has only two factors, itself and 1.

The number 8 is not prime. It has the factors 1, 2, 4, and 8 and is composite.

The numbers 9, 18, and 39 are composite. Each has more than two factors.

Thus we have

Prime: 2, 7, 11, 59;
Composite: 8, 9, 18, 39;
Neither: 1.

13. Tell whether each number is prime, composite, or neither.

1, 2, 6, 12, 13, 19, 41, 65, 73, 99

◀ Do Exercise 13.

Answers

10. Yes **11.** Yes **12.** No **13.** 2, 13, 19, 41, and 73 are prime; 6, 12, 65, and 99 are composite; 1 is neither.

Guided Solution:
10. 2, 0; 0, is

The number 2 is the *only* even prime number. It is also the smallest prime number. The number 0 is neither prime nor composite, but 0 is *not* a natural number and thus is not considered here. We are considering only natural numbers. The number 1 is the only natural number that is neither prime nor composite.

The table at right lists the prime numbers from 2 to 97. These prime numbers will be the most helpful to you in this text.

A TABLE OF PRIME NUMBERS FROM 2 TO 97

2, 3, 5, 7, 11, 13, 17, 19, 23, 29, 31, 37, 41, 43, 47, 53, 59, 61, 67, 71, 73, 79, 83, 89, 97

d PRIME FACTORIZATIONS

When we factor a composite number into a product of primes, we find the **prime factorization** of the number. To do this, we consider the primes

2, 3, 5, 7, 11, 13, 17, 19, 23, and so on,

and determine whether a given number is divisible by the primes.

EXAMPLE 7 Find the prime factorization of 39.

a) We divide by the first prime, 2.

$$
\begin{array}{r}
19 \\
2\overline{)39} \\
\underline{2} \\
19 \\
\underline{18} \\
1
\end{array}
$$

Because the remainder is not 0, 2 is not a factor of 39, and 39 is not divisible by 2.

b) We divide by the next prime, 3.

$$
\begin{array}{r}
13 \quad R = 0 \\
3\overline{)39}
\end{array}
$$

The remainder is 0, so we know that $39 = 3 \cdot 13$. Because 13 is a prime, we are finished. The prime factorization is

$$39 = 3 \cdot 13.$$

EXAMPLE 8 Find the prime factorization of 220.

a) We divide by the first prime, 2.

$$
\begin{array}{r}
110 \quad R = 0 \\
2\overline{)220}
\end{array}
\qquad 220 = 2 \cdot 110
$$

b) Because 110 is composite, we continue to divide, starting with 2 again.

$$
\begin{array}{r}
55 \quad R = 0 \\
2\overline{)110}
\end{array}
\qquad 220 = 2 \cdot 2 \cdot 55
$$

c) Since 55 is composite and is not divisible by 2 or 3, we divide by the next prime, 5.

$$
\begin{array}{r}
11 \quad R = 0 \\
5\overline{)55}
\end{array}
\qquad 220 = 2 \cdot 2 \cdot 5 \cdot 11
$$

Because 11 is prime, we are finished. The prime factorization is

$$220 = 2 \cdot 2 \cdot 5 \cdot 11.$$

CALCULATOR CORNER

Divisibility and Factors We can use a calculator to determine whether one number is divisible by another number or whether one number is a factor of another number. For example, to determine whether 387 is divisible by 9, we press 3 8 7 ÷ 9 = . The display is 43. Since 43 is a natural number, we know that 387 is a multiple of 9; that is, $387 = 43 \cdot 9$. Thus, 387 is divisible by 9, and 9 is a factor of 387.

EXERCISES For each pair of numbers, determine whether the second number is a factor of the first number.

1. 502; 8
2. 651; 21
3. 3875; 25
4. 1047; 14

We abbreviate our procedure as follows.

$$\begin{array}{r} 11 \\ 5\overline{)55} \\ 2\overline{)110} \\ 2\overline{)220} \end{array}$$

$$220 = 2 \cdot 2 \cdot 5 \cdot 11$$

Because multiplication is commutative, a factorization such as $2 \cdot 2 \cdot 5 \cdot 11$ could also be expressed as $5 \cdot 2 \cdot 2 \cdot 11$ or $2 \cdot 5 \cdot 11 \cdot 2$ (or, in exponential notation, as $2^2 \cdot 5 \cdot 11$ or $11 \cdot 2^2 \cdot 5$), but the prime factors are the same in each case. For this reason, we agree that any of these is "the" prime factorization of 220.

> Every number has just one (unique) prime factorization.

··········· Caution! ···········

Keep in mind the difference between finding all the factors of a number and finding the prime factorization. In Example 9, the prime factorization of 72 is $2 \cdot 2 \cdot 2 \cdot 3 \cdot 3$. The factors of 72 are 1, 2, 3, 4, 6, 8, 9, 12, 18, 24, 36, and 72.

EXAMPLE 9 Find the prime factorization of 72.

We can do divisions "up" as follows:

$$\begin{array}{r} 3 \leftarrow \text{Prime quotient} \\ 3\overline{)\ 9} \\ 2\overline{)18} \\ 2\overline{)36} \\ 2\overline{)72} \leftarrow \text{Begin here} \end{array}$$

$$72 = 2 \cdot 2 \cdot 2 \cdot 3 \cdot 3$$

Another way to find the prime factorization of 72 uses a **factor tree** as follows. Begin by determining any factorization you can, and then continue factoring. Any one of the following factor trees gives the prime factorization of 72:

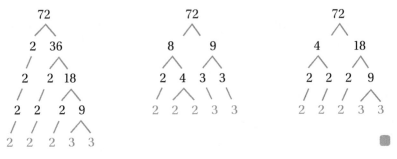

EXAMPLE 10 Find the prime factorization of 189.

We can use a string of successive divisions or a factor tree. Since 189 is not divisible by 2, we begin with 3.

$$\begin{array}{r} 7 \\ 3\overline{)21} \\ 3\overline{)63} \\ 3\overline{)189} \end{array}$$

$$189 = 3 \cdot 3 \cdot 3 \cdot 7$$

$$\begin{array}{c} 189 \\ \diagup\ \diagdown \\ 3\quad 63 \\ \diagup\ \diagdown \\ 3\quad 7\quad 9 \\ \diagup\ \diagup\ \diagup\diagdown \\ 3\quad 7\quad 3\quad 3 \end{array}$$

Find the prime factorization of each number.

14. 6

15. 12

16. 45

17. 98

18. 126

19. 144

20. 1960

21. 1925

◀ Do Exercises 14–21.

Answers

14. $2 \cdot 3$ 15. $2 \cdot 2 \cdot 3$ 16. $3 \cdot 3 \cdot 5$
17. $2 \cdot 7 \cdot 7$ 18. $2 \cdot 3 \cdot 3 \cdot 7$
19. $2 \cdot 2 \cdot 2 \cdot 2 \cdot 3 \cdot 3$ 20. $2 \cdot 2 \cdot 2 \cdot 5 \cdot 7 \cdot 7$
21. $5 \cdot 5 \cdot 7 \cdot 11$

✓ Reading Check

Determine whether each statement is true or false.

_____ **RC1.** One factorization of 20 is $4 \cdot 5$.

_____ **RC2.** One multiple of 15 is 30.

_____ **RC3.** The number 18 is divisible by 5.

_____ **RC4.** A prime number has exactly two different factors.

_____ **RC5.** The smallest prime number is 1.

_____ **RC6.** The prime factorization of 30 is $3 \cdot 10$.

a   Determine whether the second number is a factor of the first.

1. 52; 14   **2.** 52; 13   **3.** 625; 25   **4.** 680; 16

List all the factors of each number.

5. 18   **6.** 16   **7.** 54   **8.** 48

9. 4   **10.** 9   **11.** 1   **12.** 13

13. 98   **14.** 100   **15.** 255   **16.** 120

b   Multiply by 1, 2, 3, and so on, to find ten multiples of each number.

17. 4   **18.** 11   **19.** 20   **20.** 50

21. 3   **22.** 5   **23.** 12   **24.** 13

25. 10   **26.** 6   **27.** 9   **28.** 14

29. Determine whether 26 is divisible by 6.   **30.** Determine whether 48 is divisible by 8.

31. Determine whether 1880 is divisible by 8.   **32.** Determine whether 4227 is divisible by 3.

33. Determine whether 256 is divisible by 16.   **34.** Determine whether 102 is divisible by 4.

35. Determine whether 4227 is divisible by 9.   **36.** Determine whether 4143 is divisible by 7.

c Determine whether each number is prime, composite, or neither.

37. 1

38. 2

39. 9

40. 19

41. 11

42. 27

43. 29

44. 49

d Find the prime factorization of each number.

45. 8

46. 16

47. 14

48. 15

49. 42

50. 32

51. 25

52. 40

53. 50

54. 62

55. 169

56. 140

57. 100

58. 110

59. 35

60. 70

61. 72

62. 86

63. 77

64. 99

65. 2884

66. 484

67. 51

68. 91

69. 1200

70. 1800

71. 273

72. 675

73. 1122

74. 6435

Skill Maintenance

What does the digit 4 mean in each number?   [1.1a]

75. 134,895

76. 4,682,013

77. 29,745

78. 13,248,957

Round 34,562 to the nearest: [1.6a]

79. Ten.

80. Hundred.

Round 2,428,497 to the nearest: [1.6a]

81. Thousand.

82. Ten.

Synthesis

83. *Factors and Sums.*   The top number in each column of the table below can be factored as a product of two numbers whose sum is the bottom number in the column. For example, in the first column, 56 has been factored as 7 · 8, and 7 + 8 = 15. Fill in the blank spaces in the table.

PRODUCT	56	63	36	72	140	96		168	110			
FACTOR	7									9	24	3
FACTOR	8						8	8		10	18	
SUM	15	16	20	38	24	20	14		21			24

Copyright © 2015 Pearson Education, Inc.

Divisibility

Suppose you are asked to find the simplest fraction notation for

$$\frac{117}{225}.$$

Since the numbers are quite large, you might feel that the task is difficult. However, both the numerator and the denominator are divisible by 9. If you knew this, you could factor and simplify as follows:

$$\frac{117}{225} = \frac{9 \cdot 13}{9 \cdot 25} = \frac{9}{9} \cdot \frac{13}{25} = 1 \cdot \frac{13}{25} = \frac{13}{25}.$$

How did we know that both numbers have 9 as a factor? There is a simple test for determining this.

In this section, you learn quick ways to determine whether a number is divisible by 2, 3, 4, 5, 6, 8, 9, or 10. This will make simplifying fraction notation much easier.

a RULES FOR DIVISIBILITY

Divisibility by 2

You may already know the test for divisibility by 2.

> **BY 2**
>
> A number is **divisible by 2** (is *even*) if it has a ones digit of 0, 2, 4, 6, or 8 (that is, it has an even ones digit).

Let's see why this test works. Consider 354, which is

$$3 \text{ hundreds } + 5 \text{ tens } + 4.$$

Hundreds and tens are both multiples of 2. If the last digit is a multiple of 2, then the entire number is a multiple of 2.

EXAMPLES Determine whether each number is divisible by 2.

1. 355 is *not* divisible by 2; 5 is *not* even.
2. 4786 is divisible by 2; 6 is even.
3. 8990 is divisible by 2; 0 is even.
4. 4261 is *not* divisible by 2; 1 is *not* even.

Do Margin Exercises 1–4. ▶

OBJECTIVE

a Determine whether a number is divisible by 2, 3, 4, 5, 6, 8, 9, or 10.

SKILL TO REVIEW

Objective 1.2a: Add whole numbers.

Add.

1. $9 + 8 + 2 + 1$

2. $7 + 3 + 0 + 2 + 6$

Determine whether each number is divisible by 2.

1. 84 2. 59

3. 998 4. 2225

Answers

Skill to Review:
1. 20 **2.** 18

Margin Exercises:
1. Yes **2.** No **3.** Yes **4.** No

Divisibility by 3

> ### BY 3
>
> A number is **divisible by 3** if the sum of its digits is divisible by 3.

Let's illustrate why the test for divisibility by 3 works. Consider 852; since $852 = 3 \cdot 284$, 852 is divisible by 3.

$$852 = 8 \cdot 100 + 5 \cdot 10 + 2 \cdot 1$$
$$= 8(99 + 1) + 5(9 + 1) + 2(1)$$
$$= 8 \cdot 99 + 8 \cdot 1 + 5 \cdot 9 + 5 \cdot 1 + 2 \cdot 1$$

Using the distributive law: $a(b + c) = a \cdot b + a \cdot c$

Since 99 and 9 are each a multiple of 3, we see that $8 \cdot 99$ and $5 \cdot 9$ are multiples of 3. This leaves $8 \cdot 1 + 5 \cdot 1 + 2 \cdot 1$, or $8 + 5 + 2$. If $8 + 5 + 2$, the sum of the digits, is divisible by 3, then 852 is divisible by 3.

EXAMPLES Determine whether each number is divisible by 3.

5. 18 $1 + 8 = 9$
6. 93 $9 + 3 = 12$
7. 201 $2 + 0 + 1 = 3$

Each is divisible by 3 because the sum of its digits is divisible by 3.

8. 256 $2 + 5 + 6 = 13$

The sum of the digits, 13, is *not* divisible by 3, so 256 is *not* divisible by 3.

◀ Do Exercises 5–8.

Divisibility by 6

A number divisible by 6 is a multiple of 6. But $6 = 2 \cdot 3$, so the number is also a multiple of 2 and 3. Since 2 and 3 have no factors in common, we have the following.

> ### BY 6
>
> A number is **divisible by 6** if its ones digit is 0, 2, 4, 6, or 8 (is even) and the sum of its digits is divisible by 3.

EXAMPLES Determine whether each number is divisible by 6.

9. 720

Because 720 is even, it is divisible by 2. Also, $7 + 2 + 0 = 9$, so 720 is divisible by 3. Thus, 720 is divisible by 6.

72**0** $7 + 2 + 0 = 9$
↑   ↑
Even   Divisible by 3

10. 73

73 is *not* divisible by 6 because it is *not* even.

11. 256

Although 256 is even, it is *not* divisible by 6 because the sum of its digits, $2 + 5 + 6$, or 13, is *not* divisible by 3.

◀ Do Exercises 9–12.

Determine whether each number is divisible by 3.

5. 111   **6.** 1111

7. 309

8. 17,216

Add the digits:

$1 + 7 + \boxed{} + 1 + 6 = \boxed{}$

Since 17 $\boxed{}$ divisible by 3,
          is/is not

the number 17,216 $\boxed{}$
                is/is not

divisible by 3.

Determine whether each number is divisible by 6.

9. 420   **10.** 106

11. 321   **12.** 444

Answers

5. Yes   **6.** No   **7.** Yes   **8.** No   **9.** Yes
10. No   **11.** No   **12.** Yes

Guided Solution:
8. 2, 17, is not, is not

Divisibility by 9

The test for divisibility by 9 is similar to the test for divisibility by 3.

> ### BY 9
>
> A number is **divisible by 9** if the sum of its digits is divisible by 9.

EXAMPLES   Determine whether each number is divisible by 9.

12. 6984

  Because $6 + 9 + 8 + 4 = 27$ and 27 is divisible by 9, 6984 is divisible by 9.

13. 322

  Because $3 + 2 + 2 = 7$ and 7 is *not* divisible by 9, 322 is *not* divisible by 9.

                              Do Exercises 13–16. ▶

Determine whether each number is divisible by 9.

13. 16   **14.** 117

15. 930   **16.** 29,223

Divisibility by 10

> ### BY 10
>
> A number is **divisible by 10** if its ones digit is 0.

We know that this test works because the product of 10 and *any* number has a ones digit of 0.

EXAMPLES   Determine whether each number is divisible by 10.

14. 3440   is divisible by 10 because the ones digit is 0.

15. 3447   is *not* divisible by 10 because the ones digit is not 0.

                              Do Exercises 17–20. ▶

Determine whether each number is divisible by 10.

17. 305   **18.** 847

19. 300   **20.** 8760

Divisibility by 5

> ### BY 5
>
> A number is **divisible by 5** if its ones digit is 0 or 5.

EXAMPLES   Determine whether each number is divisible by 5.

16. 220   is divisible by 5 because the ones digit is 0.

17. 475   is divisible by 5 because the ones digit is 5.

18. 6514   is *not* divisible by 5 because the ones digit is neither 0 nor 5.

                              Do Exercises 21–24. ▶

Let's see why the test for 5 works. Consider 7830:

$$7830 = 10 \cdot 783 = 5 \cdot 2 \cdot 783.$$

Since 7830 is divisible by 10 and 5 is a factor of 10, 7830 is divisible by 5.

Determine whether each number is divisible by 5.

21. 5780   **22.** 3427

23. 34,678   **24.** 7775

Answers

13. No **14.** Yes **15.** No **16.** Yes
17. No **18.** No **19.** Yes **20.** Yes
21. Yes **22.** No **23.** No **24.** Yes

Consider 6734:

$$6734 = 673 \text{ tens} + 4.$$

Tens are multiples of 5, so the only number that must be checked is the ones digit. If the last digit is a multiple of 5, then the entire number is. In this case, 4 is *not* a multiple of 5, so 6734 is *not* divisible by 5.

Divisibility by 4

The test for divisibility by 4 is similar to the test for divisibility by 2.

BY 4

A number is **divisible by 4** if the number named by its last *two* digits is divisible by 4.

EXAMPLES   Determine whether the number is divisible by 4.

19. 8212   is divisible by 4 because 12 is divisible by 4.

20. 5216   is divisible by 4 because 16 is divisible by 4.

21. 8211   is *not* divisible by 4 because 11 is *not* divisible by 4.

22. 7538   is *not* divisible by 4 because 38 is *not* divisible by 4.

◀ Do Exercises 25–28.

To see why the test for divisibility by 4 works, consider 516:

$$516 = 5 \text{ hundreds} + 16.$$

Hundreds are multiples of 4. If the number named by the last two digits is a multiple of 4, then the entire number is a multiple of 4.

Divisibility by 8

The test for divisibility by 8 is an extension of the tests for divisibility by 2 and 4.

BY 8

A number is **divisible by 8** if the number named by its last *three* digits is divisible by 8.

EXAMPLES   Determine whether the number is divisible by 8.

23. 5648   is divisible by 8 because 648 is divisible by 8.

24. 96,088   is divisible by 8 because 88 is divisible by 8.

25. 7324   is *not* divisible by 8 because 324 is *not* divisible by 8.

26. 13,420   is *not* divisible by 8 because 420 is *not* divisible by 8.

◀ Do Exercises 29–32.

A Note about Divisibility by 7

There are several tests for divisibility by 7, but all of them are more complicated than simply dividing by 7. If you want to test for divisibility by 7, simply divide by 7, either by hand or using a calculator.

Determine whether each number is divisible by 4.

25. 216   **26.** 217

27. 5862

28. 23,524   (GS)

The number named by the last two digits is ____.

Since 24 ____ divisible by 4,
           is/is not

the number 23,524 ____
                        is/is not

divisible by 4.

Determine whether each number is divisible by 8.

29. 7564   **30.** 7864

31. 17,560   **32.** 25,716

Answers

25. Yes   **26.** No   **27.** No   **28.** Yes
29. No   **30.** Yes   **31.** Yes   **32.** No

Guided Solution:
28. 24; is, is

3.2 Exercise Set

✓ Reading Check

Match the beginning of each divisibility rule with the appropriate ending from the list at the right.

RC1. A number is divisible by 2 if _____ .

RC2. A number is divisible by 3 if _____ .

RC3. A number is divisible by 4 if _____ .

RC4. A number is divisible by 5 if _____ .

RC5. A number is divisible by 6 if _____ .

RC6. A number is divisible by 8 if _____ .

RC7. A number is divisible by 9 if _____ .

RC8. A number is divisible by 10 if _____ .

a) the sum of its digits is divisible by 3

b) the sum of its digits is divisible by 9

c) it has an even ones digit

d) its ones digit is 0 or 5

e) its ones digit is 0

f) it has an even ones digit and the sum of its digits is divisible by 3

g) the number named by its last two digits is divisible by 4

h) the number named by its last three digits is divisible by 8

a For Exercises 1–16, answer yes or no and give a reason based on the tests for divisibility.

1. Determine whether 84 is divisible by 3.

2. Determine whether 467 is divisible by 9.

3. Determine whether 5553 is divisible by 5.

4. Determine whether 2004 is divisible by 6.

5. Determine whether 671,500 is divisible by 10.

6. Determine whether 6120 is divisible by 5.

7. Determine whether 1773 is divisible by 9.

8. Determine whether 3286 is divisible by 3.

9. Determine whether 21,687 is divisible by 2.

10. Determine whether 64,091 is divisible by 10.

11. Determine whether 32,109 is divisible by 6.

12. Determine whether 9840 is divisible by 2.

13. Determine whether 126,930 is divisible by 4.

14. Determine whether 546,106 is divisible by 8.

15. Determine whether 796,840 is divisible by 8.

16. Determine whether 298,736 is divisible by 4.

For Exercises 17–24, test each number for divisibility by 2, 3, 4, 5, 6, 8, 9, and 10.

17. 6825

18. 12,600

19. 119,117

20. 2916

21. 127,575

22. 25,088

23. 9360

24. 143,507

To answer Exercises 25–32, consider the following numbers.

56	200	75	35
324	42	812	402
784	501	2345	111,111
55,555	3009	2001	1005

25. Which of the above are divisible by 3?

26. Which of the above are divisible by 2?

27. Which of the above are divisible by 5?

28. Which of the above are divisible by 4?

29. Which of the above are divisible by 8?

30. Which of the above are divisible by 6?

31. Which of the above are divisible by 10?

32. Which of the above are divisible by 9?

To answer Exercises 33–40, consider the following numbers.

305	313,332	876	64,000
1101	7624	1110	9990
13,205	111,126	5128	126,111

33. Which of the above are divisible by 2?

34. Which of the above are divisible by 3?

35. Which of the above are divisible by 6?

36. Which of the above are divisible by 5?

37. Which of the above are divisible by 9?

38. Which of the above are divisible by 8?

39. Which of the above are divisible by 10?

40. Which of the above are divisible by 4?

Skill Maintenance

Solve. [1.7b]

41. $56 + x = 194$

42. $y + 124 = 263$

43. $3008 = x + 2134$

44. $18 \cdot t = 1008$

45. $24 \cdot m = 624$

46. $338 = a \cdot 26$

Solve. [1.8a]

47. Marty's car has a five-speed transmission and gets 33 mpg in city driving. How many gallons of gas will it use to travel 1485 mi of city driving?

48. There are 60 min in 1 hr. How many minutes are there in 72 hr?

Synthesis

Find the prime factorization of each number. Use divisibility tests where applicable.

49. 7800

50. 2520

51. 2772

52. 1998

53. ▦ Fill in the missing digits of the number

$$95,\square\,\square\,8$$

so that it is divisible by 99.

54. A passenger in a taxicab asks for the driver's company number. The driver says abruptly, "Sure—you can have my number. Work it out: If you divide it by 2, 3, 4, 5, or 6, you will get a remainder of 1. If you divide it by 11, the remainder will be 0, and no driver has a company number that meets these requirements and is smaller than this one." Determine the number.

Copyright © 2015 Pearson Education, Inc.

The study of arithmetic begins with the set of whole numbers. But we also need to be able to use fractional parts of numbers such as halves, thirds, fourths, and so on. Here is an example.

Households in auto-dependent locations spend about $\frac{1}{4}$ of their income on transportation costs, while location-efficient households (those with easy access to public transportation) can hold transportation costs to $\frac{1}{10}$ of their income.

OBJECTIVES

a Identify the numerator and the denominator of a fraction and write fraction notation for part of an object or part of a set of objects and as a ratio.

b Simplify fraction notation like n/n to 1, $0/n$ to 0, and $n/1$ to n.

SKILL TO REVIEW

Objective 1.5a: Divide whole numbers.

Divide.

1. $36 \div 36$ **2.** $50 \div 1$

Auto-Dependent Households   **Location-Efficient Households**

$\frac{1}{4}$ Transportation $\frac{3}{4}$ Remaining $\frac{1}{10}$ Transportation $\frac{9}{10}$ Remaining

SOURCE: Based on data from U.S. Department of Transportation, Federal Highway Administration

a FRACTIONS AND THE REAL WORLD

Numbers like those above are written in **fraction notation**. The top number is called the **numerator** and the bottom number is called the **denominator**.

EXAMPLE 1   Identify the numerator and the denominator.

$\frac{7}{8}$ ← Numerator
← Denominator

Do Margin Exercises 1–3. ▶

Let's look at various situations that involve fractions.

Fractions as a Partition of an Object Divided into Equal Parts

Consider a candy bar divided into 5 equal sections. If you eat 2 sections, you have eaten $\frac{2}{5}$ of the candy bar. The denominator 5 tells us the unit, $\frac{1}{5}$. The numerator 2 tells us the number of equal parts we are considering, 2.

For each fraction, identify the numerator and the denominator.

1. About $\frac{1}{5}$ of people age 5 and older in the United States speak a language other than English at home.

   Source: 2010 American Community Survey

2. About $\frac{4}{5}$ of the parts on a Toyota Camry were produced in the United States.

   Source: "Made in America: Which Car Creates the Most Jobs?" by David Muir and Sharyn Alfonsi, on abcnews.go.com

3. It is projected that $\frac{19}{100}$ of the U.S. population in 2050 will be foreign-born.

   Source: Pew Research Center

Answers

Skill to Review:
1. 1   **2.** 50

Margin Exercises:
1. Numerator: 1; denominator: 5
2. Numerator: 4; denominator: 5
3. Numerator: 19; denominator: 100

EXAMPLE 2 What part is shaded?

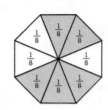

There are 8 equal parts. This tells us the unit, $\frac{1}{8}$. The *denominator* is 8. We have 5 of the units shaded. This tells us the *numerator*, 5. Thus,

$$\frac{5}{8} \begin{matrix} \leftarrow \text{5 units are shaded.} \\ \leftarrow \text{The unit is } \frac{1}{8}. \end{matrix}$$

is shaded.

EXAMPLE 3 What part is shaded?

There are 18 equal parts. Thus the unit is $\frac{1}{18}$. The denominator is 18. We have 7 units shaded. This tells us the numerator, 7. Thus, $\frac{7}{18}$ is shaded.

◀ Do Exercises 4–7.

The markings on a ruler use fractions.

EXAMPLE 4 What part of an inch is indicated?

Each inch on the ruler shown above is divided into 16 equal parts. The marked section extends to the 11th mark. Thus, $\frac{11}{16}$ of an inch is indicated.

◀ Do Exercise 8.

What part is shaded?

4.

5.

6.

7.

8. What part of an inch is indicated?

Answers

4. $\frac{5}{6}$ 5. $\frac{1}{3}$ 6. $\frac{3}{4}$ 7. $\frac{8}{15}$ 8. $\frac{15}{16}$

Fractions greater than or equal to 1, such as $\frac{24}{24}$, $\frac{10}{3}$, and $\frac{5}{4}$, correspond to situations like the following.

EXAMPLE 5 What part is shaded?

a)   **b)**

a) The rectangle is divided into 24 equal parts. Thus the unit is $\frac{1}{24}$. The denominator is 24. All 24 equal parts are shaded. This tells us that the numerator is 24. Thus, $\frac{24}{24}$ is shaded.

b) Each rectangle is divided into 6 parts. Thus the unit is $\frac{1}{6}$. The denominator is 6. We see that 11 of the equal units are shaded. This tells us that the numerator is 11. Thus, $\frac{11}{6}$ is shaded.

EXAMPLE 6 *Ice-Cream Roll-up Cake.*   What part of an ice-cream roll-up cake is shaded?

3 ice cream roll-up cakes

Each cake is divided into 6 equal slices. The unit is $\frac{1}{6}$. The *denominator* is 6. We see that 13 of the slices are shaded. This tells us that the *numerator* is 13. Thus, $\frac{13}{6}$ are shaded.

Do Exercises 9–11. ▶

Negative fractions can also be used to represent real-world situations. If the water level in a reservoir drops five-eighths inch, for example, the fraction $-\frac{5}{8}$ (read "negative five-eighths") represents this situation.

Do Exercise 12. ▶

Fractions larger than or equal to 1, such as $\frac{13}{6}$ or $\frac{9}{9}$, are sometimes referred to as "improper" fractions. We will not use this terminology because notation such as $\frac{27}{8}$, $\frac{11}{3}$, and $\frac{4}{4}$ is quite "proper" and very common in algebra.

Fractions like $\frac{2}{3}$ are not integers. A number system called the **rational numbers** contains integers and fractions. The rational numbers consist of quotients of integers with nonzero divisors.

What part is shaded?

9.

10.

GS 11.

1 gallon

2 gallons

Each gallon is divided into ☐ equal parts.

The unit is $\frac{1}{☐}$.

There are ☐ equal units shaded.

The part that is shaded is $\frac{☐}{☐}$.

12. Write a fraction that represents the situation:

The blacktop on the playground sank one-fourth inch.

Answers

9. $\frac{15}{15}$ **10.** $\frac{10}{3}$ **11.** $\frac{7}{4}$ **12.** $-\frac{1}{4}$

Guided Solution:

11. 4, 4, 7, $\frac{7}{4}$

The following are rational numbers:

$$\frac{2}{3}, \quad -\frac{2}{3}, \quad \frac{7}{1}, \quad 4, \quad -3, \quad 0, \quad \frac{23}{-8}.$$

The number $-\frac{2}{3}$ (read "negative two-thirds") can also be named $\frac{-2}{3}$ or $\frac{2}{-3}$. That is,

$$-\frac{a}{b} = \frac{-a}{b} = \frac{a}{-b}.$$

RATIONAL NUMBERS

The **rational numbers** consist of all numbers that can be named in the form $\frac{a}{b}$, where a and b are integers and b is not 0.

Fractions as Ratios

A **ratio** is a quotient of two quantities. We can express a ratio with fraction notation. (We will consider ratios in more detail in Chapter 6.)

EXAMPLE 7 *Countries of Africa.* What part of this group of countries is north of the equator? south of the equator?

Angola	Mali
Bostwana	Morocco
Egypt	Zambia
Ethiopia	

There are 7 countries in the set, and 4 of them, Egypt, Ethiopia, Mali, and Morocco, are north of the equator. Thus, 4 of 7, or $\frac{4}{7}$, are north of the equator. The 3 remaining countries are south of the equator. Thus, $\frac{3}{7}$ are south of the equator.

◀ Do Exercise 13.

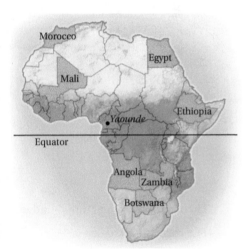

13. What part of the set of countries in Example 7 is west of Yaounde?

b SOME FRACTION NOTATION FOR INTEGERS

Fraction Notation for 1

The number 1 corresponds to situations like those shown here. If we divide an object into n parts and take n of them, we get all of the object (1 whole object).

THE NUMBER 1 IN FRACTION NOTATION

$\frac{n}{n} = 1$, for any integer n that is not 0.

Answer

13. $\frac{2}{7}$

EXAMPLES Simplify.

8. $\dfrac{5}{5} = 1$

9. $\dfrac{-9}{-9} = 1$

10. $\dfrac{23}{23} = 1$

Do Exercises 14–19. ▶

Fraction Notation for 0

Consider the fraction $\frac{0}{4}$. This corresponds to dividing an object into 4 parts and taking none of them. We get 0.

THE NUMBER 0 IN FRACTION NOTATION

$\dfrac{0}{n} = 0$, for any integer n that is not 0.

EXAMPLES Simplify.

11. $\dfrac{0}{1} = 0$

12. $\dfrac{0}{-9} = 0$

13. $\dfrac{0}{23} = 0$

Fraction notation with a denominator of 0, such as $n/0$, is meaningless because we cannot speak of an object being divided into *zero* parts. This corresponds to division by 0 being not defined.

A DENOMINATOR OF 0

$\dfrac{n}{0}$ is not defined for any integer n.

Do Exercises 20–25. ▶

Other Whole Numbers

Consider the fraction $\frac{4}{1}$. This corresponds to taking 4 objects and dividing each into 1 part. (In other words, we do not divide them.) We have 4 objects.

ANY INTEGER IN FRACTION NOTATION

Any integer divided by 1 is the integer itself. That is,

$\dfrac{n}{1} = n$, for any integer n.

EXAMPLES Simplify.

14. $\dfrac{2}{1} = 2$

15. $\dfrac{9}{1} = 9$

16. $\dfrac{-34}{1} = -34$

Do Exercises 26–29. ▶

Simplify.

14. $\dfrac{1}{1}$

15. $\dfrac{-4}{-4}$

16. $\dfrac{-34}{-34}$

17. $\dfrac{100}{100}$

18. $\dfrac{2347}{2347}$

19. $\dfrac{-103}{-103}$

Simplify, if possible.

20. $\dfrac{0}{1}$

21. $\dfrac{0}{-8}$

22. $\dfrac{0}{-107}$

 23. $\dfrac{4-4}{567} = \dfrac{\boxed{}}{567} = \boxed{}$

24. $\dfrac{15}{0}$

25. $\dfrac{0}{3-3}$

Simplify.

26. $\dfrac{8}{1}$

27. $\dfrac{-10}{1}$

28. $\dfrac{-346}{1}$

29. $\dfrac{24-1}{23-22}$

Answers

14. 1   **15.** 1   **16.** 1   **17.** 1   **18.** 1
19. 1   **20.** 0   **21.** 0   **22.** 0   **23.** 0
24. Not defined   **25.** Not defined
26. 8   **27.** −10   **28.** −346   **29.** 23

Guided Solution:
23. 0, 0

✓ Reading Check

Match each expression with the appropriate description or value from the list at the right.

RC1. The 3 in $\frac{3}{4}$ _____

a) a denominator

RC2. The 4 in $\frac{3}{4}$ _____

b) a numerator

RC3. The fraction $\frac{3}{4}$ _____

c) a ratio

RC4. $\frac{0}{-1}$ _____

d) n

RC5. $\frac{n}{0}$ _____

e) 0

RC6. $\frac{n}{1}$ _____

f) not defined

a   Identify the numerator and the denominator.

1. $\frac{3}{4}$

2. $\frac{9}{10}$

3. $\frac{11}{2}$

4. $\frac{18}{5}$

5. $\frac{0}{7}$

6. $\frac{1}{13}$

What part of each object or set of objects is shaded?

7.

1 acre

8.

1 square inch

9.

1 yard

10. 1 mile

11.

12.

1 year

13.

1 pie

14.

15.

Copyright © 2015 Pearson Education, Inc.

16.

17. 1 gold bar 2 gold bars

18. 1 mile 2 miles

19. 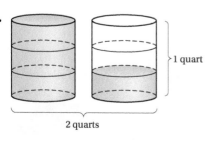 1 quart 2 quarts

20. 1 foot 3 feet

21.

22.

23.

24.

25.

26.

Write a fraction that represents the situation.

27. The water level in the well dropped one-third foot.

28. There is a depression in the road's surface that is five-sixteenths inch deep.

What part of an inch is indicated?

29.

30.

31.

32.

For each of Exercises 33–36, give fraction notation for the amount of gas **(a)** in the tank and **(b)** used from a full tank.

33.

34.

35.

36.

37. For the following set of animals, what is the ratio of:
   a) puppies to the total number of animals?
   b) puppies to kittens?
   c) kittens to the total number of animals?
   d) kittens to puppies?

38. For the following set of sports equipment, what is the ratio of:
   a) basketballs to footballs?
   b) footballs to basketballs?
   c) basketballs to the total number of balls?
   d) total number of balls to basketballs?

39. Bryce delivers car parts to auto service centers. On Thursday he had 15 deliveries scheduled. By noon he had delivered only 4 orders. What is the ratio of:
   a) orders delivered to total number of orders?
   b) orders delivered to orders not delivered?
   c) orders not delivered to total number of orders?

40. *Gas Mileage.* A Volkswagen Passat TDI® SE will travel 473 mi on 11 gal of gasoline in highway driving. What is the ratio of:
   a) miles driven to gasoline used?
   b) gasoline used to miles driven?

Source: vw.com

Copyright © 2015 Pearson Education, Inc.

For Exercises 41 and 42, use the following bar graph, which shows the number of registered nurses per 100,000 residents in each of twelve states or districts.

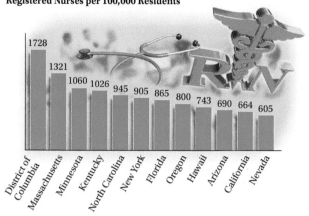

Registered Nurses per 100,000 Residents

1728, 1321, 1060, 1026, 945, 905, 865, 800, 743, 690, 664, 605

District of Columbia, Massachusetts, Minnesota, Kentucky, North Carolina, New York, Florida, Oregon, Hawaii, Arizona, California, Nevada

SOURCES: www.statehealthfacts.org; Kaiser Family Foundation, 2011

41. What is the ratio of registered nurses to 100,000 residents in the given state or district?
a) Minnesota   b) Hawaii
c) Florida   d) Kentucky
e) New York   f) District of Columbia

42. What is the ratio of registered nurses to 100,000 residents in the given state?
a) North Carolina   b) California
c) Massachusetts   d) Nevada
e) Arizona   f) Oregon

For Exercises 43 and 44, use the following set of states, as illustrated in the map.

Alabama   Nebraska   West Virginia
Arkansas   South Dakota   Wisconsin
Illinois

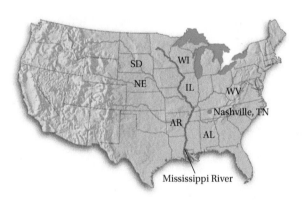

43. What part of this group of states is east of the Mississippi River?

44. What part of this group of states is north of Nashville, Tennessee?

b Simplify.

45. $\dfrac{0}{8}$

46. $\dfrac{-8}{-8}$

47. $\dfrac{8-1}{9-8}$

48. $\dfrac{16}{1}$

49. $\dfrac{-20}{-20}$

50. $\dfrac{-20}{1}$

51. $\dfrac{45}{45}$

52. $\dfrac{11-1}{10-9}$

53. $\dfrac{0}{238}$

54. $\dfrac{238}{1}$

55. $\dfrac{238}{238}$

56. $\dfrac{0}{-16}$

57. $\dfrac{3}{3}$

58. $\dfrac{56}{56}$

59. $\dfrac{87}{87}$

60. $\dfrac{98}{98}$

61. $\dfrac{18}{18}$

62. $\dfrac{0}{-18}$

63. $\dfrac{-18}{1}$

64. $\dfrac{8-8}{1247}$

65. $\dfrac{729}{0}$

66. $\dfrac{1317}{0}$

67. $\dfrac{5}{6-6}$

68. $\dfrac{13}{10-10}$

Skill Maintenance

Add. [1.2a]

69.
```
  5 7,8 7 7
+ 3 2,4 0 6
```

70.
```
  8 0 0 4
  6 7 8 9
  7 7 2 0
+ 6 8 5 1
```

Subtract. [1.3a]

71.
```
  9 0 6 0
- 4 3 8 7
```

72.
```
  7 8 0 0
- 2 4 6 2
```

Multiply. [1.4a]

73.
```
  2 1 7
×   3 0
```

74.
```
  5 3 8
×   2 7
```

Add. [2.2a]

75. $7 + (-14)$

76. $-6 + (-9)$

Synthesis

What part of each object is shaded?

77.

78.

79.

80.

Shade or mark each figure to show $\frac{3}{5}$.

81.

82.

83.

84.

Copyright © 2015 Pearson Education, Inc.

Multiplication and Applications

a MULTIPLICATION USING FRACTION NOTATION

OBJECTIVES

a Multiply a fraction by a fraction, and multiply a fraction by an integer.

b Solve applied problems involving multiplication of fractions.

SKILL TO REVIEW

Objective 1.4a: Multiply whole numbers.

Multiply.

1. $24 \cdot 17$ **2.** $5(13)$

Let's visualize the product of two fractions. We consider the multiplication

$$\frac{3}{5} \cdot \frac{3}{4}.$$

This is equivalent to finding $\frac{3}{5}$ of $\frac{3}{4}$. We first consider an object and take $\frac{3}{4}$ of it. We divide the object into 4 equal parts using vertical lines and take 3 of them. That is shown by the shading below.

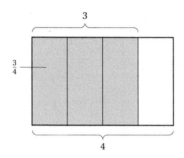

Next, we take $\frac{3}{5}$ of the shaded area. We divide it into 5 equal parts using horizontal lines and take 3 of them. That is shown by the darker shading below.

The entire object has now been divided into 20 parts, and we have shaded 9 of them twice. Thus we see that $\frac{3}{5}$ of $\frac{3}{4}$ is $\frac{9}{20}$, or

$$\frac{3}{5} \cdot \frac{3}{4} = \frac{9}{20}.$$

The figure above shows a rectangular array inside a rectangular array. The number of pieces in the entire array is $5 \cdot 4$ (the product of the denominators). The number of pieces shaded a second time is $3 \cdot 3$ (the product of the numerators). The product is represented by 9 pieces out of a set of 20, or $\frac{9}{20}$, which is the product of the numerators over the product of the denominators. This leads us to a statement of the procedure for multiplying a fraction by a fraction.

Do Margin Exercise 1. ▶

1. Draw a diagram like the one at left to show the multiplication $\frac{2}{3} \cdot \frac{4}{5}$.

Answers

Skill to Review:
1. 408 **2.** 65

Margin Exercise:
1.

We find a product such as $\frac{9}{7} \cdot \frac{3}{4}$ as follows.

> To multiply a fraction by a fraction,
>
> **a)** multiply the numerators to get the new numerator, and
>
> $$\frac{9}{7} \cdot \frac{3}{4} = \frac{9 \cdot 3}{7 \cdot 4} = \frac{27}{28}$$
>
> **b)** multiply the denominators to get the new denominator.

Multiply.

2. $\dfrac{3}{8} \cdot \dfrac{5}{7} = \dfrac{3 \cdot 5}{8 \cdot \boxed{}}$ $\quad$ **GS**

$\qquad = \dfrac{\boxed{}}{\boxed{}}$

3. $\dfrac{4}{3} \times \dfrac{8}{5}$ $\qquad$ **4.** $\dfrac{3}{10} \cdot \dfrac{1}{10}$

5. $\dfrac{5}{2} \cdot \left(-\dfrac{9}{4}\right)$

EXAMPLES Multiply.

1. $\dfrac{5}{6} \times \dfrac{7}{4} = \dfrac{5 \times 7}{\underbrace{6 \times 4}} = \dfrac{35}{24}$

 Skip writing this step whenever you can.

2. $\dfrac{3}{5} \cdot \dfrac{7}{8} = \dfrac{3 \cdot 7}{5 \cdot 8} = \dfrac{21}{40}$

3. $\dfrac{3}{5} \cdot \left(-\dfrac{4}{7}\right) = -\dfrac{3 \cdot 4}{5 \cdot 7} = -\dfrac{12}{35}$

4. $\dfrac{1}{4} \cdot \dfrac{1}{3} = \dfrac{1}{12}$

◀ Do Exercises 2–5.

Multiplication by an Integer

When multiplying a fraction by an integer, we first express the integer in fraction notation. We find a product such as $6 \cdot \frac{4}{5}$ as follows:

$$6 \cdot \dfrac{4}{5} = \dfrac{6}{1} \cdot \dfrac{4}{5} \qquad 6 = \dfrac{6}{1}$$

$$= \dfrac{6 \cdot 4}{1 \cdot 5} \qquad \text{Multiplying}$$

$$= \dfrac{24}{5}.$$

Multiply.

6. $5 \times \dfrac{2}{3} = \dfrac{5}{\boxed{}} \times \dfrac{2}{3}$ $\quad$ **GS**

$\qquad = \dfrac{5 \times 2}{\boxed{} \times 3}$

$\qquad = \dfrac{\boxed{}}{\boxed{}}$

7. $-\dfrac{3}{8} \cdot 11$

8. $23 \cdot \left(-\dfrac{2}{5}\right)$

EXAMPLES Multiply.

5. $5 \times \dfrac{3}{8} = \dfrac{5}{1} \times \dfrac{3}{8} = \dfrac{5 \times 3}{1 \times 8} = \dfrac{15}{8}$

6. $\dfrac{2}{7} \cdot 13 = \dfrac{2}{7} \cdot \dfrac{13}{1} = \dfrac{2 \cdot 13}{7 \cdot 1} = \dfrac{26}{7}$

7. $10 \cdot \left(-\dfrac{1}{3}\right) = \dfrac{10}{1} \cdot \left(-\dfrac{1}{3}\right) = -\dfrac{10 \cdot 1}{1 \cdot 3} = -\dfrac{10}{3}$

◀ Do Exercises 6–8.

Answers

2. $\dfrac{15}{56}$ $\quad$ **3.** $\dfrac{32}{15}$ $\quad$ **4.** $\dfrac{3}{100}$

5. $-\dfrac{45}{8}$ $\quad$ **6.** $\dfrac{10}{3}$ $\quad$ **7.** $-\dfrac{33}{8}$ $\quad$ **8.** $-\dfrac{46}{5}$

Guided Solutions:

2. $7, \dfrac{15}{56}$ $\quad$ **6.** $1, 1, \dfrac{10}{3}$

b APPLICATIONS AND PROBLEM SOLVING

Many problems that can be solved by multiplying fractions can be thought of in terms of rectangular arrays.

EXAMPLE 8 A real estate developer owns a plot of land and plans to use $\frac{4}{5}$ of the plot for a small strip mall and parking lot. Of this, $\frac{2}{3}$ will be needed for the parking lot. What part of the plot will be used for parking?

1. **Familiarize.** We first make a drawing to help familiarize ourselves with the problem. The land may not be rectangular, but we can think of it as a rectangle. The strip mall, including the parking lot, uses $\frac{4}{5}$ of the plot. We shade $\frac{4}{5}$ as shown on the left below. The parking lot alone uses $\frac{2}{3}$ of the part we just shaded. We shade that as shown on the right below.

2. **Translate.** We let $n =$ the part of the plot that is used for parking. We are taking "two-thirds of four-fifths." The word "of" corresponds to multiplication. Thus the following multiplication sentence corresponds to the situation:

$$\frac{2}{3} \cdot \frac{4}{5} = n.$$

3. **Solve.** The number sentence tells us what to do. We multiply:

$$\frac{2}{3} \cdot \frac{4}{5} = \frac{2 \cdot 4}{3 \cdot 5} = \frac{8}{15}.$$

Thus, $\frac{8}{15} = n$.

4. **Check.** We can do a partial check by noting that the answer is a fraction less than 1, which we expect since the developer is using only part of the original plot of land. Thus, $\frac{8}{15}$ is a reasonable answer. We can also check this in the figure above, where we see that 8 of 15 parts represent the parking lot.

5. **State.** The parking lot takes up $\frac{8}{15}$ of the plot of land.

Do Exercise 9. ▶

9. A developer plans to set aside $\frac{3}{4}$ of the land in a housing development as open (un-developed) space. Of this, $\frac{1}{2}$ will be green (natural) space. What part of the land will be green space?

Answer

9. $\frac{3}{8}$

EXAMPLE 9 *Area of a Cranberry Bog.* The length of a rectangular cranberry bog is $\frac{9}{16}$ mi. The width is $\frac{3}{8}$ mi. What is the area of the bog?

1. **Familiarize.** Recall that area is length times width. We let $A =$ the area of the cranberry bog.

2. **Translate.** Next, we translate:

$$
\underbrace{\text{Area}}_{\downarrow} \quad \underbrace{\text{is}}_{\downarrow} \quad \underbrace{\text{Length}}_{\downarrow} \quad \underbrace{\text{times}}_{\downarrow} \quad \underbrace{\text{Width}}_{\downarrow}
$$

$$
A \quad = \quad \frac{9}{16} \quad \times \quad \frac{3}{8}.
$$

3. **Solve.** The sentence tells us what to do. We multiply:

$$
A = \frac{9}{16} \cdot \frac{3}{8} = \frac{9 \cdot 3}{16 \cdot 8} = \frac{27}{128}.
$$

4. **Check.** We check by repeating the calculation. This is left to the student.

5. **State.** The area is $\frac{27}{128}$ square mile (mi^2).

◀ Do Exercise 10.

10. *Area of a Ceramic Tile.* The length of a rectangular ceramic tile inlaid on a countertop is $\frac{4}{9}$ ft. The width is $\frac{2}{9}$ ft. What is the area of the tile?

EXAMPLE 10 A recipe for oatmeal chocolate chip cookies calls for $\frac{3}{4}$ cup of brown sugar. Monica is making $\frac{1}{2}$ of the recipe. How much brown sugar should she use?

1. **Familiarize.** We first make a drawing or at least visualize the situation. We let $n =$ the amount of brown sugar that Monica should use.

$\frac{3}{4}$ cup in the recipe $\frac{1}{2} \cdot \frac{3}{4}$ cup in $\frac{1}{2}$ the recipe

2. **Translate.** We are finding $\frac{1}{2}$ of $\frac{3}{4}$, so the multiplication sentence $\frac{1}{2} \cdot \frac{3}{4} = n$ corresponds to the situation.

3. **Solve.** We carry out the multiplication:

$$
\frac{1}{2} \cdot \frac{3}{4} = \frac{1 \cdot 3}{2 \cdot 4} = \frac{3}{8}.
$$

Thus, $\frac{3}{8} = n$.

4. **Check.** We check by repeating the calculation. This is left to the student.

5. **State.** Monica should use $\frac{3}{8}$ cup of brown sugar.

◀ Do Exercise 11.

11. Of the students at Overton Junior College, $\frac{1}{8}$ participate in sports and $\frac{3}{5}$ of these play football. What fractional part of the students play football?

Answers

10. $\frac{8}{81}$ ft^2 11. $\frac{3}{40}$

✓ Reading Check

Determine whether each statement is true or false.

_____ **RC1.** Multiplying $\frac{1}{2} \cdot \frac{3}{5}$ is the same as finding $\frac{1}{2}$ of $\frac{3}{5}$.

_____ **RC2.** When we multiply two fractions, the new numerator is the product of the numerators in the two fractions.

_____ **RC3.** The whole number 6 can be written $\frac{6}{1}$.

_____ **RC4.** The product of two fractions can be smaller than either of the two fractions.

a Multiply.

1. $\frac{2}{5} \cdot \frac{2}{3}$

2. $\frac{3}{4} \cdot \frac{3}{5}$

3. $10 \cdot \frac{7}{9}$

4. $9 \cdot \frac{5}{8}$

5. $\frac{7}{8} \cdot \frac{7}{8}$

6. $\frac{4}{5} \cdot \frac{4}{5}$

7. $-\frac{2}{3} \times \frac{1}{5}$

8. $-\frac{3}{5} \times \frac{1}{5}$

9. $\frac{8}{7} \cdot \frac{5}{3}$

10. $\frac{11}{2} \cdot \frac{9}{8}$

11. $\frac{2}{5} \cdot (-3)$

12. $\frac{3}{5} \cdot (-4)$

13. $\frac{1}{2} \cdot \frac{1}{3}$

14. $\frac{1}{6} \cdot \frac{1}{4}$

15. $17 \times \frac{5}{6}$

16. $\frac{3}{7} \cdot 40$

17. $\frac{1}{10} \cdot \left(-\frac{7}{10}\right)$

18. $\frac{3}{10} \cdot \left(-\frac{7}{100}\right)$

19. $-\frac{2}{5} \cdot (-1)$

20. $-2 \cdot \left(-\frac{1}{3}\right)$

21. $-\frac{2}{3} \cdot \frac{7}{13}$

22. $-\frac{3}{11} \cdot \frac{4}{5}$

23. $5 \times \frac{1}{8}$

24. $4 \times \frac{1}{5}$

25. $\frac{1}{4} \times \frac{1}{10}$

26. $\frac{21}{4} \cdot \frac{7}{5}$

27. $\frac{8}{3} \cdot \frac{20}{9}$

28. $\frac{1}{3} \times \frac{1}{10}$

29. $-\frac{14}{15} \cdot \left(-\frac{13}{19}\right)$

30. $-\frac{12}{13} \cdot \left(-\frac{12}{13}\right)$

31. $\frac{3}{4} \cdot \frac{3}{4}$

32. $\frac{3}{7} \cdot \frac{4}{5}$

33. $\frac{2}{11} \cdot (-4)$

34. $\frac{2}{5} \cdot (-3)$

b Solve.

35. *Hair Bows.* It takes $\frac{5}{3}$ yd of ribbon to make a hair bow. How much ribbon is needed to make 8 bows?

36. A gasoline can holds $\frac{5}{2}$ gal. How much will the can hold when it is $\frac{1}{2}$ full?

37. *Basketball: High School to Pro.*   One of 35 high school basketball players plays college basketball. One of 75 college players plays professional basketball. What fractional part of high school basketball players play professional basketball?
Source: National Basketball Association

38. *Football: High School to Pro.*   One of 42 high school football players plays college football. One of 85 college players plays professional football. What fractional part of high school football players play professional football?
Source: National Football League

39. *Slices of Pizza.*   One slice of a pizza is $\frac{1}{8}$ of the pizza. How much of the pizza is $\frac{1}{2}$ slice?

40. *Tossed Salad.*   The recipe for a tossed salad calls for $\frac{3}{4}$ cup of sliced almonds. How much is needed to make $\frac{1}{2}$ of the recipe?

41. *Floor Tiling.*   The floor of a room is being covered with tile. An area $\frac{3}{5}$ of the length and $\frac{3}{4}$ of the width is covered. What fraction of the floor has been tiled?

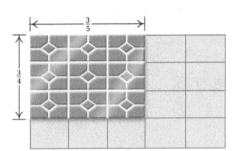

42.   A rectangular table top measures $\frac{4}{5}$ m long by $\frac{3}{5}$ m wide. What is its area?

Skill Maintenance

Solve.   [1.8a]

43. *Morel Mushrooms.*   During the spring, Kate's Country Market sold 43 pounds of fresh morel mushrooms. The mushrooms sold for $22 a pound. Find the total amount Kate took in from the sale of the mushrooms.

44.   Sandy can type 62 words per minute. How long will it take her to type 12,462 words?

45.   Write exponential notation: $4 \cdot 4 \cdot 4 \cdot 4 \cdot 4$.   [1.9a]

46.   Evaluate: 2^4.   [1.9b]

Simplify.   [1.9c]

47. $8 \cdot 12 - (63 \div 9 + 13 \cdot 3)$

48. $(10 - 3)^4 + 10^3 \cdot 4 - 10 \div 5$

Synthesis

Multiply. Write the answer using fraction notation.

49. ▦ $\dfrac{341}{517} \cdot \dfrac{209}{349}$

50. ▦ $\left(\dfrac{57}{61}\right)^3$

51. ▦ $\left(\dfrac{2}{5}\right)^3 \left(-\dfrac{7}{9}\right)$

52. ▦ $\left(-\dfrac{1}{2}\right)^5 \left(\dfrac{3}{5}\right)$

Copyright © 2015 Pearson Education, Inc.

Simplifying

a MULTIPLYING BY 1

Recall the following:

$$1 = \frac{1}{1} = \frac{2}{2} = \frac{3}{3} = \frac{4}{4} = \frac{10}{10} = \frac{45}{45} = \frac{100}{100} = \frac{n}{n}.$$

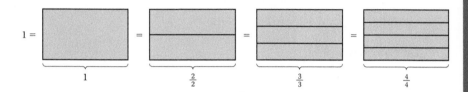

$$1 = \qquad = \frac{2}{2} \qquad = \frac{3}{3} \qquad = \frac{4}{4}$$

The multiplicative identity states that for any number a, $1 \cdot a = a \cdot 1 = a$. Since any nonzero number divided by itself is 1, we can state the multiplicative identity using fraction notation.

MULTIPLICATIVE IDENTITY FOR FRACTIONS

When we multiply a number by 1, we get the same number:

$$a = a \cdot 1 = a \cdot \frac{n}{n} = a.$$

For example, $\frac{3}{5} = \frac{3}{5} \cdot 1 = \frac{3}{5} \cdot \frac{4}{4} = \frac{12}{20}$. Since $\frac{3}{5} = \frac{12}{20}$, we say that $\frac{3}{5}$ and $\frac{12}{20}$ are **equivalent fractions**.

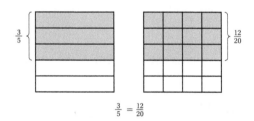

$$\frac{3}{5} = \frac{12}{20}$$

Do Margin Exercises 1–4. ▶

Suppose we want to find another name for $\frac{2}{3}$, one that has a denominator of 9. We can multiply by 1 to find equivalent fractions. Since $9 = 3 \cdot 3$, we choose $\frac{3}{3}$ for 1 in order to get a denominator of 9:

$$\frac{2}{3} = \frac{2}{3} \cdot 1 = \frac{2}{3} \cdot \frac{3}{3} = \frac{2 \cdot 3}{3 \cdot 3} = \frac{6}{9}.$$

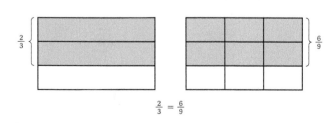

$$\frac{2}{3} = \frac{6}{9}$$

OBJECTIVES

a Multiply a number by 1 to find fraction notation with a specified denominator.

b Simplify fraction notation.

c Use the test for equality to determine whether two fractions name the same number.

SKILL TO REVIEW

Objective 3.1d: Find the prime factorization of a composite number.

Find the prime factorization.

1. 84   **2.** 2250

Multiply.

1. $\dfrac{1}{2} \cdot \dfrac{8}{8}$ 2. $\dfrac{3}{5} \cdot \dfrac{10}{10}$

3. $-\dfrac{13}{25} \cdot \dfrac{4}{4}$ 4. $\dfrac{8}{3} \cdot \dfrac{25}{25}$

Answers

Skill to Review:
1. $2 \cdot 2 \cdot 3 \cdot 7$ **2.** $2 \cdot 3 \cdot 3 \cdot 5 \cdot 5 \cdot 5$

Margin Exercises:

1. $\dfrac{8}{16}$ **2.** $\dfrac{30}{50}$ **3.** $-\dfrac{52}{100}$ **4.** $\dfrac{200}{75}$

Find another name for each number, but with the denominator indicated. Use multiplying by 1.

GS

5. $\dfrac{4}{3} = \dfrac{?}{15}$

$$\dfrac{4}{3} = \dfrac{4}{3} \cdot \dfrac{}{}$$

$$= \dfrac{4 \cdot 5}{3 \cdot 5}$$

$$= \dfrac{}{15}$$

6. $\dfrac{1}{7} = \dfrac{?}{28}$

7. $-\dfrac{9}{10} = -\dfrac{?}{100}$

8. $-\dfrac{3}{15} = -\dfrac{?}{45}$

Simplify.

9. $\dfrac{2}{8}$

10. $-\dfrac{24}{18}$

11. $\dfrac{10}{12}$

12. $\dfrac{15}{80}$

Answers

5. $\dfrac{20}{15}$ **6.** $\dfrac{4}{28}$ **7.** $-\dfrac{90}{100}$ **8.** $-\dfrac{9}{45}$ **9.** $\dfrac{1}{4}$

10. $-\dfrac{4}{3}$ **11.** $\dfrac{5}{6}$ **12.** $\dfrac{3}{16}$

Guided Solution:

5. $\dfrac{5}{5}$, 20

EXAMPLE 1 Find a name for $\frac{2}{5}$ with a denominator of 35.

Since $5 \cdot 7 = 35$, we multiply by $\frac{7}{7}$:

$$\dfrac{2}{5} = \dfrac{2}{5} \cdot \dfrac{7}{7} = \dfrac{2 \cdot 7}{5 \cdot 7} = \dfrac{14}{35}.$$

We say that $\frac{2}{5}$ and $\frac{14}{35}$ represent the same number. They are equivalent.

EXAMPLE 2 Find a name for $-\frac{2}{5}$ with a denominator of 35.

Since $5 \cdot 7 = 35$, we multiply by $\frac{7}{7}$:

$$-\dfrac{2}{5} = -\dfrac{2}{5} \cdot \dfrac{7}{7} = -\dfrac{2 \cdot 7}{5 \cdot 7} = -\dfrac{14}{35}.$$

The numbers $-\frac{2}{5}$ and $-\frac{14}{35}$ are equivalent.

◄ Do Exercises 5–8.

b   SIMPLIFYING FRACTION NOTATION

All of the following are names for three-fourths:

$$\dfrac{3}{4}, \dfrac{6}{8}, \dfrac{9}{12}, \dfrac{12}{16}, \dfrac{15}{20}.$$

We say that $\frac{3}{4}$ is **simplest** because it has the smallest numerator and the smallest denominator. That is, the numerator and the denominator have no common factor other than 1.

To simplify, we reverse the process of multiplying by 1:

$$\dfrac{12}{18} = \dfrac{2 \cdot 6}{3 \cdot 6} \quad \begin{array}{l} \leftarrow \text{Factoring the numerator} \\ \leftarrow \text{Factoring the denominator} \end{array}$$

$$= \dfrac{2}{3} \cdot \dfrac{6}{6} \qquad \text{Factoring the fraction}$$

$$= \dfrac{2}{3} \cdot 1 \qquad \dfrac{6}{6} = 1$$

$$= \dfrac{2}{3}. \qquad \text{Removing a factor of 1: } \dfrac{2}{3} \cdot 1 = \dfrac{2}{3}$$

EXAMPLES   Simplify.

3. $\dfrac{8}{20} = \dfrac{2 \cdot 4}{5 \cdot 4} = \dfrac{2}{5} \cdot \dfrac{4}{4} = \dfrac{2}{5}$

4. $\dfrac{2}{6} = \dfrac{1 \cdot 2}{3 \cdot 2} = \dfrac{1}{3} \cdot \dfrac{2}{2} = \dfrac{1}{3}$

> The number 1 allows for pairing of factors in the numerator and the denominator.

◄ Do Exercises 9–12.

The use of prime factorizations can be helpful for simplifying when numerators and/or denominators are large numbers.

EXAMPLE 5 Simplify: $\dfrac{90}{84}$.

$$\dfrac{90}{84} = \dfrac{2 \cdot 3 \cdot 3 \cdot 5}{2 \cdot 2 \cdot 3 \cdot 7}$$ Factoring the numerator and the denominator into primes

$$= \dfrac{2 \cdot 3 \cdot 3 \cdot 5}{2 \cdot 3 \cdot 2 \cdot 7}$$ Changing the order so that like primes are above and below each other

$$= \dfrac{2}{2} \cdot \dfrac{3}{3} \cdot \dfrac{3 \cdot 5}{2 \cdot 7}$$ Factoring the fraction

$$= 1 \cdot 1 \cdot \dfrac{3 \cdot 5}{2 \cdot 7}$$

$$= \dfrac{3 \cdot 5}{2 \cdot 7}$$ Removing factors of 1

$$= \dfrac{15}{14}$$

The tests for divisibility are very helpful in simplifying fraction notation. We could have shortened the preceding example had we noted that 6 is a factor of both the numerator and the denominator. Then we would have

$$\dfrac{90}{84} = \dfrac{6 \cdot 15}{6 \cdot 14} = \dfrac{6}{6} \cdot \dfrac{15}{14} = \dfrac{15}{14}.$$

EXAMPLE 6 Simplify: $\dfrac{603}{207}$.

At first glance this looks difficult. But, using the test for divisibility by 9 (sum of digits is divisible by 9), we find that both the numerator and the denominator are divisible by 9. Thus we write both numbers with a factor of 9:

$$\dfrac{603}{207} = \dfrac{9 \cdot 67}{9 \cdot 23} = \dfrac{9}{9} \cdot \dfrac{67}{23} = \dfrac{67}{23}.$$

EXAMPLE 7 Simplify: $-\dfrac{660}{1140}$.

Using the tests for divisibility, we have

$$-\dfrac{660}{1140} = -\dfrac{66 \cdot 10}{114 \cdot 10} = -\dfrac{66}{114} \cdot \dfrac{10}{10} = -\dfrac{66}{114}$$ Both 660 and 1140 are divisible by 10.

$$= -\dfrac{11 \cdot 6}{19 \cdot 6} = -\dfrac{11}{19} \cdot \dfrac{6}{6} = -\dfrac{11}{19}.$$ Both 66 and 114 are divisible by 6.

Do Exercises 13–19. ▶

Simplify.

13. $\dfrac{35}{40}$ **14.** $-\dfrac{24}{21}$

GS **15.** $\dfrac{75}{30} = \dfrac{3 \cdot 5 \cdot \square}{2 \cdot 3 \cdot \square}$

$$= \dfrac{3 \cdot 5 \cdot 5}{3 \cdot 5 \cdot 2}$$

$$= \dfrac{3}{3} \cdot \dfrac{5}{5} \cdot \dfrac{5}{\square}$$

$$= 1 \cdot \square \cdot \dfrac{5}{2}$$

$$= \dfrac{\square}{\square}$$

16. $-\dfrac{75}{300}$ **17.** $\dfrac{280}{960}$

18. $\dfrac{1332}{2880}$

19. Simplify each fraction in this circle graph.

What College Graduates Will Do If They Are Not Offered a Full-Time Job in Their First-Choice Field

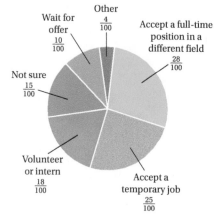

SOURCE: Yahoo Hotjobs survey

Answers

13. $\dfrac{7}{8}$ **14.** $-\dfrac{8}{7}$ **15.** $\dfrac{5}{2}$ **16.** $-\dfrac{1}{4}$ **17.** $\dfrac{7}{24}$

18. $\dfrac{37}{80}$ **19.** $\dfrac{4}{100} = \dfrac{1}{25}; \dfrac{28}{100} = \dfrac{7}{25}; \dfrac{25}{100} = \dfrac{1}{4};$

$\dfrac{18}{100} = \dfrac{9}{50}; \dfrac{15}{100} = \dfrac{3}{20}; \dfrac{10}{100} = \dfrac{1}{10}$

Guided Solution:

15. $5, 5, 5, 1, \dfrac{5}{2}$

CALCULATOR CORNER

Simplifying Fraction Notation

Fraction calculators are equipped

with a key, often labeled $\boxed{a^{b}/_{c}}$, that

allows fractions to be entered. To

simplify

$$\frac{208}{256}$$

with a fraction calculator, we enter

the fraction and press $\boxed{=}$. The

display that appears

$$\boxed{13 \lrcorner 16}$$

represents the simplified fraction

notation $\frac{13}{16}$.

EXERCISES   Use a fraction

calculator to simplify each of the

following.

1. $\dfrac{84}{90}$ 2. $\dfrac{35}{40}$

3. $\dfrac{690}{835}$ 4. $\dfrac{42}{150}$

Canceling

Canceling is a shortcut that you may have used for removing a factor of 1 when working with fraction notation. With *great* concern, we mention it as a possibility for speeding up your work. Canceling may be done only when removing common factors in numerators and denominators. Each such pair allows us to remove a factor of 1 in a fraction.

Our concern is that canceling be done with care and understanding. In effect, slashes are used to indicate factors of 1 that have been removed. For instance, Example 5 might have been done faster as follows:

$$\frac{90}{84} = \frac{2 \cdot 3 \cdot 3 \cdot 5}{2 \cdot 2 \cdot 3 \cdot 7} \qquad \text{Factoring the numerator and the denominator}$$

$$= \frac{\cancel{2} \cdot \cancel{3} \cdot 3 \cdot 5}{2 \cdot \cancel{2} \cdot \cancel{3} \cdot 7} \qquad \begin{array}{l}\text{When a factor of 1 is noted,} \\ \text{it is canceled as shown:} \dfrac{2}{2} \cdot \dfrac{3}{3} = 1.\end{array}$$

$$= \frac{3 \cdot 5}{2 \cdot 7} = \frac{15}{14}.$$

·· Caution! ··

The difficulty with canceling is that it is often applied incorrectly in situations like the following:

$$\frac{\cancel{2} + 3}{\cancel{2}} = 3; \qquad \frac{\cancel{4} + 1}{\cancel{4} + 2} = \frac{1}{2}; \qquad \frac{1\cancel{5}}{\cancel{5}4} = \frac{1}{4}.$$

      Wrong!   Wrong!   Wrong!

The correct answers are

$$\frac{2 + 3}{2} = \frac{5}{2}; \qquad \frac{4 + 1}{4 + 2} = \frac{5}{6}; \qquad \frac{15}{54} = \frac{3 \cdot 5}{3 \cdot 18} = \frac{3}{3} \cdot \frac{5}{18} = \frac{5}{18}.$$

In each situation, the number canceled was not a factor of 1. Factors are parts of products. For example, in $2 \cdot 3$, 2 and 3 are factors, but in $2 + 3$, 2 and 3 are *not* factors. Canceling may not be done when sums or differences are in numerators or denominators, as shown here. **If you cannot factor, you cannot cancel! If in doubt, do not cancel!**

···

C   A TEST FOR EQUALITY

When denominators are the same, we say that fractions have a **common denominator**. When fractions have a common denominator, we can compare them by comparing numerators. Suppose we want to compare $\frac{3}{6}$ and $\frac{2}{4}$. First, we find a common denominator. To do this, we multiply each fraction by 1, using the denominator of the other fraction to form the symbol for 1. We multiply $\frac{3}{6}$ by $\frac{4}{4}$ and $\frac{2}{4}$ by $\frac{6}{6}$:

$$\frac{3}{6} = \frac{3}{6} \cdot \frac{4}{4} = \frac{3 \cdot 4}{6 \cdot 4} = \frac{12}{24}; \qquad \text{Multiplying by } \frac{4}{4}$$

$$\frac{2}{4} = \frac{2}{4} \cdot \frac{6}{6} = \frac{2 \cdot 6}{4 \cdot 6} = \frac{12}{24}. \qquad \text{Multiplying by } \frac{6}{6}$$

Once we have a common denominator, 24, we compare the numerators. And since these numerators are both 12, the fractions are equal:

$$\frac{3}{6} = \frac{2}{4}.$$

Note in the preceding that if $\frac{3}{6} = \frac{2}{4}$, then $3 \cdot 4 = 6 \cdot 2$. This tells us that we need to check only the products $3 \cdot 4$ and $6 \cdot 2$ to compare the fractions.

A TEST FOR EQUALITY

Two fractions are equal if their cross products are equal.

We multiply these two numbers: $3 \cdot 4$.

We multiply these two numbers: $6 \cdot 2$.

$$\frac{3}{6} \;\square\; \frac{2}{4}$$

We call $3 \cdot 4$ and $6 \cdot 2$ **cross products**. Since the cross products are the same—that is, $3 \cdot 4 = 6 \cdot 2$—we know that

$$\frac{3}{6} = \frac{2}{4}.$$

If a sentence $a = b$ is true, it means that a and b name the same number. If a sentence $a \neq b$ (read "a is not equal to b") is true, it means that a and b do *not* name the same number.

EXAMPLE 8 Use $=$ or $\neq$ for $\square$ to write a true sentence:

$$\frac{6}{7} \;\square\; \frac{7}{8}.$$

We multiply these two numbers: $6 \cdot 8 = 48$.

We multiply these two numbers: $7 \cdot 7 = 49$.

$$\frac{6}{7} \;\square\; \frac{7}{8}$$

Because $48 \neq 49$, $\frac{6}{7}$ and $\frac{7}{8}$ do not name the same number. Thus,

$$\frac{6}{7} \neq \frac{7}{8}.$$

EXAMPLE 9 Use $=$ or $\neq$ for $\square$ to write a true sentence:

$$-\frac{6}{10} \;\square\; \frac{-3}{5}.$$

We rewrite $-\frac{6}{10}$ as $\frac{-6}{10}$ and then check cross products.

We multiply these two numbers: $-6 \cdot 5 = -30$.

We multiply these two numbers: $10 \cdot (-3) = -30$.

$$\frac{-6}{10} \;\square\; \frac{-3}{5}$$

Because the cross products are the same, we have

$$\frac{-6}{10} = \frac{-3}{5}, \text{ or } -\frac{6}{10} = \frac{-3}{5}.$$

Do Exercises 20 and 21. ▶

Use $=$ or $\neq$ for $\square$ to write a true sentence.

GS 20. $\frac{2}{3} \;\square\; \frac{14}{20}$

$2 \cdot \boxed{} = 40 \qquad 3 \cdot \boxed{} = 42$

$$\frac{2}{3} \;\square\; \frac{14}{20}$$

Since $40 \neq 42$, $\frac{2}{3} \;\square\; \frac{14}{20}$.

21. $\frac{-2}{6} \;\square\; -\frac{3}{9}$

Answers

20. $\neq$ **21.** $=$

Guided Solution:
20. 20, 14; $\neq$

✓ Reading Check

Complete each statement with the appropriate word from the following list.

| common | cross | equivalent | simplify |

RC1. _____ fractions name the same number.

RC2. To _____ a fraction, we find a fraction that names the same number and that has a numerator and a denominator with no common factor.

RC3. The fractions $\frac{2}{7}$ and $\frac{4}{7}$ have a _____ denominator.

RC4. Two fractions are equal if their _____ products are equal.

a Find another name for the given number, but with the denominator indicated. Use multiplying by 1.

1. $\frac{1}{2} = \frac{?}{10}$

2. $\frac{1}{6} = \frac{?}{18}$

3. $\frac{5}{8} = \frac{?}{32}$

4. $\frac{2}{9} = \frac{?}{18}$

5. $-\frac{9}{10} = -\frac{?}{30}$

6. $-\frac{5}{6} = -\frac{?}{48}$

7. $\frac{5}{12} = \frac{?}{48}$

8. $\frac{5}{3} = \frac{?}{45}$

9. $\frac{17}{18} = \frac{?}{-54}$

10. $\frac{11}{16} = \frac{?}{-256}$

11. $\frac{7}{22} = \frac{?}{132}$

12. $\frac{10}{21} = \frac{?}{126}$

b Simplify.

13. $\frac{2}{4}$

14. $\frac{4}{8}$

15. $-\frac{6}{8}$

16. $-\frac{8}{12}$

17. $\frac{3}{15}$

18. $\frac{8}{10}$

19. $\frac{-24}{8}$

20. $\frac{-36}{9}$

21. $\frac{18}{24}$

22. $\frac{42}{48}$

23. $\frac{14}{16}$

24. $\frac{15}{25}$

25. $\frac{12}{10}$

26. $\frac{16}{14}$

27. $\frac{16}{48}$

28. $\frac{100}{-20}$

29. $\frac{150}{-25}$

30. $\frac{19}{76}$

31. $-\frac{17}{51}$

32. $-\frac{425}{525}$

33. $\frac{540}{810}$

34. $\frac{1000}{1080}$

35. $-\frac{210}{2700}$

36. $-\frac{300}{2250}$

Copyright © 2015 Pearson Education, Inc.

c   Use = or ≠ for ☐ to write a true sentence.

37. $\dfrac{3}{4}$ ☐ $\dfrac{9}{12}$ **38.** $\dfrac{4}{8}$ ☐ $\dfrac{3}{6}$ **39.** $\dfrac{1}{5}$ ☐ $\dfrac{2}{9}$ **40.** $\dfrac{1}{4}$ ☐ $\dfrac{2}{9}$

41. $\dfrac{12}{9}$ ☐ $\dfrac{8}{6}$ **42.** $\dfrac{2}{6}$ ☐ $\dfrac{6}{18}$ **43.** $\dfrac{-2}{5}$ ☐ $\dfrac{-3}{7}$ **44.** $\dfrac{-1}{3}$ ☐ $\dfrac{-1}{4}$

45. $-\dfrac{5}{2}$ ☐ $\dfrac{-17}{7}$ **46.** $\dfrac{-3}{10}$ ☐ $-\dfrac{7}{24}$ **47.** $\dfrac{3}{10}$ ☐ $\dfrac{30}{100}$ **48.** $\dfrac{700}{1000}$ ☐ $\dfrac{70}{100}$

The following circle graph shows the fractional part of each day that the average person spends in various activities. For Exercises 49–52, simplify the fraction associated with the activity.

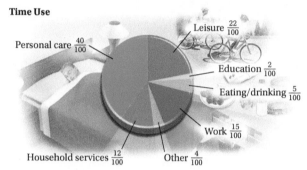

Time Use

Leisure $\frac{22}{100}$

Personal care $\frac{40}{100}$

Education $\frac{2}{100}$

Eating/drinking $\frac{5}{100}$

Work $\frac{15}{100}$

Household services $\frac{12}{100}$ Other $\frac{4}{100}$

SOURCE: Bureau of Labor Statistics

49. Personal care

50. Household services

51. Leisure

52. Eating/drinking

Skill Maintenance

Use < or > for ☐ to write a true sentence.   [1.6c]

53. 0 ☐ 23   **54.** 34 ☐ 43   **55.** 124 ☐ 98   **56.** 999 ☐ 1001

Solve.   [1.7b]

57. $5280 = 1760 + t$ **58.** $10{,}947 = 123 \cdot y$ **59.** $8797 = y + 2299$ **60.** $x \cdot 74 = 6290$

Synthesis

61. ▦ On a test of 82 questions, a student got 63 correct. On another test of 100 questions, she got 77 correct. Did she get the same portion of each test correct? Why or why not?

62. *Baseball Batting Averages.* For the 2012 season, Miguel Cabrera, of the Detroit Tigers, won the American League batting title with 205 hits in 622 times at bat. Buster Posey, of the San Francisco Giants, won the National League title with 178 hits in 530 times at bat. Did they have the same fraction of hits per times at bat (batting average)? Why or why not?

Source: Major League Baseball

Mid-Chapter Review

Concept Reinforcement

Determine whether each statement is true or false.

_____ **1.** A number a is divisible by another number b if b is a factor of a. [3.1b]

_____ **2.** If a number is not divisible by 6, then it is not divisible by 3. [3.2a]

_____ **3.** The fraction $\dfrac{13}{7}$ is larger than the fraction $\dfrac{13}{6}$. [3.5c]

_____ **4.** The number 1 is not prime. [3.1c]

Guided Solutions

 Fill in each blank with the number that creates a correct statement or solution.

5. $\dfrac{25}{\boxed{}} = 1$ [3.3b]   **6.** $\dfrac{\boxed{}}{-9} = 0$ [3.3b]   **7.** $\dfrac{-8}{\boxed{}} = -8$ [3.3b]   **8.** $\dfrac{6}{13} = \dfrac{\boxed{}}{39}$ [3.5a]

9. Simplify: $\dfrac{70}{225}$. [3.5b]

$$\dfrac{70}{225} = \dfrac{2 \cdot \boxed{} \cdot 7}{\boxed{} \cdot 3 \cdot 5 \cdot \boxed{}}$$

Factoring the numerator
Factoring the denominator

$$= \dfrac{5}{5} \cdot \dfrac{\boxed{} \cdot 7}{3 \cdot \boxed{} \cdot 5}$$

Factoring the fraction

$$= \boxed{} \cdot \dfrac{\boxed{}}{45}$$

$\dfrac{5}{5} = 1$

$$= \dfrac{\boxed{}}{\boxed{}}$$

Removing a factor of 1

Mixed Review

To answer Exercises 10–14, consider the following numbers. [3.2a]

84	132	594	350
300	500	120	14,850
17,576	180	1125	504
224	351	495	1632

10. Which of the above are divisible by 2 but not by 10?

11. Which of the above are divisible by 4 but not by 8?

12. Which of the above are divisible by 4 but not by 6?

13. Which of the above are divisible by 3 but not by 9?

14. Which of the above are divisible by 4, 5, and 6?

Copyright © 2015 Pearson Education, Inc.

Determine whether each number is prime, composite, or neither.   [3.1c]

15. 61   **16.** 2   **17.** 91   **18.** 1

Find all the factors of each composite number. Then find the prime factorization of the number.   [3.1a], [3.1d]

19. 160   **20.** 222   **21.** 98   **22.** 315

What part of each object or set of objects is shaded?   [3.3a]

23.

24.

Multiply.   [3.4a]

25. $7 \cdot \dfrac{1}{9}$ **26.** $\dfrac{4}{15} \cdot \dfrac{2}{3}$ **27.** $\dfrac{5}{11} \cdot (-8)$ **28.** $-\dfrac{3}{4} \cdot \left(-\dfrac{7}{8}\right)$

Simplify.   [3.3b], [3.5b]

29. $\dfrac{24}{60}$ **30.** $\dfrac{220}{60}$ **31.** $\dfrac{-17}{-17}$

32. $\dfrac{0}{23}$ **33.** $\dfrac{54}{-186}$ **34.** $\dfrac{36}{20}$

35. $\dfrac{75}{630}$ **36.** $\dfrac{315}{435}$ **37.** $\dfrac{-14}{0}$

Use = or ≠ for ☐ to write a true sentence.   [3.5c]

38. $\dfrac{3}{7}$ ☐ $\dfrac{48}{112}$ **39.** $\dfrac{19}{3}$ ☐ $\dfrac{95}{18}$

40. *Job Applications.*   Of every 200 online job applications started, only 25 are reviewed by a hiring manager. What is the ratio of applications reviewed to applications started?   [3.3a]

Source: Talent Function Group LLC, in "Your Résumé vs. Oblivion," wsj.com, 1/24/12

41. *Area of an Ice-Skating Rink.*   The length of a rectangular ice-skating rink in the atrium of a shopping mall is $\frac{7}{100}$ mi. The width is $\frac{3}{100}$ mi. What is the area of the rink?   [3.4b]

Understanding Through Discussion and Writing

42. Explain a method for finding a composite number that contains exactly two factors other than itself and 1.   [3.1c]

43. Which of the years from 2000 to 2020, if any, also happen to be prime numbers? Explain at least two ways in which you might go about solving this problem.   [3.2a]

44. Explain in your own words when it *is* possible to cancel and when it *is not* possible to cancel.   [3.5b]

45. Can fraction notation be simplified if the numerator and the denominator are two different prime numbers? Why or why not?   [3.5b]

STUDYING FOR SUCCESS   *A Valuable Resource—Your Instructor*

☐ Don't be afraid to ask questions in class. Other students probably have the same questions you do.
☐ Visit your instructor during office hours if you need additional help.
☐ Many instructors welcome e-mails from students who have questions.

3.6 Multiplying, Simplifying, and Applications

OBJECTIVES

a Multiply and simplify using fraction notation.

b Solve applied problems involving multiplication of fractions.

SKILL TO REVIEW

Objective 3.2a: Determine whether a number is divisible by 2, 3, 4, 5, 6, 8, 9, or 10.

Determine whether each number is divisible by 9.

1. 486   2. 129

a MULTIPLYING AND SIMPLIFYING USING FRACTION NOTATION

It is often possible to simplify after we multiply. To make such simplifying easier, it is usually best not to carry out the products in the numerator and the denominator immediately, but to factor and simplify first. Consider the product

$$\frac{3}{8} \cdot \frac{4}{9}.$$

We proceed as follows:

$$\frac{3}{8} \cdot \frac{4}{9} = \frac{3 \cdot 4}{8 \cdot 9}$$
We write the products in the numerator and the denominator, but we do not carry them out.

$$= \frac{3 \cdot 2 \cdot 2}{2 \cdot 2 \cdot 2 \cdot 3 \cdot 3}$$
Factoring the numerator and the denominator

$$= \frac{3 \cdot 2 \cdot 2 \cdot 1}{2 \cdot 2 \cdot 2 \cdot 3 \cdot 3}$$
Using the identity property of 1 to insert the number 1 as a factor

$$= \frac{3 \cdot 2 \cdot 2}{3 \cdot 2 \cdot 2} \cdot \frac{1}{2 \cdot 3}$$
Factoring the fraction

$$= 1 \cdot \frac{1}{2 \cdot 3}$$

$$= \frac{1}{2 \cdot 3}$$
Removing a factor of 1

$$= \frac{1}{6}.$$

The procedure could have been shortened had we noticed that 4 is a factor of the 8 in the denominator:

$$\frac{3}{8} \cdot \frac{4}{9} = \frac{3 \cdot 4}{8 \cdot 9} = \frac{3 \cdot 4}{4 \cdot 2 \cdot 3 \cdot 3} = \frac{3 \cdot 4}{3 \cdot 4} \cdot \frac{1}{2 \cdot 3} = 1 \cdot \frac{1}{2 \cdot 3} = \frac{1}{2 \cdot 3} = \frac{1}{6}.$$

> To multiply and simplify:
>
> **a)** Write the products in the numerator and the denominator, but do not carry them out.
> **b)** Factor the numerator and the denominator.
> **c)** Factor the fraction to remove a factor of 1, if possible.
> **d)** Carry out the remaining products.

Answers

Skill to Review:
1. Yes   2. No

EXAMPLES Multiply and simplify.

1. $\dfrac{2}{3} \cdot \dfrac{9}{4} = \dfrac{2 \cdot 9}{3 \cdot 4} = \dfrac{2 \cdot 3 \cdot 3}{3 \cdot 2 \cdot 2} = \dfrac{2 \cdot 3}{2 \cdot 3} \cdot \dfrac{3}{2} = 1 \cdot \dfrac{3}{2} = \dfrac{3}{2}$

2. $40 \cdot \left(-\dfrac{7}{8}\right) = -\dfrac{40 \cdot 7}{8} = -\dfrac{5 \cdot 8 \cdot 7}{8 \cdot 1} = -\dfrac{5 \cdot 7}{1} \cdot \dfrac{8}{8} = -\dfrac{5 \cdot 7}{1} \cdot 1$

$= -\dfrac{5 \cdot 7}{1} = -35$

.... Caution! ....

Canceling can be used as follows for these examples.

1. $\dfrac{2}{3} \cdot \dfrac{9}{4} = \dfrac{2 \cdot 9}{3 \cdot 4} = \dfrac{2 \cdot \cancel{3} \cdot 3}{\cancel{3} \cdot 2 \cdot 2} = \dfrac{3}{2}$ Removing a factor of 1: $\dfrac{2 \cdot 3}{2 \cdot 3} = 1$

2. $40 \cdot \left(-\dfrac{7}{8}\right) = -\dfrac{40 \cdot 7}{8} = -\dfrac{5 \cdot \cancel{8} \cdot 7}{\cancel{8} \cdot 1} = -\dfrac{5 \cdot 7}{1}$ Removing a factor of 1: $\dfrac{8}{8} = 1$

$= -35$

Remember: If you can't factor, you can't cancel!

Do Exercises 1–4. ▶

b APPLICATIONS AND PROBLEM SOLVING

EXAMPLE 3 *Landscaping.* Celina's Landscaping uses $\frac{2}{3}$ lb of peat moss when planting a rosebush. How much will be needed to plant 21 rosebushes?

1. **Familiarize.** We let $n =$ the number of pounds of peat moss needed. Each rosebush requires $\frac{2}{3}$ lb of peat moss, so repeated addition, or multiplication, applies.

2. **Translate.** The problem translates to the following equation:

   $n = 21 \cdot \dfrac{2}{3}.$

3. **Solve.** To solve the equation, we carry out the multiplication:

   $n = 21 \cdot \dfrac{2}{3} = \dfrac{21}{1} \cdot \dfrac{2}{3} = \dfrac{21 \cdot 2}{1 \cdot 3}$ Multiplying

   $= \dfrac{3 \cdot 7 \cdot 2}{1 \cdot 3} = \dfrac{3}{3} \cdot \dfrac{7 \cdot 2}{1} = 14.$

4. **Check.** We check by repeating the calculation. (This is left to the student.) We can also ask if the answer seems reasonable. We are putting less than a pound of peat moss on each bush, so the answer should be less than 21. Since 14 is less than 21, we have a partial check. The number 14 checks.

5. **State.** Celina's Landscaping will need 14 lb of peat moss to plant 21 rosebushes.

Do Exercise 5. ▶

Multiply and simplify.

GS **1.** $\dfrac{2}{3} \cdot \dfrac{7}{8}$

$= \dfrac{2 \cdot 7}{3 \cdot \square}$

$= \dfrac{2 \cdot 7}{3 \cdot 2 \cdot 2 \cdot \square}$

$= \dfrac{2}{\square} \cdot \dfrac{7}{3 \cdot 2 \cdot 2}$

$= \square \cdot \dfrac{7}{3 \cdot 2 \cdot 2}$

$= \dfrac{7}{\square}$

2. $-\dfrac{4}{5} \cdot \dfrac{5}{12}$ **3.** $16 \cdot \dfrac{3}{8}$

4. $\left(-\dfrac{5}{8}\right) \cdot (-4)$

5. *Candy.* Chocolate Delight sells $\frac{4}{5}$-lb boxes of truffles. How many pounds of truffles will be needed to fill 85 boxes?

85 boxes

$\frac{4}{5}$ pound of truffles in each box

Answers

1. $\dfrac{7}{12}$ **2.** $-\dfrac{1}{3}$ **3.** 6 **4.** $\dfrac{5}{2}$ **5.** 68 lb

Guided Solution:
1. 8, 2, 2, 1, 12

For Extra Help

MyMathLab®

MathXL®
PRACTICE   WATCH   READ   REVIEW

✓ Reading Check

Complete each step in the process for multiplying and simplifying using fraction notation.

RC1. a) Write the _____ in the numerator and the denominator, but do not carry them out.

RC2. b) _____ the numerator and the denominator.

RC3. c) Factor the fraction to remove a factor of _____ , if possible.

RC4. d) _____ the remaining products.

---

a   Multiply and simplify. | Don't forget to simplify! |

1. $\dfrac{2}{3} \cdot \dfrac{1}{2}$ **2.** $\dfrac{3}{8} \cdot \dfrac{1}{3}$ **3.** $\dfrac{7}{8} \cdot \dfrac{1}{7}$ **4.** $\dfrac{4}{9} \cdot \dfrac{1}{4}$

5. $-\dfrac{1}{8} \cdot \dfrac{4}{5}$ **6.** $-\dfrac{2}{5} \cdot \dfrac{1}{6}$ **7.** $\dfrac{1}{4} \cdot \dfrac{2}{3}$ **8.** $\dfrac{4}{6} \cdot \dfrac{1}{6}$

9. $\dfrac{12}{5} \cdot \dfrac{9}{8}$ **10.** $\dfrac{16}{15} \cdot \dfrac{5}{4}$ **11.** $\dfrac{10}{9} \cdot \left(-\dfrac{7}{5}\right)$ **12.** $\dfrac{25}{12} \cdot \left(-\dfrac{4}{3}\right)$

13. $9 \cdot \dfrac{1}{9}$ **14.** $4 \cdot \dfrac{1}{4}$ **15.** $\dfrac{1}{3} \cdot 3$ **16.** $\dfrac{1}{6} \cdot 6$

17. $\left(-\dfrac{7}{10}\right) \cdot \left(-\dfrac{10}{7}\right)$ **18.** $\left(-\dfrac{8}{9}\right) \cdot \left(-\dfrac{9}{8}\right)$ **19.** $\dfrac{7}{5} \cdot \dfrac{5}{7}$ **20.** $\dfrac{2}{11} \cdot \dfrac{11}{2}$

21. $\dfrac{1}{4} \cdot 8$ **22.** $\dfrac{1}{3} \cdot 18$ **23.** $-24 \cdot \dfrac{1}{6}$ **24.** $-16 \cdot \dfrac{1}{2}$

Copyright © 2015 Pearson Education, Inc.

25. $12 \cdot \dfrac{3}{4}$

26. $18 \cdot \dfrac{5}{6}$

27. $-\dfrac{3}{8} \cdot 24$

28. $-\dfrac{2}{9} \cdot 36$

29. $-35 \cdot \left(-\dfrac{3}{14}\right)$

30. $-15 \cdot \left(-\dfrac{1}{6}\right)$

31. $\dfrac{7}{10} \cdot 28$

32. $\dfrac{5}{8} \cdot 34$

33. $\dfrac{1}{6} \cdot 360$

34. $\dfrac{1}{3} \cdot 120$

35. $240 \cdot \left(-\dfrac{1}{8}\right)$

36. $150 \cdot \left(-\dfrac{1}{5}\right)$

37. $\dfrac{4}{10} \cdot \dfrac{5}{10}$

38. $\dfrac{7}{10} \cdot \dfrac{34}{150}$

39. $-\dfrac{8}{10} \cdot \dfrac{45}{100}$

40. $-\dfrac{3}{10} \cdot \dfrac{8}{10}$

41. $\dfrac{11}{24} \cdot \dfrac{3}{5}$

42. $\dfrac{15}{22} \cdot \dfrac{4}{7}$

43. $-\dfrac{10}{21} \cdot \left(-\dfrac{3}{4}\right)$

44. $-\dfrac{17}{18} \cdot \left(-\dfrac{3}{5}\right)$

 b Solve.

Construction.   The *pitch* of a screw is the distance between its threads. With each complete rotation, the screw goes in or out a distance equal to its pitch. Use this information to do Exercises 45 and 46.

}Pitch $= \frac{1}{16}$ in.

Each rotation moves the screw in or out $\frac{1}{16}$ in.

45. The pitch of a screw is $\frac{1}{16}$ in. How far will it go into a piece of oak when it is turned 10 complete rotations clockwise?

46. The pitch of a screw is $\frac{3}{32}$ in. How far will it come out of a piece of plywood when it is turned 10 complete rotations counterclockwise?

47. *World Silver Supply.* The total world supply of silver for new uses in 2011 was about 1040 million ounces. Of this, approximately $\frac{1}{4}$ was scrap silver being reused or repurposed. How many ounces of silver for new uses was supplied as scrap silver?

Source: Based on information from the *World Silver Survey 2012*

48. *Substitute Teaching.* After Jack completes 60 hr of teacher training in college, he can earn $75 for working a full day as a substitute teacher. How much will he receive for working $\frac{3}{5}$ of a day?

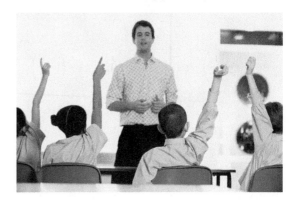

49. *Mailing-List Changes.* The United States Postal Service estimates that $\frac{4}{25}$ of the addresses on a mailing list will change in one year. A business has a mailing list of 3000 people. After one year, how many addresses on that list will be incorrect?

Source: Based on information from usps.com

50. *Shy People.* Sociologists have determined that $\frac{2}{5}$ of the people in the world are shy. A sales manager is considering 650 people for an aggressive sales position. How many of these people might be shy?

51. A recipe for piecrust calls for $\frac{2}{3}$ cup of flour. A baker is making $\frac{1}{2}$ of the recipe. How much flour should the baker use?

52. Of the students in the freshman class, $\frac{4}{5}$ have digital cameras; $\frac{1}{4}$ of these students also join the college photography club. What fraction of the students in the freshman class join the photography club?

53. A house worth $154,000 is assessed for $\frac{3}{4}$ of its value. What is the assessed value of the house?

54. Roxanne's tuition was $4600. A loan was obtained for $\frac{3}{4}$ of the tuition. How much was the loan?

55. *Map Scaling.* On a map, 1 in. represents 240 mi. What distance does $\frac{2}{3}$ in. represent?

56. *Map Scaling.* On a map, 1 in. represents 120 mi. What distance does $\frac{3}{4}$ in. represent?

Copyright © 2015 Pearson Education, Inc.

57. *Household Budgets.* A family has an annual income of $42,000. Of this, $\frac{1}{5}$ is spent for food, $\frac{1}{4}$ for housing, $\frac{1}{10}$ for clothing, $\frac{1}{14}$ for savings, $\frac{1}{5}$ for taxes, and the rest for other expenses. How much is spent for each?

58. *Household Budgets.* A family has an annual income of $28,140. Of this, $\frac{1}{5}$ is spent for food, $\frac{1}{4}$ for housing, $\frac{1}{10}$ for clothing, $\frac{1}{14}$ for savings, $\frac{1}{5}$ for taxes, and the rest for other expenses. How much is spent for each?

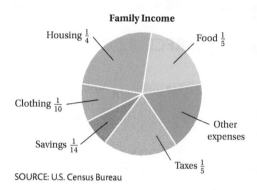

Family Income

Housing $\frac{1}{4}$ Food $\frac{1}{5}$

Clothing $\frac{1}{10}$

Savings $\frac{1}{14}$

Other expenses

Taxes $\frac{1}{5}$

SOURCE: U.S. Census Bureau

Skill Maintenance

Add.   [1.2a], [2.2a]

59. $7246 + 1341$

60. $24 + 2683$

61. $-14 + 5$

62. $-6 + (-7)$

Subtract.   [1.3a], [2.3a]

63. $9001 - 6798$

64. $2037 - 1189$

65. $8 - 12$

66. $-4 - (-4)$

Multiply.   [1.4a], [2.4a]

67. $2 \cdot 13$

68. $8 \cdot 32$

69. $17 \cdot (-25)$

70. $-5 \cdot (-6)$

Divide.   [1.5a], [2.5a]

71. $0 \div 22$

72. $22 \div 1$

73. $7140 \div (-35)$

74. $-56 \div (-7)$

Synthesis

Multiply and simplify. Use a list of prime numbers or a fraction calculator.

75. 🖩 $\dfrac{201}{535} \cdot \dfrac{4601}{6499}$

76. 🖩 $-\dfrac{5767}{3763} \cdot \dfrac{159}{395}$

77. *College Profile.* Of students entering a college, $\frac{7}{8}$ have completed high school and $\frac{2}{3}$ are older than 20. If $\frac{1}{7}$ of all students are left-handed, what fraction of students entering the college are left-handed high school graduates over the age of 20?

78. *College Profile.* Refer to the information in Exercise 77. If 480 students are entering the college, how many of them are left-handed high school graduates 20 yr old or younger?

79. *College Profile.* Refer to Exercise 77. What fraction of students entering the college did not graduate from high school, are 20 yr old or younger, and are left-handed?

OBJECTIVES

a Find the reciprocal of a number.

b Divide and simplify using fraction notation.

c Solve equations of the type $a \cdot x = b$ and $x \cdot a = b$, where a and b may be fractions.

d Solve applied problems involving division of fractions.

SKILL TO REVIEW

Objective 1.7b: Solve equations like $t + 28 = 54$, $28 \cdot x = 168$, and $98 \cdot 2 = y$.

Solve.

1. $88 = 8 \cdot y$

2. $16 \cdot x = 1152$

Find the reciprocal.

1. $\dfrac{2}{5}$ **2.** $\dfrac{10}{7}$

3. 9 **4.** $-\dfrac{1}{5}$

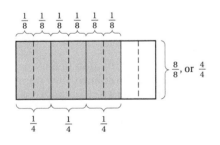

$\dfrac{8}{8}$, or $\dfrac{4}{4}$

Answers

Skill to Review:
1. 11   **2.** 72

Margin Exercises:
1. $\dfrac{5}{2}$ **2.** $\dfrac{7}{10}$ **3.** $\dfrac{1}{9}$ **4.** -5

a RECIPROCALS

Products like $8 \cdot \dfrac{1}{8}$ and $\dfrac{2}{3} \cdot \dfrac{3}{2}$ simplify to 1:

$$8 \cdot \frac{1}{8} = \frac{8}{1} \cdot \frac{1}{8} = \frac{8 \cdot 1}{1 \cdot 8} = \frac{8}{8} = 1; \qquad \frac{2}{3} \cdot \frac{3}{2} = \frac{2 \cdot 3}{3 \cdot 2} = \frac{6}{6} = 1.$$

RECIPROCALS

If the product of two numbers is 1, we say that they are **reciprocals** of each other. To find the reciprocal of a fraction, interchange the numerator and the denominator.

$$\text{Number:} \quad \frac{3}{4} \quad \longrightarrow \quad \text{Reciprocal:} \quad \frac{4}{3}$$

EXAMPLES Find the reciprocal.

1. The reciprocal of $\dfrac{4}{5}$ is $\dfrac{5}{4}$. $\dfrac{4}{5} \cdot \dfrac{5}{4} = \dfrac{20}{20} = 1$

2. The reciprocal of 24 is $\dfrac{1}{24}$.   Think of 24 as $\dfrac{24}{1}$: $\dfrac{24}{1} \cdot \dfrac{1}{24} = \dfrac{24}{24} = 1$.

3. The reciprocal of $-\dfrac{1}{3}$ is -3. $-\dfrac{1}{3} \cdot (-3) = -\dfrac{1}{3} \cdot \left(-\dfrac{3}{1}\right) = \dfrac{3}{3} = 1$

◀ **Do Margin Exercises 1–4.**

Does 0 have a reciprocal? If it did, it would have to be a number x such that $0 \cdot x = 1$. But 0 times any number is 0. Thus we have the following.

0 HAS NO RECIPROCAL

The number 0, or $\dfrac{0}{n}$, has no reciprocal. $\left(\text{Recall that } \dfrac{n}{0} \text{ is not defined.}\right)$

b DIVISION

Consider the division $\frac{3}{4} \div \frac{1}{8}$. We are asking how many $\frac{1}{8}$'s are in $\frac{3}{4}$. From the figure at left, we see that there are six $\frac{1}{8}$'s in $\frac{3}{4}$. Thus,

$$\frac{3}{4} \div \frac{1}{8} = 6.$$

We can check this by multiplying:

$$6 \cdot \frac{1}{8} = \frac{6}{1} \cdot \frac{1}{8} = \frac{6}{8} = \frac{2 \cdot 3}{2 \cdot 4} = \frac{2}{2} \cdot \frac{3}{4} = \frac{3}{4}.$$

Here is a faster way to do this division:

$$\frac{3}{4} \div \frac{1}{8} = \frac{3}{4} \cdot \frac{8}{1} = \frac{3 \cdot 8}{4 \cdot 1} = \frac{24}{4} = 6.$$ Multiplying by the reciprocal of the divisor

---

To divide fractions, multiply the dividend by the reciprocal of the divisor:

$$\frac{2}{5} \div \frac{3}{4} = \frac{2}{5} \cdot \frac{4}{3} = \frac{2 \cdot 4}{5 \cdot 3} = \frac{8}{15}.$$

EXAMPLES Divide and simplify.

4. $\dfrac{5}{6} \div \dfrac{2}{3} = \dfrac{5}{6} \cdot \dfrac{3}{2} = \dfrac{5 \cdot 3}{6 \cdot 2} = \dfrac{5 \cdot 3}{3 \cdot 2 \cdot 2} = \dfrac{3}{3} \cdot \dfrac{5}{2 \cdot 2} = \dfrac{5}{2 \cdot 2} = \dfrac{5}{4}$

5. $-\dfrac{7}{8} \div \dfrac{1}{16} = -\dfrac{7}{8} \cdot 16 = -\dfrac{7 \cdot 16}{8} = -\dfrac{7 \cdot 2 \cdot 8}{8 \cdot 1} = -\dfrac{7 \cdot 2}{1} \cdot \dfrac{8}{8}$

$= -\dfrac{7 \cdot 2}{1} = -14$

6. $\dfrac{2}{5} \div 6 = \dfrac{2}{5} \cdot \dfrac{1}{6} = \dfrac{2 \cdot 1}{5 \cdot 6} = \dfrac{2 \cdot 1}{5 \cdot 2 \cdot 3} = \dfrac{2}{2} \cdot \dfrac{1}{5 \cdot 3} = \dfrac{1}{5 \cdot 3} = \dfrac{1}{15}$

················· **Caution!** ·················

Canceling can be used as follows for Examples 4–6.

4. $\dfrac{5}{6} \div \dfrac{2}{3} = \dfrac{5}{6} \cdot \dfrac{3}{2} = \dfrac{5 \cdot 3}{6 \cdot 2} = \dfrac{5 \cdot \cancel{3}}{\cancel{3} \cdot 2 \cdot 2} = \dfrac{5}{2 \cdot 2} = \dfrac{5}{4}$ Removing a factor of 1: $\frac{3}{3} = 1$

5. $-\dfrac{7}{8} \div \dfrac{1}{16} = -\dfrac{7}{8} \cdot 16 = -\dfrac{7 \cdot 16}{8} = -\dfrac{7 \cdot \cancel{8} \cdot 2}{\cancel{8} \cdot 1}$ Removing a factor of 1: $\frac{8}{8} = 1$

$= -\dfrac{7 \cdot 2}{1} = -14$

6. $\dfrac{2}{5} \div 6 = \dfrac{2}{5} \cdot \dfrac{1}{6} = \dfrac{2 \cdot 1}{5 \cdot 6} = \dfrac{\cancel{2} \cdot 1}{5 \cdot \cancel{2} \cdot 3} = \dfrac{1}{5 \cdot 3} = \dfrac{1}{15}$ Removing a factor of 1: $\frac{2}{2} = 1$

Remember: if you can't factor, you can't cancel!

·················

Do Exercises 5–8. ▶

What is the explanation for multiplying by a reciprocal when dividing? Let's consider $\frac{2}{3} \div \frac{7}{5}$. We multiply by 1. The name for 1 that we will use is $(5/7)/(5/7)$; it comes from the reciprocal of $\frac{7}{5}$.

$$\frac{2}{3} \div \frac{7}{5} = \frac{\frac{2}{3}}{\frac{7}{5}} = \frac{\frac{2}{3}}{\frac{7}{5}} \cdot 1 = \frac{\frac{2}{3} \cdot \frac{5}{7}}{\frac{7}{5} \cdot \frac{5}{7}} = \frac{\frac{2}{3} \cdot \frac{5}{7}}{1} = \frac{2}{3} \cdot \frac{5}{7} = \frac{10}{21}$$

Thus, $\dfrac{2}{3} \div \dfrac{7}{5} = \dfrac{2}{3} \cdot \dfrac{5}{7} = \dfrac{10}{21}$.

Do Exercise 9. ▶

Divide and simplify.

GS 5. $\dfrac{6}{7} \div \dfrac{3}{4} = \dfrac{6}{7} \cdot \dfrac{}{}$

$= \dfrac{6 \cdot 4}{7 \cdot 3}$

$= \dfrac{2 \cdot 3 \cdot 2 \cdot }{7 \cdot 3}$

$= \dfrac{3}{} \cdot \dfrac{2 \cdot 2 \cdot 2}{7}$

$= \dfrac{2 \cdot 2 \cdot 2}{7}$

$= \dfrac{}{7}$

6. $-\dfrac{2}{3} \div \dfrac{1}{4}$ **7.** $\dfrac{4}{5} \div 8$

8. $-60 \div \left(-\dfrac{3}{5}\right)$

9. Divide by multiplying by 1:

$$\frac{\frac{4}{5}}{\frac{6}{7}}$$

Answers

5. $\dfrac{8}{7}$ **6.** $-\dfrac{8}{3}$ **7.** $\dfrac{1}{10}$ **8.** 100   **9.** $\dfrac{14}{15}$

Guided Solution:

5. $\dfrac{4}{3}, 2, 3, 8$

c SOLVING EQUATIONS

Now let's solve the equations $a \cdot x = b$ and $x \cdot a = b$, where a and b may be fractions. We proceed as we did with equations involving whole numbers. We divide by a on both sides.

EXAMPLE 7 Solve: $\frac{4}{3} \cdot x = \frac{6}{7}$.

We have

$$\frac{4}{3} \cdot x = \frac{6}{7}$$

$$\frac{\frac{4}{3} \cdot x}{\frac{4}{3}} = \frac{\frac{6}{7}}{\frac{4}{3}} \qquad \text{Dividing by } \tfrac{4}{3} \text{ on both sides}$$

$$x = \frac{6}{7} \cdot \frac{3}{4} \qquad \text{Multiplying by the reciprocal}$$

$$= \frac{6 \cdot 3}{7 \cdot 4} = \frac{2 \cdot 3 \cdot 3}{7 \cdot 2 \cdot 2} = \frac{2}{2} \cdot \frac{3 \cdot 3}{7 \cdot 2} = \frac{3 \cdot 3}{7 \cdot 2} = \frac{9}{14}.$$

The solution is $\frac{9}{14}$.

EXAMPLE 8 Solve: $t \cdot \frac{4}{5} = -80$.

Dividing by $\frac{4}{5}$ on both sides, we get

$$t = -80 \div \frac{4}{5} = -80 \cdot \frac{5}{4} = \frac{-80 \cdot 5}{4} = \frac{4 \cdot (-20) \cdot 5}{4 \cdot 1}$$

$$= \frac{4}{4} \cdot \frac{-20 \cdot 5}{1} = \frac{-20 \cdot 5}{1} = -100.$$

The solution is -100.

◀ Do Exercises 10 and 11.

d APPLICATIONS AND PROBLEM SOLVING

EXAMPLE 9 *Doses of an Antibiotic.* How many doses, each containing $\frac{15}{4}$ milliliters (mL), can be obtained from a bottle of a children's antibiotic that contains 60 mL?

1. **Familiarize.** We are asking the question "How many $\frac{15}{4}$'s are in 60?" Repeated addition will apply here. We make a drawing. We let $n =$ the number of doses in all.

$\frac{15}{4}$ milliliter in each dose

n doses in all

2. **Translate.** The equation that corresponds to the situation is

$$n = 60 \div \frac{15}{4}.$$

Solve.

10. $\frac{5}{6} \cdot y = \frac{2}{3}$ GS

$$\frac{\frac{5}{6} \cdot y}{\boxed{}} = \frac{\frac{2}{3}}{\boxed{}}$$

$$\boxed{} = \frac{2}{3} \cdot \frac{6}{\boxed{}}$$

$$= \frac{2 \cdot 2 \cdot \boxed{}}{3 \cdot 5}$$

$$= \frac{3}{3} \cdot \frac{2 \cdot 2}{\boxed{}}$$

$$= \frac{\boxed{}}{5}$$

11. $n \cdot \frac{3}{4} = -24$

Answers

10. $\frac{4}{5}$ **11.** -32

Guided Solution:

10. $\frac{5}{6}, \frac{5}{6}; y, 5, 3, 5, 4$

3. Solve. We solve the equation by carrying out the division:

$$n = 60 \div \frac{15}{4} = 60 \cdot \frac{4}{15} = \frac{60}{1} \cdot \frac{4}{15}$$

$$= \frac{60 \cdot 4}{1 \cdot 15} = \frac{4 \cdot 15 \cdot 4}{1 \cdot 15} = \frac{15}{15} \cdot \frac{4 \cdot 4}{1} = 1 \cdot 16 = 16.$$

4. Check. We check by multiplying the number of doses by the size of the dose: $16 \cdot \frac{15}{4} = 60$. The answer checks.

5. State. There are 16 doses in a 60-mL bottle of the antibiotic.

Do Exercise 12. ▶

EXAMPLE 10 *Bicycle Paths.* The city of Indianapolis has adopted the *Indianapolis Bicycle Master Plan* as a strategy for creating an environment where bicycling is a safe, practical, and enjoyable transportation choice. After the city finished constructing 60 mi of bike paths and on-road bike lanes, the master plan was $\frac{3}{10}$ complete. What is the total number of miles of bicycling surface that the city of Indianapolis plans to construct?

Source: *Indianapolis Bicycle Master Plan,* June 2012

1. Familiarize. We ask: "60 mi is $\frac{3}{10}$ of what length?" We make a drawing or at least visualize the problem. We let $b =$ the total number of miles of bicycling surface in the master plan.

2. Translate. We translate to an equation:

Fraction completed	of	Total miles planned	is	Amount completed
$\frac{3}{10}$	$\cdot$	b	$=$	60.

3. Solve. We divide by $\frac{3}{10}$ on both sides and carry out the division:

$$b = 60 \div \frac{3}{10} = \frac{60}{1} \cdot \frac{10}{3} = \frac{60 \cdot 10}{1 \cdot 3} = \frac{3 \cdot 20 \cdot 10}{1 \cdot 3} = \frac{3}{3} \cdot \frac{20 \cdot 10}{1} = 200.$$

4. Check. We determine whether $\frac{3}{10}$ of 200 is 60: $\frac{3}{10} \cdot 200 = 60$. The answer, 200, checks.

5. State. The *Indianapolis Bicycle Master Plan* calls for 200 mi of bicycling surface.

Do Exercise 13. ▶

12. Each loop in a spring uses $\frac{21}{8}$ in. of wire. How many loops can be made from 210 in. of wire?

13. *Sales Trip.* Ed Jacobs sells soybean seeds to seed companies. After he had driven 210 mi, $\frac{5}{6}$ of his sales trip was completed. How long was the total trip?

$\frac{5}{6}$ of the trip
210 mi

Answers

12. 80 loops **13.** 252 mi

Translating for Success

1. *Boxes of Candy.* Jane's Fudge Shop is preparing gift boxes of fudge. How many pounds of fudge will be needed to fill 80 boxes if each box contains $\frac{5}{16}$ lb?

2. *Gallons of Gasoline.* On the third day of a business trip, a sales representative used $\frac{4}{5}$ of a tank of gasoline. If the tank holds 20 gal of gasoline, how many gallons were used on the third day?

3. *Purchasing a Shirt.* Tom received $36 for his birthday. If he spends $\frac{3}{4}$ of the gift on a new shirt, what is the cost of the shirt?

4. *Checkbook Balance.* The balance in Sam's checking account is $1456. He writes a check for $28 and makes a deposit of $52. What is the new balance?

5. *Boxes of Candy.* Jane's Fudge Shop prepared 80 lb of fudge for gift boxes. If each box contains $\frac{5}{16}$ lb, how many boxes can be filled?

The goal of these matching questions is to practice step (2), Translate, of the five-step problem-solving process. Translate each problem to an equation and select a correct translation from equations A–O.

A. $x = \frac{3}{4} \cdot 36$

B. $28 \cdot x = 52$

C. $x = 80 \cdot \frac{5}{16}$

D. $x = 1456 \div 28$

E. $x = 20 - \frac{4}{5}$

F. $20 = \frac{4}{5} \cdot x$

G. $x = 12 \cdot 28$

H. $x = \frac{4}{5} \cdot 20$

I. $\frac{3}{4} \cdot x = 36$

J. $x = 1456 - 52 - 28$

K. $x \div 28 = 1456$

L. $x = 52 - 28$

M. $x = 52 \cdot 28$

N. $x = 1456 - 28 + 52$

O. $\frac{5}{16} \cdot x = 80$

Answers on page A-5

---

6. *Gasoline Tank.* A gasoline tank contains 20 gal when it is $\frac{4}{5}$ full. How many gallons can it hold when full?

7. *Knitting a Scarf.* It takes Rachel 36 hr to knit a scarf. She can knit only $\frac{3}{4}$ hr per day because she is taking 16 hr of college classes. How many days will it take her to knit the scarf?

8. *Bicycle Trip.* On a recent 52-mi bicycle trip, David stopped to make a cell-phone call after completing 28 mi. How many more miles did he bicycle after the call?

9. *Crème de Menthe Thins.* Andes Candies L.P. makes Crème de Menthe Thins. How many 28-piece packages can be filled with 1456 pieces?

10. *Cereal Donations.* The Williams family donates 28 boxes of cereal weekly to the local Family in Crisis Center. How many boxes does this family donate in one year?

✓ Reading Check

Determine whether each statement is true or false.

_____ **RC1.** The numbers $-\dfrac{1}{7}$ and -7 are reciprocals.

_____ **RC2.** The number 1 has no reciprocal.

_____ **RC3.** To divide fractions, we multiply the dividend by the reciprocal of the divisor.

_____ **RC4.** To solve $\dfrac{2}{5} \cdot x = \dfrac{3}{8}$, we divide by $\dfrac{3}{8}$ on both sides.

a Find the reciprocal of each number.

1. $\dfrac{5}{6}$

2. $\dfrac{7}{8}$

3. 6

4. 4

5. $\dfrac{1}{6}$

6. $\dfrac{1}{4}$

7. $-\dfrac{10}{3}$

8. $-\dfrac{17}{4}$

b Divide and simplify.

Don't forget to simplify!

9. $\dfrac{3}{5} \div \dfrac{3}{4}$

10. $\dfrac{2}{3} \div \dfrac{3}{4}$

11. $-\dfrac{3}{5} \div \dfrac{9}{4}$

12. $-\dfrac{6}{7} \div \dfrac{3}{5}$

13. $\dfrac{4}{3} \div \dfrac{1}{3}$

14. $\dfrac{10}{9} \div \dfrac{1}{3}$

15. $-\dfrac{1}{3} \div \left(-\dfrac{1}{6}\right)$

16. $-\dfrac{1}{4} \div \left(-\dfrac{1}{5}\right)$

17. $\dfrac{3}{8} \div 3$

18. $\dfrac{5}{6} \div 5$

19. $\dfrac{12}{7} \div 4$

20. $\dfrac{18}{5} \div 2$

21. $12 \div \left(-\dfrac{3}{2}\right)$

22. $24 \div \left(-\dfrac{3}{8}\right)$

23. $28 \div \dfrac{4}{5}$

24. $40 \div \dfrac{2}{3}$

25. $-\dfrac{5}{8} \div \dfrac{5}{8}$

26. $-\dfrac{2}{5} \div \dfrac{2}{5}$

27. $\dfrac{8}{15} \div \left(-\dfrac{4}{5}\right)$

28. $\dfrac{6}{13} \div \left(-\dfrac{3}{26}\right)$

29. $-\dfrac{9}{5} \div \left(-\dfrac{4}{5}\right)$

30. $-\dfrac{5}{12} \div \left(-\dfrac{25}{36}\right)$

31. $120 \div \dfrac{5}{6}$

32. $360 \div \dfrac{8}{7}$

 Solve.

33. $\dfrac{4}{5} \cdot x = 60$

34. $\dfrac{3}{2} \cdot t = 90$

35. $-\dfrac{5}{3} \cdot y = \dfrac{10}{3}$

36. $-\dfrac{4}{9} \cdot m = \dfrac{8}{3}$

37. $x \cdot \dfrac{25}{36} = \dfrac{5}{12}$

38. $p \cdot \dfrac{4}{5} = \dfrac{8}{15}$

39. $n \cdot \dfrac{8}{7} = -360$

40. $y \cdot \dfrac{5}{6} = -120$

d Solve.

41. *Extension Cords.* An electrical supplier sells rolls of SJO 14-3 cable to a company that makes extension cords. It takes $\frac{7}{3}$ ft of cable to make each cord. How many extension cords can be made with a roll of cable containing 2240 ft of cable?

42. Benny uses $\frac{2}{5}$ gram (g) of toothpaste each time he brushes his teeth. If Benny buys a 30-g tube, how many times will he be able to brush his teeth?

43. A pair of basketball shorts requires $\frac{3}{4}$ yd of nylon. How many pairs of shorts can be made from 24 yd of nylon?

44. A child's baseball shirt requires $\frac{5}{6}$ yd of fabric. How many shirts can be made from 25 yd of fabric?

45. How many $\frac{2}{3}$-cup sugar bowls can be filled from 16 cups of sugar?

46. How many $\frac{2}{3}$-cup cereal bowls can be filled from 10 cups of cornflakes?

47. A bucket had 12 L of water in it when it was $\frac{3}{4}$ full. How much could it hold when full?

48. A tank had 20 L of gasoline in it when it was $\frac{4}{5}$ full. How much could it hold when full?

Copyright © 2015 Pearson Education, Inc.

49. Yoshi Teramoto sells hardware tools. After driving 180 kilometers (km), he has completed $\frac{5}{8}$ of a sales trip. How long is the total trip? How many kilometers are left to drive?

50. A piece of coaxial cable $\frac{4}{5}$ meter (m) long is to be cut into 8 pieces of the same length. What is the length of each piece?

Pitch of a Screw. The pitch of a screw is the distance between its threads. With each complete rotation, the screw goes in or out a distance equal to its pitch. Use this information to do Exercises 51 and 52.

51. After a screw has been turned 8 complete rotations, it is extended $\frac{1}{2}$ in. into a piece of wallboard. What is the pitch of the screw?

52. The pitch of a screw is $\frac{3}{32}$ in. How many complete rotations are necessary to drive the screw $\frac{3}{4}$ in. into a piece of pine wood?

Skill Maintenance

Solve.   [1.8a]

53. *New York Road Runners.* The New York Road Runners, a group that runs the New York City Marathon, began in 1958 with 40 members. The membership had increased to 60,000 in 2012. How many more members were there in 2012 than in 1958?

Source: New York Road Runners

54. *Gas Mileage.* The 2013 Chevrolet Corvette coupe gets 26 mpg in highway driving. How many gallons will it use in 1846 mi of highway driving?

Source: Chevrolet

55. *Associate's Degrees.* About 849,452 associate's degrees were earned in the United States in 2010. Of these, 640,113 degrees were conferred by public institutions. How many associate's degrees were conferred by private institutions?

Source: nces.ed.gov

56. *Bachelor's Degrees and Master's Degrees.* About 693,025 master's degrees were earned in the United States in 2010. This is 956,989 fewer than the number of bachelor's degrees earned the same year. How many bachelor's degrees were earned in 2010?

57. *Tiananmen Square.* Tiananmen Square in Beijing, China, is the largest public square in the world. The length of the rectangular region is 963 yd and the width is 547 yd. What is its area? its perimeter?

58. A landscaper buys 13 small maple trees and 17 small oak trees for a project. A maple costs $23 and an oak costs $37. How much is spent altogether for the trees?

Synthesis

Simplify. Use a list of prime numbers.

59. ▦ $\dfrac{711}{1957} \div \dfrac{10,033}{13,081}$

60. ▦ $\dfrac{8633}{7387} \div \left(-\dfrac{485}{581} \right)$

61. $\left(\dfrac{9}{10} \div \dfrac{2}{5} \div \dfrac{3}{8} \right)^2$

62. $\dfrac{\left(\dfrac{3}{7} \right)^2 \div \dfrac{12}{5}}{\left(\dfrac{2}{9} \right)\left(\dfrac{9}{2} \right)}$

63. If $\frac{1}{3}$ of a number is $\frac{1}{4}$, what is $\frac{1}{2}$ of the number?

Vocabulary Reinforcement

Fill in each blank with the correct term from the list at the right. Some of the choices may not be used.

1. For any number a, $a \cdot 1 = a$. The number 1 is the _____ identity. [3.5a]

2. In the product $10 \cdot \frac{3}{4}$, 10 and $\frac{3}{4}$ are called _____. [3.1a], [3.4a]

3. A natural number that has exactly two different factors, only itself and 1, is called a(n) _____ number. [3.1c]

4. In the fraction $\frac{4}{17}$, we call 17 the _____. [3.3a]

5. Since $\frac{2}{5}$ and $\frac{6}{15}$ are two names for the same number, we say that $\frac{2}{5}$ and $\frac{6}{15}$ are _____ fractions. [3.5a]

6. The product of 6 and $\frac{1}{6}$ is 1. We say that 6 and $\frac{1}{6}$ are _____. [3.7a]

7. Since $20 = 4 \cdot 5$, we say that $4 \cdot 5$ is a _____ of 20. [3.1a]

8. Since $20 = 4 \cdot 5$, we say that 20 is a _____ of 5. [3.1b]

| |
| equivalent |
| additive |
| multiplicative |
| reciprocals |
| factors |
| prime |
| composite |
| numerator |
| denominator |
| factorization |
| variables |
| multiple |

Concept Reinforcement

Determine whether each statement is true or false.

_____ 1. For any natural number n, $\frac{n}{n} > \frac{0}{n}$. [3.3b]

_____ 2. A number is divisible by 10 if its ones digit is 0 or 5. [3.2a]

_____ 3. If a number is divisible by 9, then it is also divisible by 3. [3.2a]

_____ 4. The fraction $\frac{13}{6}$ is larger than the fraction $\frac{11}{6}$. [3.5c]

Study Guide

Objective 3.1a   Find the factors of a number.

Example   Find the factors of 84.

We find as many "two-factor" factorizations as we can.

$1 \cdot 84 \quad 4 \cdot 21$
$2 \cdot 42 \quad 6 \cdot 14$
$3 \cdot 28 \quad 7 \cdot 12 \leftarrow$ Since 8, 9, 10, and 11 are not factors, we are finished.

The factors are 1, 2, 3, 4, 6, 7, 12, 14, 21, 28, 42, and 84.

Practice Exercise

1. Find the factors of 104.

Objective 3.1d Find the prime factorization of a composite number.

Example Find the prime factorization of 84.

To find the prime factorization, we can use either successive divisions or a factor tree.

$$
\begin{array}{r}
7 \\
3\overline{)21} \\
2\overline{)42} \\
2\overline{)84}
\end{array}
$$

```
        84
       /  \
      4    21
     / \   / \
    2  2  3   7
```

Thus, $84 = 2 \cdot 2 \cdot 3 \cdot 7$.

Practice Exercise

2. Find the prime factorization of 104.

Objective 3.3b Simplify fraction notation like n/n to 1, $0/n$ to 0, and $n/1$ to n.

Example Simplify $\dfrac{6}{6}, \dfrac{0}{6}$, and $\dfrac{-6}{1}$.

$$\frac{6}{6} = 1, \qquad \frac{0}{6} = 0, \qquad \frac{-6}{1} = -6$$

Practice Exercise

3. Simplify $\dfrac{0}{18}, \dfrac{-18}{-18}$, and $\dfrac{18}{1}$.

Objective 3.5b Simplify fraction notation.

Example Simplify: $\dfrac{315}{1650}$.

Using the test for divisibility by 5, we see that both the numerator and the denominator are divisible by 5:

$$\frac{315}{1650} = \frac{5 \cdot 63}{5 \cdot 330} = \frac{5}{5} \cdot \frac{63}{330} = 1 \cdot \frac{63}{330}$$

$$= \frac{63}{330} = \frac{3 \cdot 21}{3 \cdot 110} = \frac{3}{3} \cdot \frac{21}{110} = 1 \cdot \frac{21}{110} = \frac{21}{110}.$$

Practice Exercise

4. Simplify: $\dfrac{100}{280}$.

Objective 3.5c Use the test for equality to determine whether two fractions name the same number.

Example Use = or $\neq$ for $\square$ to write a true sentence:

$$\frac{10}{54} \,\square\, \frac{15}{81}.$$

We find the cross products: $10 \cdot 81 = 810$ and $54 \cdot 15 = 810$. Because the cross products are the same, we have

$$\frac{10}{54} = \frac{15}{81}.$$

If the cross products had been different, the fractions would not be equal.

Practice Exercise

5. Use = or $\neq$ for $\square$ to write a true sentence:

$$\frac{8}{48} \,\square\, \frac{6}{44}.$$

Objective 3.6a Multiply and simplify using fraction notation.

Example Multiply and simplify: $-\dfrac{7}{16} \cdot \left(-\dfrac{40}{49}\right)$.

$$-\frac{7}{16} \cdot \left(-\frac{40}{49}\right) = \frac{7 \cdot 40}{16 \cdot 49} = \frac{7 \cdot 2 \cdot 2 \cdot 2 \cdot 5}{2 \cdot 2 \cdot 2 \cdot 2 \cdot 7 \cdot 7}$$

$$= \frac{2 \cdot 2 \cdot 2 \cdot 7}{2 \cdot 2 \cdot 2 \cdot 7} \cdot \frac{5}{2 \cdot 7} = 1 \cdot \frac{5}{14} = \frac{5}{14}$$

Practice Exercise

6. Multiply and simplify: $\dfrac{80}{3} \cdot \left(-\dfrac{21}{72}\right)$.

Objective 3.7b Divide and simplify using fraction notation.

Example Divide and simplify: $\dfrac{9}{20} \div \dfrac{18}{25}$.

$$\frac{9}{20} \div \frac{18}{25} = \frac{9}{20} \cdot \frac{25}{18} = \frac{9 \cdot 25}{20 \cdot 18} = \frac{3 \cdot 3 \cdot 5 \cdot 5}{2 \cdot 2 \cdot 5 \cdot 2 \cdot 3 \cdot 3}$$

$$= \frac{3 \cdot 3 \cdot 5}{3 \cdot 3 \cdot 5} \cdot \frac{5}{2 \cdot 2 \cdot 2} = 1 \cdot \frac{5}{8} = \frac{5}{8}$$

Practice Exercise

7. Divide and simplify: $\dfrac{9}{4} \div \dfrac{45}{14}$.

Objective 3.7d Solve applied problems involving division of fractions.

Example A rental car had 18 gal of gasoline when its gas tank was $\frac{6}{7}$ full. How much could the tank hold when full?

The equation that corresponds to the situation is

$$\frac{6}{7} \cdot g = 18.$$

We divide by $\frac{6}{7}$ on both sides and carry out the division:

$$g = 18 \div \frac{6}{7} = \frac{18}{1} \cdot \frac{7}{6} = \frac{18 \cdot 7}{1 \cdot 6}$$

$$= \frac{3 \cdot 6 \cdot 7}{1 \cdot 6} = \frac{6}{6} \cdot \frac{3 \cdot 7}{1} = 1 \cdot \frac{21}{1} = 21.$$

The rental car can hold 21 gal of gasoline.

Practice Exercise

8. A flower vase has $\frac{7}{4}$ cups of water in it when it is $\frac{3}{4}$ full. How much can it hold when full?

Review Exercises

Find all the factors of each number. [3.1a]

1. 60   **2.** 176

3. Multiply by 1, 2, 3, and so on, to find ten multiples of 8. [3.1b]

4. Determine whether 924 is divisible by 11. [3.1b]

5. Determine whether 1800 is divisible by 16. [3.1b]

Determine whether each number is prime, composite, or neither. [3.1c]

6. 37   **7.** 1   **8.** 91

Find the prime factorization of each number. [3.1d]

9. 70   **10.** 30

11. 45   **12.** 150

13. 648   **14.** 5250

To do Exercises 15–22, consider the following numbers:

140	716	93	2802
95	2432	330	711
182	4344	255,555	
475	600	780	

Which of the above are divisible by the given number? [3.2a]

15. 3   **16.** 2

17. 4   **18.** 8

19. 5   **20.** 6

21. 9   **22.** 10

23. Identify the numerator and the denominator of $\frac{2}{7}$. [3.3a]

What part of each object is shaded? [3.3a]

24. **25.**

Copyright © 2015 Pearson Education, Inc.

26. What part of the set of objects is shaded? [3.3a]

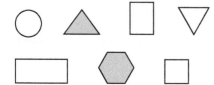

27. For a committee in the United States Senate that consists of 3 Democrats and 5 Republicans, what is the ratio of: [3.3a]
   a) Democrats to Republicans?
   b) Republicans to Democrats?
   c) Democrats to the total number of committee members?

Simplify. [3.3b], [3.5b]

28. $\dfrac{12}{30}$ **29.** $\dfrac{7}{28}$ **30.** $\dfrac{-23}{-23}$

31. $\dfrac{0}{-25}$ **32.** $\dfrac{1170}{1200}$ **33.** $\dfrac{18}{1}$

34. $\dfrac{9}{-27}$ **35.** $-\dfrac{88}{184}$ **36.** $\dfrac{18}{0}$

37. $\dfrac{48}{8}$ **38.** $\dfrac{140}{490}$ **39.** $-\dfrac{288}{2025}$

40. Simplify the fractions on this circle graph, if possible. [3.5b]

Museums in the United States

Science $\frac{15}{100}$

History $\frac{38}{100}$

Art $\frac{24}{100}$

Other $\frac{23}{100}$

Use $=$ or $\neq$ for $\square$ to write a true sentence. [3.5c]

41. $\dfrac{3}{5} \,\square\, \dfrac{4}{6}$ **42.** $\dfrac{-4}{7} \,\square\, -\dfrac{8}{14}$

43. $-\dfrac{4}{5} \,\square\, -\dfrac{5}{6}$ **44.** $\dfrac{4}{3} \,\square\, \dfrac{28}{21}$

Multiply and simplify. [3.4a], [3.6a]

45. $4 \cdot \dfrac{3}{8}$ **46.** $\dfrac{7}{3} \cdot 24$

47. $-9 \cdot \dfrac{5}{18}$ **48.** $\dfrac{6}{5} \cdot (-20)$

49. $\dfrac{3}{4} \cdot \dfrac{8}{9}$ **50.** $\dfrac{5}{7} \cdot \dfrac{1}{10}$

51. $-\dfrac{3}{7} \cdot \dfrac{14}{9}$ **52.** $\dfrac{1}{4} \cdot \dfrac{2}{11}$

53. $\dfrac{4}{25} \cdot \dfrac{15}{16}$ **54.** $-\dfrac{11}{3} \cdot \left(-\dfrac{30}{77}\right)$

Find the reciprocal. [3.7a]

55. $\dfrac{4}{5}$ **56.** -3

57. $\dfrac{1}{9}$ **58.** $-\dfrac{47}{36}$

Divide and simplify. [3.7b]

59. $6 \div \dfrac{4}{3}$ **60.** $-\dfrac{5}{9} \div \dfrac{5}{18}$

61. $\dfrac{1}{6} \div \dfrac{1}{11}$ **62.** $\dfrac{3}{14} \div \left(-\dfrac{6}{7}\right)$

63. $-\dfrac{1}{4} \div \left(-\dfrac{1}{9}\right)$ **64.** $180 \div \dfrac{3}{5}$

65. $\dfrac{23}{25} \div \dfrac{23}{25}$ **66.** $-\dfrac{2}{3} \div \left(-\dfrac{3}{2}\right)$

Solve. [3.7c]

67. $\dfrac{5}{4} \cdot t = \dfrac{3}{8}$ **68.** $x \cdot \dfrac{2}{3} = -160$

Solve. [3.6b], [3.7d]

69. A road crew repaves $\frac{1}{12}$ mi of road each day. How long will it take the crew to repave a $\frac{3}{4}$-mi stretch of road?

70. *Level of Education and Median Income.* The median yearly income of someone with an associate's degree is approximately $\frac{3}{4}$ of the median income of someone with a bachelor's degree. If the median income for those with bachelor's degrees is $42,780, what is the median income of those with associate's degrees?

Source: U.S. Census Bureau

71. After driving 600 km, the Youssi family has completed $\frac{3}{5}$ of their vacation. How long is the total trip?

72. Molly is making a pepper steak recipe that calls for $\frac{2}{3}$ cup of green bell peppers. How much would be needed to make $\frac{1}{2}$ recipe? 3 recipes?

73. Bernardo earns $105 for working a full day. How much does he receive for working $\frac{1}{7}$ of a day?

74. A book bag requires $\frac{4}{5}$ yd of fabric. How many bags can be made from 48 yd?

75. Solve: $\dfrac{2}{13} \cdot x = -\dfrac{1}{2}.$ [3.7c]

  A. $-\dfrac{1}{13}$ **B.** -13

  C. $-\dfrac{4}{13}$ **D.** $-\dfrac{13}{4}$

76. Multiply and simplify: $\dfrac{15}{26} \cdot \dfrac{13}{90}.$ [3.6a]

  A. $\dfrac{195}{234}$ **B.** $\dfrac{1}{12}$

  C. $\dfrac{3}{36}$ **D.** $\dfrac{13}{156}$

Synthesis

77. ▦ In the division below, find a and b. [3.7b]

$$\frac{19}{24} \div \frac{a}{b} = \frac{187{,}853}{268{,}224}$$

78. A prime number that remains a prime number when its digits are reversed is called a **palindrome prime**. For example, 17 is a palindrome prime because both 17 and 71 are primes. Which of the following numbers are palindrome primes? [3.1c]

  13, 91, 16, 11, 15, 24, 29, 101, 201, 37

Understanding Through Discussion and Writing

1. A student incorrectly insists that $\frac{2}{5} \div \frac{3}{4}$ is $\frac{15}{8}$. What mistake is he probably making? [3.7b]

2. Use the number 9432 to explain why the test for divisibility by 9 works. [3.2a]

3. A student claims that "taking $\frac{1}{2}$ of a number is the same as dividing by $\frac{1}{2}$." Explain the error in this reasoning. [3.7b]

4. On p. 149, we explained, using words and pictures, why $\frac{3}{5} \cdot \frac{3}{4}$ equals $\frac{9}{20}$. Present a similar explanation of why $\frac{2}{3} \cdot \frac{4}{7}$ equals $\frac{8}{21}$. [3.4a]

5. Without performing the division, explain why $5 \div \frac{1}{7}$ is a greater number than $5 \div \frac{2}{3}$. [3.5c], [3.7b]

6. If a fraction's numerator and denominator have no factors (other than 1) in common, can the fraction be simplified? Why or why not? [3.5b]

Copyright © 2015 Pearson Education, Inc.

For Extra Help For step-by-step test solutions, access the Chapter Test Prep Videos in MyMathLab® or on YouTube (search "BittingerBasicEI" and click on "Channels").

1. Find all the factors of 300.

Determine whether each number is prime, composite, or neither.

2. 41

3. 14

Find the prime factorization of the number.

4. 18

5. 60

6. Determine whether 1784 is divisible by 8.

7. Determine whether 784 is divisible by 9.

8. Determine whether 5552 is divisible by 5.

9. Determine whether 2322 is divisible by 6.

10. Identify the numerator and the denominator of $\frac{4}{5}$.

11. What part is shaded?

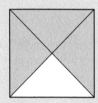

12. What part of the set is shaded?

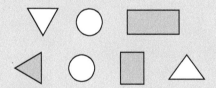

13. *Business Days.* There are approximately 259 business days in a 365-day year.

  a) What is the ratio of business days to days in the year?

  b) What is the ratio of nonbusiness days to days in the year?

Simplify.

14. $\dfrac{26}{1}$

15. $\dfrac{-12}{-12}$

16. $\dfrac{0}{16}$

17. $-\dfrac{12}{24}$

18. $\dfrac{42}{7}$

19. $\dfrac{9}{0}$

20. $\dfrac{7}{2-2}$

21. $-\dfrac{72}{108}$

Use = or ≠ for ☐ to write a true sentence.

22. $\dfrac{3}{4}$ ☐ $\dfrac{6}{8}$

23. $-\dfrac{5}{4}$ ☐ $-\dfrac{9}{7}$

Multiply and simplify.

24. $\dfrac{4}{3} \cdot 24$

25. $-5 \cdot \dfrac{3}{10}$

26. $\dfrac{2}{3} \cdot \dfrac{15}{4}$

27. $-\dfrac{22}{15} \cdot \left(-\dfrac{5}{33}\right)$

Find the reciprocal.

28. $\dfrac{5}{8}$

29. $-\dfrac{1}{4}$

30. 18

Divide and simplify.

31. $\dfrac{1}{5} \div \dfrac{1}{8}$

32. $12 \div \left(-\dfrac{2}{3}\right)$

33. $\dfrac{24}{5} \div \dfrac{28}{15}$

Solve.

34. $\dfrac{7}{8} \cdot x = -56$

35. $t \cdot \dfrac{2}{5} = \dfrac{7}{10}$

36. There are 7000 students at La Poloma College, and $\frac{5}{8}$ of them live in dorms. How many live in dorms?

37. A strip of taffy $\frac{9}{10}$ m long is cut into 12 equal pieces. What is the length of each piece?

38. A thermos of iced tea held 3 qt of tea when it was $\frac{3}{5}$ full. How much tea could it hold when full?

39. The pitch of a screw is $\frac{1}{8}$ in. How far will it go into a piece of walnut when it is turned 6 complete rotations?

40. In which figure does the shaded part represent $\frac{7}{6}$ of the figure?

A.

B.

C.

D.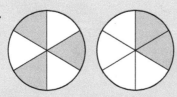

Synthesis

41. Grandma Hammons left $\frac{2}{3}$ of her $\frac{7}{8}$-acre apple farm to Karl. Karl gave $\frac{1}{4}$ of his share to his oldest daughter, Eileen. How much land did Eileen receive?

42. Simplify: $\left(\dfrac{3}{8}\right)^2 \div \dfrac{6}{7} \cdot \dfrac{2}{9} \div (-5)$.

184

Copyright © 2015 Pearson Education, Inc.

1. Write a word name: 7,453,062.

2. What does the digit 4 mean in 23,746,591?

Simplify.

3. $\dfrac{5}{1}$

4. $\dfrac{-17}{-17}$

5. $-\dfrac{56}{42}$

6. $\dfrac{32}{0}$

Find the reciprocal.

7. 8

8. $-\dfrac{3}{2}$

Calculate and simplify.

9. $4658 + 729$

10. $-3 + (-9)$

11. $5042 - 3658$

12. $-9 - 7$

13. $457 \cdot 36$

14. $-8 \cdot 12$

15. $-\dfrac{5}{6} \cdot 15$

16. $\dfrac{3}{7} \cdot \dfrac{14}{9}$

17. $10,846 \div 24$

18. $-56 \div (-7)$

19. $-\dfrac{4}{7} \div 28$

20. $\dfrac{3}{4} \div \dfrac{9}{16}$

21. $8^2 \div 8 \cdot 2 - (2 + 2 \cdot 7)$

22. $108 \div 9 - [3(18 - 5 \cdot 3)]$

23. $-20 - 10 \div 5 + 2^3$

24. $(8 - 10^2) \div (5^2 - 2)$

25. Find the average of four test scores of 85, 91, 80, and 88.

26. Round 165,739 to the nearest thousand.

Evaluate.

27. 9^2

28. 5^3

29. 2^4

Use either $<$ or $>$ for ☐ to write a true sentence.

30. -26 ☐ 2

31. 19 ☐ 17

Find the absolute value.

32. $|33|$ **33.** $|-86|$ **34.** $|0|$

Find the opposite, or additive inverse.

35. 29   **36.** -144

37. Evaluate $-(-x)$ when x is -7.

38. Graph 8 on the number line.

Determine whether each number is prime, composite, or neither.

39. 29   **40.** 1   **41.** 24

Find the prime factorization of each number.

42. 36   **43.** 135   **44.** 1350

45. Determine whether 6330 is divisible by 2; by 3; by 4; by 5; by 6; by 8; by 9; by 10.

Use $=$ or $\neq$ for ☐ to write a true sentence.

46. $\dfrac{5}{8}$ ☐ $\dfrac{7}{11}$ **47.** $-\dfrac{5}{4}$ ☐ $-\dfrac{20}{16}$

Solve.

48. $17 + x = 61$ **49.** $\dfrac{3}{5} \cdot y = -\dfrac{9}{25}$

50. *Halley's Comet.* Halley's Comet passes by Earth every 76 yr. It last appeared to people on Earth in 1986. When will it appear again?

Source: *The Cambridge Factfinder*

51. *Fundraiser.* To support a school fundraiser, Mary Ann bought 4 rolls of wrapping paper at $5 each and 2 candles at $8 each. Find the total cost of Mary Ann's order.

52. *Chemical Reaction.* The temperature of a chemical compound was 5°C at 9:00 A.M. During a reaction, it dropped 2°C per minute until 9:11 A.M. What was the temperature at 9:11 A.M.?

53. *Working Students.* An instructor determines that $\frac{2}{5}$ of the 35 students in her accounting class at Beckwith Community College have full-time jobs. How many students have full-time jobs?

Synthesis

54. Find a pair of factors whose product is 100 and:
   a) whose sum is 25.
   b) whose sum is -29.
   c) whose difference is 0.

Copyright © 2015 Pearson Education, Inc.

CHAPTER
4

Fraction Notation and Mixed Numerals

4.1 Least Common Multiples

4.2 Addition and Applications

4.3 Subtraction, Order, and Applications

Translating for Success

4.4 Mixed Numerals

Mid-Chapter Review

4.5 Addition and Subtraction Using Mixed Numerals; Applications

4.6 Multiplication and Division Using Mixed Numerals; Applications

Translating for Success

4.7 Order of Operations, Complex Fractions, and Estimation

Summary and Review

Test

Cumulative Review

STUDYING FOR SUCCESS   *Preparing for a Test*

☐ Make up your own test questions as you study.
☐ Do an overall review of the chapter focusing on the objectives and the examples.
☐ Do the exercises in the Mid-Chapter Review and in the end-of-chapter Review.
☐ Take the chapter test at the end of the chapter.

4.1   Least Common Multiples

OBJECTIVE

a Find the least common multiple, or LCM, of two or more numbers.

SKILL TO REVIEW

Objective 3.1b: Find some multiples of a number.

Multiply by 1, 2, 3, and so on, to find six multiples of each number.

1. 8   **2.** 25

When we want to add or subtract fractions, the fractions must share a common denominator. If necessary, we find equivalent fractions using the **least common denominator (LCD)**, or **least common multiple (LCM)** of the denominators.

a FINDING LEAST COMMON MULTIPLES

LEAST COMMON MULTIPLE, LCM

The **least common multiple**, or LCM, of two natural numbers is the smallest number that is a multiple of both numbers.

EXAMPLE 1   Find the LCM of 20 and 30.

First, we list some multiples of 20 by multiplying 20 by 1, 2, 3, and so on:

20, 40, 60, 80, 100, 120, 140, 160, 180, 200, 220, 240, ...

Then we list some multiples of 30 by multiplying 30 by 1, 2, 3, and so on:

30, 60, 90, 120, 150, 180, 210, 240, ...

Now we determine the smallest number *common* to both lists. The LCM of 20 and 30 is 60.

◀ Do Margin Exercise 1.

1. Find the LCM of 9 and 15 by examining lists of multiples.

Next, we develop three more efficient methods for finding LCMs. You may choose to learn only one method. (Consult with your instructor.) If you are going to study algebra, you should definitely learn method 2.

Method 1: Finding LCMs Using One List of Multiples

The first method for finding LCMs works especially well when the numbers are relatively small.

Method 1. To find the LCM of a set of numbers using a list of multiples:

a) Determine whether the largest number is a multiple of the others. If it is, it is the LCM. That is, if the largest number has the others as factors, the LCM is that number.

b) If not, check multiples of the largest number until you get one that is a multiple of each of the others.

Answers

Skill to Review:
1. 8, 16, 24, 32, 40, 48
2. 25, 50, 75, 100, 125, 150

Margin Exercise:
1. 45

EXAMPLE 2 Find the LCM of 12 and 15.

a) 15 is the larger number, but it is not a multiple of 12.

b) Check multiples of 15:

$2 \cdot 15 = 30,$ Not a multiple of 12

$3 \cdot 15 = 45,$ Not a multiple of 12

$4 \cdot 15 = 60.$ A multiple of 12: $5 \cdot 12 = 60$

The LCM $= 60$.

EXAMPLE 3 Find the LCM of 8 and 32.

32 is a multiple of 8 ($4 \cdot 8 = 32$), so the LCM $= 32$.

EXAMPLE 4 Find the LCM of 10, 20, and 50.

a) 50 is a multiple of 10 but not a multiple of 20.

b) Check multiples of 50:

$2 \cdot 50 = 100.$ A multiple of 10 and of 20:
$10 \cdot 10 = 100$ and $5 \cdot 20 = 100$

The LCM $= 100$.

Do Exercises 2–5.

Find the LCM.

2. 10, 15   **3.** 6, 8

4. 5, 10   **5.** 20, 45, 80

Method 2: Finding LCMs Using Prime Factorizations

A second method for finding LCMs uses prime factorizations. Consider again 20 and 30. Their prime factorizations are $20 = 2 \cdot 2 \cdot 5$ and $30 = 2 \cdot 3 \cdot 5$. Any multiple of 20 will have to have *two* 2's as factors and *one* 5 as a factor. Any multiple of 30 will need to have *one* 2, *one* 3, and *one* 5 as factors. The smallest number satisfying these conditions is

Two 2's, one 5; $2 \cdot 2 \cdot 3 \cdot 5$ is a multiple of 20.

$2 \cdot 2 \cdot 3 \cdot 5.$

One 2, one 3, one 5; $2 \cdot 2 \cdot 3 \cdot 5$ is a multiple of 30.

Thus the LCM of 20 and 30 is $2 \cdot 2 \cdot 3 \cdot 5$, or 60. It has all the factors of 20 and all the factors of 30, but the factors are not repeated when they are common to both numbers.

Note that each prime factor is used the greatest number of times that it occurs in either of the individual factorizations.

Method 2. To find the LCM of a set of numbers using prime factorizations:

a) Write the prime factorization of each number.

b) Create a product, using each prime factor the greatest number of times that it occurs in any one factorization.

EXAMPLE 5 Find the LCM of 6 and 8.

a) Write the prime factorization of each number.

$6 = 2 \cdot 3,$ $8 = 2 \cdot 2 \cdot 2$ The prime factors are 2's and 3's.

Answers

2. 30   **3.** 24   **4.** 10   **5.** 720

Use prime factorizations to find each LCM.

6. 8, 10

7. 18, 40   GS

a) $18 = 2 \cdot 3 \cdot$ ☐
   $40 = 2 \cdot 2 \cdot 2 \cdot$ ☐

b) Consider the factor 2. The greatest number of times that 2 occurs in any one factorization is ☐ times. Write 2 as a factor ☐ times.

   $2 \cdot 2 \cdot 2 \cdot ?$

   Consider the factor 3. The greatest number of times that 3 occurs in any one factorization is ☐ times. Write 3 as a factor ☐ times.

   $2 \cdot 2 \cdot 2 \cdot 3 \cdot 3 \cdot ?$

   Consider the factor 5. The greatest number of times that 5 occurs in any one factorization is ☐ time. Write 5 as a factor ☐ time.

   $2 \cdot 2 \cdot 2 \cdot 3 \cdot 3 \cdot 5$

   LCM = ☐

8. 32, 54

b) Create a product with the prime factors 2 and 3, using each the greatest number of times that it occurs in any one factorization.

Consider the factor 2. The greatest number of times that 2 occurs in any one factorization is three times. We write 2 as a factor three times.

$$2 \cdot 2 \cdot 2 \cdot ?$$

Consider the factor 3. The greatest number of times that 3 occurs in any one factorization is one time. We write 3 as a factor one time.

$$2 \cdot 2 \cdot 2 \cdot 3$$

Since there are no other prime factors in either factorization, the

LCM is $2 \cdot 2 \cdot 2 \cdot 3$, or 24.

EXAMPLE 6 Find the LCM of 24 and 36.

a) Write the prime factorization of each number.

$$24 = 2 \cdot 2 \cdot 2 \cdot 3, \qquad 36 = 2 \cdot 2 \cdot 3 \cdot 3 \qquad \text{The prime factors are 2's and 3's.}$$

b) Create a product with the prime factors 2 and 3, using each the greatest number of times that it occurs in any one factorization.

Consider the factor 2. The greatest number of times that 2 occurs in any one factorization is three times. We write 2 as a factor three times.

$$2 \cdot 2 \cdot 2 \cdot ?$$

Consider the factor 3. The greatest number of times that 3 occurs in any one factorization is two times. We write 3 as a factor two times.

$$2 \cdot 2 \cdot 2 \cdot 3 \cdot 3$$

Since there are no other prime factors in either factorization, the

LCM is $2 \cdot 2 \cdot 2 \cdot 3 \cdot 3$, or 72.

◀ Do Exercises 6–8.

EXAMPLE 7 Find the LCM of 81, 90, and 84.

a) Write the prime factorization of each number.

$$81 = 3 \cdot 3 \cdot 3 \cdot 3,$$
$$90 = 2 \cdot 3 \cdot 3 \cdot 5,$$
$$84 = 2 \cdot 2 \cdot 3 \cdot 7$$

The prime factors are 2's, 3's, 5's, and 7's.

b) Create a product with the prime factors 2, 3, 5, and 7, using each the greatest number of times that it occurs in any one factorization.

Consider the factor 2. The greatest number of times that 2 occurs in any one factorization is two times. We write 2 as a factor two times.

$$2 \cdot 2 \cdot ?$$

Consider the factor 3. The greatest number of times that 3 occurs in any one factorization is four times. We write 3 as a factor four times.

$$2 \cdot 2 \cdot 3 \cdot 3 \cdot 3 \cdot 3 \cdot ?$$

Answers

6. 40   **7.** 360   **8.** 864

Guided Solution:
7. (a) 3, 5; **(b)** three, three; two, two; one, one; 360

Consider the factor 5. The greatest number of times that 5 occurs in any one factorization is one time. We write 5 as a factor one time.

$$2 \cdot 2 \cdot 3 \cdot 3 \cdot 3 \cdot 3 \cdot 5 \cdot ?$$

Consider the factor 7. The greatest number of times that 7 occurs in any one factorization is one time. We write 7 as a factor one time.

$$2 \cdot 2 \cdot 3 \cdot 3 \cdot 3 \cdot 3 \cdot 5 \cdot 7$$

Since there are no other prime factors in any of the factorizations, the

LCM is $2 \cdot 2 \cdot 3 \cdot 3 \cdot 3 \cdot 3 \cdot 5 \cdot 7$, or 11,340.

Do Exercise 9. ▶

9. Find the LCM of 24, 35, and 45.

EXAMPLE 8   Find the LCM of 8 and 9.

We write the prime factorization of each number.

$$8 = 2 \cdot 2 \cdot 2, \qquad 9 = 3 \cdot 3$$

Note that the two numbers, 8 and 9, have no common prime factor. When this is the case, the LCM is just the product of the two numbers. Thus the LCM is $2 \cdot 2 \cdot 2 \cdot 3 \cdot 3$, or $8 \cdot 9$, or 72.

Find the LCM.

10. 4, 9

Do Exercises 10 and 11. ▶

11. 6, 25

EXAMPLE 9   Find the LCM of 7 and 21.

We write the prime factorization of each number. Because 7 is prime, it has no prime factorization.

$$7 = 7, \qquad 21 = 3 \cdot 7$$

Note that 7 is a factor of 21. We stated earlier that if one number is a factor of another, the LCM is the larger of the numbers. Thus the LCM is $7 \cdot 3$, or 21.

Find the LCM.

Do Exercises 12 and 13. ▶

12. 3, 18   **13.** 12, 24

Let's reconsider Example 7 using exponents. We write the prime factorizations of 81, 90, and 84 using exponential notation. The largest exponents indicate the greatest number of times that 2, 3, 5, and 7 occur as factors.

$$81 = 3 \cdot 3 \cdot 3 \cdot 3 = 3^4;$$ 4 is the largest exponent of 3 in any of the factorizations.

$$90 = 2 \cdot 3 \cdot 3 \cdot 5 = 2^1 \cdot 3^2 \cdot 5^1;$$ 1 is the largest exponent of 5 in any of the factorizations.

$$84 = 2 \cdot 2 \cdot 3 \cdot 7 = 2^2 \cdot 3^1 \cdot 7^1.$$ 2 is the largest exponent of 2 and 1 is the largest exponent of 7 in any of the factorizations.

Thus the LCM is $2^2 \cdot 3^4 \cdot 5^1 \cdot 7^1$, or 11,340.

EXAMPLE 10   Find the LCM of 25, 40, and 45 using exponential notation.

a) Write the prime factorization of each number.

$$25 = 5 \cdot 5 = 5^2,$$
$$40 = 2 \cdot 2 \cdot 2 \cdot 5 = 2^3 \cdot 5,$$
$$45 = 3 \cdot 3 \cdot 5 = 3^2 \cdot 5$$

Answers

9. 2520   **10.** 36   **11.** 150   **12.** 18   **13.** 24

b) Create a product with the prime factors 2, 3, and 5. Lining up all the powers of 2, all the powers of 3, and all the powers of 5 can help us construct the LCM.

$$25 = 5^2$$
$$40 = 2^3 \cdot 5$$
$$45 = 3^2 \cdot 5$$

The LCM is formed by choosing the greatest power of each factor, so the

$$\text{LCM} = 2^3 \cdot 3^2 \cdot 5^2 = 1800.$$

◀ **Do Exercises 14 and 15.**

14. Use exponents to find the LCM of 24, 35, and 45.

15. Redo Margin Exercises 6–8 using exponents.

Method 3: Finding LCMs Using Division by Primes

The third method is especially useful for finding the LCM of three or more numbers.

> *Method 3.* To find the LCM using division by primes:
>
> **a)** First look for any prime that divides at least two of the numbers with no remainder. Then divide, bringing down any numbers not divisible by the prime. If you cannot find a prime that divides at least two of the numbers, then the LCM is the product of the numbers.
>
> **b)** Repeat the process until you can divide no more—that is, until there are no two numbers divisible by the same prime.

EXAMPLE 11 Find the LCM of 48, 72, and 80.

We first look for any prime that divides any two of the numbers with no remainder. Then we divide. We repeat the process, bringing down any numbers not divisible by the prime, until we can divide no more—that is, until there are no two numbers divisible by the same prime:

```
2 | 48  72  80
3 | 24  36  40    ↓
2 |  8  12  40       40 is not divisible by 3.
2 |  4   6  20
2 |  2   3 |10
      1   3   5      3 is not divisible by 2.
```

No two of 1, 3, and 5 are divisible by the same prime. We stop here. The LCM is

$$2 \cdot 3 \cdot 2 \cdot 2 \cdot 2 \cdot 1 \cdot 3 \cdot 5, \quad \text{or} \quad 720.$$

EXAMPLE 12 Find the LCM of 12, 18, 21, and 40.

```
3 | 12  18  21  40  ↓
2 |  4   6   7 |40
2 |  2   3 | 7 |20
      1   3   7  10
```

No two of 1, 3, 7, and 10 are divisible by the same prime. We stop here. The LCM is $3 \cdot 2 \cdot 2 \cdot 1 \cdot 3 \cdot 7 \cdot 10$, or 2520.

◀ **Do Exercises 16–18.**

Find the LCM using division by primes.

16. 81, 90, 84

```
2 | 81  90  84
3 | 81
3 | 27
      9      14
```

The LCM is

$$2 \cdot 3 \cdot 3 \cdot 9 \cdot \boxed{} \cdot 14, \text{ or } \boxed{}.$$

17. 24, 35, 45

18. 12, 75, 80, 120

Answers

14. $2^3 \cdot 3^2 \cdot 5 \cdot 7$, or 2520   **15.** $2^3 \cdot 5$, or 40; $2^3 \cdot 3^2 \cdot 5$, or 360; $2^5 \cdot 3^3$, or 864   **16.** 11,340
17. 2520   **18.** 1200

Guided Solution:
16. 45, 42, 15, 14, 5; 5, 11,340

✓ Reading Check

Determine whether each statement is true or false.

_____ **RC1.** The least common denominator of two fractions is the LCM of their denominators.

_____ **RC2.** If one number is a multiple of a second number, the larger number is the LCM of the two numbers.

_____ **RC3.** If two numbers have no common prime factor, then the LCM of the numbers is their product.

_____ **RC4.** LCMs cannot be found using prime factorizations.

a   Find the LCM of each set of numbers.

1. 2, 4   **2.** 3, 15   **3.** 10, 25   **4.** 10, 15   **5.** 20, 40

6. 8, 12   **7.** 18, 27   **8.** 9, 11   **9.** 30, 50   **10.** 24, 36

11. 30, 40   **12.** 21, 27   **13.** 18, 24   **14.** 12, 18   **15.** 60, 70

16. 35, 45   **17.** 16, 36   **18.** 18, 20   **19.** 32, 36   **20.** 36, 48

21. 2, 3, 5   **22.** 3, 5, 7   **23.** 5, 18, 3   **24.** 6, 12, 18   **25.** 24, 36, 12

26. 8, 16, 22   **27.** 5, 12, 15   **28.** 12, 18, 40   **29.** 9, 12, 6   **30.** 8, 16, 12

31. 180, 100, 450, 60   **32.** 18, 30, 50, 48   **33.** 8, 48   **34.** 16, 32   **35.** 5, 50

36. 12, 72   **37.** 11, 13   **38.** 13, 14   **39.** 12, 35   **40.** 23, 25

41. 54, 63   **42.** 56, 72   **43.** 81, 90   **44.** 75, 100   **45.** 36, 54, 80

46. 22, 42, 51   **47.** 39, 91, 108, 26   **48.** 625, 75, 500, 25   **49.** 2000, 3000   **50.** 300, 4000

Applications of LCMs: Planet Orbits. Jupiter, Saturn, and Uranus all revolve around the sun. Jupiter takes 12 years, Saturn 30 years, and Uranus 84 years to make a complete revolution. On a certain night, you look at Jupiter, Saturn, and Uranus and wonder how many years it will take before they have the same position again. (*Hint*: To find out, you find the LCM of 12, 30, and 84. It will be that number of years.)

Source: *The Handy Science Answer Book*

51. How often will Jupiter and Saturn appear in the same direction in the night sky as seen from the earth?

52. How often will Jupiter and Uranus appear in the same direction in the night sky as seen from the earth?

53. How often will Saturn and Uranus appear in the same direction in the night sky as seen from the earth?

54. How often will Jupiter, Saturn, and Uranus appear in the same direction in the night sky as seen from the earth?

Skill Maintenance

55. Multiply and simplify: $\dfrac{6}{5} \cdot (-15)$.   [3.6a]

56. Divide: $7865 \div 132$.   [1.5a]

57. Divide and simplify: $\dfrac{4}{5} \div \dfrac{7}{10}$.   [3.7b]

58. Add: $23{,}456 + 5677 + 4002$.   [1.2a]

59. Multiply: 2118×3001.   [1.4a]

60. Subtract: $80{,}004 - 2305$.   [1.3a]

Synthesis

61. A pencil company uses two sizes of boxes, 5 in. by 6 in. and 5 in. by 8 in. These boxes are packed in bigger cartons for shipping. Find the width and the length of the smallest carton that will accommodate boxes of either size without any room left over. (Each carton can contain only one type of box and all boxes must point in the same direction.)

62. Consider 8 and 12. Determine whether each of the following is the LCM of 8 and 12. Tell why or why not.
  a) $2 \cdot 2 \cdot 3 \cdot 3$
  b) $2 \cdot 2 \cdot 3$
  c) $2 \cdot 3 \cdot 3$
  d) $2 \cdot 2 \cdot 2 \cdot 3$

Copyright © 2015 Pearson Education, Inc.

Addition and Applications

a ADDITION USING FRACTION NOTATION

Like Denominators

Addition using fraction notation corresponds to combining or putting like things together, just as addition with whole numbers does. For example,

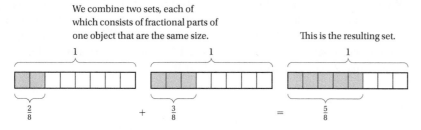

We combine two sets, each of which consists of fractional parts of one object that are the same size.

This is the resulting set.

$$\frac{2}{8} \qquad + \qquad \frac{3}{8} \qquad = \qquad \frac{5}{8}$$

2 eighths + 3 eighths = 5 eighths,

or $\quad 2 \cdot \frac{1}{8} + 3 \cdot \frac{1}{8} = 5 \cdot \frac{1}{8}, \quad$ or $\quad \frac{2}{8} + \frac{3}{8} = \frac{5}{8}.$

We see that to add when denominators are the same, we add the numerators and keep the denominator.

Do Margin Exercise 1. ▶

To add when denominators are the same,

a) add the numerators,
b) keep the denominator, and $\quad \dfrac{2}{6} + \dfrac{5}{6} = \dfrac{2+5}{6} = \dfrac{7}{6}$
c) simplify, if possible.

EXAMPLES Add and simplify.

1. $\dfrac{2}{4} + \dfrac{1}{4} = \dfrac{2+1}{4} = \dfrac{3}{4}$ No simplifying is possible.

2. $\dfrac{11}{6} + \dfrac{3}{6} = \dfrac{11+3}{6} = \dfrac{14}{6} = \dfrac{2 \cdot 7}{2 \cdot 3} = \dfrac{2}{2} \cdot \dfrac{7}{3} = 1 \cdot \dfrac{7}{3} = \dfrac{7}{3}$ Here we simplified.

3. $\dfrac{3}{12} + \dfrac{-5}{12} = \dfrac{3 + (-5)}{12} = \dfrac{-2}{12} = \dfrac{2 \cdot (-1)}{2 \cdot 6} = \dfrac{2}{2} \cdot \dfrac{-1}{6}$

$\qquad = 1 \cdot \dfrac{-1}{6} = \dfrac{-1}{6}, \text{ or } -\dfrac{1}{6} \quad$ Recall that $\dfrac{-a}{b} = -\dfrac{a}{b}.$

Do Exercises 2–5. ▶

Different Denominators

What do we do when denominators are different? We can find a common denominator by multiplying by 1. Consider adding $\frac{1}{6}$ and $\frac{3}{4}$. There are many common denominators that can be obtained. Let's look at two possibilities.

OBJECTIVES

a Add using fraction notation.

b Solve applied problems involving addition with fraction notation.

SKILL TO REVIEW

Objective 3.1d: Find the prime factorization of a composite number.

Find the prime factorization of each number.

1. 96   **2.** 1400

1. Find $\dfrac{1}{5} + \dfrac{3}{5}$.

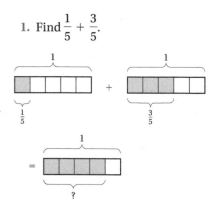

Add and simplify.

2. $\dfrac{5}{13} + \dfrac{9}{13}$ **3.** $\dfrac{1}{3} + \dfrac{2}{3}$

4. $\dfrac{5}{12} + \dfrac{1}{12}$ **5.** $\dfrac{9}{16} + \dfrac{-3}{16}$

Answers

Skill to Review:
1. $2 \cdot 2 \cdot 2 \cdot 2 \cdot 2 \cdot 3$ 2. $2 \cdot 2 \cdot 2 \cdot 5 \cdot 5 \cdot 7$

Margin Exercises:
1. $\dfrac{4}{5}$ 2. $\dfrac{14}{13}$ 3. 1   4. $\dfrac{1}{2}$ 5. $\dfrac{3}{8}$

A. $\dfrac{1}{6} + \dfrac{3}{4} = \dfrac{1}{6} \cdot 1 + \dfrac{3}{4} \cdot 1$

$\qquad\quad = \dfrac{1}{6} \cdot \dfrac{4}{4} + \dfrac{3}{4} \cdot \dfrac{6}{6}$

$\qquad\quad = \dfrac{4}{24} + \dfrac{18}{24}$

$\qquad\quad = \dfrac{22}{24}$

$\qquad\quad = \dfrac{11}{12} \qquad$ Simplifying

B. $\dfrac{1}{6} + \dfrac{3}{4} = \dfrac{1}{6} \cdot 1 + \dfrac{3}{4} \cdot 1$

$\qquad\quad = \dfrac{1}{6} \cdot \dfrac{2}{2} + \dfrac{3}{4} \cdot \dfrac{3}{3}$

$\qquad\quad = \dfrac{2}{12} + \dfrac{9}{12}$

$\qquad\quad = \dfrac{11}{12}$

We had to simplify at the end in (A) but not in (B). In (B), we used the least common multiple of the denominators, 12, as the common denominator. That number is called the **least common denominator**, or **LCD**. We may still need to simplify when using the LCD, but it is usually easier than when we use a larger common denominator.

> To add when denominators are different:
>
> **a)** Find the least common multiple of the denominators. That number is the least common denominator, LCD.
>
> **b)** Multiply by 1, using an appropriate notation, n/n, to express each number in terms of the LCD.
>
> **c)** Add the numerators, keeping the same denominator.
>
> **d)** Simplify, if possible.

EXAMPLE 4 Add: $\dfrac{3}{4} + \dfrac{1}{8}$.

The LCD is 8.   4 is a factor of 8, so the LCM of 4 and 8 is 8.

$\dfrac{3}{4} + \dfrac{1}{8} = \dfrac{3}{4} \cdot 1 + \dfrac{1}{8}$ $\leftarrow$ This fraction already has the LCD as its denominator.

$\qquad\quad = \dfrac{3}{4} \cdot \dfrac{2}{2} + \dfrac{1}{8}$ *Think:* $4 \times \square = 8$. The answer is 2, so we multiply by 1, using $\frac{2}{2}$.

$\qquad\quad = \dfrac{6}{8} + \dfrac{1}{8} = \dfrac{7}{8}$

EXAMPLE 5 Add: $\dfrac{1}{9} + \dfrac{5}{6}$.

The LCD is 18. $9 = 3 \cdot 3$ and $6 = 2 \cdot 3$, so the LCM of 9 and 6 is $2 \cdot 3 \cdot 3$, or 18.

$\dfrac{1}{9} + \dfrac{5}{6} = \dfrac{1}{9} \cdot 1 + \dfrac{5}{6} \cdot 1 = \dfrac{1}{9} \cdot \dfrac{2}{2} + \dfrac{5}{6} \cdot \dfrac{3}{3}$

Think: $6 \times \square = 18$. The answer is 3, so we multiply by 1 using $\frac{3}{3}$.

Think: $9 \times \square = 18$. The answer is 2, so we multiply by 1 using $\frac{2}{2}$.

$\qquad\quad = \dfrac{2}{18} + \dfrac{15}{18} = \dfrac{17}{18}$

◀ **Do Exercises 6 and 7.**

Add.

6. $\dfrac{2}{3} + \dfrac{1}{6}$

7. $\dfrac{3}{8} + \dfrac{5}{6}$ **GS**

The LCD is $\boxed{}$.

$\dfrac{3}{8} + \dfrac{5}{6} = \dfrac{3}{8} \cdot 1 + \dfrac{5}{6} \cdot 1$

$\qquad\quad = \dfrac{3}{8} \cdot \dfrac{3}{3} + \dfrac{5}{6} \cdot \dfrac{\square}{\square}$

$\qquad\quad = \dfrac{\square}{24} + \dfrac{\square}{24}$

$\qquad\quad = \dfrac{\square}{24}$

Answers

6. $\dfrac{5}{6}$ **7.** $\dfrac{29}{24}$

Guided Solution:

7. 24; $\dfrac{4}{4}$, 9, 20, 29

EXAMPLE 6 Add: $\dfrac{5}{9} + \dfrac{11}{18}$.

The LCD is 18.   9 is a factor of 18, so the LCM is 18.

$$\frac{5}{9} + \frac{11}{18} = \frac{5}{9} \cdot \frac{2}{2} + \frac{11}{18} = \frac{10}{18} + \frac{11}{18}$$

$$\left. \begin{array}{l} = \dfrac{21}{18} = \dfrac{3 \cdot 7}{3 \cdot 6} = \dfrac{3}{3} \cdot \dfrac{7}{6} \\[2mm] = \dfrac{7}{6} \end{array} \right\} \text{ Simplifying}$$

Do Exercise 8. ▶

8. Add: $\dfrac{1}{6} + \dfrac{7}{18}$.

EXAMPLE 7 Add: $\dfrac{1}{10} + \dfrac{3}{100} + \dfrac{-7}{1000}$.

Since 10 and 100 are factors of 1000, the LCD is 1000. Then

$$\frac{1}{10} + \frac{3}{100} + \frac{-7}{1000} = \frac{1}{10} \cdot \frac{100}{100} + \frac{3}{100} \cdot \frac{10}{10} + \frac{-7}{1000}$$

$$= \frac{100}{1000} + \frac{30}{1000} + \frac{-7}{1000} = \frac{100 + 30 + (-7)}{1000} = \frac{123}{1000}.$$

Do Exercise 9. ▶

9. Add: $\dfrac{4}{10} + \dfrac{-1}{100} + \dfrac{3}{1000}$.

EXAMPLE 8 Add: $\dfrac{13}{70} + \dfrac{11}{21} + \dfrac{8}{15}$.

We use prime factorizations to determine the LCM of 70, 21, and 15:

$$70 = 2 \cdot 5 \cdot 7, \qquad 21 = 3 \cdot 7, \qquad 15 = 3 \cdot 5.$$

The LCD is $2 \cdot 3 \cdot 5 \cdot 7$, or 210.

$$\frac{13}{70} + \frac{11}{21} + \frac{8}{15} = \frac{13}{2 \cdot 5 \cdot 7} \cdot \frac{3}{3} + \frac{11}{3 \cdot 7} \cdot \frac{2 \cdot 5}{2 \cdot 5} + \frac{8}{3 \cdot 5} \cdot \frac{7 \cdot 2}{7 \cdot 2}$$

↑   ↑   ↑

> The LCM of 70, 21, and 15 is $2 \cdot 3 \cdot 5 \cdot 7$. In each case, think of which factors are needed to get the LCD. Then multiply by 1 to obtain the LCD in each denominator.

$$= \frac{13 \cdot 3}{2 \cdot 5 \cdot 7 \cdot 3} + \frac{11 \cdot 2 \cdot 5}{3 \cdot 7 \cdot 2 \cdot 5} + \frac{8 \cdot 7 \cdot 2}{3 \cdot 5 \cdot 7 \cdot 2}$$

$$= \frac{39}{2 \cdot 3 \cdot 5 \cdot 7} + \frac{110}{2 \cdot 3 \cdot 5 \cdot 7} + \frac{112}{2 \cdot 3 \cdot 5 \cdot 7}$$

$$= \frac{261}{2 \cdot 3 \cdot 5 \cdot 7} = \frac{3 \cdot 3 \cdot 29}{2 \cdot 3 \cdot 5 \cdot 7} \quad \text{Factoring the numerator}$$

$$= \frac{3}{3} \cdot \frac{3 \cdot 29}{2 \cdot 5 \cdot 7} = \frac{3 \cdot 29}{2 \cdot 5 \cdot 7} = \frac{87}{70}$$

Add.

10. $\dfrac{7}{10} + \dfrac{2}{21} + \dfrac{6}{7}$

Do Exercises 10 and 11. ▶

11. $\dfrac{5}{18} + \dfrac{7}{24} + \dfrac{-11}{36}$

Answers

8. $\dfrac{5}{9}$ **9.** $\dfrac{393}{1000}$ **10.** $\dfrac{347}{210}$ **11.** $\dfrac{19}{72}$

b APPLICATIONS AND PROBLEM SOLVING

EXAMPLE 9 *Construction.* A contractor requires his subcontractors to use two layers of subflooring under a ceramic tile floor. First, the subcontractors install a $\frac{3}{4}$-in. layer of oriented strand board (OSB). Then a $\frac{1}{2}$-in. sheet of cement board is mortared to the OSB. The mortar is $\frac{1}{8}$-in. thick. What is the total thickness of the two installed subfloors?

1. **Familiarize.** We first make a drawing. We let T = the total thickness of the subfloors.

2. **Translate.** The problem can be translated to an equation as follows.

$$\underbrace{\frac{3}{4}}_{\text{OSB}} + \underbrace{\frac{1}{8}}_{\text{Mortar}} + \underbrace{\frac{1}{2}}_{\substack{\text{Cement}\\\text{board}}} = \underbrace{T}_{\substack{\text{Total}\\\text{thickness}}}$$

3. **Solve.** To solve the equation, we carry out the addition. The LCM of the denominators is 8 because 2 and 4 are factors of 8. We multiply by 1 in order to obtain the LCD:

$$\frac{3}{4} + \frac{1}{8} + \frac{1}{2} = T$$

$$\frac{3}{4} \cdot \frac{2}{2} + \frac{1}{8} + \frac{1}{2} \cdot \frac{4}{4} = T$$

$$\frac{6}{8} + \frac{1}{8} + \frac{4}{8} = T$$

$$\frac{11}{8} = T.$$

4. **Check.** We check by repeating the calculation. We also note that the sum should be larger than any of the individual measurements, which it is. This tells us that the answer is reasonable.

5. **State.** The total thickness of the installed subfloors is $\frac{11}{8}$ in.

◀ Do Exercise 12.

---

12. Catering. A caterer prepares a mixed berry salad with $\frac{7}{8}$ qt of strawberries, $\frac{3}{4}$ qt of raspberries, and $\frac{5}{16}$ qt of blueberries. What is the total amount of berries in the salad?

1. **Familiarize.** Let T = the total amount of berries in the salad.

2. **Translate.** To find the total amount, we add.

$$\frac{7}{\square} + \frac{3}{\square} + \frac{5}{\square} = T$$

3. **Solve.** The LCD is $\boxed{}$.

$$\frac{7}{8} \cdot \frac{2}{2} + \frac{3}{4} \cdot \frac{\square}{\square} + \frac{5}{16} = T$$

$$\frac{\square}{16} + \frac{\square}{16} + \frac{5}{16} = T$$

$$\frac{\square}{16} = T$$

4. **Check.** The answer is reasonable because it is larger than any of the individual amounts.

5. **State.** The salad contains a total of $\boxed{}$ qt of berries.

Answer

12. $\frac{31}{16}$ qt

Guided Solution:

12. 8, 4, 16; 16; $\frac{4}{4}$, 14, 12, 31; $\frac{31}{16}$

✓ Reading Check

Determine whether each statement is true or false.

_____ **RC1.** Before we can add two fractions, they must have the same denominator.

_____ **RC2.** To add fractions, we add numerators and add denominators.

_____ **RC3.** If we use the LCD to add fractions, we never need to simplify the result.

_____ **RC4.** Adding fractions with different denominators involves multiplying at least one fraction by 1.

a   Add and simplify.

1. $\dfrac{7}{8} + \dfrac{1}{8}$

2. $\dfrac{2}{5} + \dfrac{3}{5}$

3. $\dfrac{1}{8} + \dfrac{5}{8}$

4. $\dfrac{3}{10} + \dfrac{3}{10}$

5. $\dfrac{2}{3} + \dfrac{-5}{6}$

6. $\dfrac{-5}{6} + \dfrac{1}{9}$

7. $\dfrac{1}{8} + \dfrac{1}{6}$

8. $\dfrac{1}{6} + \dfrac{3}{4}$

9. $\dfrac{-4}{5} + \dfrac{7}{10}$

10. $\dfrac{3}{4} + \dfrac{-1}{12}$

11. $\dfrac{5}{12} + \dfrac{3}{8}$

12. $\dfrac{7}{8} + \dfrac{1}{16}$

13. $\dfrac{3}{20} + \dfrac{3}{4}$

14. $\dfrac{2}{15} + \dfrac{2}{5}$

15. $\dfrac{5}{6} + \dfrac{-7}{9}$

16. $\dfrac{5}{8} + \dfrac{-5}{6}$

17. $\dfrac{3}{10} + \dfrac{1}{100}$

18. $\dfrac{9}{10} + \dfrac{3}{100}$

19. $\dfrac{5}{12} + \dfrac{4}{15}$

20. $\dfrac{3}{16} + \dfrac{1}{12}$

21. $\dfrac{-9}{10} + \dfrac{99}{100}$

22. $\dfrac{-3}{10} + \dfrac{27}{100}$

23. $\dfrac{7}{8} + \dfrac{0}{1}$

24. $\dfrac{0}{1} + \dfrac{5}{6}$

25. $\dfrac{3}{8} + \dfrac{1}{6}$

26. $\dfrac{5}{8} + \dfrac{1}{6}$

27. $\dfrac{5}{12} + \dfrac{7}{24}$

28. $\dfrac{1}{18} + \dfrac{7}{12}$

29. $\dfrac{3}{16} + \dfrac{5}{16} + \dfrac{4}{16}$ **30.** $\dfrac{3}{8} + \dfrac{1}{8} + \dfrac{2}{8}$ **31.** $\dfrac{8}{10} + \dfrac{7}{100} + \dfrac{4}{1000}$ **32.** $\dfrac{1}{10} + \dfrac{2}{100} + \dfrac{3}{1000}$

33. $\dfrac{3}{8} + \dfrac{-7}{12} + \dfrac{8}{15}$ **34.** $\dfrac{1}{2} + \dfrac{-3}{8} + \dfrac{1}{4}$ **35.** $\dfrac{15}{24} + \dfrac{7}{36} + \dfrac{91}{48}$ **36.** $\dfrac{5}{7} + \dfrac{25}{52} + \dfrac{7}{4}$

   Solve.

37. *Riding a Segway®.* Tate rode a Segway® Personal Transporter $\frac{5}{6}$ mi to the library, then $\frac{3}{4}$ mi to class, and then $\frac{3}{2}$ mi to his part-time job. How far did he ride his Segway®?

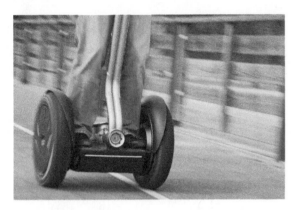

38. *Volunteering.* For a community project, an earth science class volunteered one hour per day for three days to join the state highway beautification project. The students collected trash along a $\frac{4}{5}$-mi stretch of highway the first day, a $\frac{5}{8}$-mi stretch the second day, and a $\frac{1}{2}$-mi stretch the third day. How many miles along the highway did they clean?

39. *Caffeine.* To cut back on their caffeine intake, Michelle and Gerry mix caffeinated and decaffeinated coffee beans before grinding for a customized mix. They mix $\frac{3}{16}$ lb of decaffeinated beans with $\frac{5}{8}$ lb of caffeinated beans. What is the total amount of coffee beans in the mixture?

40. *Purchasing Tea.* Alyse bought $\frac{1}{3}$ lb of orange pekoe tea and $\frac{1}{2}$ lb of English cinnamon tea. How many pounds of tea did she buy?

41. *Culinary Arts.* The campus culinary arts department is preparing brownies for the international student reception. Students in the catering program iced the $\frac{11}{16}$-in. $\left(\frac{11}{16}''\right)$ brownies with a $\frac{5}{32}$-in. $\left(\frac{5}{32}''\right)$ layer of butterscotch icing. What is the thickness of the iced brownie?

42. *Carpentry.* A carpenter glues two kinds of plywood together. He glues a $\frac{1}{4}$-in. $\left(\frac{1''}{4}\right)$ piece of cherry plywood to a $\frac{3}{8}$-in. $\left(\frac{3''}{8}\right)$ piece of less expensive plywood. What is the total thickness of these pieces?

43. A tile $\frac{5}{8}$ in. thick is glued to a board $\frac{7}{8}$ in. thick. The glue is $\frac{3}{32}$ in. thick. How thick is the result?

44. A baker used $\frac{1}{2}$ lb of flour for rolls, $\frac{1}{4}$ lb for donuts, and $\frac{1}{3}$ lb for cookies. How much flour was used?

Copyright © 2015 Pearson Education, Inc.

45. *Meteorology.* On Monday, April 15, it rained $\frac{1}{2}$ in. in the morning and $\frac{3}{8}$ in. in the afternoon. How much did it rain altogether?

46. *Medicine.* Janine took $\frac{1}{5}$ g of ibuprofen before lunch and $\frac{1}{2}$ g after lunch. How much did she take altogether?

47. *Hiking.* A park naturalist hiked $\frac{3}{5}$ mi to a lookout, another $\frac{3}{10}$ mi to an osprey's nest, and finally $\frac{3}{4}$ mi to a campsite. How far did the naturalist hike?

48. *Triathlon.* A triathlete runs $\frac{7}{8}$ mi, canoes $\frac{1}{3}$ mi, and swims $\frac{1}{6}$ mi. How many miles does the triathlete cover?

49. *Culinary Arts.* A recipe for strawberry punch calls for $\frac{1}{5}$ qt of ginger ale and $\frac{3}{5}$ qt of strawberry soda. How much liquid is needed? If the recipe is doubled, how much liquid is needed? If the recipe is halved, how much liquid is needed?

50. *Construction.* A cubic meter of concrete mix contains 420 kg of cement, 150 kg of stone, and 120 kg of sand. What is the total weight of a cubic meter of the mix? What part is cement? stone? sand? Add these fractional amounts. What is the result?

Skill Maintenance

51. *Serving of Cheesecake.* At the Cheesecake Factory, a piece of cheesecake is $\frac{1}{12}$ of cheesecake. How much of the cheesecake is $\frac{1}{2}$ piece? [3.6b]

Source: The Cheesecake Factory

52. *Milk Production.* Holstein's Dairy produced 4578 oz of milk one morning. How many 16-oz cartons could be filled? How much milk would be left over? [1.8a]

53. *Honey Production.* In 2011, 176,462,000 lb of honey was produced in the United States. The two states with the greatest honey production were North Dakota and California. North Dakota produced 46,410,000 lb of honey, and California produced 27,470,000 lb. How many more pounds of honey were produced in North Dakota than in California? [1.8a]

Source: U.S. Department of Agriculture

54. *Community Garden.* The Bingham community garden is to be split into 16 equally sized plots. If the garden occupies $\frac{3}{4}$ acre of land, how large will each plot be? [3.7d]

Synthesis

55. A guitarist's band is booked for Friday and Saturday nights at a local club. The guitarist is part of a trio on Friday and part of a quintet on Saturday. Thus the guitarist is paid one-third of one-half the weekend's pay for Friday and one-fifth of one-half the weekend's pay for Saturday. What fractional part of the band's pay did the guitarist receive for the weekend's work? If the band was paid $1200, how much did the guitarist receive?

OBJECTIVES

a Subtract using fraction notation.

b Use < or > with fraction notation to write a true sentence.

c Solve equations of the type $x + a = b$ and $a + x = b$, where a and b may be fractions.

d Solve applied problems involving subtraction with fraction notation.

SKILL TO REVIEW

Objective 1.6c: Use < or > for ☐ to write a true sentence in a situation like 6 ☐ 10.

Use < or > for ☐ to write a true sentence.

1. 218 ☐ 128

2. 41 ☐ 95

---

a SUBTRACTION USING FRACTION NOTATION

Like Denominators

Let's consider the difference $\frac{4}{8} - \frac{3}{8}$.

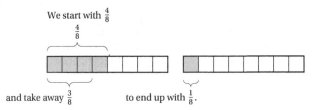

We start with $\frac{4}{8}$

$\frac{4}{8}$

and take away $\frac{3}{8}$ to end up with $\frac{1}{8}$.

We start with 4 eighths and take away 3 eighths:

$$4 \text{ eighths} - 3 \text{ eighths} = 1 \text{ eighth},$$

or $\quad 4 \cdot \frac{1}{8} - 3 \cdot \frac{1}{8} = \frac{1}{8}$, $\quad$ or $\quad \frac{4}{8} - \frac{3}{8} = \frac{1}{8}$.

To subtract when denominators are the same,

a) subtract the numerators,

b) keep the denominator, and

c) simplify, if possible.

$$\frac{7}{10} - \frac{4}{10} = \frac{7 - 4}{10} = \frac{3}{10}$$

EXAMPLES Subtract and simplify.

1. $\frac{32}{12} - \frac{25}{12} = \frac{32 - 25}{12} = \frac{7}{12}$

2. $\frac{7}{10} - \frac{3}{10} = \frac{7 - 3}{10} = \frac{4}{10} = \frac{2 \cdot 2}{5 \cdot 2} = \frac{2}{5} \cdot \frac{2}{2} = \frac{2}{5} \cdot 1 = \frac{2}{5}$

3. $\frac{25}{12} - \frac{32}{12} = \frac{25 - 32}{12} = \frac{-7}{12}$, or $-\frac{7}{12}$

◀ Do Margin Exercises 1–3.

Different Denominators

To subtract when denominators are different:

a) Find the least common multiple of the denominators. That number is the least common denominator, LCD.

b) Multiply by 1, using an appropriate notation, n/n, to express each number in terms of the LCD.

c) Subtract the numerators, keeping the same denominator.

d) Simplify, if possible.

Subtract and simplify.

1. $\frac{7}{8} - \frac{3}{8}$ $\qquad$ **2.** $\frac{10}{16} - \frac{4}{16}$

3. $\frac{3}{10} - \frac{8}{10}$

Answers

Skill to Review:
1. > $\quad$ **2.** <

Margin Exercises:
1. $\frac{1}{2}$ $\quad$ **2.** $\frac{3}{8}$ $\quad$ **3.** $-\frac{1}{2}$

EXAMPLE 4 Subtract: $\frac{2}{5} - \frac{3}{8}$.

The LCM of 5 and 8 is 40, so the LCD is 40.

$$\frac{2}{5} - \frac{3}{8} = \frac{2}{5} \cdot \frac{8}{8} - \frac{3}{8} \cdot \frac{5}{5} \leftarrow$$ *Think:* $8 \times \square = 40$. The answer is 5, so we multiply by 1, using $\frac{5}{5}$.

Think: $5 \times \square = 40$. The answer is 8, so we multiply by 1, using $\frac{8}{8}$.

$$= \frac{16}{40} - \frac{15}{40} = \frac{16 - 15}{40} = \frac{1}{40}$$

Do Exercise 4. ▶

4. Subtract: $\frac{3}{4} - \frac{2}{3}$.

EXAMPLE 5 Subtract: $\frac{7}{12} - \frac{5}{6}$.

Since 12 is a multiple of 6, the LCM of 6 and 12 is 12. The LCD is 12.

$$\frac{7}{12} - \frac{5}{6} = \frac{7}{12} - \frac{5}{6} \cdot \frac{2}{2}$$

$$= \frac{7}{12} - \frac{10}{12} = \frac{7 - 10}{12} = \frac{-3}{12}$$

$$= \frac{3 \cdot (-1)}{3 \cdot 4} = \frac{3}{3} \cdot \frac{-1}{4} = \frac{-1}{4}, \text{ or } -\frac{1}{4}$$

Do Exercises 5 and 6. ▶

Subtract.

GS 5. $\frac{5}{6} - \frac{1}{9}$

The LCD is $\boxed{}$.

$$\frac{5}{6} - \frac{1}{9} = \frac{5}{6} \cdot \frac{3}{3} - \frac{1}{9} \cdot \frac{\boxed{}}{\boxed{}}$$

$$= \frac{\boxed{}}{18} - \frac{\boxed{}}{18}$$

$$= \frac{\boxed{}}{18}$$

EXAMPLE 6 Subtract: $\frac{17}{24} - \frac{4}{15}$.

We use prime factorizations to determine the LCM of 24 and 15:

$$24 = 2 \cdot 2 \cdot 2 \cdot 3,$$
$$15 = 3 \cdot 5.$$

The LCD is $2 \cdot 2 \cdot 2 \cdot 3 \cdot 5$, or 120.

$$\frac{17}{24} - \frac{4}{15} = \frac{17}{2 \cdot 2 \cdot 2 \cdot 3} \cdot \frac{5}{5} - \frac{4}{3 \cdot 5} \cdot \frac{2 \cdot 2 \cdot 2}{2 \cdot 2 \cdot 2}$$

The LCM of 24 and 15 is $2 \cdot 2 \cdot 2 \cdot 3 \cdot 5$. In each case, we multiply by 1 to obtain the LCD.

6. $\frac{3}{10} - \frac{4}{5}$

$$= \frac{17 \cdot 5}{2 \cdot 2 \cdot 2 \cdot 3 \cdot 5} - \frac{4 \cdot 2 \cdot 2 \cdot 2}{3 \cdot 5 \cdot 2 \cdot 2 \cdot 2}$$

$$= \frac{85}{120} - \frac{32}{120} = \frac{53}{120}$$

Do Exercise 7. ▶

7. Subtract: $\frac{11}{28} - \frac{5}{16}$.

b ORDER

When two fractions share a common denominator, the fractions can be compared by comparing numerators.

Since $4 > 3$, $\frac{4}{5} > \frac{3}{5}$.

$\frac{4}{5}$ [bar diagram]

Since $3 < 4$, $\frac{3}{5} < \frac{4}{5}$.

$\frac{3}{5}$ [bar diagram]

Answers

4. $\frac{1}{12}$ **5.** $\frac{13}{18}$ **6.** $-\frac{1}{2}$ **7.** $\frac{9}{112}$

Guided Solution:

5. $18; \frac{2}{2}, 15, 2, 13$

8. Use < or > for ☐ to write a true sentence:

$$\frac{3}{8} \,\square\, \frac{5}{8}.$$

9. Use < or > for ☐ to write a true sentence:

$$\frac{7}{10} \,\square\, \frac{6}{10}.$$

Use < or > for ☐ to write a true sentence.

10. $\dfrac{2}{3} \,\square\, \dfrac{5}{8}$

11. $\dfrac{-3}{4} \,\square\, \dfrac{-8}{12}$

12. $\dfrac{5}{6} \,\square\, \dfrac{7}{8}$

The LCD is ☐.

$$\frac{5}{6} = \frac{\square}{24}$$

$$\frac{7}{8} = \frac{\square}{24}$$

Since 20 ☐ 21, it follows that

$$\frac{20}{24} \,\square\, \frac{21}{24}.$$

Thus, $\dfrac{5}{6} \,\square\, \dfrac{7}{8}.$

To compare two fractions that have a common denominator, compare the numerators:

$$\frac{6}{7} > \frac{2}{7}; \qquad \frac{2}{7} < \frac{6}{7}.$$

◀ **Do Exercises 8 and 9.**

When denominators are different, we cannot compare numerators until we multiply by 1 to make the denominators the same.

EXAMPLE 7 Use < or > for ☐ to write a true sentence:

$$\frac{2}{5} \,\square\, \frac{3}{4}.$$

The LCD is 20. We have

$$\frac{2}{5} \cdot \frac{4}{4} = \frac{8}{20}; \qquad \text{We multiply by 1 using } \frac{4}{4} \text{ to get the LCD.}$$

$$\frac{3}{4} \cdot \frac{5}{5} = \frac{15}{20}. \qquad \text{We multiply by 1 using } \frac{5}{5} \text{ to get the LCD.}$$

Now that the denominators are the same, 20, we can compare the numerators. Since $8 < 15$, it follows that $\frac{8}{20} < \frac{15}{20}$, so

$$\frac{2}{5} < \frac{3}{4}.$$

EXAMPLE 8 Use < or > for ☐ to write a true sentence:

$$\frac{-89}{100} \,\square\, \frac{-9}{10}.$$

The LCD is 100. We write $\frac{-9}{10}$ with a denominator of 100 to make the denominators the same.

$$\frac{-9}{10} \cdot \frac{10}{10} = \frac{-90}{100} \qquad \text{We multiply by } \frac{10}{10} \text{ to get the LCD.}$$

Since $-89 > -90$, it follows that $\frac{-89}{100} > \frac{-90}{100}$, so

$$\frac{-89}{100} > \frac{-9}{10}.$$

◀ **Do Exercises 10–12.**

C SOLVING EQUATIONS

Now let's solve equations of the form $x + a = b$ or $a + x = b$, where a and b may be fractions. Proceeding as we have before, we subtract a on both sides of the equation.

Answers

8. < **9.** > **10.** > **11.** < **12.** <

Guided Solution:
12. 24; 20, 21; <, <; <

EXAMPLE 9 Solve: $x + \dfrac{1}{4} = -\dfrac{3}{5}$.

$$x + \frac{1}{4} - \frac{1}{4} = -\frac{3}{5} - \frac{1}{4} \qquad \text{Subtracting } \tfrac{1}{4} \text{ on both sides}$$

$$x + 0 = -\frac{3}{5} \cdot \frac{4}{4} - \frac{1}{4} \cdot \frac{5}{5} \qquad \begin{array}{l}\text{The LCD is 20. We multiply by}\\ \text{1 to get the LCD.}\end{array}$$

$$x = -\frac{12}{20} - \frac{5}{20}$$

$$x = -\frac{7}{20}$$

Do Exercises 13 and 14. ▶

Solve.

13. $x + \dfrac{2}{3} = \dfrac{5}{6}$ 14. $\dfrac{3}{5} + t = -\dfrac{7}{8}$

d APPLICATIONS AND PROBLEM SOLVING

EXAMPLE 10 *Phases of the Moon.* The moon rotates in such a way that the same side always faces the earth. Throughout a lunar cycle, the portion of the moon that appears illuminated increases from nearly none (new moon) to nearly all (full moon), then decreases back to nearly none. These *phases* of the moon can be described by fractions between 0 and 1, indicating the portion of the moon illuminated. The partial calendar from August 2013 shows the fraction of the moon illuminated at midnight, Eastern Standard Time, for each day.

How much more of the moon appeared illuminated on August 18, 2013, than on August 15, 2013?

1. **Familiarize.** From the calendar, we see that $\frac{3}{5}$ of the moon was illuminated on August 15 and that $\frac{17}{20}$ of the moon was illuminated on August 18. We let $m =$ the additional part of the moon that appeared illuminated on August 18.

2. **Translate.** We translate to an equation.

SOURCE: Astronomical Applications Department, U.S. Naval Observatory, Washington, DC 20392-5420

Amount illuminated on August 15	plus	Additional amount illuminated	is	Amount illuminated on August 18
↓	↓	↓	↓	↓
$\dfrac{3}{5}$	$+$	m	$=$	$\dfrac{17}{20}$

3. **Solve.** To solve the equation, we subtract $\frac{3}{5}$ on both sides:

$$\frac{3}{5} + m = \frac{17}{20}$$

$$\frac{3}{5} + m - \frac{3}{5} = \frac{17}{20} - \frac{3}{5} \qquad \text{Subtracting } \tfrac{3}{5} \text{ on both sides}$$

$$m + 0 = \frac{17}{20} - \frac{3}{5} \cdot \frac{4}{4} \qquad \begin{array}{l}\text{The LCD is 20. We multiply by 1}\\ \text{to obtain the LCD.}\end{array}$$

$$m = \frac{17}{20} - \frac{12}{20} = \frac{5}{20} = \frac{5 \cdot 1}{5 \cdot 4} = \frac{5}{5} \cdot \frac{1}{4} = \frac{1}{4}.$$

4. **Check.** To check, we add:

$$\frac{3}{5} + \frac{1}{4} = \frac{3}{5} \cdot \frac{4}{4} + \frac{1}{4} \cdot \frac{5}{5} = \frac{12}{20} + \frac{5}{20} = \frac{17}{20}.$$

5. **State.** On August 18, $\frac{1}{4}$ more of the moon was illuminated than on August 15.

Do Exercise 15. ▶

15. *Phases of the Moon.* Use the calendar in Example 10 to find how much less of the moon appeared illuminated on August 31, 2013, than on August 23, 2013.

Answers

13. $\dfrac{1}{6}$ 14. $-\dfrac{59}{40}$ 15. $\dfrac{71}{100}$

Translating for Success

1. *Packaging.* One-Stop Postal Center orders bubble wrap in 64-yd rolls. On average, $\frac{3}{4}$ yd is used per small package. How many small packages can be prepared with 2 rolls of bubble wrap?

2. *Distance from College.* The post office is $\frac{7}{9}$ mi from the community college. The medical clinic is $\frac{2}{5}$ as far from the college as the post office is. How far is the clinic from the college?

3. *Swimming.* Andrew swims $\frac{7}{9}$ mi every day. One day he swims $\frac{2}{5}$ mi by 11:00 A.M. How much farther must Andrew swim to reach his daily goal?

4. *Tuition.* The average tuition at Waterside University is $12,000. If a loan is obtained for $\frac{1}{3}$ of the tuition, how much is the loan?

5. *Thermos Bottle Capacity.* A thermos bottle holds $\frac{11}{12}$ gal. How much is in the bottle when it is $\frac{4}{7}$ full?

The goal of these matching questions is to practice step (2), Translate, of the five-step problem-solving process. Translate each word problem to an equation and select a correct translation from equations A–O.

A. $\frac{3}{4} \cdot 64 = x$

B. $\frac{1}{3} \cdot 12,000 = x$

C. $\frac{1}{3} + \frac{2}{5} = x$

D. $\frac{2}{5} + x = \frac{7}{9}$

E. $\frac{2}{5} \cdot \frac{7}{9} = x$

F. $\frac{3}{4} \cdot x = 64$

G. $\frac{4}{7} = x + \frac{11}{12}$

H. $\frac{2}{5} = x + \frac{7}{9}$

I. $\frac{4}{7} \cdot \frac{11}{12} = x$

J. $\frac{3}{4} \cdot x = 128$

K. $\frac{1}{3} \cdot x = 12,000$

L. $\frac{1}{3} + \frac{2}{5} + x = 1$

M. $\frac{4}{3} \cdot 64 = x$

N. $\frac{4}{7} + x = \frac{11}{12}$

O. $\frac{1}{3} + x = \frac{2}{5}$

Answers on page A-6

6. *Cutting Rope.* A piece of rope $\frac{11}{12}$ yd long is cut into two pieces. One piece is $\frac{4}{7}$ yd long. How long is the other piece?

7. *Planting Corn.* Each year, Prairie State Farm plants 64 acres of corn. With good weather, $\frac{3}{4}$ of the planting can be completed by April 20. How many acres can be planted by April 20 with good weather?

8. *Painting Trim.* A painter used $\frac{1}{3}$ gal of white paint for the trim in the library and $\frac{2}{5}$ gal in the family room. How much paint was used for the trim in the two rooms?

9. *Lottery Winnings.* Sally won $12,000 in a state lottery and decided to give the net amount after taxes to three charities. One received $\frac{1}{3}$ of the net amount, and a second received $\frac{2}{5}$. What fractional part of the net amount did the third charity receive?

10. *Reading Assignment.* When Lowell had read 64 pages of his political science assignment, he had completed $\frac{3}{4}$ of his required reading. How many total pages were assigned?

✓ Reading Check

Complete each statement with the appropriate word or words from the following list. A word may be used more than once or not at all.

denominator   numerator
denominators   numerators

RC1. To subtract fractions with like denominators, we subtract the _____ and keep the _____.

RC2. To subtract fractions when denominators are different, we find the LCM of the _____.

RC3. To subtract fractions when denominators are different, we multiply one or both fractions by 1 to make the _____ the same.

RC4. To compare two fractions with like denominators, we compare their _____.

a   Subtract and simplify.

1. $\dfrac{5}{6} - \dfrac{1}{6}$ **2.** $\dfrac{5}{8} - \dfrac{3}{8}$ **3.** $\dfrac{11}{12} - \dfrac{2}{12}$ **4.** $\dfrac{17}{18} - \dfrac{11}{18}$ **5.** $\dfrac{1}{8} - \dfrac{3}{4}$ **6.** $\dfrac{1}{9} - \dfrac{2}{3}$

7. $\dfrac{1}{8} - \dfrac{1}{12}$ **8.** $\dfrac{1}{6} - \dfrac{1}{8}$ **9.** $\dfrac{5}{6} - \dfrac{4}{3}$ **10.** $\dfrac{1}{16} - \dfrac{7}{8}$ **11.** $\dfrac{3}{4} - \dfrac{3}{28}$ **12.** $\dfrac{2}{5} - \dfrac{2}{15}$

13. $\dfrac{3}{4} - \dfrac{3}{20}$ **14.** $\dfrac{5}{6} - \dfrac{1}{2}$ **15.** $\dfrac{1}{20} - \dfrac{3}{4}$ **16.** $\dfrac{4}{16} - \dfrac{3}{4}$ **17.** $\dfrac{5}{12} - \dfrac{2}{15}$ **18.** $\dfrac{9}{10} - \dfrac{11}{16}$

19. $\dfrac{6}{10} - \dfrac{7}{100}$ **20.** $\dfrac{9}{10} - \dfrac{3}{100}$ **21.** $\dfrac{7}{15} - \dfrac{3}{25}$ **22.** $\dfrac{18}{25} - \dfrac{4}{35}$ **23.** $\dfrac{99}{100} - \dfrac{9}{10}$ **24.** $\dfrac{78}{100} - \dfrac{11}{20}$

25. $-\dfrac{2}{3} - \dfrac{1}{8}$ **26.** $-\dfrac{3}{4} - \dfrac{1}{2}$ **27.** $\dfrac{3}{5} - \dfrac{1}{2}$ **28.** $\dfrac{5}{6} - \dfrac{2}{3}$ **29.** $\dfrac{3}{8} - \dfrac{5}{12}$ **30.** $\dfrac{2}{9} - \dfrac{7}{12}$

31. $\dfrac{7}{8} - \dfrac{1}{16}$ **32.** $\dfrac{5}{12} - \dfrac{5}{16}$ **33.** $\dfrac{4}{15} - \dfrac{17}{25}$ **34.** $\dfrac{7}{24} - \dfrac{11}{18}$ **35.** $\dfrac{23}{25} - \dfrac{112}{150}$ **36.** $\dfrac{89}{90} - \dfrac{53}{120}$

Use $<$ or $>$ for ☐ to write a true sentence.

37. $\dfrac{5}{8}$ ☐ $\dfrac{6}{8}$ **38.** $\dfrac{7}{9}$ ☐ $\dfrac{5}{9}$ **39.** $\dfrac{1}{3}$ ☐ $\dfrac{1}{4}$ **40.** $\dfrac{1}{8}$ ☐ $\dfrac{1}{6}$ **41.** $\dfrac{-5}{7}$ ☐ $\dfrac{-2}{3}$

42. $\dfrac{-4}{7}$ ☐ $\dfrac{-3}{5}$ **43.** $\dfrac{4}{5}$ ☐ $\dfrac{5}{6}$ **44.** $\dfrac{3}{2}$ ☐ $\dfrac{7}{5}$ **45.** $\dfrac{-4}{5}$ ☐ $\dfrac{-19}{20}$ **46.** $\dfrac{5}{6}$ ☐ $\dfrac{13}{16}$

47. $\dfrac{19}{20}$ ☐ $\dfrac{9}{10}$ **48.** $\dfrac{3}{4}$ ☐ $\dfrac{11}{15}$ **49.** $\dfrac{-41}{13}$ ☐ $\dfrac{-31}{21}$ **50.** $\dfrac{-132}{49}$ ☐ $\dfrac{-12}{7}$

c Solve.

51. $x + \dfrac{1}{30} = \dfrac{1}{10}$ **52.** $y + \dfrac{9}{12} = \dfrac{11}{12}$ **53.** $\dfrac{2}{3} + t = -\dfrac{4}{5}$

54. $\dfrac{2}{3} + p = -\dfrac{7}{8}$ **55.** $x + \dfrac{1}{3} = \dfrac{5}{6}$ **56.** $m + \dfrac{5}{6} = \dfrac{9}{10}$

d Solve.

57. For a research paper, Kaitlyn spent $\frac{3}{4}$ hr searching the Internet on google.com and $\frac{1}{3}$ hr on chacha.com. How many more hours did she spend on google.com than on chacha.com?

58. As part of a fitness program, Deb swims $\frac{1}{2}$ mi every day. One day she had already swum $\frac{1}{5}$ mi. How much farther should Deb swim?

59. The tread depth of an IRL Indy Car Series tire is $\frac{3}{32}$ in. Tires for a normal car have a tread depth of $\frac{5}{16}$ in. when new and are considered bald at $\frac{1}{16}$ in. How much deeper is the tread depth of an Indy Car tire than that of a bald tire for a normal car?

Sources: Indy500.com; *Consumer Reports*

60. Gerry uses $\frac{1}{3}$ lb of fresh mozzarella cheese and $\frac{1}{4}$ lb of grated Parmesan cheese on a homemade margherita pizza. How much more mozzarella cheese does he use than Parmesan cheese?

$\frac{3}{32}$ in.

61. From a $\frac{4}{5}$-lb wheel of cheese, a $\frac{1}{4}$-lb piece was served. How much cheese remained on the wheel?

62. A baker has a dispenser containing $\frac{15}{16}$ cup of icing and puts $\frac{1}{12}$ cup on a cinnamon roll. How much icing remains in the dispenser?

Copyright © 2015 Pearson Education, Inc.

63. At a party, three friends, Ashley, Cole, and Lauren, shared a big tub of popcorn. Within 30 min, the tub was empty. Ashley ate $\frac{7}{12}$ of the tub while Lauren ate only $\frac{1}{6}$ of the tub. How much did Cole eat?

64. A small community garden was divided among four local residents. Based on the time they could spend on their garden sections and their individual crop plans, each resident received a different-size plot to tend. One received $\frac{1}{4}$ of the garden, the second $\frac{1}{16}$, and the third $\frac{3}{8}$ of the garden. How much did the fourth gardener receive?

Skill Maintenance

Divide, if possible. If not possible, write "not defined."   [1.5a], [3.3b]

65. $\dfrac{-38}{-38}$

66. $\dfrac{38}{0}$

67. $\dfrac{124}{0}$

68. $\dfrac{124}{31}$

Divide and simplify.   [3.7b]

69. $\dfrac{3}{7} \div \left(-\dfrac{9}{4}\right)$

70. $-\dfrac{9}{10} \div \left(-\dfrac{3}{5}\right)$

71. $7 \div \dfrac{1}{3}$

72. $\dfrac{1}{4} \div 8$

Multiply and simplify.   [3.6a]

73. $18 \cdot \dfrac{2}{3}$

74. $\dfrac{5}{12} \cdot (-6)$

75. $\dfrac{7}{10} \cdot \dfrac{5}{14}$

76. $\left(-\dfrac{1}{10}\right) \cdot \left(-\dfrac{20}{5}\right)$

Synthesis

Solve.

77. ▦ $x + \dfrac{16}{323} = \dfrac{10}{187}$

78. ▦ $x + \dfrac{7}{253} = \dfrac{12}{299}$

79. As part of a rehabilitation program, an athlete must swim and then walk a total of $\frac{9}{10}$ km each day. If one lap in the swimming pool is $\frac{3}{80}$ km, how far must the athlete walk after swimming 10 laps?

80. *Mountain Climbing.* A mountain climber, beginning at sea level, climbs $\frac{3}{5}$ km, descends $\frac{1}{4}$ km, climbs $\frac{1}{3}$ km, and then descends $\frac{1}{7}$ km. At what elevation does the climber finish?

Simplify. Use the rules for order of operations.

81. $\dfrac{7}{8} - \dfrac{1}{10} \times \dfrac{5}{6}$

82. $\dfrac{2}{5} + \dfrac{1}{6} \div 3$

83. $\left(\dfrac{2}{3}\right)^2 - \left(\dfrac{3}{4}\right)^2$

84. $-5 \times \dfrac{3}{7} - \dfrac{1}{7} \times \dfrac{4}{5}$

Use $<$, $>$, or $=$ for ☐ to write a true sentence.

85. ▦ $\dfrac{37}{157} + \dfrac{19}{107}$ ☐ $\dfrac{6941}{16{,}799}$

86. ▦ $\dfrac{12}{97} + \dfrac{67}{139}$ ☐ $\dfrac{8167}{13{,}289}$

87. *Microsoft Interview.*   The following is a question taken from an employment interview with Microsoft. Try to answer it. "Given a gold bar that can be cut exactly twice and a contractor who must be paid one-seventh of a gold bar every day for seven days, how should the bar be cut?"

Source: *Fortune Magazine*, January 8, 2001

OBJECTIVES

a Convert between mixed numerals and fraction notation.

b Divide whole numbers, writing the quotient as a mixed numeral.

SKILL TO REVIEW

Objective 1.5a: Divide whole numbers.

Divide.

1. $735 \div 16$

2. $23\overline{)6023}$

a MIXED NUMERALS

The following figure illustrates the use of a **mixed numeral**. The bolt shown is $2\frac{3}{8}$ in. long. The length is given as a whole-number part, 2, and a fractional part less than 1, $\frac{3}{8}$. We can also represent the measurement of the bolt with fraction notation as $\frac{19}{8}$, but the meaning or interpretation of such a symbol is less understandable or less easy to visualize than that of mixed numeral notation.

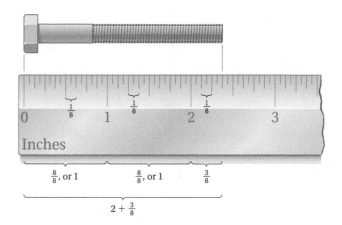

A mixed numeral like $2\frac{3}{8}$ represents a sum:

$$2\frac{3}{8} \quad \text{means} \quad 2 + \frac{3}{8}.$$

This is a whole number.   This is a fraction less than 1.

EXAMPLES Convert to a mixed numeral.

1. $7 + \frac{2}{5} = 7\frac{2}{5}$

2. $4 + \frac{3}{10} = 4\frac{3}{10}$

◀ Do Margin Exercises 1–3.

The notation $2\frac{3}{4}$ has a plus sign left out. To aid in understanding, we sometimes write the missing plus sign. This is especially helpful when we convert a mixed numeral to fraction notation.

EXAMPLES Convert to fraction notation.

3. $2\frac{3}{4} = 2 + \frac{3}{4}$ Inserting the missing plus sign

$\phantom{2\frac{3}{4}} = \frac{2}{1} + \frac{3}{4}$ $2 = \frac{2}{1}$

$\phantom{2\frac{3}{4}} = \frac{2}{1} \cdot \frac{4}{4} + \frac{3}{4}$ Finding a common denominator

$\phantom{2\frac{3}{4}} = \frac{8}{4} + \frac{3}{4} = \frac{11}{4}$

Convert to a mixed numeral.

1. $1 + \frac{2}{3} = \square\dfrac{\square}{\square}$

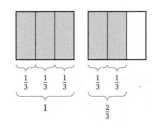

2. $2 + \frac{3}{4} = \square\dfrac{\square}{\square}$

3. $12 + \frac{2}{7}$

Answers

Skill to Review:
1. 45 R 15   **2.** 261 R 20

Margin Exercises:
1. $1\frac{2}{3}$ **2.** $2\frac{3}{4}$ **3.** $12\frac{2}{7}$

4. $4\frac{3}{10} = 4 + \frac{3}{10} = \frac{4}{1} + \frac{3}{10} = \frac{4}{1} \cdot \frac{10}{10} + \frac{3}{10} = \frac{40}{10} + \frac{3}{10} = \frac{43}{10}$

Do Exercises 4 and 5. ▶

Let's now consider a faster method for converting a mixed numeral to fraction notation.

> **To convert from a positive mixed numeral to fraction notation:**
>
> ⓐ Multiply the whole number by the denominator: $4 \cdot 10 = 40$.
>
> ⓑ Add the result to the numerator: $40 + 3 = 43$.
>
> ⓒ Keep the denominator.
>
> ⓑ ⟶ $4\frac{3}{10} = \frac{43}{10}$ ⟵ ⓒ
> ⓐ ↩

EXAMPLES Convert to fraction notation.

5. $6\frac{2}{3} = \frac{20}{3}$ $6 \cdot 3 = 18, 18 + 2 = 20$

6. $8\frac{2}{9} = \frac{74}{9}$ $8 \cdot 9 = 72, 72 + 2 = 74$ ▪

To convert a negative mixed numeral to fraction notation, we proceed as follows.

EXAMPLE 7 Convert to fraction notation: $-10\frac{7}{8}$.

$$-10\frac{7}{8} = -10 + \left(-\frac{7}{8}\right) = -\frac{10}{1} \cdot \frac{8}{8} - \frac{7}{8} = -\frac{80}{8} - \frac{7}{8} = -\frac{87}{8}$$

Do Exercises 6–9. ▶

Writing Mixed Numerals

We can find a mixed numeral for $\frac{5}{3}$ as follows:

$$\frac{5}{3} = \frac{3}{3} + \frac{2}{3} = 1 + \frac{2}{3} = 1\frac{2}{3}.$$

In terms of objects, we can think of $\frac{5}{3}$ as $\frac{3}{3}$, or 1, plus $\frac{2}{3}$, as shown below.

$$\frac{5}{3} = \quad \underbrace{}_{\frac{3}{3},\text{ or }1} \quad + \quad \underbrace{}_{\frac{2}{3}}$$

Fraction symbols like $\frac{5}{3}$ also indicate division; $\frac{5}{3}$ means $5 \div 3$. Let's divide the numerator by the denominator.

$$\begin{array}{r} 1 \\ 3\overline{)5} \\ \underline{3} \\ 2 \end{array} \leftarrow 2 \div 3 = \frac{2}{3}$$

Thus, $\frac{5}{3} = 1\frac{2}{3}$.

Convert to fraction notation.

4. $4\frac{2}{5}$ **5.** $6\frac{1}{10}$

Convert to fraction notation. Use the faster method.

GS **6.** $4\frac{5}{6}$

$$4 \cdot 6 = \boxed{}$$
$$24 + \boxed{} = 29$$
$$4\frac{5}{6} = \frac{\boxed{}}{6}$$

7. $9\frac{1}{4}$ **8.** $-20\frac{2}{3}$

9. $1\frac{9}{13}$

Answers

4. $\frac{22}{5}$ **5.** $\frac{61}{10}$ **6.** $\frac{29}{6}$ **7.** $\frac{37}{4}$

8. $-\frac{62}{3}$ **9.** $\frac{22}{13}$

Guided Solution:
6. 24, 5, 29

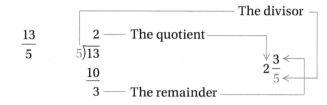

To convert from fraction notation to a mixed numeral, divide.

$\frac{13}{5}$ $5\overline{)13}$ — The quotient — 2
The divisor
$\underline{10}$
3 — The remainder
$2\frac{3}{5}$

Convert to a mixed numeral.

10. $\frac{7}{3}$ GS

11. $\frac{11}{10}$ **12.** $\frac{110}{6}$

13. $\frac{229}{18}$

EXAMPLES Convert to a mixed numeral.

8. $\frac{69}{10}$ $10\overline{)69}$ $\frac{69}{10} = 6\frac{9}{10}$
$\underline{60}$
9

9. $\frac{122}{8}$ $8\overline{)122}$ $\frac{122}{8} = 15\frac{2}{8} = 15\frac{1}{4}$
$\underline{8}$
42
$\underline{40}$
2

◀ Do Exercises 10–13.

The same type of procedure also works with negative numbers. Of course, the result will be a negative mixed numeral.

EXAMPLE 10 Convert $-\frac{17}{5}$ to a mixed numeral.

Since

$5\overline{)17}$
$\underline{15}$
2
3

we have

$$\frac{17}{5} = 3\frac{2}{5}.$$

Then

$$-\frac{17}{5} = -3\frac{2}{5}.$$

◀ Do Exercises 14 and 15.

A fraction larger than 1, such as $\frac{27}{8}$, is sometimes referred to as an "improper" fraction. We will not use this terminology because notation such as $\frac{27}{8}$, $\frac{11}{9}$, and $\frac{89}{10}$ is quite "proper" and very common in algebra.

Convert to a mixed numeral.

14. $-\frac{25}{4}$ **15.** $-\frac{33}{9}$

Answers

10. $2\frac{1}{3}$ 11. $1\frac{1}{10}$ 12. $18\frac{1}{3}$ 13. $12\frac{13}{18}$
14. $-6\frac{1}{4}$ 15. $-3\frac{2}{3}$

Guided Solution:

10. $3, 7, 2\frac{1}{3}$

b WRITING MIXED NUMERALS FOR QUOTIENTS

It is quite common when dividing whole numbers to write the quotient using a mixed numeral. The remainder is the numerator of the fraction part of the mixed numeral.

EXAMPLE 11 Divide. Write a mixed numeral for the answer.

$$4\,2\,\overline{)\,8\,9\,1\,5}$$

We first divide as usual.

$$
\begin{array}{r}
2\,1\,2 \\
4\,2\,\overline{)\,8\,9\,1\,5} \\
\underline{8\,4} \\
5\,1 \\
\underline{4\,2} \\
9\,5 \\
\underline{8\,4} \\
1\,1
\end{array}
$$

$$\frac{8915}{42} = 212\frac{11}{42}$$

The answer is $212\frac{11}{42}$.

Do Exercises 16 and 17. ▶

Divide. Write a mixed numeral for the answer.

16. $6\,\overline{)\,4\,8\,4\,6}$

17. $4\,5\,\overline{)\,6\,0\,5\,3}$

Answers

16. $807\frac{2}{3}$ **17.** $134\frac{23}{45}$

4.4 Exercise Set

For Extra Help

MyMathLab®   MathXL® PRACTICE   WATCH   READ   REVIEW

✓ Reading Check

Determine whether each statement is true or false.

_____ **RC1.** A mixed numeral consists of a whole-number part and a fraction less than 1.

_____ **RC2.** The mixed numeral $5\frac{1}{4}$ represents $5 + \frac{1}{4}$.

_____ **RC3.** It is never appropriate to use fraction notation such as $\frac{33}{25}$.

_____ **RC4.** When a quotient is written as a mixed numeral, the divisor is the denominator of the fraction part (assuming that the fraction has not been simplified).

a Solve.

1. *Stone Walkways.* In order to construct a stone paver walkway, Cheryl ordered $2\frac{1}{2}$ tons of light-colored field-stone pavers for the main portion of the walkway, $1\frac{7}{8}$ tons of dark-colored stone pavers for edging, and $1\frac{3}{4}$ tons of slab-type stones for steps. Convert $2\frac{1}{2}$, $1\frac{7}{8}$, and $1\frac{3}{4}$ to fraction notation.

2. *Greenhouse Dimensions.* A community college horticulture department builds a greenhouse that measures $32\frac{1}{2}$ ft × $20\frac{5}{6}$ ft × $11\frac{3}{4}$ ft. Convert $32\frac{1}{2}$, $20\frac{5}{6}$, and $11\frac{3}{4}$ to fraction notation.

3. *Quilt Design.* A quilt design requires three different fabrics. The quilter determines that she needs $\frac{17}{4}$ yd of a dominant fabric, $\frac{10}{3}$ yd of a contrasting fabric, and $\frac{9}{8}$ yd of a border fabric. Convert $\frac{17}{4}$, $\frac{10}{3}$, and $\frac{9}{8}$ to mixed numerals.

4. *Bake Sale.* The Valley Township Fire Department organized a bake sale as a fund-raiser for the local library. Each pie was cut into 8 pieces and each cake into 12 pieces. Sales totaled 73 pieces of pie, or $\frac{73}{8}$ pies, and 55 pieces of cake, or $\frac{55}{12}$ cakes. Convert $\frac{73}{8}$ and $\frac{55}{12}$ to mixed numerals.

Convert to fraction notation.

5. $5\dfrac{2}{3}$

6. $3\dfrac{4}{5}$

7. $3\dfrac{1}{4}$

8. $6\dfrac{1}{2}$

9. $-10\dfrac{1}{8}$

10. $-20\dfrac{1}{5}$

11. $5\dfrac{1}{10}$

12. $9\dfrac{1}{10}$

13. $20\dfrac{3}{5}$

14. $30\dfrac{4}{5}$

15. $-9\dfrac{5}{6}$

16. $-8\dfrac{7}{8}$

17. $7\dfrac{3}{10}$

18. $6\dfrac{9}{10}$

19. $1\dfrac{5}{8}$

20. $1\dfrac{3}{5}$

21. $-12\dfrac{3}{4}$

22. $-15\dfrac{2}{3}$

23. $-4\dfrac{3}{10}$

24. $-5\dfrac{7}{10}$

25. $2\dfrac{3}{100}$

26. $5\dfrac{7}{100}$

27. $66\dfrac{2}{3}$

28. $33\dfrac{1}{3}$

29. $-5\dfrac{29}{50}$

30. $-84\dfrac{3}{8}$

31. $101\dfrac{5}{16}$

32. $205\dfrac{3}{14}$

Convert to a mixed numeral.

33. $\dfrac{18}{5}$

34. $\dfrac{17}{4}$

35. $\dfrac{14}{3}$

36. $\dfrac{39}{8}$

37. $-\dfrac{27}{6}$

38. $-\dfrac{30}{9}$

39. $\dfrac{57}{10}$

40. $\dfrac{89}{10}$

41. $-\dfrac{53}{7}$

42. $-\dfrac{59}{8}$

43. $\dfrac{45}{6}$

44. $\dfrac{50}{8}$

45. $\dfrac{46}{4}$

46. $\dfrac{39}{9}$

47. $-\dfrac{12}{8}$

48. $-\dfrac{28}{6}$

49. $\dfrac{757}{100}$

50. $\dfrac{467}{100}$

51. $-\dfrac{345}{8}$

52. $-\dfrac{223}{4}$

Copyright © 2015 Pearson Education, Inc.

b Divide. Write a mixed numeral for the answer.

53. $8 \overline{)869}$

54. $3 \overline{)2126}$

55. $5 \overline{)3091}$

56. $9 \overline{)9110}$

57. $21 \overline{)852}$

58. $85 \overline{)7670}$

59. $102 \overline{)5612}$

60. $46 \overline{)1081}$

61. $35 \overline{)80,243}$

62. $152 \overline{)26,107}$

Skill Maintenance

63. Round to the nearest hundred: 45,765. [1.6a]

64. Round to the nearest ten: 45,765. [1.6a]

Simplify. [3.5b]

65. $\dfrac{200}{375}$

66. $\dfrac{63}{75}$

67. $-\dfrac{160}{270}$

68. $-\dfrac{6996}{8028}$

Use = or ≠ for ☐ to write a true sentence. [3.5c]

69. $\dfrac{3}{8}$ ☐ $\dfrac{6}{16}$

70. $\dfrac{-7}{10}$ ☐ $\dfrac{-2}{3}$

Find the reciprocal of each number. [3.7a]

71. $\dfrac{9}{7}$

72. $-\dfrac{1}{8}$

Solve. [1.7b]

73. $48 \cdot t = 1680$

74. $10,000 = m + 3593$

Synthesis

Write a mixed numeral.

75. 🖩 $\dfrac{128,236}{541}$

76. 🖩 $\dfrac{103,676}{349}$

77. $\dfrac{56}{7} + \dfrac{2}{3}$

78. $-\dfrac{72}{12} - \dfrac{5}{6}$

79. There are $\dfrac{366}{7}$ weeks in a leap year.

80. There are $\dfrac{365}{7}$ weeks in a year.

Concept Reinforcement

Determine whether each statement is true or false.

_____ 1. If $\dfrac{a}{b} > \dfrac{c}{b}$, $a, b, c > 0$, then $a > c$. [4.3b]

_____ 2. All positive mixed numerals represent numbers larger than 1. [4.4a]

_____ 3. The least common multiple of two natural numbers is the smallest number that is a factor of both. [4.1a]

_____ 4. To add fractions when denominators are the same, we keep the numerator and add the denominators. [4.2a]

Guided Solutions

GS Fill in each blank with the number that creates a correct solution.

5. Subtract: $\dfrac{11}{42} - \dfrac{3}{35}$. [4.3a]

$$\dfrac{11}{42} - \dfrac{3}{35} = \dfrac{11}{2 \cdot \boxed{} \cdot 7} - \dfrac{3}{\boxed{} \cdot 7} \qquad \text{Factoring the denominators}$$

$$= \dfrac{11}{2 \cdot 3 \cdot 7} \cdot \left(\dfrac{\boxed{}}{\boxed{}} \right) - \dfrac{3}{5 \cdot 7} \cdot \left(\dfrac{2 \cdot 3}{2 \cdot 3} \right) \qquad \text{Multiplying by 1 to get the LCD}$$

$$= \dfrac{11 \cdot \boxed{}}{2 \cdot 3 \cdot 7 \cdot \boxed{}} - \dfrac{3 \cdot 2 \cdot 3}{5 \cdot 7 \cdot 2 \cdot 3} \qquad \text{Multiplying}$$

$$= \dfrac{\boxed{}}{2 \cdot 3 \cdot 5 \cdot 7} - \dfrac{\boxed{}}{2 \cdot 3 \cdot 5 \cdot 7} \qquad \text{Simplifying}$$

$$= \dfrac{\boxed{} - \boxed{}}{2 \cdot 3 \cdot 5 \cdot 7} = \dfrac{\boxed{}}{\boxed{}} \qquad \text{Subtracting and simplifying}$$

6. Solve: $x + \dfrac{1}{8} = \dfrac{2}{3}$. [4.3c]

$$x + \dfrac{1}{8} = \dfrac{2}{3}$$

$$x + \dfrac{1}{8} - \boxed{} = \dfrac{2}{3} - \boxed{} \qquad \text{Subtracting on both sides}$$

$$x + 0 = \dfrac{2}{3} \cdot \dfrac{\boxed{}}{\boxed{}} - \dfrac{1}{8} \cdot \dfrac{\boxed{}}{\boxed{}} \qquad \text{Multiplying by 1 to get the LCD}$$

$$x = \dfrac{\boxed{}}{24} - \dfrac{\boxed{}}{24} \qquad \text{Simplifying and multiplying}$$

$$x = \dfrac{\boxed{}}{\boxed{}} \qquad \text{Subtracting}$$

Copyright © 2015 Pearson Education, Inc.

Mixed Review

7. Match each set of numbers in the first column with its least common multiple in the second column by drawing connecting lines. [4.1a]

45 and 50

50 and 80   120

30 and 24   720

18, 24, and 80   400

30, 45, and 50   450

Calculate and simplify. [4.2a], [4.3a]

8. $\frac{1}{5} + \frac{7}{45}$

9. $\frac{5}{6} + \frac{2}{3} + \frac{7}{12}$

10. $\frac{1}{6} - \frac{2}{9}$

11. $\frac{-5}{18} + \frac{1}{15}$

12. $\frac{19}{48} - \frac{11}{30}$

13. $\frac{3}{7} + \frac{15}{17}$

14. $\frac{229}{720} - \frac{5}{24}$

15. $\frac{2}{35} - \frac{8}{65}$

Solve.

16. Miguel jogs for $\frac{4}{5}$ mi, rests, and then jogs for another $\frac{2}{3}$ mi. How far does he jog in all? [4.2b]

17. One weekend, Kirby spent $\frac{39}{5}$ hr playing two iPod games—Brain Challenge: Cerebral Burn and Scrabble: Go for a Triple Word Score. She spent $\frac{11}{4}$ hr playing Scrabble. How many hours did she spend playing Brain Challenge? [4.3d]

18. Arrange in order from smallest to largest: $\frac{4}{9}, \frac{3}{10}, \frac{2}{7},$ and $\frac{1}{5}$. [4.3b]

19. Solve: $\frac{2}{5} + x = \frac{9}{16}$. [4.3c]

20. Divide: $15\overline{)263}$. Write a mixed numeral for the answer. [4.4b]

21. Which of the following is fraction notation for $9\frac{3}{8}$? [4.4a]

A. $\frac{27}{8}$ B. $\frac{93}{8}$ C. $\frac{75}{8}$ D. $\frac{80}{3}$

22. Which of the following is mixed numeral notation for $\frac{39}{4}$? [4.4a]

A. $35\frac{1}{4}$ B. $\frac{4}{39}$ C. $9\frac{3}{4}$ D. $36\frac{3}{4}$

Understanding Through Discussion and Writing

23. Is the LCM of two numbers always larger than either number? Why or why not? [4.1a]

24. Explain the role of multiplication when adding using fraction notation with different denominators. [4.2a]

25. A student made the following error:

$$\frac{8}{5} - \frac{8}{2} = \frac{8}{3}.$$

Find at least two ways to convince him of the mistake. [4.3a]

26. Are the numbers $2\frac{1}{3}$ and $2 \cdot \frac{1}{3}$ equal? Why or why not? [4.4a]

STUDYING FOR SUCCESS   *Taking a Test*

☐ Read each question carefully. Know what the question is before you answer it.
☐ Try to do all the questions the first time through, marking those to recheck if you have time at the end.
☐ Pace yourself.
☐ Write your answers in a neat and orderly manner.

4.5 Addition and Subtraction Using Mixed Numerals; Applications

OBJECTIVES

a Add using mixed numerals.

b Subtract using mixed numerals.

c Solve applied problems involving addition and subtraction with mixed numerals.

SKILL TO REVIEW

Objective 3.5b: Simplify fraction notation.

Simplify.

1. $\dfrac{18}{32}$ **2.** $\dfrac{78}{117}$

a ADDITION USING MIXED NUMERALS

To add mixed numerals, we first add the fractions. Then we add the whole numbers.

EXAMPLE 1 Add: $1\frac{5}{8} + 3\frac{1}{8}$. Write a mixed numeral for the answer.

$$1\frac{5}{8} = \qquad\qquad 1\frac{5}{8}$$
$$+\,3\frac{1}{8} = \qquad\qquad +\,3\frac{1}{8}$$
$$\overline{\frac{6}{8}}\qquad\qquad \overline{4\frac{6}{8}} = 4\frac{3}{4}$$

Simplifying: $\dfrac{6}{8} = \dfrac{3}{4}$

↑ Add the fractions.   ↑ Add the whole numbers.

Sometimes we must write the fractional parts with a common denominator before we can add.

EXAMPLE 2 Add: $5\frac{2}{3} + 3\frac{5}{6}$. Write a mixed numeral for the answer.

The LCD is 6.

$$5\frac{2}{3}\cdot\frac{2}{2} = 5\frac{4}{6}$$
$$+\,3\frac{5}{6} = +\,3\frac{5}{6}$$
$$\overline{\qquad\qquad 8\frac{9}{6}} = 8 + \frac{9}{6}$$
$$= 8 + 1\frac{1}{2} \qquad \text{Writing } \tfrac{9}{6} \text{ as a mixed numeral; } \tfrac{9}{6} = 1\tfrac{3}{6} = 1\tfrac{1}{2}$$
$$= 9\frac{1}{2}$$

◀ **Do Margin Exercises 1 and 2.**

Add.

1. $2\frac{3}{10}$
$+\,5\frac{1}{10}$

2. $8\frac{2}{5}$
$+\,3\frac{7}{10}$

Answers

Skill to Review:
1. $\frac{9}{16}$ **2.** $\frac{2}{3}$

Margin Exercises:
1. $7\frac{2}{5}$ **2.** $12\frac{1}{10}$

EXAMPLE 3 Add: $10\frac{5}{6} + 7\frac{3}{8}$.

The LCD is 24.

$$10\,\frac{5}{6} \cdot \frac{4}{4} = \quad 10\frac{20}{24}$$

$$+\ 7\,\frac{3}{8} \cdot \frac{3}{3} = +\ 7\frac{9}{24}$$

$$17\frac{29}{24} = 17 + \frac{29}{24}$$

$$= 17 + 1\frac{5}{24} \qquad \text{Writing } \frac{29}{24} \text{ as a mixed numeral, } 1\frac{5}{24}$$

$$= 18\frac{5}{24}$$

Do Exercise 3. ▶

3. Add.

$$9\frac{3}{4}$$
$$+\ 3\frac{5}{6}$$

b SUBTRACTION USING MIXED NUMERALS

Subtraction of mixed numerals is a lot like addition; we subtract the fractions and then the whole numbers.

EXAMPLE 4 Subtract: $7\frac{3}{4} - 2\frac{1}{4}$.

$$7\,\frac{3}{4} = \qquad\qquad 7\,\frac{3}{4}$$
$$-\ 2\,\frac{1}{4} = \qquad\quad -\ 2\,\frac{1}{4}$$
$$\frac{2}{4} \qquad\qquad\quad 5\,\frac{2}{4} = 5\frac{1}{2}$$

Subtract the fractions.   Subtract the whole numbers.   Simplifying: $\frac{2}{4} = \frac{1}{2}$

EXAMPLE 5 Subtract: $9\frac{4}{5} - 3\frac{1}{2}$.

The LCD is 10.

$$9\,\frac{4}{5} \cdot \frac{2}{2} = \quad 9\frac{8}{10}$$
$$-\ 3\,\frac{1}{2} \cdot \frac{5}{5} = -\ 3\frac{5}{10}$$
$$6\frac{3}{10}$$

Do Exercises 4 and 5. ▶

Subtract.

4. $10\frac{7}{8}$
$$-\ 9\frac{3}{8}$$

GS **5.** $8\frac{2}{3} = \quad 8\frac{\boxed{}}{6}$

$$-5\frac{1}{2} = -5\frac{\boxed{}}{6}$$

$$3\frac{\boxed{}}{6}$$

Answers

3. $13\frac{7}{12}$ **4.** $1\frac{1}{2}$ **5.** $3\frac{1}{6}$

Guided Solution:
5. 4, 3, 1

EXAMPLE 6 Subtract: $7\frac{1}{6} - 2\frac{1}{4}$.

The LCD is 12.

$$
\begin{array}{r}
7\dfrac{1}{6} \cdot \dfrac{2}{2} = \quad 7\dfrac{2}{12} \\
-\ 2\dfrac{1}{4} \cdot \dfrac{3}{3} = -\ 2\dfrac{3}{12}
\end{array}
\left.\vphantom{\begin{array}{r}7\\7\end{array}}\right\}
$$

We cannot subtract $\frac{3}{12}$ from $\frac{2}{12}$.
← We borrow 1, or $\frac{12}{12}$, from 7:
$7\frac{2}{12} = 6 + 1 + \frac{2}{12} = 6 + \frac{12}{12} + \frac{2}{12} = 6\frac{14}{12}$.

We can write this as

$$
\begin{array}{r}
7\dfrac{2}{12} = \quad 6\dfrac{14}{12} \\
-\ 2\dfrac{3}{12} = -\ 2\dfrac{3}{12} \\
\hline
4\dfrac{11}{12}.
\end{array}
$$

◀ Do Exercise 6.

6. Subtract.

$$
\begin{array}{r}
8\dfrac{1}{9} \\
-\ 4\dfrac{5}{6} \\
\hline
\end{array}
$$

GS **EXAMPLE 7** Subtract: $12 - 9\frac{3}{8}$.

$$
\begin{array}{r}
12 \quad = \quad 11\dfrac{8}{8} \\
-\ 9\dfrac{3}{8} = -\ 9\dfrac{3}{8} \\
\hline
2\dfrac{5}{8}
\end{array}
$$

$12 = 11 + 1 = 11 + \frac{8}{8} = 11\frac{8}{8}$

◀ Do Exercise 7.

7. Subtract: $5 - 1\frac{1}{3}$.

$$
\begin{array}{r}
5 \quad = \quad 4\dfrac{\square}{\square} \\
-\ 1\dfrac{1}{3} = -\ 1\dfrac{1}{3} \\
\hline
3\dfrac{\square}{3}
\end{array}
$$

C APPLICATIONS AND PROBLEM SOLVING

EXAMPLE 8 *Widening a Driveway.* Sherry and Woody are widening their existing $17\frac{1}{4}$-ft driveway by adding $5\frac{9}{10}$ ft on one side. What is the new width of the driveway?

$5\frac{9}{10}$ ft

$17\frac{1}{4}$ ft

1. Familiarize. We let $w =$ the new width of the driveway.

2. Translate. We translate as follows:

Existing width	+	Width of addition	=	New width
↓	↓	↓	↓	↓
$17\dfrac{1}{4}$	$+$	$5\dfrac{9}{10}$	$=$	$w.$

Answers

6. $3\dfrac{5}{18}$ 7. $3\dfrac{2}{3}$

Guided Solution:

7. $\dfrac{3}{3}$, 2

3. Solve. The translation tells us what to do. We add. The LCD is 20.

$$17\frac{1}{4} = 17\frac{1\cdot 5}{4\cdot 5} = 17\frac{5}{20}$$

$$+\ 5\frac{9}{10} = +\ 5\frac{9\cdot 2}{10\cdot 2} = +\ 5\frac{18}{20}$$

$$22\frac{23}{20} = 23\frac{3}{20}$$

Thus, $w = 23\frac{3}{20}$.

4. Check. We check by repeating the calculation. We also note that the answer is larger than either of the given widths, which means that the answer is reasonable.

5. State. The new width of the driveway is $23\frac{3}{20}$ ft.

Do Exercise 8. ▶

EXAMPLE 9 *Men's Long-Jump World Records.* On October 18, 1968, Bob Beamon set a world record of $29\frac{3}{16}$ ft for the long jump, a record that was not broken for nearly 23 years. This record-setting jump was significantly longer than the previous one of $27\frac{19}{48}$ ft, accomplished on May 29, 1965, by Ralph Boston. How much longer was Beamon's jump than Boston's?

Source: "Long jump world record progression," en.wikipedia.org

1. Familiarize. The phrase "how much longer" indicates subtraction. We let $w =$ the difference in the world records.

2. Translate. We translate as follows:

Beamon's jump	–	Boston's jump	=	Difference in length
$29\frac{3}{16}$	–	$27\frac{19}{48}$	=	w.

3. Solve. To solve the equation, we carry out the subtraction. The LCD is 48.

$$29\frac{3}{16} = 29\frac{3\cdot 3}{16\cdot 3} = 29\frac{9}{48} = 28\frac{57}{48}$$

$$-\ 27\frac{19}{48} = -\ 27\frac{19}{48} = -\ 27\frac{19}{48} = -\ 27\frac{19}{48}$$

$$1\frac{38}{48} = 1\frac{19}{24}$$

Thus, $w = 1\frac{19}{24}$.

4. Check. To check, we add the difference, $1\frac{19}{24}$, to Boston's jump:

$$27\frac{19}{48} + 1\frac{19}{24} = 27\frac{19}{48} + 1\frac{38}{48}$$

$$= 28\frac{57}{48} = 29\frac{9}{48} = 29\frac{3}{16}.$$

This checks.

5. State. Beamon's jump was $1\frac{19}{24}$ ft longer than Boston's.

Do Exercise 9. ▶

8. *Travel Distance.* On a two-day business trip, Paul drove $213\frac{7}{10}$ mi the first day and $107\frac{5}{8}$ mi the second day. What was the total distance that Paul drove?

9. *Nail Length.* A 30d nail is $4\frac{1}{2}$ in. long. A 5d nail is $1\frac{3}{4}$ in. long. How much longer is the 30d nail than the 5d nail? (The "d" stands for "penny," which was used years ago in England to specify the number of pennies needed to buy 100 nails. Today, "penny" is used only to indicate the length of the nail.)

Source: *Pocket Ref,* 2nd ed., by Thomas J. Glover, p. 280, Sequoia Publishing, Inc., Littleton, CO

Answers

8. $321\frac{13}{40}$ mi   **9.** $2\frac{3}{4}$ in.

15¼ in.

14½ in.

} 1½ in.

} 2¾ in.

EXAMPLE 10 *Locks of Love.* Locks of Love, Inc., is a non-profit organization that provides hairpieces for children who have lost their hair as a result of medical conditions. The minimum length for hair that is donated is 10 in. Karissa and Cayla allowed their hair to grow in order to donate it. The length cut from Karissa's hair was $15\frac{1}{4}$ in., and the length cut from Cayla's hair was $14\frac{1}{2}$ in. After the hair was cut, it was discovered that the ends of each lock had highlighting that needed to be trimmed. Because of the highlighting, $1\frac{1}{2}$ in. was cut from Karissa's lock of hair and $2\frac{3}{4}$ in. was cut from Cayla's. In all, what was the total usable length of hair that Karissa and Cayla donated?

1. **Familiarize.** We let l = the total usable length of hair that Karissa and Cayla donated.

2. **Translate.** The length l is the sum of the lengths that were cut, minus the sum of the lengths that were trimmed from the locks. Thus we have

$$l = \left(15\frac{1}{4} + 14\frac{1}{2}\right) - \left(1\frac{1}{2} + 2\frac{3}{4}\right).$$

3. **Solve.** This is a three-step problem.

   a) We first add the two lengths $15\frac{1}{4}$ and $14\frac{1}{2}$.

   $$\begin{aligned} 15\tfrac{1}{4} &= 15\tfrac{1}{4} \\ +\ 14\tfrac{1}{2} &= +\ 14\tfrac{2}{4} \\ \hline & 29\tfrac{3}{4} \end{aligned}$$

   b) Next, we add the two lengths $1\frac{1}{2}$ and $2\frac{3}{4}$.

   $$\begin{aligned} 1\tfrac{1}{2} &= 1\tfrac{2}{4} \\ +\ 2\tfrac{3}{4} &= +\ 2\tfrac{3}{4} \\ \hline & 3\tfrac{5}{4} = 4\tfrac{1}{4} \end{aligned}$$

   c) Finally, we subtract $4\frac{1}{4}$ from $29\frac{3}{4}$.

   $$\begin{aligned} &29\tfrac{3}{4} \\ &-\ 4\tfrac{1}{4} \\ \hline &25\tfrac{2}{4} = 25\tfrac{1}{2} \end{aligned}$$

   Thus, $l = 25\frac{1}{2}$.

4. **Check.** We can check by doing the problem a different way. We can subtract the trimmed length from each lock, then add the adjusted lengths together.

Karissa's lock	Cayla's lock	Sum of lengths
$15\frac{1}{4} = 14\frac{5}{4}$	$14\frac{1}{2} = 13\frac{6}{4}$	$13\frac{3}{4}$
$-\ 1\frac{1}{2} = -\ 1\frac{2}{4}$	$-\ 2\frac{3}{4} = -\ 2\frac{3}{4}$	$+\ 11\frac{3}{4}$
$13\frac{3}{4}$	$11\frac{3}{4}$	$24\frac{6}{4} = 25\frac{1}{2}$

   We obtained the same answer, so our answer checks.

5. **State.** The sum of the usable lengths of hair donated was $25\frac{1}{2}$ in.

◀ **Do Exercise 10.**

10. *Liquid Fertilizer.* There is $283\frac{5}{8}$ gal of liquid fertilizer in a fertilizer application tank. After applying $178\frac{2}{3}$ gal to a soybean field, the farmer requests that Braden's Farm Supply deliver an additional 250 gal to the tank. How many gallons of fertilizer are in the tank after the delivery?

Answer

10. $354\frac{23}{24}$ gal

✓ Reading Check

Match each addition or subtraction with the correct first step from the following list.

a) Add the fractions.

b) Write the fractional parts with a common denominator.

c) Rename 5 as $4\frac{9}{9}$.

d) Borrow 1 from 5 and add it to $\frac{1}{9}$.

_____ **RC1.** $\quad 5\frac{1}{9}$ $\quad\quad\quad$ _____ **RC2.** $\quad 5\frac{4}{9}$ $\quad\quad\quad$ _____ **RC3.** $\quad 5\frac{4}{9}$ $\quad\quad\quad$ _____ **RC4.** $\quad 5$

$\quad\quad\quad -3\frac{4}{9}$ $\quad\quad\quad\quad\quad\quad +3\frac{1}{9}$ $\quad\quad\quad\quad\quad\quad +3\frac{1}{18}$ $\quad\quad\quad\quad\quad -3\frac{1}{9}$

a Add. Write a mixed numeral for the answer.

1. $\quad 20$
$\quad +\ 8\frac{3}{4}$

2. $\quad 37$
$\quad +\ 18\frac{2}{3}$

3. $\quad 129\frac{7}{8}$
$\quad +\ 56$

4. $\quad 2003\frac{4}{11}$
$\quad +\quad 59$

5. $\quad 2\frac{7}{8}$
$\quad +\ 3\frac{5}{8}$

6. $\quad 4\frac{5}{6}$
$\quad +\ 3\frac{5}{6}$

7. $1\frac{1}{4} + 1\frac{2}{3}$

8. $4\frac{1}{3} + 5\frac{2}{9}$

9. $\quad 8\frac{3}{4}$
$\quad +\ 5\frac{5}{6}$

10. $\quad 4\frac{3}{8}$
$\quad +\ 6\frac{5}{12}$

11. $\quad 3\frac{2}{5}$
$\quad +\ 8\frac{7}{10}$

12. $\quad 5\frac{1}{2}$
$\quad +\ 3\frac{7}{10}$

13. $\quad 5\frac{3}{8}$
$\quad +\ 10\frac{5}{6}$

14. $\quad \frac{5}{8}$
$\quad +\ 1\frac{5}{6}$

15. $\quad 12\frac{4}{5}$
$\quad +\ 8\frac{7}{10}$

16. $\quad 15\frac{5}{8}$
$\quad +\ 11\frac{3}{4}$

17. $\quad 14\frac{5}{8}$
$\quad +\ 13\frac{1}{4}$

18. $\quad 16\frac{1}{4}$
$\quad +\ 15\frac{7}{8}$

19. $\quad 7\frac{1}{8}$
$\quad\quad 9\frac{2}{3}$
$\quad +\ 10\frac{3}{4}$

20. $\quad 45\frac{2}{3}$
$\quad\quad 31\frac{3}{5}$
$\quad +\ 12\frac{1}{4}$

b Subtract. Write a mixed numeral for the answer.

21. $4\dfrac{1}{5}$
$-\ 2\dfrac{3}{5}$

22. $5\dfrac{1}{8}$
$-\ 2\dfrac{3}{8}$

23. $6\dfrac{3}{5} - 2\dfrac{1}{2}$

24. $7\dfrac{2}{3} - 6\dfrac{1}{2}$

25. $34\dfrac{1}{3}$
$-\ 12\dfrac{5}{8}$

26. $23\dfrac{5}{16}$
$-\ 16\dfrac{3}{4}$

27. 21
$-\ 8\dfrac{3}{4}$

28. 42
$-\ 3\dfrac{7}{8}$

29. 34
$-\ 18\dfrac{5}{8}$

30. 23
$-\ 19\dfrac{3}{4}$

31. $21\dfrac{1}{6}$
$-\ 13\dfrac{3}{4}$

32. $42\dfrac{1}{10}$
$-\ 23\dfrac{7}{12}$

33. $14\dfrac{1}{8}$
$-\ \dfrac{3}{4}$

34. $28\dfrac{1}{6}$
$-\ 5$

35. $25\dfrac{1}{9}$
$-\ 13\dfrac{5}{6}$

36. $23\dfrac{5}{16}$
$-\ 14\dfrac{7}{12}$

c Solve.

37. *Planting Flowers.* A landscaper planted $4\frac{1}{2}$ flats of impatiens, $6\frac{2}{3}$ flats of snapdragons, and $3\frac{3}{8}$ flats of phlox. How many flats did she plant altogether?

38. A plumber uses two pipes, each of length $51\frac{5}{16}$ in., and one pipe of length $34\frac{3}{4}$ in. when installing a shower. How much pipe was used in all?

34$\frac{3}{4}$ in.

51$\frac{5}{16}$ in.

Copyright © 2015 Pearson Education, Inc.

39. For a family party, Dana bought packages of cheese weighing $1\frac{2}{3}$ lb and $5\frac{3}{4}$ lb. What was the total weight of the cheese?

40. Marsha's Butcher Shop sold packages of sliced turkey breast weighing $1\frac{1}{3}$ lb and $4\frac{3}{5}$ lb. What was the total weight of the meat?

41. Casey's beagle is $14\frac{1}{4}$ in. from shoulder to floor, and her basset hound is $13\frac{5}{16}$ in. from shoulder to floor. How much shorter is her basset hound?

42. *Winterizing a Swimming Pool.* To winterize their swimming pool, the Jablonskis are draining the water into a nearby field. The distance to the field is $103\frac{1}{2}$ ft. Because their only hose measures $62\frac{3}{4}$ ft, they need to buy an additional hose. How long must the new hose be?

43. *Upholstery Fabric.* Executive Car Care sells 45-in. upholstery fabric for car restoration. Art bought $9\frac{1}{4}$ yd and $10\frac{5}{6}$ yd for two car projects. How many yards did Art buy?

44. *Painting.* A painter used $1\frac{3}{4}$ gal of paint for the Garcias' living room and $1\frac{1}{3}$ gal for their family room. How much paint was used in all?

45. *Sewing from a Pattern.* Using 45-in. fabric, Regan needs $1\frac{3}{8}$ yd for a dress, $\frac{5}{8}$ yd of contrasting fabric for the band at the bottom, and $3\frac{3}{8}$ yd for a coordinating jacket. How many yards of 45-in. fabric are needed in all?

46. *Sewing from a Pattern.* Using 45-in. fabric, Sarah needs $2\frac{3}{4}$ yd for a dress and $3\frac{1}{2}$ yd for a coordinating jacket. How many yards of 45-in. fabric are needed in all?

47. Kim Park is a computer technician. One day, she drove $180\frac{7}{10}$ mi away from Los Angeles for a service call. The next day, she drove $85\frac{1}{2}$ mi back toward Los Angeles for another service call. How far was she then from Los Angeles?

48. Jose is $4\frac{1}{2}$ in. taller than his daughter, Teresa. Teresa is $66\frac{2}{3}$ in. tall. How tall is Jose?

49. Creative Glass sells a framed beveled mirror as shown below. Its dimensions are $30\frac{1}{2}$ in. wide by $36\frac{5}{8}$ in. high. What is the perimeter of (total distance around) the framed mirror?

50. *Book Size.* One standard book size is $8\frac{1}{2}$ in. by $9\frac{3}{4}$ in. What is the perimeter of (total distance around) the front cover of such a book?

51. Rene is $5\frac{1}{4}$ in. taller than his son, who is $72\frac{5}{6}$ in. tall. How tall is Rene?

52. A Boeing 767 flew 640 mi on a nonstop flight. On the return flight, it landed after having flown $320\frac{3}{10}$ mi. How far was the plane from its original point of departure?

Find the perimeter of (distance around) each figure.

53.

5$\frac{3}{4}$ yd 5$\frac{3}{4}$ yd 5$\frac{3}{4}$ yd 5$\frac{3}{4}$ yd 5$\frac{3}{4}$ yd

54.

$3\frac{7}{16}$ ft $3\frac{7}{16}$ ft $6\frac{7}{8}$ ft $6\frac{7}{8}$ ft

Find the length d in each figure.

55.

$2\frac{3}{4}$ ft $2\frac{3}{4}$ ft d $12\frac{7}{8}$ ft

56.

$2\frac{1}{5}$ in. $2\frac{1}{5}$ in. d $10\frac{1}{2}$ in.

57. *Stone Bench.* Baytown Village Stone Creations is making a custom stone bench as shown below. The recommended height for the bench is 18 in. The depth of the stone bench is $3\frac{3}{8}$ in. Each of the two supporting legs is made up of three stacked stones. Two of the stones measure $3\frac{1}{2}$ in. and $5\frac{1}{4}$ in. How much must the third stone measure?

18 in. $3\frac{3}{8}$ in. $3\frac{1}{2}$ in. $5\frac{1}{4}$ in. ?

58. *Window Dimensions.* The Sanchez family is replacing a window in their home. The original window measures $4\frac{5}{6}$ ft $\times$ $8\frac{1}{4}$ ft. The new window is $2\frac{1}{3}$ ft wider. What are the dimensions of the new window?

$4\frac{5}{6}$ ft $8\frac{1}{4}$ ft $2\frac{1}{3}$ ft ?

Copyright © 2015 Pearson Education, Inc.

59. *Carpentry.* When cutting wood with a saw, a carpenter must take into account the thickness of the saw blade. Suppose that from a piece of wood 36 in. long, a carpenter cuts a $15\frac{3}{4}$-in. length with a saw blade that is $\frac{1}{8}$ in. thick. How long is the piece that remains?

60. *Cutco Cutlery.* The Essentials 5-piece set sold by Cutco contains three knives: $7\frac{5}{8}''$ Petite Chef, $6\frac{3}{4}''$ Petite Carver, and $2\frac{3}{4}''$ Paring Knife. How much larger is the blade of the Petite Chef than that of the Petite Carver? than that of the Paring Knife?

Source: Cutco Cutlery Corporation

61. *Interior Design.* Eric worked $10\frac{1}{2}$ hr over a three-day period on an interior design project. If he worked $2\frac{1}{2}$ hr on the first day and $4\frac{1}{5}$ hr on the second, how many hours did Eric work on the third day?

62. *Painting.* Geri had $3\frac{1}{2}$ gal of paint. It took $2\frac{3}{4}$ gal to paint the family room. She estimated that it would take $2\frac{1}{4}$ gal to paint the living room. How much more paint did Geri need?

63. *Fly Fishing.* Bryn is putting together a fly fishing line and uses $58\frac{5}{8}$ ft of slow-sinking fly line and $8\frac{3}{4}$ ft of leader line. She uses $\frac{3}{8}$ ft of the slow-sinking fly line to connect the two lines. The knot used to connect the fly to the leader line uses $\frac{1}{6}$ ft of the leader line. How long is the finished fly fishing line?

64. Find the smallest length of a bolt that will pass through a piece of tubing with an outside diameter of $\frac{1}{2}$ in., a washer $\frac{1}{16}$ in. thick, a piece of tubing with a $\frac{3}{4}$-in. outside diameter, another washer, and a nut $\frac{3}{16}$ in. thick.

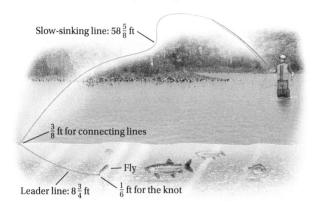

Slow-sinking line: $58\frac{5}{8}$ ft

$\frac{3}{8}$ ft for connecting lines

— Fly

Leader line: $8\frac{3}{4}$ ft $\frac{1}{6}$ ft for the knot

Skill Maintenance

Determine whether the first number is divisible by the second. [3.2a]

65. 9993 by 3

66. 9993 by 9

67. 2345 by 9

68. 2345 by 5

69. 2335 by 10

70. 7764 by 6

71. 18,888 by 8

72. 18,888 by 4

73. Write expanded notation for 38,125.   [1.1b]

74. Write a word name for 2,005,689.   [1.1c]

75. Write exponential notation for $9 \cdot 9 \cdot 9 \cdot 9$.   [1.9a]

76. Evaluate: 3^4.   [1.9b]

Synthesis

Perform the indicated operation. Write a mixed numeral for the answer.

77. $-5\frac{1}{4} + \left(-3\frac{3}{8}\right)$

78. $-8\frac{1}{3} + \left(-2\frac{5}{6}\right)$

79. $-4\frac{5}{12} - 6\frac{5}{8}$

80. $-9\frac{1}{2} - 7\frac{3}{5}$

4.6

Multiplication and Division Using Mixed Numerals; Applications

OBJECTIVES

a Multiply using mixed numerals.

b Divide using mixed numerals.

c Solve applied problems involving multiplication and division with mixed numerals.

SKILL TO REVIEW

Objective 3.7b: Divide and simplify using fraction notation.

Divide and simplify.

1. $85 \div \dfrac{17}{5}$

2. $\dfrac{7}{65} \div \left(-\dfrac{21}{25}\right)$

Multiply.

1. $6 \cdot 3\dfrac{1}{3}$

2. $2\dfrac{1}{2} \cdot \dfrac{3}{4}$

Multiply.

3. $-2 \cdot 6\dfrac{2}{5} = -\dfrac{2}{1} \cdot \dfrac{\square}{5}$

$= -\dfrac{\square}{5}$

$= -\square\dfrac{\square}{\square}$ **GS**

4. $3\dfrac{1}{3} \cdot 2\dfrac{1}{2}$

Answers

Skill to Review:

1. 25 **2.** $-\dfrac{5}{39}$

Margin Exercises:

1. 20 **2.** $1\dfrac{7}{8}$ **3.** $-12\dfrac{4}{5}$ **4.** $8\dfrac{1}{3}$

Guided Solution:

3. $32, 64, 12\dfrac{4}{5}$

---

a MULTIPLICATION USING MIXED NUMERALS

Carrying out addition and subtraction with mixed numerals is usually easier if the numbers are left as mixed numerals. With multiplication and division, however, it is easier to convert the numbers to fraction notation first.

> ### MULTIPLICATION USING MIXED NUMERALS
>
> To multiply using mixed numerals, first convert to fraction notation and multiply. Then convert the answer to a mixed numeral, if appropriate.

EXAMPLE 1 Multiply: $6 \cdot 2\dfrac{1}{2}$.

$$6 \cdot 2\dfrac{1}{2} = \dfrac{6}{1} \cdot \dfrac{5}{2} = \dfrac{6 \cdot 5}{1 \cdot 2} = \dfrac{2 \cdot 3 \cdot 5}{2 \cdot 1} = \dfrac{2}{2} \cdot \dfrac{3 \cdot 5}{1} = 1 \cdot \dfrac{3 \cdot 5}{1} = 15$$

> Convert the numbers to fraction notation first.

EXAMPLE 2 Multiply: $3\dfrac{1}{2} \cdot \dfrac{3}{4}$.

$$3\dfrac{1}{2} \cdot \dfrac{3}{4} = \dfrac{7}{2} \cdot \dfrac{3}{4} = \dfrac{21}{8} = 2\dfrac{5}{8}$$

Recall that common denominators are *not* required when multiplying fractions.

◀ Do Margin Exercises 1 and 2.

EXAMPLE 3 Multiply: $-8 \cdot 4\dfrac{2}{3}$.

$$-8 \cdot 4\dfrac{2}{3} = -\dfrac{8}{1} \cdot \dfrac{14}{3} = -\dfrac{112}{3} = -37\dfrac{1}{3}$$

EXAMPLE 4 Multiply: $2\dfrac{1}{4} \cdot 5\dfrac{2}{3}$.

$$2\dfrac{1}{4} \cdot 5\dfrac{2}{3} = \dfrac{9}{4} \cdot \dfrac{17}{3} = \dfrac{3 \cdot 3 \cdot 17}{2 \cdot 2 \cdot 3} = \dfrac{3}{3} \cdot \dfrac{3 \cdot 17}{2 \cdot 2} = \dfrac{51}{4} = 12\dfrac{3}{4}$$

◀ Do Exercises 3 and 4.

·· Caution! ··

Note that $2\dfrac{1}{4} \cdot 5\dfrac{2}{3} \ne 10\dfrac{2}{12}$. A common error is to multiply the whole numbers and then the fractions. This does not give the correct answer, $12\dfrac{3}{4}$, which is found by converting to fraction notation first.

···

b DIVISION USING MIXED NUMERALS

The division $1\frac{1}{2} \div \frac{1}{6}$ is shown here. This division means "How many $\frac{1}{6}$'s are in $1\frac{1}{2}$?" We see that the answer is 9.

$\frac{1}{6}$ goes into $1\frac{1}{2}$ nine times.

When we divide using mixed numerals, we convert to fraction notation first. Recall that to divide by a fraction, we multiply by its reciprocal.

$$1\frac{1}{2} \div \frac{1}{6} = \frac{3}{2} \div \frac{1}{6} = \frac{3}{2} \cdot \frac{6}{1}$$

$$= \frac{3 \cdot 6}{2 \cdot 1} = \frac{3 \cdot 3 \cdot 2}{2 \cdot 1} = \frac{3 \cdot 3}{1} \cdot \frac{2}{2} = \frac{3 \cdot 3}{1} \cdot 1 = 9$$

> ### DIVISION USING MIXED NUMERALS
> To divide using mixed numerals, first write fraction notation and divide. Then convert the answer to a mixed numeral, if appropriate.

EXAMPLE 5 Divide: $32 \div 3\frac{1}{5}$.

$$32 \div 3\frac{1}{5} = \frac{32}{1} \div \frac{16}{5} \quad \text{Writing fraction notation}$$

$$= \frac{32}{1} \cdot \frac{5}{16} = \frac{32 \cdot 5}{1 \cdot 16} = \frac{2 \cdot 16 \cdot 5}{1 \cdot 16} = \frac{16}{16} \cdot \frac{2 \cdot 5}{1} = 1 \cdot \frac{2 \cdot 5}{1} = 10$$

⤷ Remember to multiply by the reciprocal.

Do Exercise 5. ▶

EXAMPLE 6 Divide: $35 \div 4\frac{1}{3}$.

$$35 \div 4\frac{1}{3} = \frac{35}{1} \div \frac{13}{3} = \frac{35}{1} \cdot \frac{3}{13} = \frac{105}{13} = 8\frac{1}{13}$$

Do Exercise 6. ▶

EXAMPLE 7 Divide: $2\frac{1}{3} \div 1\frac{3}{4}$.

$$2\frac{1}{3} \div 1\frac{3}{4} = \frac{7}{3} \div \frac{7}{4} = \frac{7}{3} \cdot \frac{4}{7} = \frac{7 \cdot 4}{3 \cdot 7} = \frac{7}{7} \cdot \frac{4}{3} = 1 \cdot \frac{4}{3} = \frac{4}{3} = 1\frac{1}{3}$$ ▪

EXAMPLE 8 Divide: $-1\frac{3}{5} \div \left(-3\frac{1}{3}\right)$.

$$-1\frac{3}{5} \div \left(-3\frac{1}{3}\right) = -\frac{8}{5} \div \left(-\frac{10}{3}\right) = -\frac{8}{5} \cdot \left(-\frac{3}{10}\right)$$

$$= \frac{8 \cdot 3}{5 \cdot 10} = \frac{2 \cdot 4 \cdot 3}{5 \cdot 2 \cdot 5} = \frac{2}{2} \cdot \frac{4 \cdot 3}{5 \cdot 5} = \frac{12}{25}$$

Do Exercises 7 and 8. ▶

5. Divide: $84 \div 5\frac{1}{4}$.

6. Divide: $26 \div 3\frac{1}{2}$.

Divide.

GS 7. $2\frac{1}{4} \div 1\frac{1}{5}$

$$= \frac{\boxed{}}{4} \div \frac{\boxed{}}{5}$$

$$= \frac{9}{4} \cdot \frac{5}{\boxed{}}$$

$$= \frac{3 \cdot 3 \cdot 5}{2 \cdot 2 \cdot 2 \cdot \boxed{}}$$

$$= \frac{\boxed{}}{\boxed{}} \cdot \frac{3 \cdot 5}{2 \cdot 2 \cdot 2}$$

$$= \frac{15}{\boxed{}}$$

$$= \boxed{} \frac{\boxed{}}{\boxed{}}$$

8. $1\frac{3}{4} \div \left(-2\frac{1}{2}\right)$

Answers

5. 16 **6.** $7\frac{3}{7}$ **7.** $1\frac{7}{8}$ **8.** $-\frac{7}{10}$

Guided Solution:
7. $9, 6, 6, 3, \frac{3}{3}, 8, 1\frac{7}{8}$

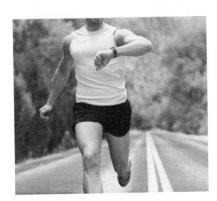

c APPLICATIONS AND PROBLEM SOLVING

EXAMPLE 9 *Training Regimens.* Fitness trainers suggest training regimens for athletes who are preparing to run marathons and mini-marathons. One suggested twelve-week regimen combines days of short, easy running with other days of cross-training, rest, and long-distance running. During week nine, this regimen calls for a long-distance run of 10 mi, which is $2\frac{1}{2}$ times the length of the long-distance run recommended for week one. What is the length of the long-distance run recommended for week one?

Source: shape.com

1. **Familiarize.** We ask the question "10 is $2\frac{1}{2}$ times what number?" We let $r =$ the length of the long-distance run recommended for week one.

2. **Translate.** The problem can be translated to an equation.

$$\underbrace{\text{Length of run for week nine}}_{\downarrow} \quad \underset{\downarrow}{\text{is}} \quad \underset{\downarrow}{2\frac{1}{2}} \quad \underset{\downarrow}{\text{times}} \quad \underbrace{\text{Length of run for week one}}_{\downarrow}$$

$$10 \quad = \quad 2\frac{1}{2} \quad \cdot \quad r$$

3. **Solve.** To solve the equation, we divide on both sides.

$$10 = \frac{5}{2} \cdot r \qquad \text{Converting } 2\frac{1}{2} \text{ to fraction notation}$$

$$10 \div \frac{5}{2} = r \qquad \text{Dividing by } \frac{5}{2} \text{ on both sides}$$

$$10 \cdot \frac{2}{5} = r \qquad \text{Multiplying by the reciprocal of } \frac{5}{2}$$

$$4 = r \qquad \text{Simplifying: } 10 \cdot \frac{2}{5} = \frac{20}{5} = 4$$

4. **Check.** If the length of the long-distance run recommended for week one is 4 mi, we find the length of the run recommended for week nine by multiplying 4 by $2\frac{1}{2}$.

$$2\frac{1}{2} \cdot 4 = \frac{5}{2} \cdot 4 = \frac{20}{2} = 10$$

The answer checks.

5. **State.** The regimen recommends a long-distance run of 4 mi for week one.

◀ **Do Exercises 9 and 10.**

EXAMPLE 10 *Flooring.* Ann and Tony plan to redo the floor of their living room. Since part of the room will be covered by a rug, they want to lay a hardwood floor only on the part of the room not under the rug. If the room is $22\frac{1}{2}$ ft by $15\frac{1}{2}$ ft and the rug is 9 ft by 12 ft, how much hardwood flooring do they need? How much hardwood flooring would it take to cover the entire floor of the room?

Solve.

9. Kyle's pickup truck travels on an interstate highway at 65 mph for $3\frac{1}{2}$ hr. How far does it travel?

10. Holly's minivan traveled 302 mi on $15\frac{1}{10}$ gal of gas. How many miles per gallon did it get?

Answers

9. $227\frac{1}{2}$ mi   10. 20 mpg

1. **Familiarize.** We draw a diagram and let $B = $ the area of the room, $R = $ the area of the rug, and $H = $ the area to be covered by hardwood flooring.

2. **Translate.** This is a multistep problem. We first find the area of the room, B, and the area of the rug, R. Then $H = B - R$. We find each area using the formula for the area of a rectangle: $A = l \times w$.

3. **Solve.** We carry out the calculations.

$$B = \text{length} \times \text{width}$$
$$= 22\frac{1}{2} \cdot 15\frac{1}{2}$$
$$= \frac{45}{2} \cdot \frac{31}{2}$$
$$= \frac{1395}{4} = 348\frac{3}{4} \text{ sq ft}$$

$$R = \text{length} \times \text{width}$$
$$= 12 \cdot 9$$
$$= 108 \text{ sq ft}$$

Then $H = B - R$

$$= 348\frac{3}{4} \text{ sq ft} - 108 \text{ sq ft}$$

$$= 240\frac{3}{4} \text{ sq ft}$$

4. **Check.** We can perform a check by repeating the calculations.

5. **State.** Ann and Tony will need $240\frac{3}{4}$ sq ft of hardwood flooring. It would take $348\frac{3}{4}$ sq ft of hardwood flooring to cover the entire floor of the room.

Do Exercise 11. ▶

11. *Koi Pond.* Colleen designed a koi fish pond for her backyard. Using the dimensions shown in the diagram below, determine the area of Colleen's backyard remaining after the pond was completed.

Sources: en.wikipedia.org; pondliner.com

CALCULATOR CORNER

Operations on Fractions and Mixed Numerals Fraction calculators can add, subtract, multiply, and divide fractions and mixed numerals. The $\boxed{a^b/_c}$ key is used to enter fractions and mixed numerals. The fraction $\frac{3}{4}$ is entered by pressing $\boxed{3}$ $\boxed{a^b/_c}$ $\boxed{4}$, and it appears on the display as $\boxed{\quad 3 \lrcorner 4}$. The mixed numeral $1\frac{5}{16}$ is entered by pressing $\boxed{1}$ $\boxed{a^b/_c}$ $\boxed{5}$ $\boxed{a^b/_c}$ $\boxed{1}$ $\boxed{6}$, and it is displayed as $\boxed{1 \lrcorner 5 \lrcorner 16}$. Fraction results that are greater than 1 are always displayed as mixed numerals. To express the result for $1\frac{5}{16}$ as a fraction, we press $\boxed{\text{SHIFT}}$ $\boxed{d/c}$. We get $\boxed{\quad 21 \lrcorner 16}$, or $\frac{21}{16}$. Some calculators display fractions and mixed numerals in the way in which we write them.

EXERCISES Perform each calculation. Give the answer in fraction notation.

1. $\dfrac{1}{3} + \dfrac{1}{4}$

2. $\dfrac{7}{5} - \dfrac{3}{10}$

3. $\dfrac{15}{4} \cdot \dfrac{7}{12}$

4. $\dfrac{4}{5} \div \dfrac{8}{3}$

Perform each calculation. Give the answer as a mixed numeral.

5. $4\dfrac{1}{3} + 5\dfrac{4}{5}$

6. $9\dfrac{2}{7} - 8\dfrac{1}{4}$

7. $2\dfrac{1}{3} \cdot 4\dfrac{3}{5}$

8. $10\dfrac{7}{10} \div 3\dfrac{5}{6}$

Answer

11. 945 sq yd

Translating for Success

The goal of these matching questions is to practice step (2), Translate, of the five-step problem-solving process. Translate each word problem to an equation and select a correct translation from equations A–O.

1. **Raffle Tickets.** At the Happy Hollow Camp Fall Festival, Rico and Becca, together, spent $270 on raffle tickets that sell for $\$\frac{9}{20}$ each. How many tickets did they buy?

2. **Irrigation Pipe.** Jed uses two pipes, one of which measures $5\frac{1}{3}$ ft, to repair the irrigation system in the Aguilars' lawn. The total length of the two pipes is $8\frac{7}{12}$ ft. How long is the other pipe?

3. **Vacation Days.** Together, Oscar and Claire have 36 vacation days a year. Oscar has 22 vacation days per year. How many does Claire have?

4. **Enrollment in Japanese Classes.** Last year at the Lakeside Community College, 225 students enrolled in basic mathematics. This number is $4\frac{1}{2}$ times as many as the number who enrolled in Japanese. How many enrolled in Japanese?

5. **Bicycling.** Cole rode his bicycle $5\frac{1}{3}$ mi on Saturday and $8\frac{7}{12}$ mi on Sunday. How far did he ride on the weekend?

A. $13\frac{11}{12} = x + 5\frac{1}{3}$

B. $\frac{3}{4} \cdot x = 1\frac{2}{3}$

C. $270 - \frac{20}{9} = x$

D. $225 = 4\frac{1}{2} \cdot x$

E. $98 \div 2\frac{1}{3} = x$

F. $22 + x = 36$

G. $x = 4\frac{1}{2} \cdot 225$

H. $x = 5\frac{1}{3} + 8\frac{7}{12}$

I. $22 \cdot x = 36$

J. $x = \frac{3}{4} \cdot 1\frac{2}{3}$

K. $5\frac{1}{3} + x = 8\frac{7}{12}$

L. $\frac{9}{20} \cdot 270 = x$

M. $1\frac{2}{3} + \frac{3}{4} = x$

N. $98 - 2\frac{1}{3} = x$

O. $\frac{9}{20} \cdot x = 270$

Answers on page A-7

6. **Deli Order.** For a promotional open house for contractors last year, the Bayside Builders Association ordered 225 turkey sandwiches. Due to increased registrations this year, $4\frac{1}{2}$ times as many sandwiches are needed. How many sandwiches should be ordered?

7. **Dog Ownership.** In Sam's community, $\frac{9}{20}$ of the households own at least one dog. There are 270 households. How many own dogs?

8. **Magic Tricks.** Samantha has 98 ft of rope and needs to cut it into $2\frac{1}{3}$-ft pieces to be used in a magic trick. How many pieces can be cut from the rope?

9. **Painting.** Laura needs $1\frac{2}{3}$ gal of paint to paint the ceiling of the exercise room and $\frac{3}{4}$ gal of the same paint for the bathroom. How much paint does Laura need?

10. **Chocolate Fudge Bars.** A recipe for chocolate fudge bars that serves 16 includes $1\frac{2}{3}$ cups of sugar. How much sugar is needed for $\frac{3}{4}$ of this recipe?

✓ Reading Check

Determine whether each statement is true or false.

_____ **RC1.** To multiply using mixed numerals, we first convert to fraction notation.

_____ **RC2.** To divide using mixed numerals, we first convert to fraction notation.

_____ **RC3.** The product of mixed numerals is generally written as a mixed numeral, unless it is a whole number or less than 1.

_____ **RC4.** To divide fractions, we multiply by the reciprocal of the divisor.

a   Multiply. Write a mixed numeral for the answer.

1. $8 \cdot 2\frac{5}{6}$

2. $5 \cdot 3\frac{3}{4}$

3. $3\frac{5}{8} \cdot \left(-\frac{2}{3}\right)$

4. $6\frac{2}{3} \cdot \left(-\frac{1}{4}\right)$

5. $3\frac{1}{2} \cdot 2\frac{1}{3}$

6. $4\frac{1}{5} \cdot 5\frac{1}{4}$

7. $3\frac{2}{5} \cdot 2\frac{7}{8}$

8. $2\frac{3}{10} \cdot 4\frac{2}{5}$

9. $-4\frac{7}{10} \cdot 5\frac{3}{10}$

10. $-6\frac{3}{10} \cdot 5\frac{7}{10}$

11. $-20\frac{1}{2} \cdot 10\frac{1}{5} \cdot \left(-4\frac{2}{3}\right)$

12. $-21\frac{1}{3} \cdot 11\frac{1}{3} \cdot \left(-3\frac{5}{8}\right)$

b   Divide. Write a mixed numeral for the answer.

13. $20 \div 3\frac{1}{5}$

14. $18 \div 2\frac{1}{4}$

15. $8\frac{2}{5} \div 7$

16. $3\frac{3}{8} \div 3$

17. $-4\frac{3}{4} \div 1\frac{1}{3}$

18. $-5\frac{4}{5} \div 2\frac{1}{2}$

19. $1\frac{7}{8} \div 1\frac{2}{3}$

20. $4\frac{3}{8} \div 2\frac{5}{6}$

21. $5\frac{1}{10} \div 4\frac{3}{10}$

22. $4\frac{1}{10} \div 2\frac{1}{10}$

23. $-20\frac{1}{4} \div (-90)$

24. $-12\frac{1}{2} \div (-50)$

C   Solve.

25. *Art Prices.*   A 1966 Andy Warhol portrait of Marlon Brando on his motorcycle sold for $5 million at Christie's in 2003. On November 14, 2012, the work was sold again by Christie's for about $4\frac{4}{5}$ times the amount paid in 2003. How much was paid for the portrait in 2012?

Source: Businessweek.com

26. *Spreading Grass Seed.*   Emily seeds lawns for Sam's Superior Lawn Care. When she walks at a rapid pace, the wheel on the broadcast spreader completes $150\frac{2}{3}$ revolutions per minute. How many revolutions does the wheel complete in 15 min?

27. *Population.*   The population of Alabama is $6\frac{2}{3}$ times that of Alaska. The population of Alaska is approximately 720,000. What is the population of Alabama?

Source: U.S. Census Bureau

28. *Population.*   The population of New York is $32\frac{1}{2}$ times the population of Wyoming. The population of Wyoming is approximately 600,000. What is the population of New York?

Source: U.S. Census Bureau

29. *Mural.*   A student artist painted a mural on the wall under a bridge. The dimensions of the mural are $6\frac{2}{3}$ ft by $9\frac{3}{8}$ ft. What is the area of the mural?

30. *Sodium Consumption.*   The average American woman consumes $1\frac{2}{5}$ tsp of sodium each day. How much sodium do 10 average American women consume in one day?

Source: Based on information from mayoclinic.com

31. *Sidewalk.*   A sidewalk alongside a garden at the conservatory is to be $14\frac{2}{5}$ yd long. Rectangular stone tiles that are each $1\frac{1}{8}$ yd long are used to form the sidewalk. How many tiles are used?

32. *Aeronautics.*   Most space shuttles orbit the earth once every $1\frac{1}{2}$ hr. How many orbits are made every 24 hr?

33. *Weight of Water.*   The weight of water is $62\frac{1}{2}$ lb per cubic foot. What is the weight of $5\frac{1}{2}$ cubic feet of water?

34. *Weight of Water.*   The weight of water is $62\frac{1}{2}$ lb per cubic foot. What is the weight of $2\frac{1}{4}$ cubic feet of water?

Copyright © 2015 Pearson Education, Inc.

35. *Temperature.* Fahrenheit temperature can be obtained from Celsius (Centigrade) temperature by multiplying by $1\frac{4}{5}$ and adding 32°. What Fahrenheit temperature corresponds to a Celsius temperature of 20°?

36. *Temperature.* Fahrenheit temperature can be obtained from Celsius (Centigrade) temperature by multiplying by $1\frac{4}{5}$ and adding 32°. What Fahrenheit temperature corresponds to the Celsius temperature of boiling water, 100°?

37. *Apple Net Income.* Apple, Inc., reported net income of about $8,000,000,000 in fiscal year 2009. In fiscal year 2012, Apple's net income was about $5\frac{1}{4}$ times that amount. What was Apple's net income for fiscal year 2012?

38. *Median Income.* Median household income in the United States was about $12,000 in 1975. By 2011, median household income was $4\frac{1}{6}$ times that amount. What was the median household income in 2011?

Source: U.S. Census Bureau

39. *Average Speed in Indianapolis 500.* Arie Luyendyk won the Indianapolis 500 in 1990 with a record average speed of about 186 mph. This record held through 2012 and is about $2\frac{12}{25}$ times the average speed of the first winner, Ray Harroun, in 1911. What was the average speed in the first Indianapolis 500?

Source: Indianapolis Motor Speedway

40. *Population.* The population of Cleveland is about $1\frac{1}{3}$ times the population of Cincinnati. In 2013, the population of Cincinnati was approximately 294,750. What was the population of Cleveland in 2013?

Source: U.S. Census Bureau

41. *Doubling a Recipe.* The chef of a five-star hotel is doubling a recipe for chocolate cake. The original recipe requires $2\frac{3}{4}$ cups of flour and $1\frac{1}{3}$ cups of sugar. How much flour and sugar will she need?

42. *Half of a Recipe.* A caterer is following a salad dressing recipe that calls for $1\frac{7}{8}$ cups of mayonnaise and $1\frac{1}{6}$ cups of sugar. How much mayonnaise and sugar will he need if he prepares $\frac{1}{2}$ of the amount of salad dressing?

43. *Mileage.* A car traveled 213 mi on $14\frac{2}{10}$ gal of gas. How many miles per gallon did it get?

44. *Mileage.* A car traveled 385 mi on $15\frac{4}{10}$ gal of gas. How many miles per gallon did it get?

45. *Weight of Water.*   The weight of water is $62\frac{1}{2}$ lb per cubic foot. How many cubic feet would be occupied by 25,000 lb of water?

46. *Weight of Water.*   The weight of water is $8\frac{1}{3}$ lb per gallon. Harry rolls his lawn with an 800-lb capacity roller. Express the water capacity of the roller in gallons.

47. *Servings of Salmon.*   A serving of filleted fish is generally considered to be about $\frac{1}{3}$ lb. How many servings can be prepared from $5\frac{1}{2}$ lb of salmon fillet?

48. *Servings of Tuna.*   A serving of fish steak (cross section) is generally $\frac{1}{2}$ lb. How many servings can be prepared from a cleaned $18\frac{3}{4}$-lb tuna?

Find the area of each shaded region.

49.

$s = 6\frac{7}{8}$ in.

$\frac{1}{2} \cdot s$

$\frac{1}{2} \cdot s$

$6\frac{7}{8}$ in.

50.

$10\frac{1}{2}$ ft

$8\frac{1}{2}$ ft

4 ft

$10\frac{1}{2}$ ft

51. *Building a Ziggurat.*   The dimensions of all of the square bricks that King Nebuchadnezzar used over 2500 years ago to build ziggurats were $13\frac{1}{4}$ in. $\times$ $13\frac{1}{4}$ in. $\times$ $3\frac{1}{4}$ in. What is the perimeter and the area of the $13\frac{1}{4}$ in. $\times$ $13\frac{1}{4}$ in. side? of the $13\frac{1}{4}$ in. $\times$ $3\frac{1}{4}$ in. side?

Source: www.eartharchitecture.org

52. *Word Processing.*   For David's design report, he needs to create a table containing two columns, each $1\frac{1}{2}$ in. wide, and five columns, each $\frac{3}{4}$ in. wide. Will this table fit on a piece of standard paper that is $8\frac{1}{2}$ in. wide? If so, how wide will each side margin be if the margins on each side are to be of equal width?

Copyright © 2015 Pearson Education, Inc.

Skill Maintenance

Solve.

53. *Checking Account Balance.* The balance in Laura's checking account is $457. She uses her debit card to buy a digital picture frame that costs $49. Find the new balance in her checking account. [1.8a]

54. Anita buys 12 gift cards at $15 each and pays for them with $20 bills. How many $20 bills does it take? [1.8a]

55. About $\frac{9}{25}$ of all pizzas that Americans order have pepperoni as a topping. If Americans eat 350 slices of pizza every second, how many of those slices are topped with pepperoni? [3.6b]

Source: inventors.about.com

56. A batch of fudge requires $\frac{3}{4}$ cup of sugar. How much sugar is needed to make 12 batches? [3.6b]

57. After her company was restructured, Meghan's pay was $\frac{9}{10}$ of what it had been. If she is now making $32,850 a year, what was she making before the reorganization? [3.7d]

58. Rick's Market sells Swiss cheese in $\frac{3}{4}$-lb packages. How many packages can be made from a 12-lb slab of cheese? [3.7d]

59. Find the perimeter of the figure. [1.2b]

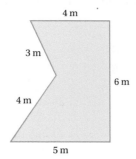

60. Find the area of the region. [1.4b]

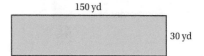

Synthesis

Multiply. Write the answer as a mixed numeral whenever possible.

61. 🖩 $15\frac{2}{11} \cdot 23\frac{31}{43}$

62. 🖩 $17\frac{23}{31} \cdot 19\frac{13}{15}$

Simplify.

63. $8 \div \frac{1}{2} + \frac{3}{4} - \left(5 - \frac{5}{8}\right)^2$

64. $\left(\frac{5}{9} - \frac{1}{4}\right) \times 12 + \left(4 - \frac{3}{4}\right)^2$

65. $\frac{1}{3} \div \left(\frac{1}{2} - \frac{1}{5}\right) \times \frac{1}{4} + \frac{1}{6}$

66. $\frac{7}{8} - 1\frac{1}{8} \times \frac{2}{3} - \frac{9}{10} \div \frac{3}{5}$

67. $4\frac{1}{2} \div 2\frac{1}{2} + 8 - 4 \div \frac{1}{2}$

68. $6 - 2\frac{1}{3} \times \frac{3}{4} + \frac{5}{8} \div \frac{2}{3}$

OBJECTIVES

a Simplify expressions using the rules for order of operations.

b Simplify complex fractions.

c Estimate with fraction notation and mixed numerals.

SKILL TO REVIEW

Objective 1.9c: Simplify expressions using the rules for order of operations.

Simplify.

1. $22 - 3 \cdot 4$

2. $6(4 + 1)^2 - 3^4 \div 3$

Simplify.

1. $\dfrac{2}{5} \cdot \dfrac{5}{8} + \dfrac{1}{4}$

2. $\dfrac{1}{3} \cdot \dfrac{3}{4} \div \dfrac{5}{8} - \dfrac{1}{10}$

$$= \dfrac{\square}{12} \div \dfrac{5}{8} - \dfrac{1}{10} = \dfrac{3}{12} \cdot \dfrac{\square}{5} - \dfrac{1}{10}$$

$$= \dfrac{3 \cdot 2 \cdot 2 \cdot \square}{3 \cdot 2 \cdot 2 \cdot 5} - \dfrac{1}{10} = \dfrac{\square}{5} - \dfrac{1}{10}$$

$$= \dfrac{\square}{10} - \dfrac{1}{10} = \dfrac{\square}{10}$$

3. Simplify: $\dfrac{3}{4} \cdot 16 + 8\dfrac{2}{3}$.

Answers

Skill to Review:
1. 10   2. 123

Margin Exercises:
1. $\dfrac{1}{2}$ 2. $\dfrac{3}{10}$ 3. $20\dfrac{2}{3}$, or $\dfrac{62}{3}$

Guided Solution:
2. 3, 8, 2, 2, 4, 3

a ORDER OF OPERATIONS; FRACTION NOTATION AND MIXED NUMERALS

The rules for order of operations that we use with whole numbers apply when we are simplifying expressions involving fraction notation and mixed numerals. For review, these rules are listed below.

RULES FOR ORDER OF OPERATIONS

1. Do all calculations within parentheses before operations outside.
2. Evaluate all exponential expressions.
3. Do all multiplications and divisions in order from left to right.
4. Do all additions and subtractions in order from left to right.

EXAMPLE 1 Simplify: $\dfrac{1}{6} + \dfrac{2}{3} \div \dfrac{1}{2} \cdot \dfrac{5}{8}$.

$$\dfrac{1}{6} + \dfrac{2}{3} \div \dfrac{1}{2} \cdot \dfrac{5}{8} = \dfrac{1}{6} + \dfrac{2}{3} \cdot \dfrac{2}{1} \cdot \dfrac{5}{8}$$

    Doing the division first by multiplying by the reciprocal of $\frac{1}{2}$

$$= \dfrac{1}{6} + \dfrac{2 \cdot 2 \cdot 5}{3 \cdot 1 \cdot 8}$$

    Doing the multiplications in order from left to right

$$= \dfrac{1}{6} + \dfrac{2 \cdot 2 \cdot 5}{3 \cdot 1 \cdot 2 \cdot 2 \cdot 2}$$

    Factoring in order to simplify

$$= \dfrac{1}{6} + \dfrac{5}{6}$$

    Removing a factor of 1: $\dfrac{2 \cdot 2}{2 \cdot 2} = 1$; simplifying

$$= \dfrac{6}{6}, \text{ or } 1$$

    Doing the addition

◀ Do Margin Exercises 1 and 2.

EXAMPLE 2 Simplify: $\dfrac{2}{3} \cdot 24 - 11\dfrac{1}{2}$.

$$\dfrac{2}{3} \cdot 24 - 11\dfrac{1}{2} = \dfrac{2 \cdot 24}{3 \cdot 1} - 11\dfrac{1}{2}$$

    Doing the multiplication first

$$= \dfrac{2 \cdot 3 \cdot 8}{3 \cdot 1} - 11\dfrac{1}{2}$$

    Factoring the fraction

$$= 2 \cdot 8 - 11\dfrac{1}{2}$$

    Removing a factor of 1: $\dfrac{3}{3} = 1$

$$= 16 - 11\dfrac{1}{2}$$

    Completing the multiplication

$$= 4\dfrac{1}{2}, \text{ or } \dfrac{9}{2}$$

    Doing the subtraction

◀ Do Exercise 3.

EXAMPLE 3 Simplify: $\left(\dfrac{7}{8} - \dfrac{1}{3}\right) \times 48 + \left(13 + \dfrac{4}{5}\right)^2$.

$\left(\dfrac{7}{8} - \dfrac{1}{3}\right) \times 48 + \left(13 + \dfrac{4}{5}\right)^2$

$= \left(\dfrac{7}{8} \cdot \dfrac{3}{3} - \dfrac{1}{3} \cdot \dfrac{8}{8}\right) \times 48 + \left(13 \cdot \dfrac{5}{5} + \dfrac{4}{5}\right)^2$ Carrying out operations inside parentheses first. To do so, we first multiply by 1 to obtain each LCD.

$= \left(\dfrac{21}{24} - \dfrac{8}{24}\right) \times 48 + \left(\dfrac{65}{5} + \dfrac{4}{5}\right)^2$

$= \dfrac{13}{24} \times 48 + \left(\dfrac{69}{5}\right)^2$ Completing the operations within parentheses

$= \dfrac{13}{24} \times 48 + \dfrac{4761}{25}$ Evaluating the exponential expression next

$= 26 + \dfrac{4761}{25}$ Doing the multiplication

$= 26 + 190\dfrac{11}{25}$ Converting to a mixed numeral

$= 216\dfrac{11}{25}$, or $\dfrac{5411}{25}$ Adding

Answers can be given using either fraction notation or mixed numerals.

Do Exercise 4. ▶

4. Simplify:
$\left(\dfrac{2}{3} + \dfrac{3}{4}\right) \div 2\dfrac{1}{3} - \left(\dfrac{1}{2}\right)^3$.

b   COMPLEX FRACTIONS

A **complex fraction** is a fraction in which the numerator and/or the denominator contains one or more fractions. The following are some examples of complex fractions.

$\dfrac{\dfrac{7}{3}}{2}$ ← The numerator contains a fraction.

$\dfrac{\dfrac{1}{5}}{\dfrac{9}{10}}$ ← The numerator contains a fraction.
← The denominator contains a fraction.

Since a fraction bar represents division, complex fractions can be rewritten using the division symbol ÷.

EXAMPLE 4 Simplify: $\dfrac{\dfrac{7}{3}}{2}$

$\dfrac{\dfrac{7}{3}}{2} = \dfrac{7}{3} \div 2$ Rewriting using a division symbol

$= \dfrac{7}{3} \cdot \dfrac{1}{2}$ Multiplying by the reciprocal of the divisor

$= \dfrac{7 \cdot 1}{3 \cdot 2}$ Multiplying numerators and multiplying denominators

$= \dfrac{7}{6}$ This expression cannot be simplified.

Answer

4. $\dfrac{27}{56}$

EXAMPLE 5 Simplify: $\dfrac{-\dfrac{1}{5}}{\dfrac{9}{10}}$.

$$\dfrac{-\dfrac{1}{5}}{\dfrac{9}{10}} = -\dfrac{1}{5} \div \dfrac{9}{10}$$

Rewriting using a division symbol

$$= -\dfrac{1}{5} \cdot \dfrac{10}{9}$$

Multiplying by the reciprocal of the divisor

$$= -\dfrac{1 \cdot 2 \cdot 5}{5 \cdot 3 \cdot 3}$$

Multiplying numerators and multiplying denominators; factoring

$$= -\dfrac{2}{9}$$

Removing a factor of 1 and simplifying

◀ **Do Exercises 5 and 6.**

When the numerator or denominator of a complex fraction consists of more than one term, first simplify that numerator or denominator separately.

EXAMPLE 6 Simplify: $\dfrac{\dfrac{2}{3} - \dfrac{1}{2}}{1\dfrac{7}{8}}$.

$$\dfrac{\dfrac{2}{3} - \dfrac{1}{2}}{1\dfrac{7}{8}} = \dfrac{\dfrac{4}{6} - \dfrac{3}{6}}{\dfrac{15}{8}}$$

Writing the fractions in the numerator with a common denominator

Writing the mixed numeral in the denominator as a fraction

$$= \dfrac{\dfrac{1}{6}}{\dfrac{15}{8}}$$

Subtracting in the numerator of the complex fraction

$$= \dfrac{1}{6} \div \dfrac{15}{8}$$

Rewriting using a division symbol

$$= \dfrac{1}{6} \cdot \dfrac{8}{15}$$

Multiplying by the reciprocal of the divisor

$$= \dfrac{1 \cdot 2 \cdot 2 \cdot 2}{2 \cdot 3 \cdot 3 \cdot 5}$$

Multiplying numerators and multiplying denominators; factoring

$$= \dfrac{4}{45}$$

Removing a factor of 1: $\dfrac{2}{2} = 1$

◀ **Do Exercises 7 and 8.**

EXAMPLE 7 *Harvesting Walnut Trees.* A woodland owner decided to harvest five walnut trees in order to improve the growing conditions of the remaining trees. The logs she sold measured $7\frac{5}{8}$ ft, $8\frac{1}{4}$ ft, $8\frac{3}{4}$ ft, $9\frac{1}{8}$ ft, and $10\frac{1}{2}$ ft. What is the average length of the logs?

Simplify.

5. $\dfrac{\dfrac{10}{5}}{8}$

6. $\dfrac{-\dfrac{7}{5}}{\dfrac{10}{7}}$

Simplify.

7. $\dfrac{\dfrac{7}{12} + \dfrac{5}{6}}{\dfrac{4}{9}}$

GS

8. $\dfrac{\dfrac{3}{5}}{\dfrac{7}{10} - \dfrac{2}{3}}$

$$= \dfrac{\dfrac{3}{5}}{\dfrac{7}{10} \cdot \dfrac{3}{3} - \dfrac{2}{3} \cdot \dfrac{\square}{\square}} = \dfrac{\dfrac{3}{5}}{\dfrac{21}{30} - \dfrac{\square}{30}}$$

$$= \dfrac{\dfrac{3}{5}}{\dfrac{\square}{30}} = \dfrac{3}{5} \div \dfrac{1}{30}$$

$$= \dfrac{3}{5} \cdot \dfrac{\square}{1} = \dfrac{3 \cdot 6 \cdot 5}{5 \cdot 1} = \square$$

Answers

5. 16   6. $-\dfrac{49}{50}$ 7. $\dfrac{51}{16}$, or $3\dfrac{3}{16}$ 8. 18

Guided Solution:

8. $\dfrac{10}{10}$, 20, 1, 30, 18

Recall that to compute an average, we add the numbers and then divide the sum by the number of addends. We have

$$\frac{7\frac{5}{8} + 8\frac{1}{4} + 8\frac{3}{4} + 9\frac{1}{8} + 10\frac{1}{2}}{5} = \frac{7\frac{5}{8} + 8\frac{2}{8} + 8\frac{6}{8} + 9\frac{1}{8} + 10\frac{4}{8}}{5}$$

$$= \frac{42\frac{18}{8}}{5} = \frac{42\frac{9}{4}}{5} = \frac{\frac{177}{4}}{5} \quad \begin{array}{l}\text{Adding,}\\ \text{simplifying, and}\\ \text{converting to}\\ \text{fraction notation}\end{array}$$

$$= \frac{177}{4} \cdot \frac{1}{5} \quad \begin{array}{l}\text{Multiplying by}\\ \text{the reciprocal}\end{array}$$

$$= \frac{177}{20} = 8\frac{17}{20}. \quad \begin{array}{l}\text{Converting to a}\\ \text{mixed numeral}\end{array}$$

The average length of the logs is $8\frac{17}{20}$ ft.

Do Exercises 9–11.

9. Rachel has triplets. Their birth weights are $3\frac{1}{2}$ lb, $2\frac{3}{4}$ lb, and $3\frac{1}{8}$ lb. What is the average weight of her babies?

10. Find the average of $\frac{1}{2}, \frac{1}{3},$ and $\frac{5}{6}$.

11. Find the average of $\frac{3}{4}$ and $\frac{4}{5}$.

c ESTIMATION WITH FRACTION NOTATION AND MIXED NUMERALS

EXAMPLES Estimate each of the following as $0, \frac{1}{2},$ or 1.

8. $\frac{2}{17}$

A fraction is close to 0 when the numerator is small in comparison to the denominator. Since 2 is small in comparison to 17, we have $\frac{2}{17} \approx 0$.

9. $\frac{11}{23}$

A fraction is close to $\frac{1}{2}$ when the denominator is about twice the numerator. Twice the numerator of this fraction is 22, and 22 is close to 23. Thus, $\frac{11}{23} \approx \frac{1}{2}$.

10. $\frac{43}{41}$

A fraction is close to 1 when the numerator is nearly equal to the denominator. Since 43 is nearly equal to 41, we have $\frac{43}{41} \approx 1$.

Do Exercises 12–15.

Estimate each of the following as $0, \frac{1}{2},$ or 1.

12. $\frac{3}{59}$ 13. $\frac{61}{59}$

14. $\frac{29}{59}$ 15. $\frac{57}{59}$

EXAMPLE 11 Estimate $16\frac{8}{9} + 11\frac{2}{13} - 4\frac{22}{43}$ by estimating each mixed numeral as a whole number or as a mixed numeral where the fractional part is $\frac{1}{2}$.

We estimate each mixed numeral. Then we calculate:

$$16\frac{8}{9} + 11\frac{2}{13} - 4\frac{22}{43} \approx 17 + 11 - 4\frac{1}{2}$$

$$= 28 - 4\frac{1}{2} = 23\frac{1}{2}.$$

Estimate each of the following by estimating each mixed numeral as a whole number or as a mixed numeral where the fractional part is $\frac{1}{2}$ and estimating each fraction as $0, \frac{1}{2},$ or 1.

16. $5\frac{9}{10} + 26\frac{1}{2} - 10\frac{3}{29}$

17. $10\frac{7}{8} \cdot \left(25\frac{11}{13} - 14\frac{1}{9}\right)$

18. $\left(10\frac{4}{5} + 7\frac{5}{9}\right) \div \frac{17}{30}$

Do Exercises 16–18.

Answers

9. $3\frac{1}{8}$ lb   10. $\frac{5}{9}$ 11. $\frac{31}{40}$ 12. 0   13. 1

14. $\frac{1}{2}$ 15. 1   16. $22\frac{1}{2}$ 17. 132   18. 37

☑ Reading Check

Match the beginning of each statement with the correct ending from the list at the right so that the rules for order of operations are listed in the correct order.

RC1. Do all _____.

RC2. Evaluate all _____.

RC3. Do all _____.

RC4. Do all _____.

a) multiplications and divisions in order from left to right

b) additions and subtractions in order from left to right

c) calculations within parentheses

d) exponential expressions

a   Simplify.

1. $\dfrac{5}{8} \div \dfrac{1}{4} - \dfrac{2}{3} \cdot \dfrac{4}{5}$

2. $\dfrac{4}{7} \cdot \dfrac{7}{15} + \dfrac{2}{3} \div 8$

3. $\dfrac{3}{4} - \dfrac{2}{3} \cdot \left(\dfrac{1}{2} + \dfrac{2}{5} \right)$

4. $\dfrac{3}{4} \div \dfrac{1}{2} \cdot \left(\dfrac{8}{9} - \dfrac{2}{3} \right)$

5. $28\dfrac{1}{8} - 5\dfrac{1}{4} + 3\dfrac{1}{2}$

6. $10\dfrac{3}{5} - 4\dfrac{1}{10} - 1\dfrac{1}{2}$

7. $\dfrac{7}{8} \div \dfrac{1}{2} \cdot \dfrac{1}{4}$

8. $\dfrac{7}{10} \cdot \dfrac{4}{5} \div \dfrac{2}{3}$

9. $\left(\dfrac{2}{3} \right)^2 - \dfrac{1}{3} \cdot 1\dfrac{1}{4}$

10. $\left(\dfrac{3}{4} \right)^2 + 3\dfrac{1}{2} \div 1\dfrac{1}{4}$

11. $\dfrac{1}{2} - \left(\dfrac{1}{2} \right)^2 + \left(\dfrac{1}{2} \right)^3$

12. $-1 + \dfrac{1}{4} + \left(\dfrac{1}{4} \right)^2 - \left(\dfrac{1}{4} \right)^3$

13. $\left(\dfrac{2}{3} + \dfrac{3}{4} \right) \div \left(\dfrac{5}{6} - \dfrac{1}{3} \right)$

14. $\left(\dfrac{3}{5} - \dfrac{1}{2} \right) \div \left(\dfrac{3}{4} - \dfrac{3}{10} \right)$

15. $\left(\dfrac{1}{2} + \dfrac{1}{3} \right)^2 \cdot 144 - \dfrac{5}{8} \div 10\dfrac{1}{2}$

16. $\left(3\dfrac{1}{2} - 2\dfrac{1}{3} \right)^2 + 6 \cdot 2\dfrac{1}{2} \div 32$

b   Simplify.

17. $\dfrac{\frac{3}{8}}{\frac{11}{8}}$

18. $\dfrac{\frac{1}{8}}{\frac{3}{4}}$

19. $\dfrac{-4}{\frac{6}{7}}$

20. $\dfrac{-\frac{3}{8}}{12}$

21. $\dfrac{\frac{1}{40}}{\frac{1}{50}}$

Copyright © 2015 Pearson Education, Inc.

22. $\dfrac{\dfrac{7}{9}}{\dfrac{3}{9}}$

23. $\dfrac{\dfrac{1}{10}}{10}$

24. $\dfrac{\dfrac{28}{7}}{4}$

25. $\dfrac{-\dfrac{5}{18}}{1\dfrac{2}{3}}$

26. $\dfrac{2\dfrac{1}{5}}{-\dfrac{7}{10}}$

27. $\dfrac{\dfrac{5}{9} - \dfrac{1}{6}}{\dfrac{2}{3}}$

28. $\dfrac{\dfrac{7}{12}}{\dfrac{5}{8} - \dfrac{1}{4}}$

29. $\dfrac{\dfrac{3}{8} - \dfrac{1}{4}}{\dfrac{7}{8} - \dfrac{1}{2}}$

30. $\dfrac{\dfrac{3}{5} - \dfrac{1}{2}}{\dfrac{1}{2} - \dfrac{2}{5}}$

31. Find the average of $\dfrac{2}{3}$ and $\dfrac{7}{8}$.

32. Find the average of $\dfrac{1}{4}$ and $\dfrac{1}{5}$.

33. Find the average of $\dfrac{1}{6}, \dfrac{1}{8}$, and $\dfrac{3}{4}$.

34. Find the average of $\dfrac{4}{5}, \dfrac{1}{2}$, and $\dfrac{1}{10}$.

35. Find the average of $3\dfrac{1}{2}$ and $9\dfrac{3}{8}$.

36. Find the average of $10\dfrac{2}{3}$ and $24\dfrac{5}{6}$.

37. *Hiking the Appalachian Trail.* Ellen camped and hiked for three consecutive days along a section of the Appalachian Trail. The distances she hiked on the three days were $15\dfrac{5}{32}$ mi, $20\dfrac{3}{16}$ mi, and $12\dfrac{7}{8}$ mi. Find the average of these distances.

38. *Vertical Leaps.* Eight-year-old Zachary registered vertical leaps of $12\dfrac{3}{4}$ in., $13\dfrac{3}{4}$ in., $13\dfrac{1}{2}$ in., and 14 in. Find his average vertical leap.

39. *Black Bear Cubs.* Black bears typically have two cubs. In January 2007 in northern New Hampshire, a black bear sow gave birth to a litter of 5 cubs. This is so rare that Tom Sears, a wildlife photographer, spent 28 hr per week for six weeks watching for the perfect opportunity to photograph this family of six. At the time of this photo, an observer estimated that the cubs weighed $7\dfrac{1}{2}$ lb, 8 lb, $9\dfrac{1}{2}$ lb, $10\dfrac{5}{8}$ lb, and $11\dfrac{3}{4}$ lb. What was the average weight of the cubs?

Source: Andrew Timmins, New Hampshire Fish and Game Department, *Northcountry News*, Warren, NH; Tom Sears, photographer

40. *Acceleration.* The results of a *Road & Track* road acceleration test for five cars are given in the graph below. The test measures the time in seconds required to go from 0 mph to 60 mph. What was the average time?

Acceleration: 0 mph to 60 mph

SOURCE: *Road & Track*, October 2008, pp.156–157

Copyright © 2015 Pearson Education, Inc.

C Estimate each of the following as 0, $\frac{1}{2}$, or 1.

41. $\dfrac{2}{47}$ **42.** $\dfrac{5}{12}$ **43.** $\dfrac{7}{8}$ **44.** $\dfrac{1}{13}$ **45.** $\dfrac{6}{11}$ **46.** $\dfrac{11}{13}$

47. $\dfrac{7}{15}$ **48.** $\dfrac{1}{16}$ **49.** $\dfrac{7}{100}$ **50.** $\dfrac{5}{9}$ **51.** $\dfrac{19}{20}$ **52.** $\dfrac{4}{5}$

Estimate each of the following by estimating each mixed numeral as a whole number or as a mixed numeral where the fractional part is $\frac{1}{2}$ and by estimating each fraction as 0, $\frac{1}{2}$, or 1.

53. $2\dfrac{7}{8}$ **54.** $12\dfrac{5}{6}$ **55.** $\dfrac{4}{5} + \dfrac{7}{8}$ **56.** $\dfrac{1}{12} \cdot \dfrac{7}{15}$

57. $24 \div 7\dfrac{8}{9}$ **58.** $43\dfrac{16}{17} \div 11\dfrac{2}{13}$ **59.** $7\dfrac{29}{60} + 10\dfrac{12}{13} \cdot 24\dfrac{2}{17}$

60. $1\dfrac{5}{8} + 1\dfrac{27}{28} \cdot 6\dfrac{35}{74}$ **61.** $16\dfrac{1}{5} \div 2\dfrac{1}{11} + 25\dfrac{9}{10} - 4\dfrac{11}{23}$ **62.** $96\dfrac{2}{13} \div 5\dfrac{19}{20} + 3\dfrac{1}{7} \cdot 5\dfrac{18}{21}$

Skill Maintenance

Simplify.

63. $12 + 30 \div 3 - 2$ [1.9c]

64. $5 \cdot 2^2 \div 10$ [1.9c]

65. $10^2 - [3 \cdot 2^4 \div (10 - 2) + 5 \cdot 2]$ [1.9d]

66. $(10 + 3 \cdot 4 \div 6)^2 - 11 \cdot 2^2$ [1.9c]

67. List all the factors of 42.   [3.1a]

68. Determine whether 114 is divisible by 7.   [3.1b]

69. Classify the given numbers as prime, composite, or neither.   [3.1c]

     $1, 5, 7, 9, 14, 23, 43$

70. Find the prime factorization of 150.   [3.1d]

Synthesis

71. 🖩 In the sum below, a and b are digits. Find a and b.

$$\dfrac{a}{17} + \dfrac{1b}{23} = \dfrac{35a}{391}$$

72. 🖩 Consider only the numbers 3, 4, 5, and 6. Assume each can be placed in a blank in the following.

$$\square + \dfrac{\square}{\square} \cdot \square = \, ?$$

What placement of the numbers in the blanks yields the largest sum?

73. 🖩 Consider only the numbers 2, 3, 4, and 5. Assume each is placed in a blank in the following.

$$\dfrac{\square}{\square} + \dfrac{\square}{\square} = \, ?$$

What placement of the numbers in the blanks yields the largest sum?

74. 🖩 Use a calculator to arrange the following in order from smallest to largest.

$$\dfrac{3}{4}, \dfrac{17}{21}, \dfrac{13}{15}, \dfrac{7}{9}, \dfrac{15}{17}, \dfrac{13}{12}, \dfrac{19}{22}$$

Vocabulary Reinforcement

Complete each statement with the correct term from the given list. Some of the choices may not be used and some may be used more than once.

1. The _____ of two numbers is the smallest number that is a multiple of both numbers. [4.1a]

2. A _____ represents a sum of a whole number and a fraction less than 1. [4.4a]

3. To multiply using mixed numerals, we first convert to _____ notation. [4.6a]

4. A _____ contains a fraction in its numerator and/or denominator. [4.7b]

5. To add fractions, the _____ of the fractions must be the same. [4.2a]

6. The least common denominator of two fractions is the _____ of the denominators of the fractions. [4.2a]

7. When finding the LCM of a set of numbers using prime factorizations, we use each prime number the _____ number of times that it appears in any one factorization. [4.1a]

8. To compare two fractions with a common denominator, we compare their _____. [4.3b]

greatest

least

numerators

denominators

fraction

decimal

mixed numeral

complex fraction

least common multiple

greatest common factor

Concept Reinforcement

Determine whether each statement is true or false.

_____ 1. The mixed numeral $5\frac{2}{3}$ can be represented by the sum $5 \cdot \frac{3}{3} + \frac{2}{3}$. [4.4a]

_____ 2. The least common multiple of two numbers is always larger than or equal to the larger number. [4.1a]

_____ 3. The sum of any two mixed numerals is a mixed numeral. [4.5a]

_____ 4. The product of any two mixed numerals is greater than 1. [4.6a]

Study Guide

Objective 4.1a Find the least common multiple, or LCM, of two or more numbers.

Example Find the LCM of 105 and 90.
$$105 = 3 \cdot 5 \cdot 7,$$
$$90 = 2 \cdot 3 \cdot 3 \cdot 5;$$
$$\text{LCM} = 2 \cdot 3 \cdot 3 \cdot 5 \cdot 7 = 630$$

Practice Exercise

1. Find the LCM of 52 and 78.

Objective 4.2a Add using fraction notation.

Example Add: $\dfrac{5}{24} + \dfrac{7}{45}$.

$$\dfrac{5}{24} + \dfrac{7}{45} = \dfrac{5}{2 \cdot 2 \cdot 2 \cdot 3} \cdot \dfrac{3 \cdot 5}{3 \cdot 5} + \dfrac{7}{3 \cdot 3 \cdot 5} \cdot \dfrac{2 \cdot 2 \cdot 2}{2 \cdot 2 \cdot 2}$$

$$= \dfrac{75}{360} + \dfrac{56}{360} = \dfrac{131}{360}$$

Practice Exercise

2. Add: $\dfrac{19}{60} + \dfrac{11}{36}$.

Objective 4.3a Subtract using fraction notation.

Example Subtract: $\dfrac{7}{12} - \dfrac{11}{60}$.

$$\dfrac{7}{12} - \dfrac{11}{60} = \dfrac{7}{12} \cdot \dfrac{5}{5} - \dfrac{11}{60} = \dfrac{35}{60} - \dfrac{11}{60}$$

$$= \dfrac{35 - 11}{60} = \dfrac{24}{60} = \dfrac{2 \cdot \cancel{12}}{5 \cdot \cancel{12}} = \dfrac{2}{5}$$

Practice Exercise

3. Subtract: $\dfrac{29}{35} - \dfrac{5}{7}$.

Objective 4.3b Use $<$ or $>$ with fraction notation to write a true sentence.

Example Use $<$ or $>$ for $\square$ to write a true sentence:

$\dfrac{5}{12} \,\square\, \dfrac{9}{16}$.

Writing both fractions with the LCD, 48, we have

$\dfrac{20}{48} \,\square\, \dfrac{27}{48}$.

Since $20 < 27$, $\dfrac{20}{48} < \dfrac{27}{48}$ and thus $\dfrac{5}{12} < \dfrac{9}{16}$.

Practice Exercise

4. Use $<$ or $>$ for $\square$ to write a true sentence:

$\dfrac{3}{13} \,\square\, \dfrac{5}{12}$.

Objective 4.3c Solve equations of the type $x + a = b$ and $a + x = b$, where a and b may be fractions.

Example Solve: $x - \dfrac{1}{6} = -\dfrac{5}{8}$.

$$x - \dfrac{1}{6} = -\dfrac{5}{8}$$

$$x - \dfrac{1}{6} + \dfrac{1}{6} = -\dfrac{5}{8} + \dfrac{1}{6}$$

$$x = -\dfrac{5}{8} \cdot \dfrac{3}{3} + \dfrac{1}{6} \cdot \dfrac{4}{4}$$

$$x = -\dfrac{15}{24} + \dfrac{4}{24} = -\dfrac{11}{24}$$

Practice Exercise

5. Solve: $\dfrac{2}{9} + x = -\dfrac{9}{11}$.

Objective 4.4a Convert between mixed numerals and fraction notation.

Example Convert $2\dfrac{5}{13}$ to fraction notation: $2\dfrac{5}{13} = \dfrac{31}{13}$.

Example Convert $-\dfrac{40}{9}$ to a mixed numeral:

$-\dfrac{40}{9} = -4\dfrac{4}{9}$.

Practice Exercises

6. Convert $8\dfrac{2}{3}$ to fraction notation.

7. Convert $-\dfrac{47}{6}$ to a mixed numeral.

Objective 4.5b Subtract using mixed numerals.

Example   Subtract: $3\dfrac{3}{8} - 1\dfrac{4}{5}$.

$$3\dfrac{3}{8} = \quad 3\dfrac{15}{40} = \quad 2\dfrac{55}{40}$$

$$-1\dfrac{4}{5} = -1\dfrac{32}{40} = -1\dfrac{32}{40}$$

$$1\dfrac{23}{40}$$

Practice Exercise

8. Subtract: $10\dfrac{5}{7} - 2\dfrac{3}{4}$.

Objective 4.6a Multiply using mixed numerals.

Example   Multiply: $7\dfrac{1}{4} \cdot \left(-5\dfrac{3}{10}\right)$. Write a mixed numeral for the answer.

$$7\dfrac{1}{4} \cdot \left(-5\dfrac{3}{10}\right) = \dfrac{29}{4} \cdot \left(-\dfrac{53}{10}\right)$$

$$= -\dfrac{1537}{40} = -38\dfrac{17}{40}$$

Practice Exercise

9. Multiply: $-4\dfrac{1}{5} \cdot 3\dfrac{7}{15}$.

Objective 4.6c Solve applied problems involving multiplication and division with mixed numerals.

Example   The population of New York is $3\frac{1}{3}$ times that of Missouri. The population of New York is approximately 19,000,000. What is the population of Missouri?

Translate:

$$19{,}000{,}000 = 3\dfrac{1}{3} \cdot x.$$

Solve:

$$19{,}000{,}000 = \dfrac{10}{3} \cdot x$$

$$\dfrac{19{,}000{,}000}{\dfrac{10}{3}} = \dfrac{\dfrac{10}{3} \cdot x}{\dfrac{10}{3}}$$

$$19{,}000{,}000 \cdot \dfrac{3}{10} = x$$

$$5{,}700{,}000 = x.$$

The population of Missouri is about 5,700,000.

Practice Exercise

10. The population of Louisiana is $2\frac{1}{2}$ times the population of West Virginia. The population of West Virginia is approximately 1,800,000. What is the population of Louisiana?

Objective 4.7a Simplify expressions using the rules for order of operations.

Example   Simplify: $\left(\dfrac{4}{5}\right)^2 - \dfrac{1}{5} \cdot 2\dfrac{1}{8}$.

$$\left(\dfrac{4}{5}\right)^2 - \dfrac{1}{5} \cdot 2\dfrac{1}{8} = \dfrac{16}{25} - \dfrac{1}{5} \cdot \dfrac{17}{8}$$

$$= \dfrac{16}{25} - \dfrac{17}{40} = \dfrac{16}{25} \cdot \dfrac{8}{8} - \dfrac{17}{40} \cdot \dfrac{5}{5}$$

$$= \dfrac{128}{200} - \dfrac{85}{200} = \dfrac{43}{200}$$

Practice Exercise

11. Simplify: $\dfrac{3}{2} \cdot 1\dfrac{1}{3} \div \left(\dfrac{2}{3}\right)^2$.

Example Estimate

$$3\frac{2}{5} + \frac{7}{10} + 6\frac{5}{9}$$

by estimating each mixed numeral as a whole number or as a mixed numeral where the fractional part is $\frac{1}{2}$ and by estimating each fraction as 0, $\frac{1}{2}$, or 1.

$$3\frac{2}{5} + \frac{7}{10} + 6\frac{5}{9} \approx 3\frac{1}{2} + \frac{1}{2} + 6\frac{1}{2} = 10\frac{1}{2}$$

Practice Exercise

12. Estimate

$$1\frac{19}{20} + 3\frac{1}{8} - \frac{8}{17}$$

by estimating each mixed numeral as a whole number or as a mixed numeral where the fractional part is $\frac{1}{2}$ and by estimating each fraction as 0, $\frac{1}{2}$, or 1.

Review Exercises

Find the LCM.   [4.1a]

1. 12 and 18

2. 18 and 45

3. 3, 6, and 30

4. 26, 36, and 54

Add and simplify.   [4.2a]

5. $\dfrac{6}{5} + \dfrac{3}{8}$

6. $\dfrac{-5}{16} + \dfrac{1}{12}$

7. $\dfrac{6}{5} + \dfrac{11}{15} + \dfrac{3}{20}$

8. $\dfrac{1}{1000} + \dfrac{19}{100} + \dfrac{7}{10}$

Subtract and simplify.   [4.3a]

9. $\dfrac{5}{9} - \dfrac{2}{9}$

10. $\dfrac{7}{8} - \dfrac{3}{4}$

11. $\dfrac{2}{9} - \dfrac{11}{27}$

12. $-\dfrac{5}{6} - \dfrac{2}{9}$

Use < or > for $\square$ to write a true sentence.   [4.3b]

13. $\dfrac{4}{7} \,\square\, \dfrac{5}{9}$

14. $\dfrac{-11}{13} \,\square\, \dfrac{-8}{9}$

Solve.   [4.3c]

15. $x + \dfrac{2}{5} = \dfrac{7}{8}$

16. $\dfrac{1}{2} + y = -\dfrac{9}{10}$

Convert to fraction notation.   [4.4a]

17. $7\dfrac{1}{2}$

18. $8\dfrac{3}{8}$

19. $4\dfrac{1}{3}$

20. $-10\dfrac{5}{7}$

Convert to a mixed numeral.   [4.4a]

21. $\dfrac{7}{3}$

22. $\dfrac{27}{4}$

23. $-\dfrac{63}{5}$

24. $\dfrac{7}{2}$

Divide. Write a mixed numeral for the answer.   [4.4b]

25. $9\,\overline{)\,7\,8\,9\,6}$

26. $2\,3\,\overline{)\,1\,0,4\,9\,3}$

Add. Write a mixed numeral for the answer where appropriate.   [4.5a]

27. $\begin{array}{r} 5\frac{3}{5} \\ + 4\frac{4}{5} \\ \hline \end{array}$

28. $\begin{array}{r} 8\frac{1}{3} \\ + 3\frac{2}{5} \\ \hline \end{array}$

29. $\begin{array}{r} 5\frac{5}{6} \\ + 4\frac{5}{6} \\ \hline \end{array}$

30. $\begin{array}{r} 2\frac{3}{4} \\ + 5\frac{1}{2} \\ \hline \end{array}$

Subtract. Write a mixed numeral for the answer where appropriate.   [4.5b]

31. $\begin{array}{r} 12 \\ - 4\frac{2}{9} \\ \hline \end{array}$

32. $\begin{array}{r} 9\frac{3}{5} \\ - 4\frac{13}{15} \\ \hline \end{array}$

33. $\begin{array}{r} 10\frac{1}{4} \\ - 6\frac{1}{10} \\ \hline \end{array}$

34. $\begin{array}{r} 24 \\ - 10\frac{5}{8} \\ \hline \end{array}$

Multiply. Write a mixed numeral for the answer where appropriate.   [4.6a]

35. $6 \cdot 2\dfrac{2}{3}$

36. $5\dfrac{1}{4} \cdot \left(-\dfrac{2}{3}\right)$

37. $2\dfrac{1}{5} \cdot 1\dfrac{1}{10}$

38. $-2\dfrac{2}{5} \cdot 2\dfrac{1}{2}$

Copyright © 2015 Pearson Education, Inc.

Divide. Write a mixed numeral for the answer where appropriate. [4.6b]

39. $-27 \div 2\frac{1}{4}$

40. $2\frac{2}{5} \div 1\frac{7}{10}$

41. $3\frac{1}{4} \div 26$

42. $\left(-4\frac{1}{5}\right) \div \left(-4\frac{2}{3}\right)$

Solve. [4.2b], [4.3d], [4.5c], [4.6c]

43. *Sewing.* Gloria wants to make a dress and a jacket. She needs $1\frac{5}{8}$ yd of 60-in. fabric for the dress and $2\frac{5}{8}$ yd for the jacket. How many yards in all does Gloria need to make the outfit?

44. What is the sum of the areas in the figure below?

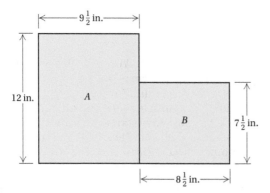

45. In the figure above, how much larger is the area of rectangle *A* than the area of rectangle *B*?

46. *Carpentry.* A board $\frac{9}{10}$ in. thick is glued to a board $\frac{4}{5}$ in. thick. The glue is $\frac{3}{100}$ in. thick. How thick is the result?

47. *Turkey Servings.* Turkey contains $1\frac{1}{3}$ servings per pound. How many pounds are needed for 32 servings?

48. *Cake Recipe.* A wedding-cake recipe requires 12 cups of shortening. Being calorie-conscious, the wedding couple decides to reduce the shortening by $3\frac{5}{8}$ cups and replace it with prune purée. How many cups of shortening are used in their new recipe?

49. *Painting a Border.* Katie hired an artist to paint a decorative border around the top of her son's bedroom. The artist charges $20 per foot. The room measures $11\frac{3}{4}$ ft $\times$ $9\frac{1}{2}$ ft. What is Katie's cost for the project?

$9\frac{1}{2}$ ft

$11\frac{3}{4}$ ft

50. *Running.* Janelle has mapped a $1\frac{1}{2}$-mi running route in her neighborhood. One Saturday, she ran this route $2\frac{1}{2}$ times. How many miles did she run?

51. *Humane Society Pie Sale.* Green River's Humane Society recently hosted its annual pie sale. Each of the 83 pies donated was cut into 6 pieces. At the end of the evening, 382 pieces of pie had been sold. How many pies were sold? How many were left over? Express your answers in mixed numerals.

Simplify each expression using the rules for order of operations. [4.7a]

52. $\dfrac{1}{8} \div \dfrac{1}{4} + \dfrac{1}{2}$

53. $\dfrac{4}{5} - \dfrac{1}{2} \cdot \left(1 + \dfrac{1}{4}\right)$

54. $20\dfrac{3}{4} - 1\dfrac{1}{2} \times 12 + \left(\dfrac{1}{2}\right)^2$

Simplify. [4.7b]

55. $\dfrac{-\dfrac{2}{3}}{\dfrac{5}{6}}$

56. $\dfrac{10}{\dfrac{1}{2} - \dfrac{1}{6}}$

57. Find the average of $\dfrac{1}{2}, \dfrac{1}{4}, \dfrac{1}{3}$, and $\dfrac{1}{5}$. [4.7b]

Estimate each of the following as $0, \frac{1}{2}$, or 1. [4.7c]

58. $\dfrac{29}{59}$ **59.** $\dfrac{2}{59}$ **60.** $\dfrac{61}{59}$

Estimate by estimating each mixed numeral as a whole number or as a mixed numeral where the fractional part is $\frac{1}{2}$ and by estimating each fraction as $0, \frac{1}{2}$, or 1. [4.7c]

61. $6\dfrac{7}{8}$ **62.** $10\dfrac{2}{17}$

63. $\dfrac{11}{12} \cdot 5\dfrac{6}{13}$ **64.** $\dfrac{1}{15} \cdot \dfrac{2}{3}$

65. $\dfrac{6}{11} + \dfrac{5}{6} + \dfrac{31}{29}$

66. $32\dfrac{14}{15} + 27\dfrac{6}{7} - 4\dfrac{25}{28} \cdot 6\dfrac{37}{76}$

67. Simplify: $\dfrac{1}{4} + \dfrac{2}{5} \div 5^2$. [4.7a]

  A. $\dfrac{133}{500}$ **B.** $\dfrac{3}{500}$

  C. $\dfrac{117}{500}$ **D.** $\dfrac{5}{2}$

68. Solve: $x + \dfrac{2}{3} = -5$. [4.3c]

  A. $\dfrac{17}{3}$ **B.** $\dfrac{13}{3}$

  C. $-\dfrac{13}{3}$ **D.** $-\dfrac{17}{3}$

Synthesis

69. *Orangutan Circus Act.* Yuri and Olga are orangutans that perform in a circus by riding bicycles around a circular track. It takes Yuri 6 min and Olga 4 min to make one trip around the track. Suppose they start at the same point and then complete their act when they again reach the same point. How long is their act? [4.1a]

70. Place the numbers 3, 4, 5, and 6 in the boxes in order to make a true equation: [4.5a]

$$\dfrac{\square}{\square} + \dfrac{\square}{\square} = 3\dfrac{1}{4}.$$

Understanding Through Discussion and Writing

1. Is the sum of two mixed numerals always a mixed numeral? Why or why not? [4.5a]

2. Write a problem for a classmate to solve. Design the problem so that its solution is found by performing the multiplication $4\frac{1}{2} \cdot 33\frac{1}{3}$. [4.6c]

3. A student insists that $3\frac{2}{5} \cdot 1\frac{3}{7} = 3\frac{6}{35}$. What mistake is he making and how should he have proceeded? [4.6a]

4. Discuss the role of least common multiples in adding and subtracting with fraction notation. [4.2a], [4.3a]

5. Find a real-world situation that fits this equation:

$$2 \cdot 15\dfrac{3}{4} + 2 \cdot 28\dfrac{5}{8} = 88\dfrac{3}{4}. \quad \text{[4.5c], [4.6c]}$$

6. A student insists that $5 \cdot 3\frac{2}{7} = (5 \cdot 3) \cdot \left(5 \cdot \frac{2}{7}\right)$. What mistake is she making and how should she have proceeded? [4.6a], [4.7a]

Copyright © 2015 Pearson Education, Inc.

CHAPTER

4   Test

For Extra Help   For step-by-step test solutions, access the Chapter Test Prep Videos in MyMathLab® or on YouTube (search "BittingerBasicEI" and click on "Channels").

Find the LCM.

1. 16 and 12

2. 15, 40, and 50

Add and simplify.

3. $\dfrac{1}{2} + \dfrac{5}{2}$

4. $\dfrac{-7}{8} + \dfrac{2}{3}$

5. $\dfrac{7}{10} + \dfrac{19}{100} + \dfrac{31}{1000}$

Subtract and simplify.

6. $\dfrac{5}{6} - \dfrac{3}{6}$

7. $\dfrac{5}{6} - \dfrac{3}{4}$

8. $-\dfrac{17}{24} - \dfrac{1}{15}$

Solve.

9. $\dfrac{1}{4} + y = 4$

10. $x + \dfrac{2}{3} = \dfrac{11}{12}$

11. Use < or > for $\square$ to write a true sentence:

$\dfrac{6}{7} \square \dfrac{21}{25}$.

Convert to fraction notation.

12. $3\dfrac{1}{2}$

13. $-9\dfrac{7}{8}$

Convert to a mixed numeral.

14. $\dfrac{9}{2}$

15. $-\dfrac{74}{9}$

Divide. Write a mixed numeral for the answer.

16. $1\,1\overline{)1\,7\,8\,9}$

Add. Write a mixed numeral for the answer.

17. $6\dfrac{2}{5}$

$+\ 7\dfrac{4}{5}$

18. $9\dfrac{1}{4}$

$+\ 5\dfrac{1}{6}$

Subtract. Write a mixed numeral for the answer.

19. $10\dfrac{1}{6}$

$-\ 5\dfrac{7}{8}$

20. 14

$-\ 7\dfrac{5}{6}$

Multiply. Write a mixed numeral for the answer, if appropriate.

21. $9 \cdot 4\dfrac{1}{3}$

22. $-6\dfrac{3}{4} \cdot \dfrac{2}{3}$

Divide. Write a mixed numeral for the answer, if appropriate.

23. $2\dfrac{1}{3} \div 1\dfrac{1}{6}$

24. $2\dfrac{1}{12} \div (-75)$

25. *Weightlifting.*   In 2002, Hossein Rezazadeh of Iran did a clean and jerk of 263 kg. This amount was about $2\dfrac{1}{2}$ times his body weight. How much did Rezazadeh weigh?

Source: *The Guinness Book of Records,* 2005

26. *Book Order.*   An order of books for a math course weighs 220 lb. Each book weighs $2\dfrac{3}{4}$ lb. How many books are in the order?

27. *Carpentry.* The following diagram shows a middle drawer support guide for a cabinet drawer. Find each of the following.

a) The short length a across the top

b) The length b across the bottom

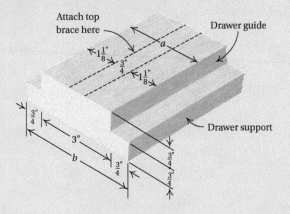

28. *Carpentry.* In carpentry, some pieces of plywood that are called "$\frac{3}{4}$-inch" plywood are actually $\frac{11}{16}$ in. thick. How much thinner is such a piece than its name indicates?

29. *Women's Dunks.* The first three women in the history of college basketball to dunk a basketball are listed below, along with their heights and universities:

Michelle Snow, $6\frac{5}{12}$ ft, Tennessee;
Charlotte Smith, $5\frac{11}{12}$ ft, North Carolina;
Georgeann Wells, $6\frac{7}{12}$ ft, West Virginia.

Find the average height of these women.
Source: *USA Today*, 11/30/00, p. 3C

Simplify.

30. $\dfrac{2}{3} + 1\dfrac{1}{3} \cdot 2\dfrac{1}{8}$

31. $1\dfrac{1}{2} - \dfrac{1}{2}\left(\dfrac{1}{2} \div \dfrac{1}{4}\right) + \left(\dfrac{1}{2}\right)^2$

32. $\dfrac{\frac{2}{3} + \frac{1}{6}}{5}$

Estimate each of the following as 0, $\frac{1}{2}$, or 1.

33. $\dfrac{3}{82}$

34. $\dfrac{93}{91}$

35. Estimate the following by estimating the mixed numeral as a whole number or as a mixed numeral where the fractional part is $\frac{1}{2}$.

$$256 \div 15\dfrac{19}{21}$$

36. Find the LCM of 12, 36, and 60.

A. 6 **B.** 12
C. 60 **D.** 180

Synthesis

37. The students in a math class can be organized into study groups of 8 each so that no students are left out. The same class of students can also be organized into groups of 6 so that no students are left out.

a) Find some class sizes for which this will work.

b) Find the smallest such class size.

38. Rebecca walks 17 laps at her health club. Trent walks 17 laps at his health club. If the track at Rebecca's health club is $\frac{1}{7}$ mi long, and the track at Trent's is $\frac{1}{8}$ mi long, who walks farther? How much farther?

Copyright © 2015 Pearson Education, Inc.

Solve.

1. *Cross-Country Skiing.* During a three-day holiday weekend trip, David and Sally Jean cross-country skied $3\frac{2}{3}$ mi on Friday, $6\frac{1}{8}$ mi on Saturday, and $4\frac{3}{4}$ mi on Sunday.

 a) Find the total number of miles they skied.

 b) Find the average number of miles they skied per day. Express your answer as a mixed numeral.

2. How many people can receive equal $16 shares from a total of $496?

3. A recipe calls for $\frac{4}{5}$ tsp of salt. How much salt should be used for $\frac{1}{2}$ recipe? for 5 recipes?

4. How many pieces, each $2\frac{3}{8}$ ft long, can be cut from a piece of wire 38 ft long?

5. An emergency food pantry fund contains $423. From this fund, $148 and $167 are withdrawn for expenses. How much is left in the fund?

6. In a walkathon, Jermaine walked $\frac{9}{10}$ mi and Oleta walked $\frac{3}{4}$ mi. What was the total distance they walked?

What part is shaded?

7.

8.

Calculate and simplify.

9. $\begin{array}{r} 3704 \\ +\,5278 \\ \hline \end{array}$

10. $\begin{array}{r} 7605 \\ -\,3087 \\ \hline \end{array}$

11. $-27 + 12$

12. $\dfrac{3}{8} + \dfrac{1}{24}$

13. $-20 - (-6)$

14. $-\dfrac{3}{4} - \dfrac{1}{3}$

15. $\begin{array}{r} 2\frac{3}{4} \\ +\,5\frac{1}{2} \\ \hline \end{array}$

16. $\begin{array}{r} 2\frac{1}{3} \\ -\,1\frac{1}{6} \\ \hline \end{array}$

17. $15 \cdot (-5)$

18. $\dfrac{9}{10} \cdot \dfrac{5}{3}$

19. $-18 \cdot \left(-\dfrac{5}{6}\right)$

20. $2\dfrac{1}{5} \div \dfrac{3}{10}$

Divide. Write the answer in the form 34 R 7.

21. $6\overline{)4\,2\,9\,0}$ **22.** $4\,5\overline{)2\,5\,3\,1}$

23. Write a mixed numeral for the answer in Exercise 22.

24. In the number 2753, what digit names tens?

25. *Room Carpeting.*   The Chandlers are carpeting an L-shaped family room consisting of one rectangle that is $8\frac{1}{2}$ ft by 11 ft and another rectangle that is $6\frac{1}{2}$ ft by $7\frac{1}{2}$ ft.

  a) Find the area of the carpet.

  b) Find the perimeter of the carpet.

26. Round 38,478 to the nearest hundred.

27. Find the LCM of 18 and 24.

28. Simplify:

$$\left(\frac{1}{2} + \frac{2}{5}\right)^2 \div 3 + 6 \times \left(2 + \frac{1}{4}\right).$$

Use $<$, $>$, or $=$ for ☐ to write a true sentence.

29. $\dfrac{4}{5}$ ☐ $\dfrac{4}{6}$ **30.** $\dfrac{3}{13}$ ☐ $\dfrac{9}{39}$ **31.** $\dfrac{-3}{7}$ ☐ $\dfrac{-5}{12}$

Estimate each of the following as 0, $\frac{1}{2}$, or 1.

32. $\dfrac{29}{30}$ **33.** $\dfrac{15}{29}$ **34.** $\dfrac{2}{43}$

Simplify.

35. $\dfrac{36}{45}$ **36.** $\dfrac{0}{-27}$ **37.** $\dfrac{320}{10}$

38. Convert to fraction notation: $4\dfrac{5}{8}$.

39. Convert to a mixed numeral: $\dfrac{17}{3}$.

Solve.

40. $x + 24 = 117$ **41.** $x + \dfrac{7}{9} = \dfrac{4}{3}$

42. $\dfrac{7}{9} \cdot t = -\dfrac{4}{3}$ **43.** $y = 32,580 \div 36$

44. *Matching.*   Match each item in the first column with the appropriate item in the second column by drawing connecting lines. There can be more than one correct correspondence for an item.

Factors of 68	12, 54, 72, 300
Factorization of 68	2, 3, 17, 19, 23, 31, 47, 101
Prime factorization of 68	$2 \cdot 2 \cdot 17$
Numbers divisible by 6	$2 \cdot 34$
Numbers divisible by 8	8, 16, 24, 32, 40, 48, 64, 864
Numbers divisible by 5	1, 2, 4, 17, 34, 68
Prime numbers	70, 95, 215

Synthesis

45. Find the smallest prime number that is larger than 2000.

Copyright © 2015 Pearson Education, Inc.

CHAPTER

5

Decimal Notation

5.1 Decimal Notation, Order, and Rounding

5.2 Addition and Subtraction

5.3 Multiplication

5.4 Division

Mid-Chapter Review

5.5 Converting from Fraction Notation to Decimal Notation

5.6 Estimating

5.7 Applications and Problem Solving

Translating for Success

Summary and Review

Test

Cumulative Review

STUDYING FOR SUCCESS *Time Management*

☐ As a rule, budget 2–3 hours for doing homework and studying for every hour you spend in class.

☐ Balance work and study carefully. Be honest with yourself about how much time you have available to work, attend class, and study.

☐ Make an hour-by-hour schedule of your week, planning time for leisure as well as work and study.

☐ Use your syllabus to help you plan your time. Transfer project deadlines and test dates to your calendar.

5.1 Decimal Notation, Order, and Rounding

OBJECTIVES

a Given decimal notation, write a word name.

b Convert between decimal notation and fraction notation.

c Given a pair of numbers in decimal notation, tell which is larger.

d Round decimal notation to the nearest thousandth, hundredth, tenth, one, ten, hundred, or thousand.

SKILL TO REVIEW

Objective 1.6a: Round to the nearest ten, hundred, or thousand.

Round 4735 to the nearest:

1. Ten.

2. Hundred.

Recall that the set of **rational numbers** consists of the integers, . . . , −3, −2, −1, 0, 1, 2, 3, . . . , and fractions like $\frac{1}{2}, -\frac{5}{3}, \frac{9}{8}, -\frac{17}{10}$, and so on. (See Section 3.3.) In this chapter, we use **decimal notation** to represent the set of rational numbers. For example, $\frac{1}{2}$ can be written as 0.5 in decimal notation and $3\frac{1}{10}$ can be written as 3.1.

The word *decimal* comes from the Latin word *decima*, meaning a tenth part. Since our counting system is based on tens, decimal notation is a natural extension of a system with which we are already familiar.

a DECIMAL NOTATION AND WORD NAMES

One model of the Magellan GPS navigation system sells for \$249.98. The dot in \$249.98 is called a **decimal point**. Since \$0.98, or 98¢, is $\frac{98}{100}$ of a dollar, it follows that

$$\$249.98 = \$249 + \$0.98.$$

Also, since \$0.98, or 98¢, has the same value as 9 dimes + 8 cents and 1 dime is $\frac{1}{10}$ of a dollar and 1 cent is $\frac{1}{100}$ of a dollar, we can write

$$249.98 = 2 \cdot 100 + 4 \cdot 10 + 9 \cdot 1 + 9 \cdot \frac{1}{10} + 8 \cdot \frac{1}{100}.$$

This is an extension of the expanded notation for whole numbers that we used in Chapter 1. The place values are 100, 10, 1, $\frac{1}{10}$, $\frac{1}{100}$, and so on. We can see this on a **place-value chart**. The value of each place is $\frac{1}{10}$ as large as that of the one to its left.

Let's consider decimal notation using a place-value chart to represent 2.0677 min, the women's 200-meter backstroke world record held by Missy Franklin from the United States.

PLACE-VALUE CHART							
Hundreds	Tens	Ones	Tenths	Hundredths	Thousandths	Ten-Thousandths	Hundred-Thousandths
100	10	1	$\frac{1}{10}$	$\frac{1}{100}$	$\frac{1}{1000}$	$\frac{1}{10,000}$	$\frac{1}{100,000}$
		2 .	0	6	7	7	

Answers

Skill to Review:
1. 4740 **2.** 4700

The decimal notation 2.0677 means

$$2 + \frac{0}{10} + \frac{6}{100} + \frac{7}{1000} + \frac{7}{10,000}, \quad \text{or} \quad 2\frac{677}{10,000}.$$

We read both 2.0677 and $2\frac{677}{10,000}$ as

"Two *and* six hundred seventy-seven ten-thousandths."

We can also read 2.0677 as

"Two *point* zero six seven seven."

To write a word name from decimal notation,

a) write a word name for the whole number (the number named to the left of the decimal point),

397.685 ⟶ Three hundred ninety-seven

b) write the word "and" for the decimal point, and

397.685 ⟶ Three hundred ninety-seven and

c) write a word name for the number named to the right of the decimal point, followed by the place value of the last digit.

397.685 ⟶ Three hundred ninety-seven and six hundred eighty-five *thousandths*

EXAMPLE 1 *Median Age.* The median age of residents in Maine is 42.7 years. The median age of residents in Utah is 29.2 years. Write word names for 42.7 and 29.2.

Source: U.S. Census Bureau

Forty-two and seven tenths

Twenty-nine and two tenths

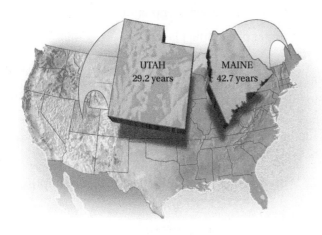

UTAH 29.2 years
MAINE 42.7 years

EXAMPLE 2 Write a word name for 410.87.

Four hundred ten and eighty-seven hundredths

1. *Life Expectancy.* The life expectancy at birth in Kenya in 2011 was 61.3 years for males and 64.2 years for females. Write word names for 61.3 and 64.2.

   Source: World Health Organization

2. *10,000-Meter Record.* Wang Junxia of China holds the women's world record for the 10,000-meter run: 29.5297 min. Write a word name for 29.5297.

Write a word name for each number.

3. 245.89

4. −34.0064

5. 31,079.756

6. *Temperature Extremes.* The lowest average annual temperature in the United States is −12.6°C. It occurs in Barrow, Alaska.

   Source: *Time Almanac* 2005

Answers

1. Sixty-one and three tenths; sixty-four and two tenths
2. Twenty-nine and five thousand, two hundred ninety-seven ten-thousandths
3. Two hundred forty-five and eighty-nine hundredths
4. Negative thirty-four and sixty-four ten-thousandths
5. Thirty-one thousand, seventy-nine and seven hundred fifty-six thousandths
6. Negative twelve and six tenths

EXAMPLE 3 *Record Price.* Edvard Munch's painting *The Scream* sold for $119.9225 million at Sotheby's in New York City on May 2, 2012. This price set a world record as the highest paid for a work of art sold at auction. Write a word name for 119.9225.

Source: Sotheby's

> One hundred nineteen and nine thousand, two hundred twenty-five ten-thousandths

EXAMPLE 4 Write a word name for −1788.045.

> Negative one thousand, seven hundred eighty-eight and forty-five thousandths

◀ Do Exercises 1–6.

b CONVERTING BETWEEN DECIMAL NOTATION AND FRACTION NOTATION

Given decimal notation, we can convert to fraction notation as follows:

$$9.875 = 9 + \frac{8}{10} + \frac{7}{100} + \frac{5}{1000}$$

$$= 9 \cdot \frac{1000}{1000} + \frac{8}{10} \cdot \frac{100}{100} + \frac{7}{100} \cdot \frac{10}{10} + \frac{5}{1000}$$

$$= \frac{9000}{1000} + \frac{800}{1000} + \frac{70}{1000} + \frac{5}{1000} = \frac{9875}{1000}.$$

To convert from decimal to fraction notation,

a) count the number of decimal places,   4.98
                                           2 places

b) move the decimal point that many   4.98.   Move
   places to the right, and   2 places.

c) write the answer over a denominator   498
   with a 1 followed by that number of zeros. 100   2 zeros

EXAMPLE 5 Write fraction notation for 0.876. Do not simplify.

0.876   0.876. $0.876 = \dfrac{876}{1000}$

3 places   3 zeros

For a number like 0.876, we generally write a 0 before the decimal point to draw attention to the presence of the decimal point.

EXAMPLE 6 Write fraction notation for 56.23. Do not simplify.

$$56.23 \qquad 56.23. \qquad 56.23 = \frac{5623}{100}$$

2 places   2 zeros

EXAMPLE 7 Write fraction notation for −1.5018. Do not simplify.

$$-1.5018 \qquad -1.5018. \qquad -1.5018 = -\frac{15{,}018}{10{,}000}$$

4 places   4 zeros

Do Exercises 7–10. ▶

If fraction notation has a denominator that is a power of ten, such as 10, 100, 1000, and so on, we convert to decimal notation by reversing the procedure that we used before.

> To convert from fraction notation to decimal notation when the denominator is 10, 100, 1000, and so on,
>
> **a)** count the number of zeros, and
>
> $$\frac{8679}{1000}$$
>
> 3 zeros
>
> **b)** move the decimal point that number of places to the left. Leave off the denominator.
>
> 8.679.   Move 3 places.
>
> $$\frac{8679}{1000} = 8.679$$

EXAMPLE 8 Write decimal notation for $\frac{47}{10}$.

$$\frac{47}{10} \qquad 4.7. \qquad \frac{47}{10} = 4.7$$

1 zero   1 place

EXAMPLE 9 Write decimal notation for $\frac{13}{1000}$.

$$\frac{13}{1000} \qquad 0.013. \qquad \frac{13}{1000} = 0.013$$

3 zeros   3 places

EXAMPLE 10 Write decimal notation for $-\frac{570}{100{,}000}$.

$$-\frac{570}{100{,}000} \qquad -0.00570. \qquad -\frac{570}{100{,}000} = -0.0057$$

5 zeros   5 places

Note that when we write the decimal notation, it is not necessary to include the 0 that follows the 7.

Do Exercises 11–15. ▶

Write fraction notation.

GS **7.** 0.896

0.896. ☐ places

$$0.896 = \frac{896}{1\,\square}$$

8. 23.78

9. −5.6789

10. 1.9

Write decimal notation.

GS **11.** $\frac{743}{100}$

$$\frac{743}{100} \qquad 7.43.$$

☐ zeros   ☐ places

$$\frac{743}{100} = 7.\square$$

12. $\frac{406}{1000}$

13. $\frac{67{,}089}{10{,}000}$

14. $-\frac{9}{10}$

15. $-\frac{830}{10{,}000}$

Answers

7. $\frac{896}{1000}$ **8.** $\frac{2378}{100}$ **9.** $-\frac{56{,}789}{10{,}000}$ **10.** $\frac{19}{10}$

11. 7.43 **12.** 0.406 **13.** 6.7089 **14.** −0.9

15. −0.083

Guided Solutions:

7. 3, 000 **11.** 2, 2, 43

When denominators are numbers other than 10, 100, and so on, we will use another method for conversion. It will be considered in Section 5.5.

If a mixed numeral has a fraction part with a denominator that is a power of ten, such as 10, 100, or 1000, and so on, we first write the mixed numeral as a sum of a whole number and a fraction. Then we convert to decimal notation.

EXAMPLE 11 Write decimal notation for $23\frac{59}{100}$.

$$23\frac{59}{100} = 23 + \frac{59}{100} = 23 \text{ and } \frac{59}{100} = 23.59$$

EXAMPLE 12 Write decimal notation for $-772\frac{129}{10,000}$.

First we consider $772\frac{129}{10,000}$.

$$772\frac{129}{10,000} = 772 + \frac{129}{10,000} = 772 \text{ and } \frac{129}{10,000} = 772.0129$$

Since $772\frac{129}{10,000} = 772.0129$, we have $-772\frac{129}{10,000} = -772.0129$.

◀ **Do Exercises 16–18.**

Write decimal notation.

16. $4\frac{3}{10}$

17. $283\frac{71}{100}$

18. $-456\frac{13}{1000}$

C ORDER

To understand how to compare numbers in decimal notation, consider 0.85 and 0.9. First note that $0.9 = 0.90$ because $\frac{9}{10} = \frac{90}{100}$. Then $0.85 = \frac{85}{100}$ and $0.90 = \frac{90}{100}$. Since $\frac{85}{100} < \frac{90}{100}$, it follows that $0.85 < 0.90$. This leads us to a quick way to compare two numbers in decimal notation.

COMPARING POSITIVE DECIMALS

To compare two positive numbers in decimal notation, start at the left and compare corresponding digits moving from left to right. If two digits differ, the number with the larger digit is the larger of the two numbers. To ease the comparison, extra zeros can be written to the right of the last decimal place.

EXAMPLE 13 Which of 2.109 and 2.1 is larger?

Think.

2.109 → 2.109

2.1 → 2.100

Same ⌐Different; 9 > 0

Thus, 2.109 is larger than 2.1. That is, $2.109 > 2.1$.

Answers

16. 4.3   **17.** 283.71   **18.** −456.013

EXAMPLE 14 Which of 0.09 and 0.108 is larger?

Think.

0.09   0.090

0.108   0.108

Same ⌐— Different; 1 > 0

Thus, 0.108 is larger than 0.09. That is, 0.108 > 0.09.

Do Exercises 19–24. ▶

How do we compare negative decimals? Using the number line, we see that $-1 > -2$. Similarly, $-1.4 > -1.5$.

This leads to the following procedure.

COMPARING NEGATIVE DECIMALS

To compare two negative numbers in decimal notation, start at the left and compare corresponding digits. When two digits differ, the number with the smaller digit is the larger of the two numbers.

EXAMPLE 15 Which of -5.6 and -5.63 is larger?

Think.

-5.6 -5.60

-5.63 -5.63

Same ⌐—Different; 0 < 3

Thus, -5.6 is larger than -5.63. That is, $-5.6 > -5.63$.

Do Exercises 25–28. ▶

d ROUNDING

Rounding of numbers in decimal notation is done as for whole numbers. To understand, we first consider an example using the number line. It might help to review Section 1.6.

EXAMPLE 16 Round 0.37 to the nearest tenth.

Here is part of a number line.

We see that 0.37 is closer to 0.40 than to 0.30. Thus, 0.37 rounded to the nearest tenth is 0.4.

Which number is larger?

19. 2.04, 2.039

20. 0.06, 0.008

21. 0.5, 0.58

22. 1, 0.9999

23. 0.8989, 0.09898

24. 21.006, 21.05

Which number is larger?

25. -7.56, -6.18

26. -21.006, -21.05

27. -0.44, -0.46

28. -13.94, -13.79

Answers

19. 2.04   **20.** 0.06   **21.** 0.58   **22.** 1
23. 0.8989   **24.** 21.05   **25.** -6.18
26. -21.006 **27.** -0.44 **28.** -13.79

ROUNDING DECIMAL NOTATION

To round to a certain place:

a) Locate the digit in that place.

b) Consider the next digit to the right.

c) If the digit to the right is 5 or higher, round up. If the digit to the right is 4 or lower, round down.

EXAMPLE 17   Round 3872.2459 to the nearest tenth.

a) Locate the digit in the tenths place, 2.

$$3\ 8\ 7\ 2\ .\ 2\ 4\ 5\ 9$$
$$\uparrow$$

b) Consider the next digit to the right, 4.

$$3\ 8\ 7\ 2\ .\ 2\ 4\ 5\ 9$$
$$\uparrow$$

·············· **Caution!** ··············

3872.3 is not a correct answer to Example 17. It is *incorrect* to round from the ten-thousandths digit over to the tenths digit, as follows:

$$3872.246 \rightarrow 3872.25 \rightarrow 3872.3.$$

c) Since that digit, 4, is 4 or lower, round down.

$$3\ 8\ 7\ 2\ .\ 2 \longleftarrow \text{This is the answer.}$$

EXAMPLE 18   Round 3872.2459 to the nearest thousandth, hundredth, tenth, one, ten, hundred, and thousand.

Thousandth:	3872.246	One:	3872	Thousand:	4000
Hundredth:	3872.25	Ten:	3870		
Tenth:	3872.2	Hundred:	3900		

EXAMPLE 19   Round −14.8973 to the nearest hundredth.

a) Locate the digit in the hundredths place, 9.

$$-1\ 4\ .\ 8\ 9\ 7\ 3$$
$$\uparrow$$

b) Consider the next digit to the right, 7.

$$-1\ 4\ .\ 8\ 9\ 7\ 3$$
$$\uparrow$$

c) Since that digit, 7, is 5 or higher, round the digit 9 up. When we make the hundredths digit a 10, we carry 1 to the tenths place.

The answer is −14.90. The 0 in −14.90 indicates that the answer is correct to the nearest hundredth. Note that when we rounded the digit 9 up, we actually rounded −14.8973 down. That is, −14.90 < −14.8973.

EXAMPLE 20   Round 0.008 to the nearest tenth.

a) Locate the digit in the tenths place, 0.

$$0\ .\ 0\ 0\ 8$$
$$\uparrow$$

b) Consider the next digit to the right, 0.

$$0\ .\ 0\ 0\ 8$$
$$\uparrow$$

c) Since that digit, 0, is less than 5, round down.

The answer is 0.0.

◀ Do Exercises 29–47.

Round to the nearest tenth.

29. 2.76   **30.** 13.85

31. 234.448   **32.** 7.009

Round to the nearest hundredth.

33. 0.636   **34.** 7.834

35. 34.675   **36.** 0.025

Round to the nearest thousandth.

37. 0.9434   **38.** 8.0038

39. 43.1119   **40.** 37.4005

Round 7459.3548 to the nearest:

41. Thousandth.

42. Hundredth.

43. Tenth.

44. One.

45. Ten. (*Caution:* "Tens" are not "tenths.")

46. Hundred.

47. Thousand.

Answers

29. 2.8   **30.** 13.9   **31.** 234.4   **32.** 7.0
33. 0.64   **34.** 7.83   **35.** 34.68   **36.** 0.03
37. 0.943   **38.** 8.004   **39.** 43.112
40. 37.401   **41.** 7459.355   **42.** 7459.35
43. 7459.4   **44.** 7459   **45.** 7460
46. 7500   **47.** 7000

Reading Check

Name the digit that represents each place value in the number 436.81205.

RC1. Hundred-thousandths _____

RC2. Thousandths _____

RC3. Tens _____

RC4. Ten-thousandths _____

RC5. Tenths _____

RC6. Hundreds _____

RC7. Hundredths _____

RC8. Ones _____

a

1. *Currency Conversion.* One Japanese yen was worth about $0.0119 in U.S. currency recently. Write a word name for 0.0119.

   Source: finance.yahoo.com

2. *Currency Conversion.* One U.S. dollar was worth 0.9949 Canadian dollars recently. Write a word name for 0.9949.

   Source: finance.yahoo.com

3. *Birth Rate.* There were 137.6 triplet births per 100,000 live births in a recent year in the United States. Write a word name for 137.6.

   Source: U.S. Centers for Disease Control and Prevention

4. *Coffee Consumption.* Annual per capita coffee consumption in Finland is 26.7 lb. In Spain, annual per capita coffee consumption is only 9.4 lb. Write word names for 26.7 and 9.4.

   Source: International Coffee Organization

5. *Stock Price.* Apple, Inc.'s stock price was recently $519.22 per share. Write a word name for 519.22.

   Source: NASDAQ

6. *Indianapolis 500.* Dario Franchitti won the 2012 Indianapolis 500 race with a time of 21 hr 58 min 51.2532 sec. In second place, Scott Dixon finished 0.0295 sec later. Write a word name for 0.0295.

   Source: Indianapolis Motor Speedway

Write a word name for the number in each sentence.

7. One gallon of paint is equal to 3.785 L of paint.

8. *Water Weight.* One gallon of water weighs 8.35 lb.

Write a word name.

9. -34.891

10. -27.1245

b Write fraction notation. Do not simplify.

11. 8.3

12. 203.6

13. 3.56

14. 0.17

15. 20.003

16. 1.509

17. −1.0008

18. −2.0114

19. 37.2

20. 4567.2

21. −0.00013

22. −6.14057

Write decimal notation.

23. $\dfrac{8}{10}$

24. $\dfrac{51}{10}$

25. $\dfrac{3798}{1000}$

26. $\dfrac{780}{1000}$

27. $-\dfrac{889}{100}$

28. $-\dfrac{92}{100}$

29. $\dfrac{19}{100,000}$

30. $\dfrac{56,788}{100,000}$

31. $\dfrac{78}{10,000}$

32. $\dfrac{13,463}{10,000}$

33. $-\dfrac{376,193}{1,000,000}$

34. $-\dfrac{8,953,074}{1,000,000}$

35. $2\dfrac{9}{10}$

36. $9243\dfrac{1}{10}$

37. $3\dfrac{98}{1000}$

38. $4\dfrac{67}{1000}$

39. $99\dfrac{44}{100}$

40. $67\dfrac{83}{100}$

41. $-2\dfrac{1739}{10,000}$

42. $-2256\dfrac{3059}{10,000}$

c Which number is larger?

43. 0.06, 0.58

44. 0.008, 0.8

45. 0.905, 0.91

46. 42.06, 42.1

47. −0.0009, −0.001

48. −7.067, −7.054

49. 234.07, 235.07

50. 0.99999, 1

51. 0.004, $\dfrac{4}{100}$

52. $\dfrac{73}{10}$, 0.73

53. −0.432, −0.4325

54. −0.8437, −0.84384

d Round to the nearest tenth.

55. 0.11

56. 0.85

57. −0.49

58. −0.5394

59. 2.7449

60. 4.78

61. −123.65

62. −36.049

Copyright © 2015 Pearson Education, Inc.

Round to the nearest hundredth.

63. 0.893

64. 0.675

65. 0.6666

66. 6.524

67. −0.995

68. −207.9976

69. −0.094

70. −11.4246

Round to the nearest thousandth.

71. 0.3246

72. 0.6666

73. −17.0014

74. −123.4562

75. 10.1011

76. 0.1161

77. −9.9989

78. −67.100602

Round 809.5732 to the nearest:

79. Hundred.

80. Tenth.

81. Thousandth.

82. Hundredth.

83. One.

84. Ten.

Round 34.54389 to the nearest:

85. Ten-thousandth.

86. Thousandth.

87. Hundredth.

88. Tenth.

89. One.

90. Ten.

Skill Maintenance

Round 6172 to the nearest: [1.6a]

91. Ten.

92. Hundred.

93. Thousand.

Find the prime factorization. [3.1d]

Simplify. [3.5b]

94. 2000

95. 1530

96. $\dfrac{30}{126}$

97. $\dfrac{120}{100}$

Synthesis

98. Arrange the following numbers in order from smallest to largest.

−0.99, −0.099, −1, −0.9999, −0.89999, −1.00009, −0.909, −0.9889

99. Arrange the following numbers in order from smallest to largest.

−2.1, −2.109, −2.108, −2.018, −2.0119, −2.0302, −2.000001

Truncating.   There are other methods of rounding decimal notation. To round using **truncating**, we drop off all decimal places past the rounding place, which is the same as changing all digits to the right to zeros. For example, rounding 6.78093456285102 to the ninth decimal place, using truncating, gives us 6.780934562. Use truncating to round each of the following to the fifth decimal place—that is, the hundred-thousandth place.

100. 6.78346623

101. 6.783465902

102. 99.999999999

103. 0.030303030303

OBJECTIVES

a Add using decimal notation for positive numbers.

b Subtract using decimal nota-tion for positive numbers.

c Add and subtract negative decimals.

d Solve equations of the type $x + a = b$ and $a + x = b$, where a and b may be in decimal notation.

SKILLS TO REVIEW

Objective 1.2a: Add whole numbers.
Objective 1.3a: Subtract whole numbers.

Add or subtract.

1. 3 8 7
    + 2 5 4

2. 4 0 2 3
    − 1 6 6 7

a ADDITION

Adding positive decimal numbers is similar to adding whole numbers. First, we line up the decimal points so that we can add corresponding place-value digits. Then we add digits from the right. For example, we add the thousandths, then the hundredths, and so on, carrying if necessary. If desired, we can write extra zeros to the right of the decimal point so that the number of places is the same in all of the addends.

EXAMPLE 1 Add: 56.314 + 17.78.

      5 6 . 3 1 4   Lining up the decimal points in order to add
   + 1 7 . 7 8 0   Writing an extra zero to the right of the
                            decimal point

      5 6 . 3 1 4
   + 1 7 . 7 8 0
                  4   Adding thousandths

      5 6 . 3 1 4
   + 1 7 . 7 8 0
               9 4   Adding hundredths

      ¹
      5 6 . 3 1 4   Adding tenths
   + 1 7 . 7 8 0   We get 10 tenths = 1 one + 0 tenths,
            . 0 9 4   so we carry the 1 to the ones column.
                            Writing a decimal point in the answer

    ¹ ¹
      5 6 . 3 1 4   Adding ones
   + 1 7 . 7 8 0   We get 14 ones = 1 ten + 4 ones, so we
         4 . 0 9 4   carry the 1 to the tens column.

    ¹ ¹
      5 6 . 3 1 4
   + 1 7 . 7 8 0
      7 4 . 0 9 4   Adding tens

◀ **Do Margin Exercises 1–2.**

Add.

1.   0.8 4 7   **2.**   2.1
       + 1 0.0 7   0.7 3
                          + 3 1.3 6 8

Add.

3. 0.02 + 4.3 + 0.649

4. 0.12 + 3.006 + 0.4357

5. 0.4591 + 0.2374 + 8.70894

EXAMPLE 2 Add: 3.42 + 0.237 + 14.1.

      3 . 4 2 0   Lining up the decimal points
      0 . 2 3 7   and writing extra zeros
   + 1 4 . 1 0 0
   1 7 . 7 5 7   Adding

◀ **Do Exercises 3–5.**

Answers

Skills to Review:
1. 641   **2.** 2356

Margin Exercises:
1. 10.917   **2.** 34.198   **3.** 4.969
4. 3.5617   **5.** 9.40544

Now we consider the addition 3456 + 19.347. Keep in mind that any whole number has an "unwritten" decimal point at the right that can be followed by zeros. For example, 3456 can also be written 3456.000. When adding, we can always write in the decimal point and extra zeros if desired.

EXAMPLE 3   Add: 3456 + 19.347.

$$
\begin{array}{r}
\overset{1}{} \\
3\,4\,5\,6\,.\,0\,0\,0 \\
+\quad\ \ 1\,9\,.\,3\,4\,7 \\
\hline
3\,4\,7\,5\,.\,3\,4\,7
\end{array}
$$

Writing in the decimal point and extra zeros
Lining up the decimal points
Adding

Do Exercises 6 and 7. ▶

b   SUBTRACTING POSITIVE DECIMALS

Subtracting positive decimals is similar to subtracting whole numbers. First, we line up the decimal points so that we can subtract corresponding place-value digits. Then we subtract digits from the right. For example, we subtract the thousandths, then the hundredths, the tenths, and so on, borrowing if necessary.

EXAMPLE 4   Subtract: 56.314 − 17.78.

$$
\begin{array}{r}
5\,6\,.\,3\,1\,4 \\
-\,1\,7\,.\,7\,8\,0 \\
\hline
\end{array}
$$
Lining up the decimal points in order to subtract
Writing an extra 0

$$
\begin{array}{r}
5\,6\,.\,3\,1\,4 \\
-\,1\,7\,.\,7\,8\,0 \\
\hline
4
\end{array}
$$
Subtracting thousandths

$$
\begin{array}{r}
{}^{2\ 11}\\
5\,6\,.\,3\,\cancel{1}\,4 \\
-\,1\,7\,.\,7\,8\,0 \\
\hline
3\ 4
\end{array}
$$
Borrowing tenths to subtract hundredths
Subtracting hundredths

$$
\begin{array}{r}
{}^{12}\\
{}^{5\ \cancel{2}\ 11}\\
5\,\cancel{6}\,.\,\cancel{3}\,\cancel{1}\,4 \\
-\,1\,7\,.\,7\,8\,0 \\
\hline
.5\ 3\ 4
\end{array}
$$
Borrowing ones to subtract tenths
Subtracting tenths; writing a decimal point

$$
\begin{array}{r}
{}^{15\ 12}\\
{}^{4\ 5\ \cancel{2}\ 11}\\
\cancel{5}\,\cancel{6}\,.\,\cancel{3}\,\cancel{1}\,4 \\
-\,1\,7\,.\,7\,8\,0 \\
\hline
8\,.5\ 3\ 4
\end{array}
$$
Borrowing tens to subtract ones
Subtracting ones

$$
\begin{array}{r}
{}^{15\ 12}\\
{}^{4\ 5\ \cancel{2}\ 11}\\
\cancel{5}\,\cancel{6}\,.\,\cancel{3}\,\cancel{1}\,4 \\
-\,1\,7\,.\,7\,8\,0 \\
\hline
3\,8\,.5\ 3\ 4
\end{array}
$$
Subtracting tens

Check by adding:
$$
\begin{array}{r}
\overset{1\ \ 1\ \ 1}{} \\
3\,8\,.\,5\,3\,4 \\
+\,1\,7\,.\,7\,8\,0 \\
\hline
5\,6\,.\,3\,1\,4
\end{array}
$$
◀ The answer checks because this is the top number in the subtraction.

Do Exercises 8 and 9. ▶

Add.

6. 789 + 123.67

7. 45.78 + 2467 + 1.993

$$
\begin{array}{r}
\boxed{}\ 1\ \boxed{}\ \ 1 \\
4\,5\,.\,7\,8\,0 \\
2\,4\,6\,7\,.\,0\,0\,0 \\
+\qquad\ \ 1\,.\,9\,9\,3 \\
\hline
2\ \boxed{}\ 4\,.\,\boxed{}\ 7\ 3
\end{array}
$$

Subtract.

8. 37.428 − 26.674

$$
\begin{array}{r}
{}^{6\ \ \ 3\ \ \boxed{}}\\
3\,7\,.\,4\,\cancel{2}\,8 \\
-\,2\,6\,.\,6\,7\,4 \\
\hline
1\ \boxed{}\,.\,7\ \boxed{}\ 4
\end{array}
$$

9.
$$
\begin{array}{r}
0\,.\,3\,4\,7 \\
-\,0\,.\,0\,0\,8 \\
\hline
\end{array}
$$

Answers

6. 912.67   **7.** 2514.773   **8.** 10.754
9. 0.339

Guided Solutions:
7. 1, 1, 5, 7   **8.** 13, 12, 0, 5

EXAMPLE 5 Subtract: 13.07 − 9.205.

$$
\begin{array}{r}
{\scriptstyle 12} \\
{\scriptstyle \cancel{2}\ 10\ 6\ 10} \\
\cancel{1}\,3.0\,7\,0 \\
-\quad 9.2\,0\,5 \\
\hline
3.8\,6\,5
\end{array}
$$ Writing an extra zero

Subtracting

EXAMPLE 6 Subtract: 23.08 − 5.0053.

$$
\begin{array}{r}
{\scriptstyle 1\ 13\quad 7\ 9\ 10} \\
2\,\cancel{3}.0\,\cancel{8}\,\cancel{0}\,\cancel{0} \\
-\quad 5.0\,0\,5\,3 \\
\hline
1\,8.0\,7\,4\,7
\end{array}
$$ Writing two extra zeros

Subtracting

Check by adding:

$$
\begin{array}{r}
{\scriptstyle 1\qquad 1\ 1} \\
1\,8.0\,7\,4\,7 \\
+\quad 5.0\,0\,5\,3 \\
\hline
2\,3.0\,8\,0\,0
\end{array}
$$

◀ **Do Exercises 10–12.**

When subtraction involves a whole number, again keep in mind that there is an "unwritten" decimal point that can be written in if desired. Extra zeros can also be written in to the right of the decimal point.

EXAMPLE 7 Subtract: 456 − 2.467.

$$
\begin{array}{r}
{\scriptstyle 5\ 9\ 9\ 10} \\
4\,5\,6.0\,0\,0 \\
-\quad 2.4\,6\,7 \\
\hline
4\,5\,3.5\,3\,3
\end{array}
$$ Writing in the decimal point and extra zeros

Subtracting

◀ **Do Exercises 13 and 14.**

C ADDING AND SUBTRACTING NEGATIVE DECIMALS

Negative decimals are added or subtracted just like negative integers.

ADDITION INVOLVING NEGATIVE NUMBERS
1. *Negative numbers*: Add absolute values. The answer is negative.
2. *A positive and a negative number*:
• If the numbers have the same absolute value, the answer is 0.
• If the numbers have different absolute values, subtract the smaller absolute value from the larger. Then:
a) If the positive number has the greater absolute value, the answer is positive.
b) If the negative number has the greater absolute value, the answer is negative.
3. *One number is zero*: The sum is the other number.

Subtract.

10. 1.2345 − 0.7

11. 0.9564 − 0.4392

12. 7.37 − 0.00008

Subtract.

13. 1277 − 82.78

14. 5 − 0.0089   GS

$$
\begin{array}{r}
{\scriptstyle \boxed{}\ 10} \\
5.0\,0\,0\,0 \\
-\,0.0\,0\,8\,9 \\
\hline
4.\boxed{}\,9\,1\,\boxed{}
\end{array}
$$

Answers

10. 0.5345 **11.** 0.5172 **12.** 7.36992
13. 1194.22 **14.** 4.9911

Guided Solution:
14. 4999, 9, 1

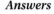

EXAMPLE 8 Add: $-5.103 + (-6.275)$.

$$\begin{array}{r} 5.103 \\ +\ 6.275 \\ \hline 11.378 \end{array}$$ The absolute values are 5.103 and 6.275.

Adding the absolute values

The answer is negative: $-5.103 + (-6.275) = -11.378$.

EXAMPLE 9 Add: $-9.48 + 2.37$.

$$\begin{array}{r} 9.48 \\ -\ 2.37 \\ \hline 7.11 \end{array}$$ Finding the difference of the absolute values

The negative number has the greater absolute value, so the answer is negative: $-9.48 + 2.37 = -7.11$.

Do Exercises 15–18. ▶

To subtract, we add the opposite of the number being subtracted.

EXAMPLE 10 Subtract: $-3.1 - 4.8$.

$$\begin{aligned} -3.1 - 4.8 &= -3.1 + (-4.8) \\ &= -7.9 \end{aligned}$$

Adding the opposite of 4.8

The sum of two negative numbers is negative.

EXAMPLE 11 Subtract: $-7.9 - (-8.5)$.

$$\begin{aligned} -7.9 - (-8.5) &= -7.9 + 8.5 \\ &= 0.6 \end{aligned}$$

Adding the opposite of -8.5

Finding the difference of the absolute values. The answer is positive since 8.5 has the greater absolute value.

Do Exercises 19–22. ▶

d SOLVING EQUATIONS

Now let's solve equations $x + a = b$ and $a + x = b$, where a and b may be in decimal notation. Proceeding as we have before, we subtract a on both sides.

EXAMPLE 12 Solve: $x + 28.89 = 74.567$.

We have

$$x + 28.89 - 28.89 = 74.567 - 28.89$$ Subtracting 28.89 on both sides

$$x = 45.677.$$

$$\begin{array}{r} \overset{13\ \ 14}{\overset{6\ \ 3\ \ 4\ \ 16}{7\,4.5\,6\,7}} \\ 2\,8.8\,9\,0 \\ \hline 4\,5.6\,7\,7 \end{array}$$

The solution is 45.677.

Add.

15. $12.064 + (-7.591)$

16. $-2.81 + (-8.432)$

17. $7.42 + (-9.38)$

18. $-4.201 + 7.36$

Subtract.

19. $9.25 - 13.41$

20. $-5.72 - 4.19$

21. $9.8 - (-2.6)$

22. $-5.9 - (-3.2)$

Answers

15. 4.473 **16.** −11.242 **17.** −1.96
18. 3.159 **19.** −4.16 **20.** −9.91
21. 12.4 **22.** −2.7

EXAMPLE 13 Solve: $0.8879 + y = 9.0026$.

We have

$$0.8879 + y - 0.8879 = 9.0026 - 0.8879 \qquad \text{Subtracting 0.8879 on both sides}$$
$$y = 8.1147.$$

$$\begin{array}{r} \overset{11}{} \\ {}^{8}\cancel{9}\ {}^{9}\cancel{9}\ {}^{1}\cancel{0}\ {}^{16}\cancel{0}\cancel{6} \\ 9.0026 \\ -\ 0.8879 \\ \hline 8.1147 \end{array}$$

The solution is 8.1147.

◀ **Do Exercises 23 and 24.**

Solve.

23. $x + 17.78 = 56.314$

24. $8.906 + t = 23.07$

EXAMPLE 14 Solve: $x + 7.4 = 5.6$.

We have

$$x + 7.4 - 7.4 = 5.6 - 7.4 \qquad \text{Subtracting 7.4 on both sides}$$
$$x = -1.8. \qquad 5.6 - 7.4 = 5.6 + (-7.4) = -1.8$$

25. Solve: $10.6 + y = 2.8$.

The solution is -1.8.

Answers

23. 38.534   **24.** 14.164   **25.** −7.8

◀ **Do Exercise 25.**

5.2 Exercise Set

For Extra Help
MyMathLab®
MathXL®
PRACTICE   WATCH   READ   REVIEW

✓ Reading Check

Complete each subtraction and its check by selecting a number from the list at right.

RC1.
$$\begin{array}{r} 2\,3.7 \\ -\ \ 1.876 \\ \hline \boxed{} \end{array}$$

Check:
$$\begin{array}{r} 2\,1.824 \\ +\ \ 1.876 \\ \hline \boxed{} \end{array}$$

RC2.
$$\begin{array}{r} 1\,8\,7.623 \\ -\ \ 40.9 \\ \hline \boxed{} \end{array}$$

Check:
$$\begin{array}{r} 1\,4\,6.723 \\ +\ \boxed{} \\ \hline 1\,8\,7.623 \end{array}$$

| |
| 23.7 |
| 187.623 |
| 21.824 |
| 40.9 |
| 1.876 |
| 146.723 |

a Add.

1.
$$\begin{array}{r} 3\,1\,6.25 \\ +\ \ 1\,8.12 \\ \hline \end{array}$$

2.
$$\begin{array}{r} 6\,4\,1.803 \\ +\ \ 1\,4.935 \\ \hline \end{array}$$

3.
$$\begin{array}{r} 6\,5\,9.403 \\ +9\,1\,6.812 \\ \hline \end{array}$$

4.
$$\begin{array}{r} 4\,2\,0\,3.28 \\ +\ \ \ \ \ 3.39 \\ \hline \end{array}$$

Copyright © 2015 Pearson Education, Inc.

5.
```
      9.1 0 4
+ 1 2 3.4 5 6
```

6.
```
   8 1.0 0 8
 +   3.4 0 9
```

7. 20.0124 + 30.0124

8. 0.687 + 0.9

9. 39 + 1.007

10. 2.3 + 0.729 + 23

11.
```
     4 7.8
   2 1 9.8 5 2
     4 3.5 9
 + 6 6 6.7 1 3
```

12.
```
    1 3.7 2
     9.1 1 2
 6 5 4 2.7 9 0 8
 +   2 3.9 0 1
```

13. 0.34 + 3.5 + 0.127 + 768

14. 17 + 3.24 + 0.256 + 0.3689

15. 99.6001 + 7285.18 + 500.042 + 870

16. 65.987 + 9.4703 + 6744.02 + 1.0003 + 200.895

b   Subtract.

17.
```
   5 1.3 1
 −    2.2 9
```

18.
```
   4 4.3 4 5
 −    3.1 0 5
```

19.
```
   9 2.3 4 1
 −    6.4 2
```

20.
```
   9 7.0 1
 −    3.1 5
```

21.
```
   2.5
 − 0.0 0 2 5
```

22.
```
   3 9.0
 −    0.2 8
```

23.
```
   3.4
 − 0.0 0 3
```

24.
```
   2.8
 − 2.0 8
```

25. 28.2 − 19.35

26. 100.16 − 0.118

27. 34.07 − 30.7

28. 36.2 − 16.28

29. 8.45 − 7.405

30. 3.801 − 2.81

31. 6.003 − 2.3

32. 9.087 − 8.807

33. 1 − 0.0098

34. 2 − 1.0908

35. 100 − 0.34

36. 624 − 18.79

37. $7.48 - 2.6$

38. $18.4 - 5.92$

39. $3 - 2.006$

40. $263.7 - 102.08$

41. $19 - 1.198$

42. $2548.98 - 2.007$

43. $65 - 13.87$

44. $45 - 0.999$

45.
$$\begin{array}{r} 3\,2.7\,9\,7\,8 \\ -\ \ \ \ 0.0\,5\,9\,2 \\ \hline \end{array}$$

46.
$$\begin{array}{r} 0.4\,9\,6\,3\,4 \\ -\ 0.1\,2\,6\,7\,8 \\ \hline \end{array}$$

47.
$$\begin{array}{r} 6.0\,7 \\ -\ 2.0\,0\,7\,8 \\ \hline \end{array}$$

48.
$$\begin{array}{r} 1.0 \\ -\ 0.9\,9\,9\,9 \\ \hline \end{array}$$

---

c   Add or subtract, as indicated.

49. $-5.02 + 1.73$

50. $-4.31 + 7.66$

51. $12.9 - 15.4$

52. $27.2 - 31.9$

53. $-2.9 + (-4.3)$

54. $-7.49 - 1.82$

55. $-4.301 + 7.68$

56. $-5.952 + 7.98$

57. $-12.9 - 3.7$

58. $-8.7 - 12.4$

59. $-2.1 - (-4.6)$

60. $-4.3 - (-2.5)$

61. $14.301 + (-17.82)$

62. $13.45 + (-18.701)$

63. $7.201 - (-2.4)$

64. $2.901 - (-5.7)$

65. $96.9 + (-21.4)$

66. $43.2 + (-10.9)$

67. $-8.9 - (-12.7)$

68. $-4.5 - (-7.3)$

69. $-4.9 - 5.392$

70. $89.3 - 92.1$

71. $14.7 - 23.5$

72. $-7.201 - 1.9$

Copyright © 2015 Pearson Education, Inc.

d Solve.

73. $x + 17.5 = 29.15$

74. $t + 50.7 = 54.07$

75. $17.95 + p = 402.63$

76. $w + 1.3004 = 47.8$

77. $x + 2349 = -17{,}684.3$

78. $1830.4 + t = -23{,}067$

79. $13{,}083.3 = x + 12{,}500.33$

80. $100.23 = 67.8 + z$

81. $643.2 + w = 109.6$

82. $7375.4 + z = 984.56$

83. $y + 2.39 = -4.6$

84. $x + 16.47 = -15.49$

Skill Maintenance

85. Round 34,567 to the nearest thousand.   [1.6a]

86. Round 34,496 to the nearest thousand.   [1.6a]

Subtract.

87. $\dfrac{13}{24} - \dfrac{3}{8}$ [4.3a]

88. $\dfrac{8}{9} - \dfrac{2}{15}$ [4.3a]

89. $8805 - 2639$ [1.3a]

90. $8005 - 2639$ [1.3a]

Solve.

91. A serving of filleted fish is generally considered to be about $\frac{1}{3}$ lb. How many servings can be prepared from $5\frac{1}{2}$ lb of flounder fillet?   [4.6c]

92. A photocopier technician drove $125\frac{7}{10}$ mi away from Scottsdale for a repair call. The next day he drove $65\frac{1}{2}$ mi back toward Scottsdale for another service call. How far was the technician from Scottsdale?   [4.5c]

Synthesis

93. A student presses the wrong button when using a calculator and adds 235.7 instead of subtracting it. The incorrect answer is 817.2. What is the correct answer?

OBJECTIVES

a Multiply using decimal notation.

b Convert from notation like 45.7 million to standard notation, and convert between dollars and cents.

SKILL TO REVIEW

Objective 1.4a: Multiply whole numbers.

Multiply.

1. $\begin{array}{r} 4\ 2 \\ \times\ 6\ 3 \\ \hline \end{array}$ **2.** $\begin{array}{r} 7\ 1\ 6 \\ \times\ \ \ 5\ 8 \\ \hline \end{array}$

a **MULTIPLICATION**

Let's find the product

$$2.3 \times 1.12.$$

To understand how we find such a product, we first convert each factor to fraction notation. Next, we multiply the numerators and then divide by the product of the denominators.

$$2.3 \times 1.12 = \frac{23}{10} \times \frac{112}{100} = \frac{23 \times 112}{10 \times 100} = \frac{2576}{1000} = 2.576$$

Note the number of decimal places.

$$\begin{array}{r} 1.1\,2 \quad (2\text{ decimal places}) \\ \times\ \ \ 2.3 \quad (1\text{ decimal place}) \\ \hline 2.5\,7\,6 \quad (3\text{ decimal places}) \end{array}$$

Now consider

$$0.011 \times 15.0002 = \frac{11}{1000} \times \frac{150{,}002}{10{,}000} = \frac{1{,}650{,}022}{10{,}000{,}000} = 0.1650022.$$

Note the number of decimal places.

$$\begin{array}{r} 1\,5.0\,0\,0\,2 \quad (4\text{ decimal places}) \\ \times\ \ \ \ \ 0.0\,1\,1 \quad (3\text{ decimal places}) \\ \hline 0.1\,6\,5\,0\,0\,2\,2 \quad (7\text{ decimal places}) \end{array}$$

To multiply using decimals: 0.8×0.43

a) Ignore the decimal points and multiply as though both factors were integers.

$$\begin{array}{r} \overset{2}{} \\ 0.4\,3 \\ \times\ \ \ 0.8 \\ \hline 3\,4\,4 \end{array}$$ Ignore the decimal points for now.

b) Then place the decimal point in the result. The number of decimal places in the product is the sum of the numbers of places in the factors. (Count places from the right.)

$$\begin{array}{r} 0.4\,3 \quad (2\text{ decimal places}) \\ \times\ \ \ 0.8 \quad (1\text{ decimal place}) \\ \hline 0.3\,4\,4 \quad (3\text{ decimal places}) \end{array}$$

EXAMPLE 1 Multiply: 8.3×74.6.

a) We ignore the decimal points and multiply as though factors were integers.

$$\begin{array}{r} 7\,4.6 \\ \times\ \ \ \ 8.3 \\ \hline 2\,2\,3\,8 \\ 5\,9\,6\,8\,0 \\ \hline 6\,1\,9\,1\,8 \end{array}$$

Answers

Skill to Review:
1. 2646 **2.** 41,528

b) We place the decimal point in the result. The number of decimal places in the product is the sum of the numbers of places in the factors, $1 + 1$, or 2.

$$
\begin{array}{r}
7\ 4.6 \quad (1\text{ decimal place}) \\
\times \quad\quad 8.3 \quad (1\text{ decimal place}) \\
\hline
2\ 2\ 3\ 8 \\
5\ 9\ 6\ 8\ 0 \\
\hline
6\ 1\ 9.1\ 8 \quad (2\text{ decimal places})
\end{array}
$$

Do Exercise 1. ▶

EXAMPLE 2 Multiply: 0.0032×2148.

$$
\begin{array}{r}
2\ 1\ 4\ 8 \quad (0\text{ decimal places}) \\
\times\ 0.0\ 0\ 3\ 2 \quad (4\text{ decimal places}) \\
\hline
4\ 2\ 9\ 6 \\
6\ 4\ 4\ 4\ 0 \\
\hline
6.8\ 7\ 3\ 6 \quad (4\text{ decimal places})
\end{array}
$$

EXAMPLE 3 Multiply: -0.14×0.867.
First we multiply the absolute values.

$$
\begin{array}{r}
0.8\ 6\ 7 \quad (3\text{ decimal places}) \\
\times \quad\quad 0.1\ 4 \quad (2\text{ decimal places}) \\
\hline
3\ 4\ 6\ 8 \\
8\ 6\ 7\ 0 \\
\hline
0.1\ 2\ 1\ 3\ 8 \quad (5\text{ decimal places})
\end{array}
$$

Since the product of a negative number and a positive number is negative, the answer is -0.12138.

Do Exercises 2 and 3. ▶

Multiplying by 0.1, 0.01, 0.001, and So On

Now let's consider some special kinds of products. The first involves multiplying by a tenth, hundredth, thousandth, ten-thousandth, and so on. Let's look at such products.

$$0.1 \times 38 = \frac{1}{10} \times 38 = \frac{38}{10} = 3.8$$

$$0.01 \times 38 = \frac{1}{100} \times 38 = \frac{38}{100} = 0.38$$

$$0.001 \times 38 = \frac{1}{1000} \times 38 = \frac{38}{1000} = 0.038$$

$$0.0001 \times 38 = \frac{1}{10,000} \times 38 = \frac{38}{10,000} = 0.0038$$

Note in each case that the product is *smaller* than 38. That is, the decimal point in each product is farther to the left than the unwritten decimal point in 38.

---

1. Multiply.

$$
\begin{array}{r}
8\ 5.4 \\
\times \quad 6.2 \\
\end{array}
$$

Multiply.

2.
$$
\begin{array}{r}
1\ 2\ 3\ 4 \\
\times\ 0.0\ 0\ 4\ 1 \\
\end{array}
$$

GS **3.** $-4\ 2.6\ 5 \times 0.8\ 0\ 4$
First we multiply the absolute values.

$$
\begin{array}{r}
4\ 2.6\ 5 \\
\times\ \ 0.8\ 0\ 4 \\
\hline
1\ \boxed{\ }\ 0\ 6\ 0 \\
3\ 4\ \ 1\ 2\ 0\ \ \ \ 0 \\
\hline
3\ 4.\ \ \boxed{\ }\ 9\ 0\ \ \ 0
\end{array}
$$

Since the product of a negative number and a positive number is _____, the answer
\quad\quad\quad positive/negative
is \boxed{\ \ }.

Answers
1. 529.48 **2.** 5.0594 **3.** −34.2906
Guided Solution:
3. 7, 0, 2, 6; negative, −34.2906

To multiply any number by 0.1, 0.01, 0.001, and so on,

a) count the number of decimal places in the tenth, hundredth, or thousandth, and so on, and

$$0.001 \times 34.45678$$
$$\longrightarrow 3 \text{ places}$$

b) move the decimal point in the other number that many places to the left.

$$0.001 \times 34.45678 = 0.034.45678$$

Move 3 places to the left.

$$0.001 \times 34.45678 = 0.03445678$$

EXAMPLES Multiply.

4. $0.1 \times 14.605 = 1.4605$ 1.4.605

5. $0.01 \times 14.605 = 0.14605$

6. $0.001 \times 14.605 = 0.014605$ We write an extra zero.

7. $0.0001 \times 14.605 = 0.0014605$ We write two extra zeros.

◀ **Do Exercises 4–7.**

Multiply.

4. 0.1×3.48

5. 0.01×3.48

6. 0.001×3.48

7. 0.0001×3.48

Multiplying by 10, 100, 1000, and So On

Next, let's consider multiplying by 10, 100, 1000, and so on. Let's look at some of these products.

$$10 \times 97.34 = 973.4$$
$$100 \times 97.34 = 9734$$
$$1000 \times 97.34 = 97,340$$

Note in each case that the product is *larger* than 97.34. That is, the decimal point in each product is farther to the right than the decimal point in 97.34.

To multiply any number by 10, 100, 1000, and so on,

a) count the number of zeros, and

$$1000 \times 34.45678$$
$$\longrightarrow 3 \text{ zeros}$$

b) move the decimal point in the other number that many places to the right.

$$1000 \times 34.45678 = 34.456.78$$

Move 3 places to the right.

$$1000 \times 34.45678 = 34,456.78$$

Multiply.

8. 10×3.48

9. 100×3.48

10. 1000×3.48

11. $10,000 \times 3.48$

EXAMPLES Multiply.

8. $10 \times 14.605 = 146.05$ 14.6.05

9. $100 \times 14.605 = 1460.5$

10. $1000 \times 14.605 = 14,605$

11. $10,000 \times 14.605 = 146,050$ 14.6050. We write an extra zero.

◀ **Do Exercises 8–11.**

Answers

4. 0.348   **5.** 0.0348   **6.** 0.00348
7. 0.000348   **8.** 34.8   **9.** 348
10. 3480   **11.** 34,800

b NAMING LARGE NUMBERS; MONEY CONVERSION

Naming Large Numbers

We often see notation like the following in newspapers and magazines and on television and the Internet.

- In 2012, wildfires burned over 9.1 million acres in the United States.
  Source: National Interagency Fire Center

- The number of valid U.S. passports in circulation in 2011 exceeded 113.4 million.
  Source: U.S. State Department

- Each day, about 144.8 billion e-mails are sent worldwide.
  Source: Mashable.com

- At one point in 2013, the U.S. national debt was approximately $16.501 trillion. The national debt has increased, on average, by $3.81 billion per day since 2007.
  Source: www.usdebtclock.org

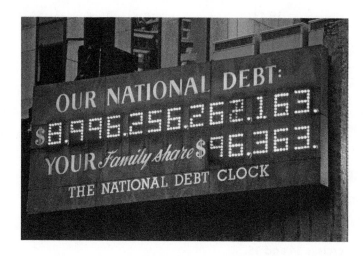

To understand such notation, consider the information in the following table.

NAMING LARGE NUMBERS

1 hundred = 1$\underline{00}$ = $10 \cdot 10$ = 10^2
$\qquad$ ⟶ 2 zeros

1 thousand = 1$\underline{000}$ = $10 \cdot 10 \cdot 10$ = 10^3
$\qquad$ ⟶ 3 zeros

1 million = 1,$\underline{000,000}$ = $10 \cdot 10 \cdot 10 \cdot 10 \cdot 10 \cdot 10$ = 10^6
$\qquad$ ⟶ 6 zeros

1 billion = 1,$\underline{000,000,000}$ = 10^9
$\qquad$ ⟶ 9 zeros

1 trillion = 1,$\underline{000,000,000,000}$ = 10^{12}
$\qquad$ ⟶ 12 zeros

Convert the number in each sentence to standard notation.

12. The largest building in the world is the Pentagon, which has 3.7 million square feet of floor space.

13. *Text Messages.* In the United States, 2.2 trillion text messages are sent each year.
Source: CNNTech, Forrester Research

To convert a large number to standard notation, we proceed as follows.

EXAMPLE 12 *Text Messages.* Worldwide, 8.6 trillion text messages are sent each year. Convert 8.6 trillion to standard notation.
Source: CNNTech, Portio Research

$$8.6 \text{ trillion} = 8.6 \times 1 \text{ trillion}$$
$$= 8.6 \times 1,\underline{000,000,000,000}$$

$\longrightarrow$ 12 zeros

$$= 8,600,000,000,000 \quad \text{Moving the decimal point 12 places to the right}$$

◀ Do Exercises 12 and 13.

Money Conversion

Converting from dollars to cents is like multiplying by 100. To see why, consider $19.43.

$$\$19.43 = 19.43 \times \$1 \quad \text{We think of } \$19.43 \text{ as } 19.43 \times 1 \text{ dollar, or } 19.43 \times \$1.$$
$$= 19.43 \times 100¢ \quad \text{Substituting } 100¢ \text{ for } \$1: \$1 = 100¢$$
$$= 1943¢ \quad \text{Multiplying}$$

Convert from dollars to cents.

14. $15.69
$$\$15.69 = 15.69 \times \$1$$
$$= 15.69 \times \boxed{} ¢$$
$$= \boxed{} ¢$$

GS

15. $0.17

DOLLARS TO CENTS

To convert from dollars to cents, move the decimal point two places to the right and change the $ sign in front to a ¢ sign at the end.

EXAMPLES Convert from dollars to cents.

13. $189.64 = 18,964¢

14. $0.75 = 75¢

◀ Do Exercises 14 and 15.

Converting from cents to dollars is like multiplying by 0.01. To see why, consider 65¢.

$$65¢ = 65 \times 1¢ \quad \text{We think of } 65¢ \text{ as } 65 \times 1 \text{ cent, or } 65 \times 1¢.$$
$$= 65 \times \$0.01 \quad \text{Substituting } \$0.01 \text{ for } 1¢: 1¢ = \$0.01$$
$$= \$0.65 \quad \text{Multiplying}$$

CENTS TO DOLLARS

To convert from cents to dollars, move the decimal point two places to the left and change the ¢ sign at the end to a $ sign in front.

Convert from cents to dollars.
16. 35¢

17. 577¢

EXAMPLES Convert from cents to dollars.

15. 395¢ = $3.95

16. 8503¢ = $85.03

◀ Do Exercises 16 and 17.

Answers

12. 3,700,000   **13.** 2,200,000,000,000
14. 1569¢   **15.** 17¢   **16.** $0.35   **17.** $5.77

Guided Solution:
14. 100, 1569

✓ Reading Check

Match each expression with an equivalent expression from the list at the right.

RC1. 0.001×38 _____   **a)** 3800¢

RC2. 1000×38 _____   **b)** 380

RC3. 38¢ _____   **c)** 0.038

RC4. $38 _____   **d)** $3.80

RC5. 380¢ _____   **e)** 38,000

RC6. 10×38 _____   **f)** $0.38

a Multiply.

1. 8.6
   $\times$ 7

2. 5.7
   $\times$ 0.8

3. 0.8 4
   $\times$ 8

4. 9.4
   $\times$ 0.6

5.   6.3
   $\times$ 0.0 4

6.   9.8
   $\times$ 0.0 8

7.   8 7
   $\times$ 0.0 0 6

8.   1 8.4
   $\times$ 0.0 7

9. 10×23.76

10. 100×3.8798

11. -1000×583.686852

12. -0.34×1000

13. -7.8×100

14. $0.00238 \times (-10)$

15. 0.1×89.23

16. 0.01×789.235

17. 0.001×97.68

18. 8976.23×0.001

19. -78.2×0.01

20. -0.0235×0.1

21. 3 2.6
   $\times$ 1 6

22. 9.2 8
   $\times$ 8.6

23. 0.9 8 4
   $\times$ 3.3

24. 8.4 8 9
   $\times$ 7.4

25. $(374)(-2.4)$

26. $(865)(-1.08)$

27. $-749(-0.43)$

28. $-978(-20.5)$

29.   0.8 7
    $\times$ 6 4

30.   7.2 5
    $\times$ 6 0

31.   4 6.5 0
    $\times$ 7 5

32.   8.2 4
    $\times$ 7 0 3

33.   8 1.7
    $\times$ 0.6 1 2

34.   3 1.8 2
    $\times$ 7.1 5

35.   1 0.1 0 5
    $\times$ 1 1.3 2 4

36.   1 5 1.2
    $\times$ 4.5 5 5

37.   1 2.3
    $\times$ 1.0 8

38.   7.8 2
    $\times$ 0.0 2 4

39.   3 2.4
    $\times$ 2.8

40.   8.0 9
    $\times$ 0.0 0 7 5

41.   0.0 0 3 4 2
    $\times$ 0.8 4

42.   2.0 0 5 6
    $\times$ 3.8

43.   0.3 4 7
    $\times$ 2.0 9

44.   2.5 3 2
    $\times$ 1.0 6 7

45. $3.005 \times (-0.623)$

46. $(-6.4)(-15.6)$

47. 1000×45.678

48. 0.001×45.678

b   Convert from dollars to cents.

49. $28.88

50. $67.43

51. $0.66

52. $1.78

Convert from cents to dollars.

53. 34¢

54. 95¢

55. 3445¢

56. 933¢

Copyright © 2015 Pearson Education, Inc.

57. *Farming Area.* China has 3.48 million hectares of land devoted to farming. This area is approximately 24% of China's total area. Convert 3.48 million to standard notation.

Source: Viking Cruises

58. *Doll Sales.* In the United States, spending on dolls totaled $2.7 billion in 2011. Convert 2.7 billion to standard notation.

Source: The NPD Group

59. *Spending on Pets.* In 2011, Americans spent approximately $50.96 billion on their pets, of which $13.41 billion was for veterinary care. Convert 50.96 billion and 13.41 billion to standard notation.

Source: American Pet Association

60. *Library of Congress.* The Library of Congress is the largest public library in the United States. It holds about 33.5 million books. Convert 33.5 million to standard notation.

Source: American Library Association

61. *Safe Water.* Worldwide, about 2.2 million people die each year because of diseases caused by unsafe water. Convert 2.2 million to standard notation.

Source: United Nations Environment Programme

62. *Overdraft Charges.* Revenue of U.S. banks from checking account overdraft charges rose to $31.5 billion in the fiscal year ending in June 2012. Convert 31.5 billion to standard notation.

Sources: Moebs Services; abcNews, *Consumer Report*, September 27, 2012

Skill Maintenance

Calculate.

63. $2\frac{1}{3} \cdot 4\frac{4}{5}$ [4.6a]

64. $-2\frac{1}{3} \div 4\frac{4}{5}$ [4.6b]

65. $4\frac{4}{5} - 2\frac{1}{3}$ [4.5b]

66. $4\frac{4}{5} + 2\frac{1}{3}$ [4.5a]

Divide. [1.5a], [2.5a]

67. $4\,0\,\overline{)\,3\,4\,8\,0}$

68. $1\,7\,\overline{)\,2\,0,0\,0\,6}$

69. $49 \div (-7)$

70. $-56 \div 4$

Synthesis

Consider the following names for large numbers in addition to those already discussed in this section:

$$1 \text{ quadrillion} = 1{,}000{,}000{,}000{,}000{,}000 = 10^{15};$$

$$1 \text{ quintillion} = 1{,}000{,}000{,}000{,}000{,}000{,}000 = 10^{18};$$

$$1 \text{ sextillion} = 1{,}000{,}000{,}000{,}000{,}000{,}000{,}000 = 10^{21};$$

$$1 \text{ septillion} = 1{,}000{,}000{,}000{,}000{,}000{,}000{,}000{,}000 = 10^{24}.$$

Find each of the following. Express the answer with a name that is a power of 10.

71. (1 trillion) · (1 billion)

72. (1 million) · (1 billion)

73. (1 trillion) · (1 trillion)

74. Is a billion millions the same as a million billions? Explain.

Division

OBJECTIVES

a Divide using decimal notation.

b Solve equations of the type $a \cdot x = b$, where a and b may be in decimal notation.

c Simplify expressions using the rules for order of operations.

SKILL TO REVIEW

Objective 1.5a: Divide whole numbers.

Divide.

1. $5 \overline{)\,2\,4\,5}$

2. $2\,3 \overline{)\,1\,9\,7\,8}$

a DIVISION

Whole-Number Divisors

We use the following method when we divide a decimal quantity by a whole number.

To divide by a whole number,

a) place the decimal point directly above the decimal point in the dividend, and

b) divide as though dividing whole numbers.

$$
\begin{array}{r}
0.8\,4 \leftarrow \text{Quotient} \\
\text{Divisor} \rightarrow 7 \overline{)\,5.8\,8} \leftarrow \text{Dividend} \\
\underline{5\,6} \\
2\,8 \\
\underline{2\,8} \\
0 \leftarrow \text{Remainder}
\end{array}
$$

EXAMPLE 1   Divide: $379.2 \div 8$.

Place the decimal point.

$$
\begin{array}{r}
4\,7.4 \\
8 \overline{)\,3\,7\,9.2} \\
\underline{3\,2} \\
5\,9 \\
\underline{5\,6} \\
3\,2 \\
\underline{3\,2} \\
0
\end{array}
$$

Divide as though dividing whole numbers.

EXAMPLE 2   Divide: $82.08 \div (-24)$.

First we consider $82.08 \div 24$.

Place the decimal point.

$$
\begin{array}{r}
3.4\,2 \\
2\,4 \overline{)\,8\,2.0\,8} \\
\underline{7\,2} \\
1\,0\,0 \\
\underline{9\,6} \\
4\,8 \\
\underline{4\,8} \\
0
\end{array}
$$

Divide as though dividing whole numbers.

Since a positive number divided by a negative number is negative, the answer is -3.42.

◀ Do Margin Exercises 1–3.

Divide.

1. $9 \overline{)\,5.4}$

2. $1\,5 \overline{)\,2\,2.5}$

3. $38.54 \div (-82)$

Answers

Skill to Review:
1. 49   **2.** 86

Margin Exercises:
1. 0.6   **2.** 1.5   **3.** −0.47

We can think of a whole-number dividend as having a decimal point at the end with as many zeros as we wish after the decimal point. For example, 12 = 12. = 12.0 = 12.00 = 12.000, and so on. We can also add zeros after the last digit in the decimal portion of a number: 3.6 = 3.60 = 3.600, and so on.

EXAMPLE 3 Divide: 30 ÷ 8.

```
     3.
  8 ) 3 0.
     2 4
       6
```
Place the decimal point and divide to find how many ones.

```
     3.
  8 ) 3 0.0
     2 4
       6 0
```
Write an extra zero.

```
     3.7
  8 ) 3 0.0
     2 4
       6 0
       5 6
         4
```
Divide to find how many tenths.

```
     3.7
  8 ) 3 0.0 0
     2 4
       6 0
       5 6
         4 0
```
Write another zero.

```
     3.7 5
  8 ) 3 0.0 0
     2 4
       6 0
       5 6
         4 0
         4 0
           0
```
Divide to find how many hundredths.

Check:
```
        6 4
      3.7 5
   ×      8
    3 0.0 0
```

EXAMPLE 4 Divide: − 4 ÷ 25.

First we consider 4 ÷ 25.

```
     0.1 6
  2 5 ) 4.0 0
       2 5
       1 5 0
       1 5 0
           0
```

Check:
```
        1
        3
      0.1 6
   ×   2 5
        8 0
      3 2 0
      4.0 0
```

Since a negative number divided by a positive number is negative, the answer is −0.16.

Do Exercises 4–6. ▶

CALCULATOR CORNER

Calculations with Decimal Notation · To use a calculator to add, subtract, multiply, and divide when any of the numbers are in decimal notation, we use the decimal key, $\boxed{\cdot}$, the operation keys, $\boxed{+}$, $\boxed{-}$, $\boxed{\times}$, and $\boxed{\div}$, the negative number key, $\boxed{+/-}$, and the equals key, $\boxed{=}$.

EXERCISES Calculate.

1. 1.7 + 14.56 + 0.89
2.   52.34
    − 18.51
3. 489 − 34.26
4. 0.04 × 12.69
5. 49)125.44‾
6. 1.6 ÷ 25

Divide.

4. 2 5)‾ 8   5. −15 ÷ 4

GS 6. 2.15 ÷ 86

```
         0.  2
  8 6 ) 2. 1 5 0
        1 7 2
          4 3
          4 3 0
              0
```

Answers

4. 0.32   5. −3.75   6. 0.025

Guided Solution:
6. 0, 5, 0

Divisors That Are Not Whole Numbers

Consider the division

$$0.2\,4\,)\overline{8.2\,0\,8}$$

We write the division as $\dfrac{8.208}{0.24}$. Then we multiply by 1 to change to a whole-number divisor:

The division $0.24)\overline{8.208}$ is the same as $24)\overline{820.8}$.

$$\frac{8.208}{0.24} = \frac{8.208}{0.24} \times \frac{100}{100} = \frac{820.8}{24}.$$

The divisor is now a whole number.

To divide when the divisor is not a whole number,

a) move the decimal point (multiply by 10, 100, and so on) to make the divisor a whole number;

$$0.2\,4\,)\overline{8.2\,0\,8}$$

Move 2 places to the right.

b) move the decimal point in the dividend the same number of places (multiply the same way); and

$$0.2\,4\,)\overline{8.2\,0\,8}$$

Move 2 places to the right.

c) place the decimal point directly above the new decimal point in the dividend and divide as though dividing whole numbers.

$$
\begin{array}{r}
3\ 4.2 \\
0.2\,4\,)\overline{8.2\,0\,8} \\
7\ 2 \\
\hline
1\ 0\ 0 \\
9\ 6 \\
\hline
4\ 8 \\
4\ 8 \\
\hline
0
\end{array}
$$

(The new decimal point in the dividend is indicated by a caret.)

Divide.

7. $0.375 \div 0.25$

$$\frac{0.375}{0.25} = \frac{0.375}{0.25} \times \frac{\boxed{}}{100}$$

$$= \frac{37.5}{\boxed{}}$$

$$
\begin{array}{r}
1.\boxed{} \\
0.2\,5\,)\overline{0.3\,7\wedge5} \\
2\ 5 \\
\hline
1\ 2\boxed{} \\
1\ 2\ 5 \\
\hline
0
\end{array}
$$

8. $0.8\,3\,)\overline{4.0\,6\,7}$

9. $3.5\,)\overline{4\,4.8}$

EXAMPLE 5 Divide: $5.848 \div 8.6$.

$$8.6\,)\overline{5.8\,4\,8}$$

Multiply the divisor by 10. (Move the decimal point 1 place.) Multiply the same way in the dividend. (Move 1 place.)

$$
\begin{array}{r}
0.6\ 8 \\
8.6\,)\overline{5.8\wedge4\ 8} \\
5\ 1\ 6 \\
\hline
6\ 8\ 8 \\
6\ 8\ 8 \\
\hline
0
\end{array}
$$

Place a decimal point above the new decimal point in the dividend and then divide.

Note: $\dfrac{5.848}{8.6} = \dfrac{5.848}{8.6} \cdot \dfrac{10}{10} = \dfrac{58.48}{86}.$

◀ Do Exercises 7–9.

Answers

7. 1.5   **8.** 4.9   **9.** 12.8

Guided Solution:

7. 100, 25; 5, 5

EXAMPLE 6 Divide: $-12 \div 0.64$.

First we consider $12 \div 0.64$.

$$0.64 \overline{\smash{)}12.}$$

Place a decimal point at the end of the whole number.

$$0.64 \overline{\smash{)}12.00}$$

Multiply the divisor by 100 (move the decimal point 2 places). Multiply the same way in the dividend (move 2 places).

$$
\begin{array}{r}
1\ 8.7\ 5 \\
0.64 \overline{\smash{)}1\ 2.0\ 0_\wedge 0\ 0} \\
\underline{6\ 4} \\
5\ 6\ 0 \\
\underline{5\ 1\ 2} \\
4\ 8\ 0 \\
\underline{4\ 4\ 8} \\
3\ 2\ 0 \\
\underline{3\ 2\ 0} \\
0
\end{array}
$$

Place a decimal point above the new decimal point in the dividend and then divide.

Since $12 \div 0.64 = 18.75$, we have $-12 \div 0.64 = -18.75$.

Do Exercise 10. ▶

10. Divide: $-25 \div 1.6$.

Dividing by 10, 100, 1000, and So On

It is often helpful to be able to divide quickly by a ten, hundred, or thousand, or by a tenth, hundredth, or thousandth. Each procedure we use is based on multiplying by 1. Consider the following example:

$$\frac{23.789}{1000} = \frac{23.789}{1000} \cdot \frac{1000}{1000} = \frac{23{,}789}{1{,}000{,}000} = 0.023789.$$

We are dividing by a number greater than 1: The result is *smaller* than 23.789.

To divide by 10, 100, 1000, and so on,

a) count the number of zeros in the divisor, and

$$\frac{713.49}{100}$$

↳ 2 zeros

b) write the quotient by moving the decimal point in the dividend that number of places to the left.

$$\frac{713.49}{100}, \quad 7.13.49, \quad \frac{713.49}{100} = 7.1349$$

2 places to the left

EXAMPLE 7 Divide: $\dfrac{0.0104}{10}$.

$$\frac{0.0104}{10}, \quad 0.0.0104, \quad \frac{0.0104}{10} = 0.00104$$

1 zero   1 place to the left

Answer

10. 15.625

Dividing by 0.1, 0.01, 0.001, and So On

Now consider the following example:

$$\frac{23.789}{0.01} = \frac{23.789}{0.01} \cdot \frac{100}{100} = \frac{2378.9}{1} = 2378.9.$$

We are dividing by a number less than 1: The result is *larger* than 23.789. We use the following procedure.

To divide by 0.1, 0.01, 0.001, and so on,

a) count the number of decimal places in the divisor, and

$$\frac{713.49}{0.001}$$

⌐→ 3 places

b) write the quotient by moving the decimal point in the dividend that number of places to the right.

$$\frac{713.49}{0.001}, \quad 713.490., \quad \frac{713.49}{0.001} = 713,490$$

3 places to the right to change 0.001 to 1

EXAMPLE 8 Divide: $\dfrac{23.738}{0.001}$.

$$\frac{23.738}{0.001}, \quad 23.738., \quad \frac{23.738}{0.001} = 23,738$$

3 places   3 places to the right

◀ **Do Exercises 11–14.**

Divide.

11. $\dfrac{0.1278}{0.01}$

12. $\dfrac{0.1278}{100}$

13. $\dfrac{98.47}{1000}$

14. $\dfrac{-6.7832}{0.1}$

b SOLVING EQUATIONS

Now let's solve equations of the type $a \cdot x = b$, where a and b may be in decimal notation. Proceeding as before, we divide by a on both sides.

EXAMPLE 9 Solve: $8 \cdot x = 27.2$.

We have

$$\frac{8 \cdot x}{8} = \frac{27.2}{8} \qquad \text{Dividing by 8 on both sides}$$

$$x = 3.4. \qquad \begin{array}{r} 3.4 \\ 8\overline{)27.2} \\ \underline{24} \\ 32 \\ \underline{32} \\ 0 \end{array}$$

The solution is 3.4.

Answers

11. 12.78   **12.** 0.001278   **13.** 0.09847
14. −67.832

EXAMPLE 10 Solve: $2.9 \cdot t = -0.14616$.

We have

$$\frac{2.9 \cdot t}{2.9} = \frac{-0.14616}{2.9} \quad \text{Dividing by 2.9 on both sides}$$

$$t = -0.0504. \qquad 2.9)\overline{0.1_\wedge 4\,6\,1\,6}$$

$$\begin{array}{r} 0.0\,5\,0\,4 \\ 2.9)\overline{0.1_\wedge 4\,6\,1\,6} \\ \underline{1\,4\,5} \\ 1\,1\,6 \\ \underline{1\,1\,6} \\ 0 \end{array}$$

Since $0.14616 \div 2.9 = 0.0504$, then $-0.14616 \div 2.9 = -0.0504$. Thus the solution is -0.0504.

Do Exercises 15 and 16. ▶

Solve.

GS **15.** $100 \cdot x = 78.314$

$$\frac{100 \cdot x}{100} = \frac{78.314}{\boxed{}}$$

$$x = 0.7\boxed{}\,314$$

16. $0.25 \cdot y = -276.4$

c ORDER OF OPERATIONS: DECIMAL NOTATION

The same rules for order of operations that we use with integers and fraction notation apply when simplifying expressions with decimal notation.

> ### RULES FOR ORDER OF OPERATIONS
>
> **1.** Do all calculations within grouping symbols before operations outside.
> **2.** Evaluate all exponential expressions.
> **3.** Do all multiplications and divisions in order from left to right.
> **4.** Do all additions and subtractions in order from left to right.

EXAMPLE 11 Simplify: $2.56 \times 25.6 \div 25{,}600 \times 256$.

There are no exponents or parentheses, so we multiply and divide from left to right:

$$\begin{aligned} 2.56 \times 25.6 \div 25{,}600 \times 256 &= 65.536 \div 25{,}600 \times 256 & \text{Doing all} \\ &= 0.00256 \times 256 & \text{multiplications} \\ &= 0.65536. & \text{and divisions} \\ & & \text{in order from} \\ & & \text{left to right} \end{aligned}$$

EXAMPLE 12 Simplify: $(5 - 0.06) \div (-2) + 3.42 \times 0.1$.

$$\begin{aligned} (5 - 0.06) \div (-2) + 3.42 \times 0.1 &= 4.94 \div (-2) + 3.42 \times 0.1 & \text{Carrying out the} \\ & & \text{operation inside} \\ & & \text{parentheses} \\ &= -2.47 + 0.342 & \text{Doing all multiplications} \\ & & \text{and divisions in order} \\ & & \text{from left to right} \\ &= -2.128 & \text{Adding} \end{aligned}$$

Answers

15. 0.78314   **16.** −1105.6

Guided Solution:
15. 100, 8

Simplify.

17. $625 \div 62.5 \times 25 \div 6250$

$= \boxed{} \times 25 \div 6250$

$= \boxed{} \div 6250$

$= 0.04$

GS

18. $0.25 \cdot (-1 + 0.08) - 0.0274$

19. $20^2 - 3.4^2 +$
$\{2.5[20(9.2 - 5.6)] + 5(10 - 5)\}$

EXAMPLE 13 Simplify: $10^2 \times \{[(3 - 0.24) \div 2.4] - (0.21 - 0.092)\}$.

$10^2 \times \{[(3 - 0.24) \div 2.4] - (0.21 - 0.092)\}$

$= 10^2 \times \{[2.76 \div 2.4] - 0.118\}$ Doing the calculations in the innermost parentheses first

$= 10^2 \times \{1.15 - 0.118\}$ Again, doing the calculations in the innermost grouping symbols

$= 10^2 \times 1.032$ Subtracting inside the grouping symbols

$= 100 \times 1.032$ Evaluating the exponential expression

$= 103.2$

◀ **Do Exercises 17–19.**

EXAMPLE 14 *Population Density.* The table below shows the number of residents per square mile in the six New England states. Find the average number of residents per square mile for this group of states.

Source: 2010 U.S. Census

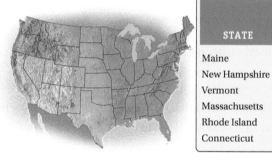

STATE	NUMBER OF RESIDENTS PER SQUARE MILE
Maine	43.1
New Hampshire	147.0
Vermont	67.9
Massachusetts	839.4
Rhode Island	1018.1
Connecticut	738.1

20. *Population Density.* The table below shows the number of residents per square mile in five northwestern states. Find the average number of residents per square mile for this group of states.

Source: 2010 U.S. Census

STATE	RESIDENTS PER SQUARE MILE
Washington	101.2
Oregon	39.9
Idaho	19
Montana	6.8
Wyoming	5.8

The **average** of a set of numbers is the sum of the numbers divided by the number of addends. We find the sum of the population densities per square mile and divide it by the number of addends, 6:

$$\frac{43.1 + 147 + 67.9 + 839.4 + 1018.1 + 738.1}{6} = \frac{2853.6}{6} = 475.6.$$

Thus the average number of residents per square mile for these six states is 475.6.

◀ **Do Exercise 20.**

Answers

17. 0.04   **18.** −0.2574   **19.** 593.44   **20.** 34.54

Guided Solution:
17. 10, 250

✓ Reading Check

Name the operation that should be performed first in evaluating each expression. Do not calculate.

RC1. $(2 - 0.04) \div 4 + 8.5$ _____

RC2. $0.02 + 2.06 \div 0.01$ _____

RC3. $5 \times 2.1 + 0.1 - 8^3$ _____

RC4. $18.2 - (4.1 + 6.9)$ _____

RC5. $16 - 9 \div 3 + 7.3$ _____

RC6. $4(10 - 5) \times 14.2$ _____

a Divide.

1. $2 \overline{)5.9\,8}$

2. $5 \overline{)1\,8}$

3. $4 \overline{)9\,5.1\,2}$

4. $8 \overline{)2\,5.9\,2}$

5. $1\,2 \overline{)8\,9.7\,6}$

6. $2\,3 \overline{)2\,5.0\,7}$

7. $3\,3 \overline{)2\,3\,7.6}$

8. $5\,4 \overline{)4\,4\,8.2}$

9. $-9.144 \div 8$

10. $4.5 \div (-9)$

11. $12.123 \div (-3)$

12. $-12.4 \div 4$

13. $0.0\,6 \overline{)3.3\,6}$

14. $0.0\,4 \overline{)1.6\,8}$

15. $0.1\,2 \overline{)8.4}$

16. $0.3\,6 \overline{)2.8\,8}$

17. $3.4 \overline{)6\,8}$

18. $0.2\,5 \overline{)5}$

19. $-6 \div (-15)$

20. $-1.8 \div (-12)$

21. $3\,6 \overline{)1\,4.7\,6}$

22. $5\,2 \overline{)1\,1\,9.6}$

23. $3.2 \overline{)2\,7.2}$

24. $8.5 \overline{)2\,7.2}$

25. $4.2 \overline{)\, 3\,9.0\,6}$ **26.** $4.8 \overline{)\, 0.1\,1\,0\,4}$ **27.** $-5 \div 8$ **28.** $-3 \div 8$

29. $0.4\,7 \overline{)\, 0.1\,2\,2\,2}$ **30.** $1.0\,8 \overline{)\, 0.5\,4}$ **31.** $4.8 \overline{)\, 7\,5}$

32. $0.2\,8 \overline{)\, 6\,3}$ **33.** $0.0\,3\,2 \overline{)\, 0.0\,7\,4\,8\,8}$ **34.** $0.0\,1\,7 \overline{)\, 1.5\,8\,1}$

35. $8\,2 \overline{)\, 3\,8.5\,4}$ **36.** $3\,4 \overline{)\, 0.1\,4\,6\,2}$ **37.** $\dfrac{213.4567}{1000}$ **38.** $\dfrac{769.3265}{1000}$

39. $\dfrac{-23.59}{10}$ **40.** $\dfrac{-83.57}{10}$ **41.** $\dfrac{426.487}{100}$ **42.** $\dfrac{591.348}{100}$

43. $\dfrac{-16.94}{0.1}$ **44.** $\dfrac{-100.7604}{0.1}$ **45.** $\dfrac{1.0237}{0.001}$ **46.** $\dfrac{3.4029}{0.001}$

47. $\dfrac{-42.561}{0.01}$ **48.** $\dfrac{-98.473}{0.01}$

b Solve.

49. $4.2 \cdot x = 39.06$ **50.** $36 \cdot y = 14.76$ **51.** $1000 \cdot y = -9.0678$

52. $-789.23 = 0.25 \cdot q$ **53.** $1048.8 = 23 \cdot t$ **54.** $28.2 \cdot x = 423$

Copyright © 2015 Pearson Education, Inc.

C Simplify.

55. $14 \times (82.6 + 67.9)$

56. $(26.2 - 14.8) \times 12$

57. $0.003 - 3.03 \div 0.01$

58. $9.94 + 118.8 \div (-6.2 - 4.6) - 0.9$

59. $42 \times (10.6 + 0.024)$

60. $(18.6 - 4.9) \times 13$

61. $4.2 \times 5.7 + 0.7 \div 3.5$

62. $123.3 - 4.24 \times 1.01$

63. $-9.0072 + 0.04 \div 0.1^2$

64. $-12 \div 0.03 + 12 \times 0.03^2$

65. $(8 - 0.04)^2 \div 4 + 8.7 \times 0.4$

66. $(5 - 2.5)^2 \div 100 + 0.1 \times 6.5$

67. $86.7 + 4.22 \times (9.6 - 0.03)^2$

68. $2.48 \div (1 - 0.504) + 24.3 - 11 \times 2$

69. $4 \div (-0.4) + 0.1 \times 5 - 0.1^2$

70. $6 \times (-0.9) + 0.1 \div 4 - 0.2^3$

71. $5.5^2 \times [(6 - 4.2) \div 0.06 + 0.12]$

72. $12^2 \div (12 + 2.4) - [(2 - 1.6) \div 0.8]$

73. $200 \times \{[(4 - 0.25) \div 2.5] - (4.5 - 4.025)\}$

74. $0.03 \times \{1 \times 50.2 - [(8 - 7.5) \div 0.05]\}$

75. Find the average of $1276.59, $1350.49, $1123.78, and $1402.58.

76. Find the average weight of two wrestlers who weigh 308 lb and 296.4 lb.

77. *Mountain Peaks in Colorado.* The elevations of four mountain peaks in Colorado are listed in the table below. Find the average elevation of these peaks.

MOUNTAIN PEAK	ELEVATION (in feet)
Mount Elbert	14,440
Mount Evans	14,271
Pikes Peak	14,115
Crested Butte	12,168

78. *Driving Costs.* The table below shows the cost per mile when specific types of vehicles are driven 15,000 miles in a year. Find the average cost per mile for the listed vehicles.

TYPE OF VEHICLE	COST PER MILE (in cents)
Small sedan	44.9
Medium sedan	58.5
Minivan	63.4
Large sedan	75.5
SUV 4WD	75.7

SOURCE: AAA

Skill Maintenance

Simplify. [3.5b]

79. $\dfrac{38}{146}$

80. $-\dfrac{92}{124}$

Find the prime factorization. [3.1d]

81. 684

82. 2005

83. Add: $10\frac{1}{2} + 4\frac{5}{8}$. [4.5a]

84. Subtract: $10\frac{1}{2} - 4\frac{5}{8}$. [4.5b]

Evaluate. [1.9b]

85. 7^3

86. 2^6

Solve. [1.7b]

87. $235 = 5 \cdot z$

88. $q + 31 = 72$

Synthesis

Simplify.

89. ▦ $9.0534 - 2.041^2 \times 0.731 \div 1.043^2$

90. ▦ $23.042(7 - 4.037 \times 1.46 - 0.932^2)$

In Exercises 91–94, find the missing value.

91. $439.57 \times 0.01 \div 1000 \times \boxed{} = 4.3957$

92. $5.2738 \div 0.01 \times 1000 \div \boxed{} = 52.738$

93. $0.0329 \div 0.001 \times 10^4 \div \boxed{} = 3290$

94. $0.0047 \times 0.01 \div 10^4 \times \boxed{} = 4.7$

Copyright © 2015 Pearson Education, Inc.

Mid-Chapter Review

Concept Reinforcement

Determine whether each statement is true or false.

_____ **1.** In the number 308.00567, the digit 6 names the tens place.   [5.1a]

_____ **2.** When writing a word name for decimal notation, we write the word "and" for the decimal point.   [5.1a]

_____ **3.** To multiply any number by 10, 100, 1000, and so on, count the number of zeros and move the decimal point that many places to the right.   [5.3a]

Guided Solutions

 Fill in each blank with the number that creates a correct statement or solution.

4. Solve: $y + 12.8 = 23.35$.   [5.2d]

$$y + 12.8 = 23.35$$
$$y + 12.8 - \boxed{} = 23.35 - \boxed{} \qquad \text{Subtracting 12.8 on both sides}$$
$$y + \boxed{} = \boxed{} \qquad \text{Carrying out the subtraction}$$
$$y = \boxed{}$$

5. Simplify: $5.6 + 4.3 \times (6.5 - 0.25)^2$.   [5.4c]

$$5.6 + 4.3 \times (6.5 - 0.25)^2 = 5.6 + 4.3 \times (\boxed{})^2 \qquad \text{Carrying out the operation inside parentheses}$$
$$= 5.6 + 4.3 \times \boxed{} \qquad \text{Evaluating the exponential expression}$$
$$= 5.6 + \boxed{} \qquad \text{Multiplying}$$
$$= \boxed{} \qquad \text{Adding}$$

Mixed Review

6. *Mile Run Record.*   The difference between the men's record for the mile run, held by Hicham El Guerrouj of Morocco (with a time of 3 min 43.13 sec) and the women's record for the mile run, held by Svetlana Masterkova of Russia (with a time of 4 min 12.56 sec) is 29.43 sec. Write a word name for 29.43.   [5.1a]

Source: International Association of Athletics Federations (iaaf.org)

7. *Skin Allergies.*   Skin allergies are the most common allergies among children. In 2010, 9.4 million children in the United States suffered from skin allergies. Convert 9.4 million to standard notation.   [5.3b]

Source: CDC National Center for Health Statistics

Write fraction notation.   [5.1b]

8. 4.53

9. −0.287

Which number is larger?   [5.1c]

10. 0.07, 0.13

11. −5.2, −5.09

Write decimal notation.   [5.1b]

12. $\dfrac{7}{10}$

13. $\dfrac{-639}{100}$

14. $35\dfrac{67}{100}$

15. $8\dfrac{2}{1000}$

Round 28.4615 to the nearest: [5.1d]

16. Thousandth.

17. Hundredth.

18. Tenth.

19. One.

Add. [5.2a], [5.2c]

20. 4 7.6 3 8
     + 2.4 5 7

21.   1 5.6
         2 3 4.7 2 9
              3.0 8
      + 9 6 1.4 5 3

22. −4.5 + 0.728

23. 16 + 0.34 + 1.9

Subtract. [5.2b], [5.2c]

24. 3 2 1.5 7
     −   4 9.3 8

25.   5.6
       − 0.0 0 7

26. 34.3 − 18.75

27. −49.07 − 9.7

Multiply. [5.3a]

28.   4.6
       × 0.9

29.   1 5.3
       ×   6.0 7

30. −100 × 81.236

31. 0.1 × 29.37

Divide. [5.4a]

32. 20.24 ÷ 4

33. −21.76 ÷ 6.8

34. 76.34 ÷ 0.1

35. 914.036 ÷ 1000

36. Convert $20.45 to cents. [5.3b]

37. Convert 147¢ to dollars. [5.3b]

38. Solve: $46.3 + x = -59.$ [5.2d]

39. Solve: $42.84 = 5.1 \cdot y.$ [5.4b]

Simplify. [5.4c]

40. $6.594 + 0.5318 \div 0.01$

41. $7.3 \times 4.6 - 0.8 \div (-3.2)$

Understanding Through Discussion and Writing

42. A fellow student rounds 236.448 to the nearest one and gets 237. Explain the possible error. [5.1d]

43. Explain the error in the following: [5.2b]
Subtract.

$$73.089 - 5.0061 = 2.3028$$

44. Explain why $10 \div 0.2 = 100 \div 2.$ [5.4a]

45. Kayla made these two computational mistakes:

$$0.247 \div 0.1 = 0.0247; \quad 0.247 \div 10 = 2.47.$$

In each case, how could you convince her that a mistake has been made? [5.4a]

Copyright © 2015 Pearson Education, Inc.

STUDYING FOR SUCCESS   *As You Study*

☐ Find a quiet place to study.
☐ Be disciplined about your use of video games, the Internet, and television. Study first!
☐ Pace yourself. It is usually better to study for shorter periods several times a week than to study in one marathon session each week.

Converting from Fraction Notation to Decimal Notation

5.5

a FRACTION NOTATION TO DECIMAL NOTATION

When a denominator has no prime factors other than 2's and 5's, we can find decimal notation by multiplying by 1. We multiply to get a denominator that is a power of ten, like 10, 100, or 1000.

EXAMPLE 1 Find decimal notation for $\frac{3}{5}$.

$$\frac{3}{5} = \frac{3}{5} \cdot \frac{2}{2} = \frac{6}{10} = 0.6$$

$5 \cdot 2 = 10$, so we use $\frac{2}{2}$ for 1 to get a denominator of 10.

EXAMPLE 2 Find decimal notation for $-\frac{87}{25}$.

$$-\frac{87}{25} = -\frac{87}{25} \cdot \frac{4}{4} = -\frac{348}{100} = -3.48$$

$25 \cdot 4 = 100$, so we use $\frac{4}{4}$ for 1 to get a denominator of 100.

EXAMPLE 3 Find decimal notation for $\frac{9}{40}$.

$$\frac{9}{40} = \frac{9}{40} \cdot \frac{25}{25} = \frac{225}{1000} = 0.225$$

$40 \cdot 25 = 1000$, so we use $\frac{25}{25}$ for 1 to get a denominator of 1000.

Do Margin Exercises 1–3. ▶

We can always divide to find decimal notation.

EXAMPLE 4 Find decimal notation for $\frac{3}{5}$.

$$\frac{3}{5} = 3 \div 5 \qquad \begin{array}{r} 0.6 \\ 5\overline{)3.0} \\ \underline{3\ 0} \\ 0 \end{array} \qquad \frac{3}{5} = 0.6$$

EXAMPLE 5 Find decimal notation for $-\frac{7}{8}$.

First we consider $\frac{7}{8}$.

$$\frac{7}{8} = 7 \div 8 \qquad \begin{array}{r} 0.8\ 7\ 5 \\ 8\overline{)7.0\ 0\ 0} \\ \underline{6\ 4} \\ 6\ 0 \\ \underline{5\ 6} \\ 4\ 0 \\ \underline{4\ 0} \\ 0 \end{array} \qquad \frac{7}{8} = 0.875$$

Since $\frac{7}{8} = 0.875$, we have $-\frac{7}{8} = -0.875$.

OBJECTIVES

a Convert from fraction notation to decimal notation.

b Round numbers named by repeating decimals in problem solving.

c Calculate using fraction notation and decimal notation together.

SKILL TO REVIEW

Objective 5.4a: Divide using decimal notation.

Divide.

1. $3 \div 4$ **2.** $25 \div 8$

Find decimal notation. Use multiplying by 1.

1. $\dfrac{4}{5}$

GS 2. $\dfrac{9}{20} = \dfrac{9}{20} \cdot \dfrac{5}{\boxed{}} = \dfrac{\boxed{}}{100} = \boxed{}$

3. $-\dfrac{11}{40}$

Answers

Skill to Review:
1. 0.75   **2.** 3.125

Margin Exercises:
1. 0.8   **2.** 0.45   **3.** −0.275

Guided Solution:
2. 5, 45, 0.45

Find decimal notation.

4. $-\dfrac{2}{5}$ **5.** $\dfrac{3}{8}$

Find decimal notation.

6. $\dfrac{1}{6}$ GS

$$\dfrac{1}{6} = \boxed{} \div 6$$

$$
\begin{array}{r}
0.1\ \boxed{}\ 6 \\
\boxed{}\,)\overline{1.0\ 0\ 0} \\
\underline{6} \\
4\ 0 \\
\underline{3\ 6} \\
\boxed{}\ 0 \\
\underline{3\ 6} \\
\boxed{}
\end{array}
$$

$$\dfrac{1}{6} = 0.1666\ldots = 0.1\overline{6}$$

7. $\dfrac{2}{3}$

Find decimal notation.

8. $\dfrac{5}{11}$ **9.** $-\dfrac{12}{11}$

Answers

4. -0.4 5. 0.375 6. $0.1\overline{6}$ 7. $0.\overline{6}$
8. $0.\overline{45}$ 9. $-1.\overline{09}$

Guided Solution:
6. 1; 6, 6, 4, 4

◀ **Do Exercises 4 and 5.**

In Examples 4 and 5, the division *terminated,* meaning that eventually we got a remainder of 0. A **terminating decimal** occurs when the denominator of a fraction has only 2's or 5's, or both, as factors, as in $\frac{17}{25}$, $\frac{5}{8}$, or $\frac{83}{100}$. This assumes that the fraction notation has been simplified.

Consider a different situation: $\frac{5}{6}$, or $5/(2 \cdot 3)$. Since 6 has a 3 as a factor, the division will not terminate. Although we can still use division to get decimal notation, the answer will be a **repeating decimal**, as follows.

EXAMPLE 6 Find decimal notation for $\frac{5}{6}$.

$$\dfrac{5}{6} = 5 \div 6$$

$$
\begin{array}{r}
0.8\ 3\ 3 \\
6\,)\overline{5.0\ 0\ 0} \\
\underline{4\ 8} \\
2\ 0 \\
\underline{1\ 8} \\
2\ 0 \\
\underline{1\ 8} \\
2
\end{array}
$$

Since 2 keeps reappearing as a remainder, the digits repeat and will continue to do so; therefore,

$$\dfrac{5}{6} = 0.83333\ldots.$$

The red dots indicate an endless sequence of digits in the quotient. When there is a repeating pattern, the dots are often replaced by a bar to indicate the repeating part—in this case, only the 3:

$$\dfrac{5}{6} = 0.8\overline{3}.$$

◀ **Do Exercises 6 and 7.**

EXAMPLE 7 Find decimal notation for $-\frac{4}{11}$.

First we consider $\frac{4}{11}$.

$$\dfrac{4}{11} = 4 \div 11$$

$$
\begin{array}{r}
0.3\ 6\ 3\ 6 \\
11\,)\overline{4.0\ 0\ 0\ 0} \\
\underline{3\ 3} \\
7\ 0 \\
\underline{6\ 6} \\
4\ 0 \\
\underline{3\ 3} \\
7\ 0 \\
\underline{6\ 6} \\
4
\end{array}
$$

Since 7 and 4 keep repeating as remainders, the sequence of digits "36" repeats in the quotient, and

$$\dfrac{4}{11} = 0.363636\ldots, \text{ so we have } -\dfrac{4}{11} = -0.363636\ldots, \text{ or } -0.\overline{36}.$$

◀ **Do Exercises 8 and 9.**

EXAMPLE 8 Find decimal notation for $\frac{5}{7}$.

$$
\begin{array}{r}
0.7\,1\,4\,2\,8\,5 \\
7\overline{)5.0\,0\,0\,0\,0\,0} \\
\underline{4\,9} \\
1\,0 \\
\underline{7} \\
3\,0 \\
\underline{2\,8} \\
2\,0 \\
\underline{1\,4} \\
6\,0 \\
\underline{5\,6} \\
4\,0 \\
\underline{3\,5} \\
5
\end{array}
$$

Since 5 appears again as a remainder, the sequence of digits "714285" repeats in the quotient, and

$$\frac{5}{7} = 0.714285714285\ldots, \quad \text{or} \quad 0.\overline{714285}.$$

The length of a repeating part can be very long—too long to find on a calculator. An example is $\frac{5}{97}$, which has a repeating part of 96 digits.

Do Exercise 10. ▷

10. Find decimal notation for $\frac{3}{7}$.

b ROUNDING IN PROBLEM SOLVING

In applied problems, repeating decimals are rounded to get approximate answers. To round a repeating decimal, we can extend the decimal notation at least one place past the rounding digit, and then round as usual.

EXAMPLES Round each of the following to the nearest tenth, hundredth, and thousandth.

	Nearest tenth	*Nearest hundredth*	*Nearest thousandth*
9. $0.8\overline{3} = 0.83333\ldots$	0.8	0.83	0.833
10. $0.\overline{09} = 0.090909\ldots$	0.1	0.09	0.091
11. $-0.\overline{714285} = -0.714285714285\ldots$	-0.7	-0.71	-0.714

Do Exercises 11–13. ▷

Round each to the nearest tenth, hundredth, and thousandth.

11. $0.\overline{6}$

12. $0.\overline{80}$

13. $-6.2\overline{45}$

Converting Ratios to Decimal Notation

When solving applied problems, we often convert ratios to decimal notation.

EXAMPLE 12 *Gas Mileage.* A car travels 457 mi on 16.4 gal of gasoline. The ratio of number of miles driven to amount of gasoline used is the *gas mileage.* Find the gas mileage and convert the ratio to decimal notation rounded to the nearest tenth.

$$\frac{\text{Miles driven}}{\text{Gasoline used}} = \frac{457}{16.4} \approx 27.86 \qquad \text{Dividing to 2 decimal places}$$

$$\approx 27.9 \qquad \text{Rounding to 1 decimal place}$$

The gas mileage is 27.9 miles to the gallon.

Answers

10. $0.\overline{428571}$ **11.** 0.7; 0.67; 0.667
12. 0.8; 0.81; 0.808 **13.** -6.2; -6.25; -6.245

14. *Coin Tossing.* A coin is tossed 51 times. It lands heads 26 times. Find the ratio of heads to tosses and convert it to decimal notation rounded to the nearest thousandth. (This is also the experimental probability of getting heads.)

15. *Gas Mileage.* A car travels 380 mi on 15.7 gal of gasoline. Find the gasoline mileage and convert the ratio to decimal notation rounded to the nearest tenth.

EXAMPLE 13 *Space Travel.* The space shuttle *Columbia* traveled about 121,700,000 mi in 28 flights. Find the ratio of number of miles traveled to number of flights and convert it to decimal notation. Round to the nearest tenth.

Source: NASA

We have

$$\frac{\text{Miles traveled}}{\text{Number of flights}} = \frac{121{,}700{,}000}{28}$$
$$\approx 4{,}346{,}428.571$$
$$\approx 4{,}346{,}428.6.$$

The ratio is about 4,346,428.6 mi per flight.

◀ Do Exercises 14 and 15.

Averages

EXAMPLE 14 *Price of Gold.* The price of gold more than doubled between 2007 and 2012. The graph below shows the average price of gold per troy ounce for those years. Find the average price of gold over the entire period. Round to the nearest hundredth.

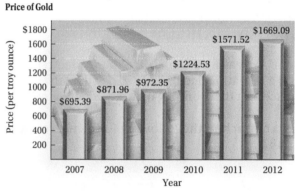

Price of Gold

SOURCES: www.nma.org; *Wall Street Journal*

16. *Gold Prices.* Refer to the data on the price of gold in Example 14. Find the average price of gold per troy ounce for the period 2009–2012. Round the answer to the nearest hundredth.

We add the prices of gold and divide by the number of addends, 6. The average is

$$\frac{695.39 + 871.96 + 972.35 + 1224.53 + 1571.52 + 1669.09}{6}$$
$$= \frac{7004.84}{6} = 1167.47\overline{3} \approx 1167.47.$$

From 2007 to 2012, the price of gold averaged about $1167.47 per troy ounce.

◀ Do Exercise 16.

Answers

14. 0.510   **15.** 24.2 mpg   **16.** $1359.37

CALCULATIONS WITH FRACTION NOTATION AND DECIMAL NOTATION TOGETHER

In certain kinds of calculations, fraction notation and decimal notation occur together. In such cases, there are at least three ways in which we might proceed.

EXAMPLE 15   Calculate: $\frac{3}{5} \times 0.56$.

Method 1:   One way to do this calculation is to convert the fraction notation to decimal notation so that both numbers are in decimal notation.

$$\frac{3}{5} \times 0.56 = 0.6 \times 0.56 = 0.336$$

Method 2:   A second way to do this calculation is to convert the decimal notation to fraction notation so that both numbers are in fraction notation. The answer can be left in fraction notation and simplified, or we can convert to decimal notation and round, if appropriate.

$$\frac{3}{5} \times 0.56 = \frac{3}{5} \cdot \frac{56}{100} = \frac{3 \cdot 2 \cdot 2 \cdot 2 \cdot 7}{5 \cdot 2 \cdot 2 \cdot 5 \cdot 5}$$
$$= \frac{2 \cdot 2}{2 \cdot 2} \cdot \frac{3 \cdot 2 \cdot 7}{5 \cdot 5 \cdot 5} = 1 \cdot \frac{3 \cdot 2 \cdot 7}{5 \cdot 5 \cdot 5}$$
$$= \frac{3 \cdot 2 \cdot 7}{5 \cdot 5 \cdot 5} = \frac{42}{125}, \quad \text{or} \quad 0.336$$

Method 3:   A third way to do this calculation is to treat 0.56 as $\frac{0.56}{1}$. Then we multiply 0.56 by 3 and divide the result by 5.

$$\frac{3}{5} \times 0.56 = \frac{3}{5} \times \frac{0.56}{1} = \frac{3 \times 0.56}{5} = \frac{1.68}{5} = 0.336$$

Do Exercise 17. ▶

EXAMPLE 16   Calculate: $\frac{2}{3} \times 0.576 - 3.287 \div \frac{4}{5}$.

   We use the rules for order of operations, doing first the multiplication and then the division. Then we add. Since $\frac{2}{3}$ would convert to a repeating decimal that would need to be rounded, method 1 would give an approximation. Here we use method 3.

$$\frac{2}{3} \times 0.576 - 3.287 \div \frac{4}{5} = \frac{2}{3} \times \frac{0.576}{1} - \frac{3.287}{1} \times \frac{5}{4}$$
$$= \frac{2 \times 0.576}{3} - \frac{3.287 \times 5}{4}$$
$$= 0.384 - 4.10875$$
$$= -3.72475$$

Do Exercises 18 and 19. ▶

GS **17.** Calculate: $\frac{3}{4} \times 0.62$.

Method 1:
$$\frac{3}{4} \times 0.62 = 0.\boxed{}5 \times 0.62$$
$$= 0.465$$

Method 2:
$$\frac{3}{4} \times 0.62 = \frac{3}{4} \cdot \frac{62}{\boxed{}}$$
$$= \frac{1\boxed{}6}{400}, \quad \text{or} \quad 0.465$$

Method 3:
$$\frac{3}{4} \times 0.62 = \frac{3}{4} \times \frac{0.62}{\boxed{}}$$
$$= \frac{1.8\boxed{}}{4}, \quad \text{or} \quad 0.465$$

Calculate.

18. $\frac{1}{3} \times 0.384 + \frac{5}{8} \times 0.6784$

19. $\frac{5}{6} \times 0.864 - 14.3 \div \frac{8}{5}$

Answers

17. 0.465   **18.** 0.552   **19.** −8.2175

Guided Solution:
17. 7; 100, 8; 1, 6

For Extra Help

MyMathLab®   MathXL®
                     PRACTICE   WATCH   READ   REVIEW

✓ Reading Check

Determine whether the decimal notation for each fraction is terminating or repeating.

RC1. $\dfrac{4}{9}$ _____   **RC2.** $\dfrac{3}{32}$ _____

RC3. $\dfrac{39}{40}$ _____   **RC4.** $\dfrac{7}{12}$ _____

RC5. $\dfrac{2}{11}$ _____   **RC6.** $\dfrac{80}{125}$ _____

a Find decimal notation.

1. $\dfrac{23}{100}$ **2.** $\dfrac{9}{100}$ **3.** $\dfrac{3}{5}$ **4.** $\dfrac{19}{20}$ **5.** $-\dfrac{13}{40}$ **6.** $-\dfrac{3}{16}$

7. $\dfrac{1}{5}$ **8.** $\dfrac{4}{5}$ **9.** $-\dfrac{17}{20}$ **10.** $-\dfrac{11}{20}$ **11.** $\dfrac{3}{8}$ **12.** $\dfrac{7}{8}$

13. $-\dfrac{39}{40}$ **14.** $-\dfrac{31}{40}$ **15.** $\dfrac{13}{25}$ **16.** $\dfrac{61}{125}$ **17.** $-\dfrac{2502}{125}$ **18.** $-\dfrac{181}{200}$

19. $\dfrac{1}{4}$ **20.** $\dfrac{1}{2}$ **21.** $-\dfrac{29}{25}$ **22.** $-\dfrac{37}{25}$ **23.** $\dfrac{19}{16}$ **24.** $\dfrac{5}{8}$

25. $\dfrac{4}{15}$ **26.** $\dfrac{7}{9}$ **27.** $\dfrac{1}{3}$ **28.** $\dfrac{1}{9}$ **29.** $-\dfrac{4}{3}$ **30.** $-\dfrac{8}{9}$

31. $-\dfrac{7}{6}$ **32.** $-\dfrac{7}{11}$ **33.** $\dfrac{4}{7}$ **34.** $\dfrac{14}{11}$ **35.** $-\dfrac{11}{12}$ **36.** $-\dfrac{5}{12}$

Copyright © 2015 Pearson Education, Inc.

37.–47. *Odds.* Round each answer for odd-numbered Exercises 25–35 to the nearest tenth, hundredth, and thousandth.

38.–48. *Evens.* Round each answer for even-numbered Exercises 26–36 to the nearest tenth, hundredth, and thousandth.

Round each to the nearest tenth, hundredth, and thousandth.

49. $0.\overline{18}$

50. $0.\overline{83}$

51. $-0.2\overline{7}$

52. $-3.5\overline{4}$

53. For this set of people, what is the ratio, in decimal notation rounded to the nearest thousandth, where appropriate, of:
  a) women to the total number of people?
  b) women to men?
  c) men to the total number of people?
  d) men to women?

54. For this set of pennies and quarters, what is the ratio, in decimal notation rounded to the nearest thousandth, where appropriate, of:
  a) pennies to quarters?
  b) quarters to pennies?
  c) pennies to total number of coins?
  d) total number of coins to pennies?

55. *Batting Average.* During the 2012 season, Brandon Phillips, a second baseman for the Cincinnati Reds, had 163 hits in 580 at bats. Find the ratio of number of hits to number of at bats. This is a *batting average.* Give Phillips's batting average in decimal notation rounded to the nearest thousandth.

Source: Major League Baseball

56. *Batting Average.* During the 2012 season, Buster Posey, a catcher for the San Francisco Giants, had 178 hits in 530 at bats. Find the ratio of number of hits to number of at bats. This is a *batting average.* Give Posey's batting average in decimal notation rounded to the nearest thousandth.

Source: Major League Baseball

Gas Mileage. In each of Exercises 57–60, find the gas mileage rounded to the nearest tenth.

57. 285 mi; 18 gal

58. 396 mi; 17 gal

59. 324.8 mi; 18.2 gal

60. 264.8 mi; 12.7 gal

Use the following table for Exercises 61 and 62.

YEAR	U.S. IMPORTS FROM CHINA (in billions of dollars)	U.S. EXPORTS TO CHINA
2007	$321.5	$65.2
2008	337.8	71.5
2009	296.4	69.5
2010	364.9	91.9
2011	399.3	103.9
2012	425.6	110.6

SOURCE: U.S. Census Bureau

61. Find the average amount, in billions of dollars per year, of imports from China to the United States for the period 2007–2012. Round to the nearest tenth.

62. Find the average amount, in billions of dollars per year, of exports from the United States to China for the period 2007–2012. Round to the nearest tenth.

63. *Windy Cities.* Although nicknamed the Windy City, Chicago is not the windiest city in the United States. Listed in the table below are the five windiest cities and their average wind speeds, as well as that on Mt. Washington (the windiest location in the United States). Find the average of these wind speeds and round your answer to the nearest tenth.

Source: *The Handy Geography Answer Book*

CITY	AVERAGE WIND SPEED (in miles per hour)
Mt. Washington, NH	35.3
Boston, MA	12.5
Honolulu, HI	11.3
Dallas, TX	10.7
Kansas City, MO	10.7
Chicago, IL	10.4

64. *Areas of the New England States.* The table below lists the areas of the New England states. Find the average area of this group of states and round your answer to the nearest tenth.

Source: *The New York Times Almanac*

STATE	TOTAL AREA (in square miles)
Maine	33,265
New Hampshire	9,279
Vermont	9,614
Massachusetts	8,284
Connecticut	5,018
Rhode Island	1,211

c Calculate.

65. $\frac{7}{8} \times 12.64$

66. $\frac{4}{5} \times 384.8$

67. $2\frac{3}{4} + 5.65$

68. $4\frac{4}{5} + 3.25$

69. $\frac{47}{9} \times (-79.95)$

70. $\frac{7}{11} \times (-2.7873)$

71. $\frac{1}{2} - 0.5$

72. $3\frac{1}{8} - 2.75$

Copyright © 2015 Pearson Education, Inc.

73. $4.875 - 2\frac{1}{16}$

74. $55\frac{3}{5} - 12.22$

75. $\frac{5}{6} \times 0.0765 - \frac{5}{4} \times 0.1124$

76. $\frac{2}{5} \times 114.8 - \frac{3}{8} \times 156.56$

77. $\frac{4}{5} \times 384.8 + 24.8 \div \frac{8}{3}$

78. $102.4 \div \frac{2}{5} - 12 \times \frac{5}{6}$

79. $\frac{7}{8} \times 0.86 - 0.76 \times \frac{3}{4}$

80. $17.95 \div \frac{5}{8} + \frac{3}{4} \times 16.2$

81. $3.375 \times 5\frac{1}{3}$

82. $2.5 \times 3\frac{5}{8}$

83. $6.84 \div \left(-2\frac{1}{2}\right)$

84. $-8\frac{1}{2} \div 2.125$

Skill Maintenance

Calculate.

85. $9 \cdot 2\frac{1}{3}$ [4.6a]

86. $16\frac{1}{10} - 14\frac{3}{5}$ [4.5b]

87. $-84 \div 8\frac{2}{5}$ [4.6b]

88. $14\frac{3}{5} + 16\frac{1}{10}$ [4.5a]

Solve.   [4.5c]

89. A recipe for bread calls for $\frac{2}{3}$ cup of water, $\frac{1}{4}$ cup of milk, and $\frac{1}{8}$ cup of oil. How many cups of liquid ingredients does the recipe call for?

90. A board $\frac{7}{10}$ in. thick is glued to a board $\frac{3}{5}$ in. thick. The glue is $\frac{3}{100}$ in. thick. How thick is the result?

Synthesis

91. 🖩 Find decimal notation for $\frac{1}{7}, \frac{2}{7}, \frac{3}{7}, \frac{4}{7}$, and $\frac{5}{7}$. Observe the pattern and guess the decimal notation for $\frac{6}{7}$.

92. Find decimal notation for $\frac{1}{9}, \frac{1}{99}$, and $\frac{1}{999}$. Observe the pattern and guess the decimal notation for $\frac{1}{9999}$.

SKILL TO REVIEW

Objective 1.6b: Estimate sums, differences, products, and quotients by rounding.

Estimate by first rounding to the nearest ten.

1.
$$\begin{array}{r} 4\ 6\ 7 \\ -\ 2\ 8\ 4 \end{array}$$

2.
$$\begin{array}{r} 5\ 4 \\ \times\ 2\ 9 \end{array}$$

a ESTIMATING SUMS, DIFFERENCES, PRODUCTS, AND QUOTIENTS

Estimating has many uses. It can be done before we even attempt a problem in order to get an idea of the answer. It can be done afterward as a check, even when we are using a calculator. In many situations, an estimate is all we need. We usually estimate by rounding the numbers so that there are one or two nonzero digits, depending on how accurate we want our estimate to be. Consider the following prices for Examples 1–3.

$289.95

16.2 Megapixel Digital Camera

19" Flat-Panel HDTV

Four-Burner Gas Grill

$139.97

$449.99

EXAMPLE 1 Estimate by rounding to the nearest ten the total cost of one grill and one TV.

We are estimating the sum

$289.95 + $449.99 = total cost.

The estimate found by rounding the addends to the nearest ten is

$290 + $450 = $740.   (Estimated total cost)

◀ Do Margin Exercise 1.

EXAMPLE 2 About how much more does the TV cost than the camera? Estimate by rounding to the nearest ten.

We are estimating the difference

$449.99 − $139.97 = price difference.

The estimate, found by rounding the minuend and the subtrahend to the nearest ten, is

$450 − $140 = $310.   (Estimated price difference)

◀ Do Exercise 2.

1. Estimate by rounding to the nearest ten the total cost of one grill and one camera. Which of the following is an appropriate estimate?

   a) $43   **b)** $400
   c) $410   **d)** $430

2. About how much more does the TV cost than the grill? Estimate by rounding to the nearest ten. Which of the following is an appropriate estimate?

   a) $100   **b)** $150
   c) $160   **d)** $300

Answers

Skill to Review:
1. 190   **2.** 1500

Margin Exercises:
1. (d)   **2.** (c)

EXAMPLE 3 Estimate the total cost of four cameras.

We are estimating the product

$$4 \times \$139.97 = \text{total cost}.$$

The estimate is found by rounding 139.97 to the nearest ten:

$$4 \times \$140 = \$560.$$

Do Exercise 3. ▷

EXAMPLE 4 A student government group is planning an event for in-coming freshmen. Since the local weather is often rainy, the group decides to purchase umbrellas bearing the university logo for door prizes. About how many umbrellas that cost $39.99 each can be purchased for $356?

We are estimating the quotient

$$\$356 \div \$39.99.$$

Since we want a whole-number estimate, we need to round appropriately. Rounding $39.99 to the nearest one, we get $40. Since $356 is close to $360, which is a multiple of $40, we estimate

$$\$360 \div \$40 = 9.$$

The answer is about 9 umbrellas.

Do Exercise 4. ▷

EXAMPLE 5 Estimate: 4.8×52. Do not find the actual product. Which of the following is an appropriate estimate?

a) 25   **b)** 250   **c)** 2500   **d)** 360

We round 4.8 to the nearest one and 52 to the nearest ten:

$$5 \times 50 = 250. \quad \text{(Estimated product)}$$

Thus an approximate estimate is (b).

Other estimates that we might have used in Example 5 are

$$5 \times 52 = 260, \quad \text{or} \quad 4.8 \times 50 = 240.$$

The estimate used in Example 5, $5 \times 50 = 250$, is the easiest to do because the factors have the fewest nonzero digits.

Do Exercises 5–10. ▷

EXAMPLE 6 Estimate: $82.08 \div 24$. Which of the following is an appropriate estimate?

a) 400   **b)** 16   **c)** 40   **d)** 4

This is about $80 \div 20$, so the answer is about 4. Thus an appropriate estimate is (d).

3. Estimate the total cost of six TVs. Which of the following is an appropriate estimate?

  a) $450   **b)** $2700

  c) $4500   **d)** $27,000

4. Refer to the umbrella price in Example 4. About how many umbrellas can be purchased for $675?

Estimate each product. Do not find the actual product. Which of the choices is an appropriate estimate?

5. 2.4×8

  a) 16   **b)** 34

  c) 125   **d)** 5

6. 24×0.6

  a) 200   **b)** 5

  c) 110   **d)** 20

7. 0.86×0.432

  a) 0.04   **b)** 0.4

  c) 1.1   **d)** 4

8. 0.82×0.1

  a) 800   **b)** 8

  c) 0.08   **d)** 80

9. 0.12×18.248

  a) 180   **b)** 1.8

  c) 0.018   **d)** 18

10. 24.234×5.2

  a) 200   **b)** 120

  c) 12.5   **d)** 234

Answers

3. (b)   **4.** 17 umbrellas   **5.** (a)   **6.** (d)
7. (b)   **8.** (c)   **9.** (b)   **10.** (b)

Estimate each quotient. Which of the choices is an appropriate estimate?

11. 59.78 ÷ 29.1
    a) 200   b) 20
    c) 2   d) 0.2

12. 82.08 ÷ 2.4
    a) 40   b) 4.0
    c) 400   d) 0.4

13. 0.1768 ÷ 0.08
    a) 8   b) 10
    c) 2   d) 20

14. Estimate: 0.0069 ÷ 0.15. Which of the following is an appropriate estimate?
    a) 0.5   b) 50
    c) 0.05   d) 0.004

Answers

11. (c)   12. (a)   13. (c)   14. (c)

EXAMPLE 7   Estimate: 94.18 ÷ 3.2. Which of the following is an appropriate estimate?

a) 30   b) 300   c) 3   d) 60

This is about 90 ÷ 3, so the answer is about 30. Thus an appropriate estimate is (a).

EXAMPLE 8   Estimate: 0.0156 ÷ 1.3. Which of the following is an appropriate estimate?

a) 0.2   b) 0.002   c) 0.02   d) 20

This is about 0.02 ÷ 1, so the answer is about 0.02. Thus an appropriate estimate is (c).

◀ Do Exercises 11–13.

In some cases, it is easier to estimate a quotient directly rather than by rounding the divisor and the dividend.

EXAMPLE 9   Estimate: 0.0074 ÷ 0.23. Which of the following is an appropriate estimate?

a) 0.3   b) 0.03   c) 300   d) 3

We estimate 3 for a quotient. We check by multiplying.

   $0.23 \times 3 = 0.69$

We make the estimate smaller. We estimate 0.3 and check by multiplying.

   $0.23 \times 0.3 = 0.069$

We make the estimate smaller. We estimate 0.03 and check by multiplying.

   $0.23 \times 0.03 = 0.0069$

This is about 0.0074, so the quotient is about 0.03. Thus an appropriate estimate is (b).

◀ Do Exercise 14.

5.6   Exercise Set

For Extra Help
MyMathLab®   MathXL® PRACTICE   WATCH   READ   REVIEW

☑ Reading Check

Match each calculation with the most appropriate estimate from the list at the right.

RC1. 0.1003 × 0.8   _____   a) 0.8

RC2. 38.41 + 41.777   _____   b) 0.08

RC3. 0.00152 × 4025   _____   c) 8

RC4. 1632 ÷ 1.9   _____   d) 80

RC5. 9.054 − 8.3111   _____   e) 800

RC6. 162,105 × 0.0496 _____   f) 8000

Copyright © 2015 Pearson Education, Inc.

a For Exercises 1–6, use the prices shown below to estimate each sum, difference, product, or quotient. Indicate which of the choices is an appropriate estimate.

2 Quart Ice Cream Maker $79.⁹⁹

Satellite Radio Receiver $149.⁹⁹

Black & White Multifunction Printer/Copier/Scanner $279.⁸⁹

1. About how much more does the printer cost than the satellite radio?

   a) $1300   **b)** $200   **c)** $130   **d)** $13

2. About how much more does the satellite radio cost than the ice cream maker?

   a) $7000   **b)** $70   **c)** $130   **d)** $700

3. Estimate the total cost of six ice cream makers.

   a) $480   **b)** $48   **c)** $240   **d)** $4800

4. Estimate the total cost of four printers.

   a) $1200   **b)** $1120   **c)** $11,200   **d)** $600

5. About how many ice cream makers can be purchased for $830?

   a) 120   **b)** 100   **c)** 10   **d)** 1000

6. About how many printers can be purchased for $5627?

   a) 200   **b)** 20   **c)** 1800   **d)** 2000

Estimate by rounding as directed.

7. $0.02 + 1.31 + 0.34$; nearest tenth

8. $0.88 + 2.07 + 1.54$; nearest one

9. $6.03 + 0.007 + 0.214$; nearest one

10. $1.11 + 8.888 + 99.94$; nearest one

11. $52.367 + 1.307 + 7.324$; nearest one

12. $12.9882 + 1.2115$; nearest tenth

13. $2.678 - 0.445$; nearest tenth

14. $12.9882 - 1.0115$; nearest one

15. $198.67432 - 24.5007$; nearest ten

Estimate. Indicate which of the choices is an appropriate estimate.

16. $234.12321 - 200.3223$

   a) 600   **b)** 60
   c) 300   **d)** 30

17. 49×7.89

   a) 400   **b)** 40
   c) 4   **d)** 0.4

18. 7.4×8.9

   a) 95   **b)** 63
   c) 124   **d)** 6

19. 98.4×0.083
  a) 80   **b)** 12
  c) 8   **d)** 0.8

20. 78×5.3
  a) 400   **b)** 800
  c) 40   **d)** 8

21. $3.6 \div 4$
  a) 10   **b)** 1
  c) 0.1   **d)** 0.01

22. $0.0713 \div 1.94$
  a) 3.5   **b)** 0.35
  c) 0.035 **d)** 35

23. $74.68 \div 24.7$
  a) 9   **b)** 3
  c) 12   **d)** 120

24. $914 \div 0.921$
  a) 10   **b)** 100
  c) 1000 **d)** 1

25. *Fence Posts.* A zoo plans to construct a fence around a proposed exhibit featuring animals of the Great Plains. The perimeter of the area to be fenced is 1760 ft. Estimate the number of wooden fence posts needed if the posts are placed 8.625 ft apart.

26. *Ticketmaster.* Recently, Ticketmaster stock sold for $22.25 per share. Estimate how many shares can be purchased for $4400.

27. *Day-Care Supplies.* Helen wants to buy 12 boxes of crayons at $1.89 per box for the day care center that she runs. Estimate the total cost of the crayons.

28. *Batteries.* Oscar buys 6 packages of AAA batteries at $5.29 per package. Estimate the total cost of the purchase.

Skill Maintenance

Simplify. [1.9c]

29. $2^4 \div 4 - 2$

30. $3 \cdot 60 - (12 + 3)$

31. $200 + 40 \div 4$

Solve. [1.7b]

32. $p + 14 = 83$

33. $50 = 5 \cdot t$

34. $270 + y = 800$

Synthesis

The following were done on a calculator. Estimate to determine whether the decimal point was placed correctly.

35. $19.7236 - 1.4738 \times 4.1097 = 1.366672414$

36. $28.46901 \div 4.9187 - 2.5081 = 3.279813473$

37. ▦ Use one of $+$, $-$, $\times$, and $\div$ in each blank to make a true sentence.

  a) $(0.37 \,\square\, 18.78) \,\square\, 2^{13} = 156{,}876.8$

  b) $2.56 \,\square\, 6.4 \,\square\, 51.2 \,\square\, 17.4 = 312.84$

Copyright © 2015 Pearson Education, Inc.

Applications and Problem Solving

a SOLVING APPLIED PROBLEMS

Solving applied problems with decimals is like solving applied problems with integers. We translate first to an equation that corresponds to the situation. Then we solve the equation.

EXAMPLE 1 *Window Code.* To meet building codes, the area of the opening when the lower part of a double-sash window is raised must be 5 ft^2 (720 in^2) for first-floor windows and 5.7 ft^2 (820.8 in^2) for second-floor windows. A contractor orders windows that have an opening measuring 27.063 in. × 28.563 in. Find the area of the opening and determine if the windows meet the first-floor code.

Sources: Matt Beecher Builders; Paul's Glass

1. Familiarize. We first make a drawing.

27.063 in.

28.563 in.

2. Translate. We use the formula $A = l \cdot w$ and substitute.

$$A = l \cdot w = 27.063 \times 28.563$$

3. Solve. We solve by carrying out the multiplication.

```
        2 8.5 6 3
    ×   2 7.0 6 3
        8 5 6 8 9
    1 7 1 3 7 8 0
  1 9 9 9 4 1 0 0 0
  5 7 1 2 6 0 0 0 0
  7 7 3.0 0 0 4 6 9
```

Thus, $A = 773.000469$ in^2.

4. Check. We obtain a partial check by estimating the product:

$$A = 27.063 \times 28.563 \approx 25 \times 30 = 750.$$

The estimate is close to 773, so the answer is probably correct.

5. State. The area of the opening is about 773 in^2. Since $773 > 720$, the windows meet the first-floor code.

Do Margin Exercise 1. ▶

OBJECTIVE

a Solve applied problems involving decimals.

SKILL TO REVIEW

Objective 1.7b: Solve equations like $t + 28 = 54$, $28 \cdot x = 168$, and $98 \cdot 2 = y$.

Solve.

1. $16 + q = 41$

2. $45 \cdot x = 405$

1. *Window Code.* Refer to Example 1. A contractor orders windows that have an opening measuring 26.535 in. × 29.265 in. Find the area of the opening and determine if the windows meet code for the second floor. Round to the nearest tenth.

Answers

Skill to Review:
1. 25   **2.** 9

Margin Exercise:
1. 776.5 in^2; the windows do not meet the second-floor code.

EXAMPLE 2 *Canals.* The Panama Canal in Panama is 50.7 mi long. The Suez Canal in Egypt is 119.9 mi long. How much longer is the Suez Canal?

Panama Canal   Suez Canal

1. **Familiarize.** We let l = the distance in miles by which the length of the longer canal differs from the length of the shorter canal.

2. **Translate.** We translate as follows, using the given information:

Length of Panama Canal, the shorter canal	plus	Additional length	is	Length of Suez Canal, the longer canal
↓	↓	↓	↓	↓
50.7 mi	+	l	=	119.9 mi.

3. **Solve.** We solve the equation by subtracting 50.7 mi on both sides:

$$50.7 + l = 119.9$$
$$50.7 + l - 50.7 = 119.9 - 50.7$$
$$l = 69.2.$$

4. **Check.** We can check by adding.

$$\begin{array}{r} 5\,0.7 \\ +\ 6\,9.2 \\ \hline 1\,1\,9.9 \end{array}$$

The answer checks.

5. **State.** The Suez Canal is 69.2 mi longer than the Panama Canal.

◀ Do Exercise 2.

EXAMPLE 3 *iPad Purchase.* A large architectural firm spent $10,399.74 on 26 iPads for its architects. How much did each iPad cost?

1. **Familiarize.** We let c = the cost of each iPad.

2. **Translate.** We translate as follows:

Number of iPads purchased	times	Cost of each iPad	is	Total cost of purchase
↓	↓	↓	↓	↓
26	·	c	=	$10,399.74.

---

2. *Debit-Card Transactions.* U.S. debit-card transactions in 2009 totaled 38.5 billion. The number of transactions in 2012 was 52.6 billion. How many more debit-card transactions were there in 2012 than in 2009?

Source: *The Nilson Report*

Answer

2. 14.1 billion transactions

3. Solve. We solve the equation by dividing by 26 on both sides, and then we carry out the division.

$$\frac{26 \cdot c}{26} = \frac{10{,}399.74}{26}$$

$$c = \frac{10{,}399.74}{26}$$

$$c = 399.99$$

```
          3 9 9.9 9
  2 6)1 0,3 9 9.7 4
        7 8
        2 5 9
        2 3 4
          2 5 9
          2 3 4
            2 5 7
            2 3 4
              2 3 4
              2 3 4
                  0
```

4. Check. We check by estimating:

$$10{,}399.74 \div 26 \approx 10{,}000 \div 25 = 400.$$

Since 400 is close to 399.99, the answer is probably correct.

5. State. The cost of each iPad was $399.99.

Do Exercise 3. ▶

3. One pound of lean boneless ham contains 4.5 servings. It costs $7.99 per pound. What is the cost per serving? Round to the nearest cent.

EXAMPLE 4 *IRS Driving Allowance.* The Internal Revenue Service allowed a tax deduction of 55.5¢ per mile driven for business purposes in 2012. What deduction, in dollars, was allowed for driving 8407 mi during the year?

Source: Internal Revenue Service

1. Familiarize. We first make a drawing or at least visualize the situation. Repeated addition fits this situation. We let $d =$ the deduction, in dollars, allowed for driving 8407 mi.

8407 mi

2. Translate. We translate as follows, writing 55.5¢ as $0.555:

Deduction for each mile	times	Number of miles driven	is	Total deduction
↓	↓	↓	↓	↓
$0.555	×	8407	=	d.

3. Solve. To solve the equation, we carry out the multiplication.

```
        8 4 0 7
    ×  0.5 5 5
      4 2 0 3 5
    4 2 0 3 5 0
  4 2 0 3 5 0 0
  4 6 6 5.8 8 5
```

Thus, $d = 4665.885 \approx 4665.89$.

Answer

3. $1.78 per serving

4. *Printing Costs.* At Kwik Copy, the cost of copying is 11 cents per page. How much, in dollars, would it cost to make 466 copies?

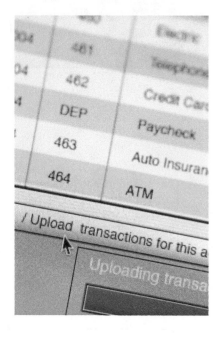

4. Check. We can obtain a partial check by rounding and estimating:

$$8407 \times 0.555 \approx 8000 \times 0.6 = 4800 \approx 4665.89.$$

5. State. The total allowable deduction was $4665.89.

◀ Do Exercise 4.

Multistep Problems

EXAMPLE 5 *Tracking a Bank Balance.* Revenue of U.S. banks from checking account overdraft charges was $31.5 billion in a recent fiscal year. (**Source:** Moebs Services) To avoid overdrafts and to track her spending, Maggie keeps a running account of her banking transactions. She checks her balance online, but because of pending amounts that post later, she keeps a separate record. Maggie had $2432.27 in her account. She used her debit card to pay her rent of $835 and make purchases of $14.13, $38.60, and $205.98. She then deposited her weekly pay of $748.35. What was her balance after these transactions?

1. Familiarize. We first find the total of the debits. Then we find how much is left in the account after the debits are deducted. Finally, we add to this amount the deposit to find the balance in the account after all the transactions.

2, 3. Translate and Solve. We let d = the total amount of the debits. We are combining amounts: $835 + \$14.13 + \$38.60 + \$205.98 = d$. To solve the equation, we add.

$$
\begin{array}{rl}
835.00 & \text{First debit} \\
14.13 & \text{Second debit} \\
38.60 & \text{Third debit} \\
+\ 205.98 & \text{Fourth debit} \\
\hline
1093.71 & \text{Total debits} \qquad \text{Thus, } d = 1093.71.
\end{array}
$$

Now let a = the amount in the account after the debits are deducted. We subtract: $2432.27 - \$1093.71 = a$.

$$
\begin{array}{rl}
2432.27 & \text{Original amount} \\
-\ 1093.71 & \text{Total debits} \\
\hline
1338.56 & \text{New amount} \qquad \text{Thus, } a = 1338.56.
\end{array}
$$

Finally, we let f = the amount in the account after the paycheck is deposited.

Amount after debits	plus	Amount of deposit	is	Final amount
↓	↓	↓	↓	↓
1338.56	+	748.35	=	f

To solve the equation, we add.

$$
\begin{array}{rl}
1338.56 & \text{Balance after debits} \\
+\ 748.35 & \text{Paycheck deposit} \\
\hline
2086.91 & \text{Final amount}
\end{array}
$$

Answer
4. $51.26

4. Check. We repeat the computations.

5. State. Maggie had $2086.91 in her account after all the transactions.

Do Exercise 5. ▷

EXAMPLE 6 *Gas Mileage.* Ava filled her gas tank and noted that the odometer read 67,507.8. After the next fill-up, the odometer read 68,006.1. It took 16.5 gal to fill the tank. How many miles per gallon did Ava get?

1. Familiarize. We first make a drawing.

This is a two-step problem. First, we find the number of miles that have been driven between fill-ups. We let $n =$ the number of miles driven.

2, 3. Translate and Solve. We translate and solve as follows:

First odometer reading	plus	Number of miles driven	is	Second odometer reading
↓	↓	↓	↓	↓
67,507.8	+	n	=	68,006.1.

To solve the equation, we subtract 67,507.8 on both sides:

$n = 68,006.1 - 67,507.8$
$\quad = 498.3.$

$$\begin{array}{r} 6\ 8,0\ 0\ 6.1 \\ -\ 6\ 7,5\ 0\ 7.8 \\ \hline 4\ 9\ 8.3 \end{array}$$

Next, we divide the total number of miles driven by the number of gallons. This gives us $m =$ the number of miles per gallon—that is, the gas mileage. The division that corresponds to the situation is $498.3 \div 16.5 = m$. To find the number m, we divide.

$$\begin{array}{r} 3\ 0.2 \\ 1\ 6.5\,\overline{)4\ 9\ 8.3\ 0} \\ \underline{4\ 9\ 5} \\ 3\ 3\ 0 \\ \underline{3\ 3\ 0} \\ 0 \end{array}$$

Thus, $m = 30.2$.

4. Check. To check, we first multiply the number of miles per gallon times the number of gallons to find the number of miles driven:

$$16.5 \times 30.2 = 498.3.$$

Then we add 498.3 to 67,507.8 to find the new odometer reading:

$$67,507.8 + 498.3 = 68,006.1.$$

The gas mileage of 30.2 checks.

5. State. Ava got 30.2 miles per gallon.

Do Exercise 6. ▷

5. *Bank Balance.* Stephen had $915.22 in his checking account. He used his debit card to pay a charge card minimum payment of $36 and to make purchases of $67.50, $178.23, and $429.05. He then deposited his weekly pay of $570.91. How much was in his account after these transactions?

6. *Gas Mileage.* John filled his gas tank and noted that the odometer read 38,320.8. After the next fill-up, the odometer read 38,735.5. It took 14.5 gal to fill the tank. How many miles per gallon did John get?

Answers

5. $775.35   **6.** 28.6 mpg

Translating for Success

1. **Gas Mileage.** Art filled his SUV's gas tank and noted that the odometer read 38,271.8. At the next fill-up, the odometer read 38,677.92. It took 28.4 gal to fill the tank. How many miles per gallon did the SUV get?

2. **Dimensions of a Parking Lot.** A store's parking lot is a rectangle that measures 85.2 ft by 52.3 ft. What is the area of the parking lot?

3. **Game Snacks.** Three students pay $18.40 for snacks at a football game. What is each student's share of the cost?

4. **Electrical Wiring.** An electrician needs 1314 ft of wiring cut into $2\frac{1}{2}$-ft pieces. How many pieces will she have?

5. **College Tuition.** Wayne needs $4638 for the fall semester's tuition. On the day of registration, he has only $3092. How much does he need to borrow?

The goal of these matching questions is to practice step (2), Translate, of the five-step problem-solving process. Translate each word problem to an equation and select a correct translation from equations A–O.

A. $2\frac{1}{2} \cdot n = 1314$

B. $18.4 \times 3.87 = n$

C. $n = 85.2 \times 52.3$

D. $1314.28 - 437 = n$

E. $3 \times 18.40 = n$

F. $2\frac{1}{2} \cdot 1314 = n$

G. $3092 + n = 4638$

H. $18.4 \cdot n = 3.87$

I. $\dfrac{406.12}{28.4} = n$

J. $52.3 \cdot n = 85.2$

K. $n = 1314.28 + 437$

L. $52.3 + n = 85.2$

M. $3092 + 4638 = n$

N. $3 \cdot n = 18.40$

O. $85.2 + 52.3 = n$

Answers on page A-9

6. **Cost of Gasoline.** What is the cost, in dollars, of 18.4 gal of gasoline at $3.87 per gallon?

7. **Savings Account Balance.** Margaret has $1314.28 in her savings account. Before using her debit card to buy an office chair, she transferred $437 to her checking account. How much was left in her savings account?

8. **Acres Planted.** This season Sam planted 85.2 acres of corn and 52.3 acres of soybeans. Find the total number of acres that he planted.

9. **Amount Inherited.** Tara inherited $2\frac{1}{2}$ times as much as her cousin. Her cousin received $1314. How much did Tara receive?

10. **Travel Funds.** The athletic department needs travel funds of $4638 for the tennis team and $3092 for the golf team. What is the total amount needed for travel?

✓ Reading Check

Complete each step in the five-step problem-solving strategy with the correct word from the following list.

Solve   Familiarize   State   Translate   Check

Five-Step Problem Solving Strategy

RC1. _____ yourself with the problem situation.

RC2. _____ the problem to an equation.

RC3. _____ the equation.

RC4. _____ the solution.

RC5. _____ the answer using a complete sentence.

a   Solve.

International Travel.   The chart below shows the numbers of U.S. citizens who traveled internationally in 2007–2011. Use this chart in Exercises 1 and 2.

YEAR	U.S. CITIZENS WHO TRAVELED INTERNATIONALLY (in millions)
2007	64
2008	63.6
2009	61.4
2010	60.3
2011	58.7

SOURCE: Office of Travel and Tourism

1. Find the average number of citizens per year who traveled internationally during 2007–2011.

2. How many more U.S. citizens traveled internationally in 2007 than in 2011?

3. *Lottery Winnings.*   A group of 28 employees won $300,000 in a lottery. After $33\frac{1}{3}\%$ was withheld for taxes, the remaining amount, $200,000, was split equally among the employees. How much was each winner's share?

4. *Lunch Costs.*   A group of 4 students pays $47.84 for lunch and splits the cost equally. What is each person's share?

5. *Body Temperature.*   Normal body temperature is 98.6°F. During an illness, a patient's temperature rose 4.2° higher than normal. What was the new temperature?

6. *Gasoline Cost.*   What is the cost, in dollars, of 12.6 gal of gasoline at $3.79 per gallon? Round the answer to the nearest cent.

7. Find the perimeter.

8.9 cm   23.8 cm   4.7 cm   18.6 cm   22.1 cm

8. Find the length *d*.

0.8 cm — d — 0.8 cm   3.91 cm

9. *Odometer Reading.* The Lanosga family's odometer reads 22,456.8 at the beginning of a trip. The family's online driving directions tell them that they will be driving 234.7 mi. What will the odometer read at the end of the trip?

10. *Miles Driven.* Petra bought gasoline when the odometer read 14,296.3. At the next gasoline purchase, the odometer read 14,515.8. How many miles had been driven?

11. *100-Meter Record.* The fastest speed clocked for a cheetah running a distance of 100 m is 5.95 sec. The men's world record for the 100-m dash is held by Jamaican Usain Bolt. His time was 3.63 sec more than the cheetah's. What is the men's 100-m record held by Usain Bolt?

Source: "Cheetahs on the Edge," by Roff Smith, *National Geographic*, November 2012.

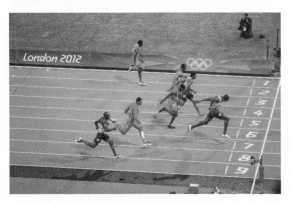

12. *Record Movie Openings.* The movie *Marvel's The Avengers* took in $207.4 million on its first weekend. This topped the previous record for opening-weekend revenue set by *Harry Potter and the Deathly Hallows: Part II* by $38.2 million. How much did *Harry Potter and the Deathly Hallows: Part II* take in on its opening weekend?

Source: Nash Information Services

13. *Tank Capacity.* The water in a filled tank weighs 748.45 lb. One cubic foot of water weighs 62.5 lb. How many cubic feet of water does the tank hold?

14. Lot A measures 250.1 ft by 302.7 ft. Lot B measures 389.4 ft by 566.2 ft. What is the total area of the two lots?

15. *Cost of Bottled Water.* The cost of a year's supply of a popular brand of bottled water, based on the recommended consumption of 64 oz per day, at the supermarket price of $3.99 for a six-pack of half-liter bottles, is $918.82. This is $918.31 more than the cost of drinking the same amount of tap water for a year. What is the cost of drinking tap water for a year?

Source: American Water Works Association

16. *Highway Routes.* You can drive from home to work using either of two routes:

> *Route A*: Via interstate highway, 7.6 mi, with a speed limit of 65 mph.

> *Route B*: Via a country road, 5.6 mi, with a speed limit of 50 mph.

Assuming you drive at the posted speed limit, which route takes less time? (Use the formula *distance* = *speed* × *time*.)

17. Andrew bought a DVD of the movie *Horton Hears a Who* for his nephew for $23.99 plus $1.68 sales tax. He paid for it with a $50 bill. How much change did he receive?

18. Claire bought a copy of the book *Make Way for Ducklings* for her daughter for $16.95 plus $0.85 sales tax. She paid for it with a $20 bill. How much change did she receive?

Copyright © 2015 Pearson Education, Inc.

19. *Gas Mileage.* Peggy filled her van's gas tank and noted that the odometer read 26,342.8. After the next fill-up, the odometer read 26,736.7. It took 19.5 gal to fill the tank. How many miles per gallon did the van get?

20. *Gas Mileage.* Henry filled his Honda's gas tank and noted that the odometer read 18,943.2. After the next fill-up, the odometer read 19,306.2. It took 13.2 gal to fill the tank. How many miles per gallon did the car get?

21. A rectangular yard is 20 ft by 15 ft. The yard is covered with grass except for an 8.5-ft-square flower garden. How much grass is in the yard?

22. Rita receives a gross pay (before deductions) of $495.72. Her deductions are $59.60 for federal income tax, $29.00 for FICA, and $29.00 for medical insurance. What is her take-home pay?

23. *Pole Vault Pit.* Find the area and the perimeter of the landing area of the pole vault pit shown here.

16.4 ft

16.4 ft

Landing area

24. *Stamp.* Find the area and the perimeter of the stamp shown here.

2.5 cm

3.25 cm

25. *Loose Change.* In 2010, passengers at New York's John F. Kennedy International Airport left $46,918.06 in loose change at airport checkpoints. This was $27,807.23 more than passengers left that year at Los Angeles International Airport. How much change was left at the Los Angeles airport?

Source: Transportation Security Administration

26. *Online Ad Spending.* It is projected that $132.1 billion will be spent for online advertising in 2015. This is $63.7 billion more than in 2010. What was spent on online advertising in 2010?

Source: eMarketer, June 2011

27. *Loan Payment.* In order to make money on loans, financial institutions are paid back more money than they loan. Suppose you borrow $120,000 to buy a house and agree to make monthly payments of $880.52 for 30 years. How much do you pay back altogether? How much more do you pay back than the amount of the loan?

28. *Loan Payment.* In order to make money on loans, financial institutions are paid back more money than they loan. Suppose you borrow $270,000 to buy a house and agree to make monthly payments of $1105.73 for 30 years. How much do you pay back altogether? How much more do you pay back than the amount of the loan?

29. *Calories Burned Mowing.*   A person weighing 150 lb burns 7.3 calories per minute while mowing a lawn with a power lawnmower. How many calories would be burned in 2 hr of mowing?

Source: *The Handy Science Answer Book*

30. *Weight Loss.*   A person weighing 170 lb burns 8.6 calories per minute while mowing a lawn. One must burn about 3500 calories in order to lose 1 lb. How many pounds would be lost by mowing for 2 hr? Round to the nearest tenth.

31. *Construction Pay.*   A construction worker is paid $18.50 per hour for the first 40 hr of work, and time and a half, or $27.75 per hour, for any overtime exceeding 40 hr per week. One week she works 46 hr. How much is her pay?

32. *Summer Work.*   Zachary worked 53 hr during a week one summer. He earned $7.50 per hour for the first 40 hr and $11.25 per hour for overtime (hours exceeding 40). How much did Zachary earn during the week?

33. *Corn Production.*   The table below lists 2012 corn production for six of the top ten corn-producing nations. Find the average corn production for the top two countries.

RANK	COUNTRY	CORN PRODUCTION (in millions of metric tons)
1	United States	272.4
2	China	200.0
3	Brazil	70.0
7	Mexico	20.7
9	South Africa	13.5
10	Canada	11.6

SOURCE: www.indexmundi.com

34. *Projected World Population.*   Using the information in the bar graph below, determine the average population of the world for the years 1950 through 2050. Round to the nearest thousandth of a billion.

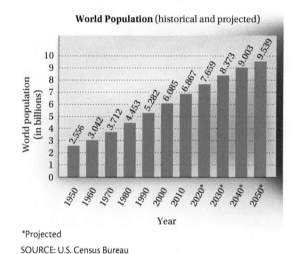

World Population (historical and projected)

*Projected

SOURCE: U.S. Census Bureau

35. *Checking Account Balance.*   Jacob had $1218.30 in his bank account. After using his debit card for three purchases, writing a check for his rent, and receiving his weekly paycheck by direct deposit, he checked what he had calculated as his balance against his online account balance. They did not match. Find his errors and correct the numbers in the balance column.

DATE	DEBIT CARD	CHECK NUMBER	DESCRIPTION	(−) PAYMENT/ DEBIT	(+) DEPOSIT/ CREDIT	BALANCE $1218.30
1/28	✓		Walgreen's	38 15		1186 15
2/1		2578	Rent	680 00		506 15
2/5			Paycheck		416 27	922 42
2/7	✓		Kroger	40 95		963 37
2/10	✓		Bookstore	110 64		852 73

Copyright © 2015 Pearson Education, Inc.

36. *Checking Account Balance.* Lynn had $3425.24 in her bank account. After paying her mortgage payment with a check, making two purchases with her debit card, making an online utility payment, and depositing her paycheck, she checked what she had calculated as her balance against her online account balance. They did not match. Find her errors and correct the numbers in the balance column.

DATE	DEBIT CARD	CHECK NUMBER	DESCRIPTION	(−) PAYMENT/ DEBIT	(+) DEPOSIT/ CREDIT	BALANCE $3425.24
7/20		471	Mortgage payment	905 17		2525 24
7/25			Paycheck		1210 48	3735 72
7/28			PE Energy	89 20		3646 52
8/3	✓		Groceries	32 49		3614 03
8/11	✓		Gas	62 17		3676 20

37. *Body Temperature.* Normal body temperature is 98.6°F. A baby's bath water should be 100°F. How many degrees above normal body temperature is this?

38. *Body Temperature.* Normal body temperature is 98.6°F. The lowest body temperature at which a patient has survived is 69°F. How many degrees below normal is this?

39. *Property Taxes.* The Brunners own a house with an assessed value of $165,500. For every $1000 of assessed value, they pay $8.50 in property taxes each year. How much do they pay in property taxes each year?

40. *Property Taxes.* The Colavitos own a house with an assessed value of $184,500. For every $1000 of assessed value, they pay $7.68 in property taxes each year. How much do they pay in property taxes each year?

Skill Maintenance

Add.

41. $-\dfrac{5}{6} - \dfrac{7}{10}$ [4.2a]

42. $4\dfrac{1}{3} + 2\dfrac{1}{2}$ [4.5a]

Subtract.

43. $\dfrac{2}{3} - \dfrac{5}{8}$ [4.3a]

44. $4569 - 1766$ [1.3a]

Simplify. [3.5b]

45. $\dfrac{125}{400}$

46. $-\dfrac{325}{625}$

47. If a bicycle wheel made 480 revolutions at a rate of $66\frac{2}{3}$ revolutions per minute, for how long did it rotate?

[4.6c]

Synthesis

48. Suppose you buy a half-dozen packs of basketball cards with a dozen cards in each pack. The cost is twelve dozen cents for each half-dozen cards. How much do you pay for the cards?

Vocabulary Reinforcement

Complete each statement with the correct word from the list at the right.

1. A _____ decimal occurs when we convert a fraction to a decimal and the denominator of the fraction has at least one factor other than 2 or 5. [5.5a]

2. A _____ decimal occurs when we convert a fraction to a decimal and the denominator of the fraction has only 2's or 5's, or both, as factors. [5.5a]

3. One _____ = 1,000,000,000. [5.3b]

4. One _____ = 1,000,000. [5.3b]

5. One _____ = 1,000,000,000,000. [5.3b]

6. The _____ consist of the integers, . . . , −3, −2, −1, 0, 1, 2, 3, . . . , and fractions like $\frac{1}{2}$, $-\frac{4}{5}$, and $\frac{31}{25}$. [5.1a]

trillion
million
billion
repeating
terminating
whole numbers
rational numbers

Concept Reinforcement

Determine whether each statement is true or false.

_____ 1. One thousand billion is one trillion. [5.3b]

_____ 2. The number of decimal places in the product of two numbers is the product of the numbers of places in the factors. [5.3a]

_____ 3. An estimate found by rounding to the nearest ten is usually more accurate than one found by rounding to the nearest hundred. [5.6a]

_____ 4. For a fraction with a factor other than 2 or 5 in its denominator, decimal notation terminates. [5.5a]

Study Guide

Objective 5.1b Convert between decimal notation and fraction notation.

Example Write fraction notation for 5.347.

5.347   5.347. $\frac{5347}{1000}$

↑   ⤵   ↑
3 decimal places   Move 3 places to the right.   3 zeros

Example Write decimal notation for $-\frac{29}{1000}$.

$-\frac{29}{1000}$ −0.029. $-\frac{29}{1000} = -0.029$

↑   ⤸
3 zeros   Move 3 places to the left.

Practice Exercise

1. Write fraction notation for 50.93.

Practice Exercise

2. Write decimal notation for $-\frac{817}{10}$.

Example Write decimal notation for $4\frac{63}{100}$.

$$4\frac{63}{100} = 4 + \frac{63}{100} = 4 \text{ and } \frac{63}{100} = 4.63$$

Practice Exercise

3. Write decimal notation for $42\frac{159}{1000}$.

Objective 5.1d Round decimal notation to the nearest thousandth, hundredth, tenth, one, ten, hundred, or thousand.

Example Round 19.7625 to the nearest hundredth.

Locate the digit in the hundredths place, 6. Consider the next digit to the right, 2. Since that digit, 2, is 4 or lower, round down.

19.7625

$\downarrow$

19.76

Practice Exercise

4. Round 153.346 to the nearest hundredth.

Objective 5.2a Add using decimal notation for positive numbers.

Example Add: 14.26 + 63.589.

$$\begin{array}{r} {\scriptstyle 1} \\ 1\,4.2\,6\,0 \\ +\,6\,3.5\,8\,9 \\ \hline 7\,7.8\,4\,9 \end{array}$$

   Writing an extra zero

Practice Exercise

5. Add: 5.54 + 33.071.

Objective 5.2b Subtract using decimal notation for positive numbers.

Example Subtract: 67.345 − 24.28.

$$\begin{array}{r} {\scriptstyle 2\ 14} \\ 6\,7.\cancel{3}\,\cancel{4}\,5 \\ -\,2\,4.2\,8\,0 \\ \hline 4\,3.0\,6\,5 \end{array}$$

   Writing an extra zero

Practice Exercise

6. Subtract: 221.04 − 13.192.

Objective 5.3a Multiply using decimal notation.

Example Multiply: 1.8×0.04.

$$\begin{array}{r} 1.8 \quad (1 \text{ decimal place}) \\ \times\,0.0\,4 \quad (2 \text{ decimal places}) \\ \hline 0.0\,7\,2 \quad (3 \text{ decimal places}) \end{array}$$

Example Multiply: 0.001×87.1.

$0.001 \times 87.1 \qquad 0.087.1$

$\uparrow$ $\curvearrowleft$

3 decimal places   Move 3 places to the left.
We write an extra zero.

$0.001 \times 87.1 = 0.0871$

Example Multiply: -63.4×100.

$-63.4 \times 100 \qquad -63.40.$

        $\uparrow$ $\curvearrowright$

2 zeros   Move 2 places to the right.
We write an extra zero.

$-63.4 \times 100 = -6340$

Practice Exercise

7. Multiply: 5.46×3.5.

Practice Exercise

8. Multiply: -17.6×0.01.

Practice Exercise

9. Multiply: 1000×60.437.

Objective 5.4a Divide using decimal notation.

Example Divide: $21.35 \div 6.1$.

$$
\begin{array}{r}
3.5 \\
6.1\,) \overline{\,2\,1.3\,5\,} \\
\underline{1\,8\,3} \\
3\,0\,5 \\
\underline{3\,0\,5} \\
0
\end{array}
$$

Practice Exercise

10. Divide: $26.64 \div 3.6$.

Example Divide: $\dfrac{16.7}{1000}$.

$\dfrac{16.7}{1000}$ 0.016.7

3 zeros   Move 3 places to the left.

$\dfrac{16.7}{1000} = 0.0167$

Practice Exercise

11. Divide: $\dfrac{4.7}{100}$.

Example Divide: $\dfrac{-42.93}{0.001}$.

$\dfrac{-42.93}{0.001}$ $-42.930.$

3 decimal places   Move 3 places to the right.

$\dfrac{-42.93}{0.001} = -42{,}930$

Practice Exercise

12. Divide: $\dfrac{-156.9}{0.01}$.

Review Exercises

Convert the number in each sentence to standard notation. [5.3b]

1. Russia has the largest total area of any country in the world, at 6.59 million square miles.

2. Americans eat more than 3.1 billion pounds of chocolate each year.

Source: Chocolate Manufacturers' Association

Write a word name. [5.1a]

3. 3.47

4. 0.031

5. 27.0001

6. −0.9

Write fraction notation. [5.1b]

7. 0.09

8. 4.561

9. −0.089

10. −3.0227

Write decimal notation. [5.1b]

11. $\dfrac{34}{1000}$

12. $-\dfrac{42{,}603}{10{,}000}$

13. $27\dfrac{91}{100}$

14. $-867\dfrac{6}{1000}$

Which number is larger? [5.1c]

15. 0.034, 0.0185

16. 0.91, 0.19

17. 0.741, 0.6943

18. −1.038, −1.041

Round 17.4287 to the nearest: [5.1d]

19. Tenth.

20. Hundredth.

21. Thousandth.

22. One.

Copyright © 2015 Pearson Education, Inc.

Add. [5.2a]

23.
```
      2 . 0 4 8
    6 5 . 3 7 1
  + 5 0 7 . 1
```

24.
```
      0 . 6
      0 . 0 0 4
      0 . 0 7
  + 0 . 0 0 9 8
```

25. $-219.3 + 2.8 + 7$

26. $0.41 + 4.1 + 41 + 0.041$

Subtract. [5.2b, c]

27.
```
    3 0 . 0
  -  0 . 7 9 0 8
```

28.
```
    8 4 5 . 0 8
  -    5 4 . 7 9
```

29. $37.645 - (-8.497)$

30. $-70.8 - 0.0109$

Multiply. [5.3a]

31.
```
      4 8
  × 0 . 2 7
```

32. $-0.174 \cdot (-0.83)$

33. 100×0.043

34. 0.001×-24.68

Divide. [5.4a]

35. $-60 \div 8$

36. $5\,2\,)\overline{2\,3.4}$

37. $2.6\,)\overline{1\,1\,7.5\,2}$

38. $2.1\,4\,)\overline{2.1\,8\,7\,0\,8}$

39. $\dfrac{276.3}{1000}$

40. $\dfrac{-13.892}{0.01}$

Solve. [5.2d], [5.4b]

41. $x + 51.748 = 548.0275$

42. $3 \cdot x = -20.85$

43. $10 \cdot y = 425.4$

44. $0.0089 + y = 5$

Solve. [5.7a]

45. Cole earned $620.80 working as a coronary intensive-care nurse for 40 hr one week. What is his hourly wage?

46. *Nutrition.* The average person eats 688.6 lb of fruits and vegetables in a year. What is the average consumption in one day? (Use 1 year = 365 days.) Round to the nearest tenth of a pound.

Source: U.S. Department of Agriculture

47. Derek had $1034.46 in his bank account. He used his debit card to buy a Wii game system for $249.99. How much was left in his account?

48. *Scanning Posters.* A high school club needs to scan posters designed by students and load them onto a flash drive. The copy center charges $12.99 for the flash drive and $1.09 per square foot for scanning. If the club needs to scan 13 posters at 3 sq ft per poster, what will the total cost be?

49. *Gas Mileage.* Ellie wants to estimate the gas mileage of her car. At 36,057.1 mi, she fills the tank with 10.7 gal. At 36,217.6 mi, she fills the tank with 11.1 gal. Find the mileage per gallon. Round to the nearest tenth.

50. *Books in Libraries.* The table below lists the numbers of books, in millions, held in the five largest public libraries in the United States. Find the average number of books per library. Round to the nearest tenth.

LIBRARY	NUMBER OF BOOKS (in millions)
Library of Congress	33.5
Boston Public Library	24.1
New York Public Library	16.6
Harvard University	16.6
University of Illinois–Urbana	12.8

SOURCE: American Library Association

Estimate each of the following. [5.6a]

51. The product 7.82×34.487 by rounding to the nearest one

52. The difference $219.875 - 4.478$ by rounding to the nearest one

53. The sum $\$45.78 + \$78.99$ by rounding to the nearest one

Find decimal notation. Use multiplying by 1. [5.5a]

54. $\dfrac{13}{25}$ **55.** $-\dfrac{9}{20}$ **56.** $\dfrac{11}{4}$

Find decimal notation. Use division. [5.5a]

57. $-\dfrac{13}{4}$ **58.** $\dfrac{7}{6}$ **59.** $\dfrac{17}{11}$

Round the answer to Exercise 59 to the nearest: [5.5b]

60. Tenth.   **61.** Hundredth.   **62.** Thousandth.

Convert from cents to dollars. [5.3b]

63. 8273¢   **64.** 487¢

Convert from dollars to cents. [5.3b]

65. $24.93   **66.** $9.86

Calculate. [5.4c], [5.5c]

67. $(8 - 1.23) \div (-4) + 5.6 \times 0.02$

68. $(1 + 0.07)^2 + 10^3 \div 10^2$
$\quad + [4(10.1 - 5.6) + 8(11.3 - 7.8)]$

69. $\dfrac{3}{4} \times (-20.85)$

70. Divide: $\dfrac{346.295}{0.001}$. [5.4a]

   A. 0.346295   **B.** 3.46295
   C. 34,629.5   **D.** 346,295

71. Estimate the quotient $82.304 \div 17.287$ by rounding to the nearest ten. [5.6a]

   A. 0.4   **B.** 4
   C. 40   **D.** 400

Synthesis

72. 🔳 In each of the following, use one of $+$, $-$, $\times$, and $\div$ in each blank to make a true sentence. [5.4c]

   a) $2.56 \;\square\; 6.4 \;\square\; 51.2 \;\square\; 17.4 \;\square\; 89.7 = 72.62$
   b) $(11.12 \;\square\; 0.29) \;\square\; 3^4 = 877.23$

73. Use the fact that $\frac{1}{3} = 0.\overline{3}$ to find repeating decimal notation for 1. Explain how you got your answer. [5.5a]

Understanding Through Discussion and Writing

1. Describe in your own words a procedure for converting from decimal notation to fraction notation. [5.1b]

2. A student insists that $346.708 \times 0.1 = 3467.08$. How could you convince him that a mistake had been made without checking on a calculator? [5.3a]

3. When is long division *not* the fastest way to convert from fraction notation to decimal notation? [5.5a]

4. Consider finding decimal notation for $\frac{44}{125}$. Discuss as many ways as you can for finding such notation and give the answer. [5.5a]

Copyright © 2015 Pearson Education, Inc.

CHAPTER

5 | **Test**

For Extra Help For step-by-step test solutions, access the Chapter Test Prep Videos in MyMathLab® or on YouTube (search "BittingerBasicEl" and click on "Channels").

1. In a recent year, 2.6 billion ducks were killed for food worldwide. Convert 2.6 billion to standard notation.

Sources: FAO; *National Geographic*, May 2011, Nigel Holmes

2. Write a word name for 123.0047.

Write fraction notation.

3. 0.91

4. −2.769

Which number is larger?

5. 0.07, 0.162

6. −0.078, −0.06

Write decimal notation.

8.7047

7. $\dfrac{074}{1000}$

8. $-\dfrac{37,047}{10,000}$

756.09

9. $756\dfrac{9}{100}$

Round 5.6783 to the nearest:

10. One.

11. Thousandth.

12. Tenth.

Calculate.

13. −102.4 + 6.1 + 78

14.
$$\begin{array}{r} 5\,2.6\,7\,8 \\ -\quad 4.3\,2\,1 \\ \hline \end{array}$$

15.
$$\begin{array}{r} 2\,0.0 \\ -\quad 0.9\,0\,9\,9 \\ \hline \end{array}$$

16.
$$\begin{array}{r} 0.1\,2\,5 \\ \times\quad 0.2\,4 \\ \hline \end{array}$$

17. 0.001 × (−213.45)

18. −19 ÷ 4

19. $3.3\,\overline{)\,1\,0\,0\,3.2}$

$33\,\overline{)\,100\,8.2}$

20. $8\,2\,\overline{)\,1\,5.5\,8}$

21. $\dfrac{-346.89}{1000}$

Solve.

22. −4.8 · y = 404.448

23. x + 0.018 = 9

Calculate.

24. $256 \div 3.2 \div 2 - 1.56 + 78.325 \times 0.02$

25. $-\dfrac{7}{8} \times (-345.6)$

Find decimal notation.

26. $\dfrac{7}{20}$

27. $\dfrac{22}{25}$

28. $\dfrac{9}{11}$

29. $-\dfrac{89}{12}$

Round the answer to Exercise 28 to the nearest:

30. Tenth.

31. Hundredth.

32. Thousandth.

Estimate each of the following.

33. The product 8.91×22.457 by rounding to the nearest one

34. The quotient $78.2209 \div 16.09$ by rounding to the nearest ten

35. *Scanning Blueprints.* A building contractor needs to scan and load blueprints onto a flash drive. The copy center charges $10.99 for the flash drive and $1.19 per square foot for scanning. If the contractor needs to scan 5 blueprints at 6 sq ft per print, what will the total cost be?

36. *Gas Mileage.* Tina wants to estimate the gas mileage in her economy car. At 76,843 mi, she fills the tank with 14.3 gal of gasoline. At 77,310 mi, she fills the tank with 16.5 gal of gasoline. Find the mileage per gallon. Round to the nearest tenth.

37. *Life Expectancy.* Life expectancies at birth for seven Asian countries are listed in the table below. Find the average life expectancy for this group of countries. Round to the nearest tenth.

COUNTRY	LIFE EXPECTANCY (in years)
Japan	82.25
South Korea	79.05
People's Republic of China	73.47
India	69.9
Russia	66.03
North Korea	63.81
Afghanistan	44.64

SOURCE: *CIA Factbook* 2011

38. The office manager for the law firm Drake, Smith, and Hartner buys 7 cases of copy paper at $41.99 per case. What is the total cost?

39. Convert from cents to dollars: 949¢.
   A. 0.949¢   **B.** $9.49   **C.** $94.90   **D.** $949

Synthesis

40. The Silver's Health Club charges a $79 membership fee and $42.50 a month. Allise has a coupon that will allow her to join the club for $299 for 6 months. How much will Allise save if she uses the coupon?

41. ▦ Arrange from smallest to largest.

$$-\dfrac{2}{3}, \ -\dfrac{15}{19}, \ -\dfrac{11}{13}, \ -\dfrac{5}{7}, \ -\dfrac{13}{15}, \ -\dfrac{17}{20}$$

Copyright © 2015 Pearson Education, Inc.

Convert to fraction notation.

1. $2\frac{2}{9}$

2. -3.051

Find decimal notation.

3. $-\frac{7}{5}$

4. $\frac{6}{11}$

5. Determine whether 43 is prime, composite, or neither.

6. Determine whether 2,053,752 is divisible by 4.

Calculate.

7. $48 + 12 \div 4 - 10 \times 2 + 6892 \div 4$

8. $0.2 - \{0.1[1.2(3.95 - 1.65) + 1.5 \div 2.5]\}$

Round to the nearest hundredth.

9. 584.973

10. $218.\overline{5}$

11. Estimate the product 16.392×9.715 by rounding to the nearest one.

12. Estimate by rounding to the nearest tenth:
$$2.714 + 4.562 - 3.31 - 0.0023.$$

13. Estimate the product 6418×1984 by rounding to the nearest hundred.

14. Estimate the quotient $717.832 \div 124.998$ by rounding to the nearest ten.

Add and simplify.

15. $2\frac{1}{4}$
   $+ 3\frac{4}{5}$

16. $3\,4{,}9\,2\,1$
     $9\,3{,}0\,9\,2$
   $+ 1\,1{,}1\,0\,3$

17. $\frac{1}{6} + \frac{2}{3} + \frac{8}{9}$

18. $-143.9 + 2.053$

Subtract and simplify.

19. $723{,}041 - 12{,}904$

20. $19 - 5.903$

21. $5\frac{1}{7} - 4\frac{3}{7}$

22. $\frac{9}{10} - \frac{10}{11}$

Multiply and simplify.

23. $\frac{3}{8} \cdot \left(-\frac{4}{9}\right)$

24. $2\,5\,3\,2$
   $\times\ 2\,1\,0\,0$

25. $2\,3.9$
   $\times\ \ \ 0.2$

26. $2\,7.9\,4\,3\,1$
   $\times\ \ \ \ \ 0.0\,0\,1$

Divide and simplify.

27. $1\,6.5\,)\overline{\,3\,5.0\,1\,3\,}$

28. $2\,6\,)\overline{\,4\,7{,}9\,1\,8\,}$

29. $13.8621 \div 0.001$

30. $-\dfrac{4}{9} \div \left(-\dfrac{8}{15} \right)$

Solve.

31. $8.32 + x = 9.1$

32. $75 \cdot x = 2100$

33. $y \cdot 9.47 = -81.6314$

34. $1062 + y = 368{,}313$

35. $t + \dfrac{5}{6} = \dfrac{8}{9}$

36. $-\dfrac{7}{8} \cdot t = \dfrac{7}{16}$

37. *Dominant Languages.* The table below lists the numbers of first-language speakers (people who acquired the language as infants) for the top five languages spoken worldwide.

LANGUAGE	FIRST-LANGUAGE SPEAKERS (in millions)
Chinese	1213
Spanish	329
English	328
Arabic	221
Hindi	182

SOURCES: Living Tongues Institute for Endangered Languages; UNESCO; SIL International

How many people in the world are first-language speakers of Spanish, Arabic, or Hindi?

38. Refer to the table in Exercise 37. How many more people in the world are first-language speakers of Chinese than first-language speakers of English?

39. After Lauren made a $450 down payment on a sofa, $\dfrac{3}{10}$ of the total cost was paid. How much did the sofa cost?

40. Joshua's tuition was $3600. He obtained a loan for $\dfrac{2}{3}$ of the tuition. How much was the loan?

41. The balance in Elliott's bank account is $314.79. After a debit transaction for $56.02, what is the balance in the account?

42. A clerk in Leah's Delicatessen sold $1\dfrac{1}{2}$ lb of ham, $2\dfrac{3}{4}$ lb of turkey, and $2\dfrac{1}{4}$ lb of roast beef. How many pounds of meat were sold altogether?

43. A baker used $\dfrac{1}{2}$ lb of sugar for cookies, $\dfrac{2}{3}$ lb of sugar for pie, and $\dfrac{5}{6}$ lb of sugar for cake. How much sugar was used in all?

44. The Currys' rectangular family room measures 19.8 ft by 23.6 ft. What is its area?

Simplify.

45. $\left(\dfrac{3}{4} \right)^2 - \dfrac{1}{8} \cdot \left(3 - 1\dfrac{1}{2} \right)^2$

46. $-1.2 \times 12.2 \div 0.1 \times 3.6$

Synthesis

47. Using a manufacturer's coupon, Lucy bought 2 cartons of orange juice and received a third carton free. The price of each carton was $3.59. What was the cost per carton with the coupon? Round to the nearest cent.

48. A carton of gelatin mix packages weighs $15\dfrac{3}{4}$ lb. Each package weighs $1\dfrac{3}{4}$ oz. How many packages are in the carton? (1 lb = 16 oz)

Copyright © 2015 Pearson Education, Inc.

Percent Notation

7.1 Percent Notation

7.2 Percent Notation and Fraction Notation

7.3 Solving Percent Problems Using Percent Equations

7.4 Solving Percent Problems Using Proportions

MID-CHAPTER REVIEW

7.5 Applications of Percent

TRANSLATING FOR SUCCESS

7.6 Sales Tax, Commission, and Discount

7.7 Simple Interest and Compound Interest; Credit Cards

Summary and Review

Test

Cumulative Review

STUDYING FOR SUCCESS   *Quiz and Test Follow-up*

☐ Immediately after completing a chapter quiz or test, write out a step-by-step solution for each question that you missed.

☐ Meet with your instructor or tutor for help with problems that are still giving you trouble.

☐ Keep your tests and quizzes along with their corrections to use as a study guide for the final exam.

7.1 Percent Notation

OBJECTIVES

a Write three kinds of notation for a percent.

b Convert between percent notation and decimal notation.

SKILL TO REVIEW

Objective 5.3a: Multiply using decimal notation.

Multiply.

1. 68.3 × 0.01

2. 3013 × 2.4

a   UNDERSTANDING PERCENT NOTATION

Today almost half of the world's population lives in cities. It is estimated that by 2050, 70% of the population will live in cities. What does 70% mean? It means that of every 100 people on Earth in 2050, 70 will live in cities. Thus, 70% is a ratio of 70 to 100, or $\frac{70}{100}$.

Sources: DuPont, 2011; *National Geographic*, December 2011

70 of 100 squares are shaded.

70% or $\frac{70}{100}$ or 0.70 of the large square is shaded.

We encounter percent notation frequently. Here are some examples.

- The 1964–2013 Washington quarter is 91.67% copper and 8.33% nickel. The 1946–2013 Jefferson nickel is 75% copper and 25% nickel.
  Source: Coinflation.com

- A blood alcohol level of 0.08% is the standard used by most states as the legal limit for drunk driving.
  Source: The National Highway Safety Administration

- Educational loans of $20,000 or more per year are obtained by 16% of college students.
  Source: TRU Survey

- Of senior citizens aged 76 and older, 31% own a laptop.
  Source: Internet & American Life Project

Percent notation is often represented using a circle graph, or pie chart, to show how the parts of a quantity are related. For example, the circle graph at left illustrates the percentages of coffee drinkers who get their coffee at selected locations.

Where Coffee Drinkers Get Their Coffee

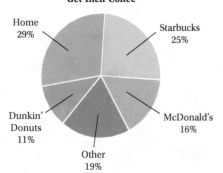

Home 29%

Starbucks 25%

Dunkin' Donuts 11%

Other 19%

McDonald's 16%

SOURCE: "Starbucks' Big Mug," *TIME*, June 25, 2012

> **PERCENT NOTATION**
>
> The notation *n*% means "*n* per hundred."

Answers

Skill to Review:
1. 0.683   **2.** 7231.2

This definition leads us to the following equivalent ways of defining percent notation.

NOTATION FOR $n\%$

Percent notation, $n\%$, can be expressed using:

ratio $\longrightarrow n\% =$ the ratio of n to $100 = \dfrac{n}{100}$,

fraction notation $\longrightarrow n\% = n \times \dfrac{1}{100}$, or

decimal notation $\longrightarrow n\% = n \times 0.01$.

EXAMPLE 1 Write three kinds of notation for 67.8%.

Using ratio: $\qquad\qquad\qquad 67.8\% = \dfrac{67.8}{100} \qquad$ A ratio of 67.8 to 100

Using fraction notation: $\quad 67.8\% = 67.8 \times \dfrac{1}{100} \qquad$ Replacing % with $\times \dfrac{1}{100}$

Using decimal notation: $\quad 67.8\% = 67.8 \times 0.01 \qquad$ Replacing % with $\times 0.01$

Do Exercises 1–4. ▶

b CONVERTING BETWEEN PERCENT NOTATION AND DECIMAL NOTATION

Consider 78%. To convert to decimal notation, we can think of percent notation as a ratio and write

$$78\% = \frac{78}{100} \qquad \text{Using the definition of percent as a ratio}$$
$$= 0.78. \qquad \text{Dividing}$$

Similarly,

$$4.9\% = \frac{4.9}{100} = 0.049.$$

We can also convert 78% to decimal notation by replacing "%" with "$\times 0.01$" and writing

$$78\% = 78 \times 0.01 \qquad \text{Replacing % with } \times 0.01$$
$$= 0.78. \qquad \text{Multiplying}$$

Similarly,

$$4.9\% = 4.9 \times 0.01 = 0.049.$$

Dividing by 100 amounts to moving the decimal point two places to the left, which is the same as multiplying by 0.01. This leads us to a quick way to convert from percent notation to decimal notation: We drop the percent symbol and move the decimal point two places to the left.

During 2011, 42.2% of electricity in the United States was generated using coal.

Source: U.S. Energy Information Administration

Write three kinds of notation for each percent, as in Example 1.

1. 70%   2. 23.4%

3. 100%   4. 0.6%

It is thought that the Roman emperor Augustus began percent notation by taxing goods sold at a rate of $\frac{1}{100}$. In time, the symbol "%" evolved by interchanging the parts of the symbol "100" to "0/0" and then to "%."

Answers

1. $\dfrac{70}{100}$; $70 \times \dfrac{1}{100}$; 70×0.01

2. $\dfrac{23.4}{100}$; $23.4 \times \dfrac{1}{100}$; 23.4×0.01

3. $\dfrac{100}{100}$; $100 \times \dfrac{1}{100}$; 100×0.01

4. $\dfrac{0.6}{100}$; $0.6 \times \dfrac{1}{100}$; 0.6×0.01

CALCULATOR CORNER

Converting from Percent Notation to Decimal Notation

Many calculators have a %️ key that can be used to convert from percent notation to decimal notation. This is often the second operation associated with a particular key and is accessed by first pressing a 2nd or SHIFT key. To convert 57.6% to decimal notation, for example, you might press 5 7 · 6 2nd %️ or 5 7 · 6 SHIFT %️ . The display would read [0.576], so 57.6% = 0.576.

EXERCISES Use a calculator to find decimal notation.

1. 14%   **2.** 0.069%

3. 43.8%   **4.** 125%

Find decimal notation.

5. 34%   **6.** 78.9%

Find decimal notation for the percent notation(s) in each sentence.

7. *Energy Use.* The United States consumes 19% of the world's energy. Russia consumes only 6% of the world's energy.
Source: U.S. Energy Information Administration

8. *Blood Alcohol Level.* A blood alcohol level of 0.08% is the standard used by the most states as the legal limit for drunk driving.

To convert from percent notation to decimal notation,	36.5%
a) replace the percent symbol % with $\times$ 0.01, and	36.5 $\times$ 0.01
b) multiply by 0.01, which means move the decimal point two places to the left.	0.36.5 Move 2 places to the left.
	36.5% = 0.365

EXAMPLE 2 Find decimal notation for 99.44%.

a) Replace the percent symbol with $\times$ 0.01.   99.44 $\times$ 0.01

b) Move the decimal point two places to the left.   0.99.44

Thus, 99.44% = 0.9944.

EXAMPLE 3 The interest rate on a $2\frac{1}{2}$-year certificate of deposit is $6\frac{3}{8}$%. Find decimal notation for $6\frac{3}{8}$%.

a) Convert $6\frac{3}{8}$ to decimal notation and replace the percent symbol with $\times$ 0.01. $6\frac{3}{8}$%   6.375 $\times$ 0.01

b) Move the decimal point two places to the left.   0.06.375

Thus, $6\frac{3}{8}$% = 0.06375.

◀ **Do Exercises 5–8.**

To convert 0.38 to percent notation, we can first write fraction notation, as follows:

$$0.38 = \frac{38}{100} \quad \text{Converting to fraction notation}$$

$$= 38\%. \quad \text{Using the definition of percent as a ratio}$$

Note that 100% = 100 $\times$ 0.01 = 1. Thus to convert 0.38 to percent notation, we can multiply by 1, using 100% as a symbol for 1.

$$0.38 = 0.38 \times 1$$
$$= 0.38 \times 100\%$$
$$= 0.38 \times 100 \times 0.01 \quad \text{Replacing 100\% with 100} \times 0.01$$
$$= (0.38 \times 100) \times 0.01 \quad \text{Using the associative law of multiplication}$$
$$= 38 \times 0.01$$
$$= 38\% \quad \text{Replacing} \times 0.01 \text{ with \%}$$

Even more quickly, since 0.38 = 0.38 $\times$ 100%, we can simply multiply 0.38 by 100 and write the % symbol.

To convert from decimal notation to percent notation, we multiply by 100%. That is, we move the decimal point two places to the right and write a percent symbol.

Answers

5. 0.34   **6.** 0.789
7. 0.19; 0.06   **8.** 0.0008

To convert from decimal notation to percent notation, multiply by 100%. That is,	$0.675 = 0.675 \times 100\%$
a) move the decimal point two places to the right and	0.67.5 Move 2 places to the right.
b) write a % symbol.	67.5% $0.675 = 67.5\%$

EXAMPLE 4 Of the time off that employees take as sick leave, 0.21 is actually used for family issues. Find percent notation for 0.21.
Source: CCH Inc.

a) Move the decimal point two places to the right.   0.21.

b) Write a % symbol.   21%

Thus, $0.21 = 21\%$.

EXAMPLE 5 Find percent notation for 5.6.

a) Move the decimal point two places to the right, adding an extra zero.   5.60.

b) Write a % symbol.   560%

Thus, $5.6 = 560\%$.

EXAMPLE 6 Of those who play golf, 0.149 play 8–24 rounds per year. Find percent notation for 0.149.
Source: U.S. Golf Association

a) Move the decimal point two places to the right.   0.14.9

b) Write a % symbol.   14.9%

Thus, $0.149 = 14.9\%$.

Do Exercises 9–14. ▶

Find percent notation.

9. 0.24   **10.** 3.47

11. 1   **12.** 0.05

Find percent notation for the decimal notation(s) in each sentence.

13. *Women in Congress.* In 2012, 0.19 of the members of the United States Congress were women.
Source: *Wall Street Journal*

14. *Soccer.* Of Americans in the 18–24 age group, 0.311 have played soccer. Of those in the 12–17 age group, 0.396 have played soccer.
Source: ESPN Sports Poll, a service of TNS Sport

Answers
9. 24%   **10.** 347%   **11.** 100%   **12.** 5%
13. 19%   **14.** 31.1%; 39.6%

7.1   Exercise Set

For Extra Help   MyMathLab®   MathXL® PRACTICE   WATCH   READ   REVIEW

Reading Check

Find percent notation for each shaded area.

RC1.

RC2.

RC3.

RC4.

a   Write three kinds of notation, as in Example 1 on p. 383.

1. 90%
     2. 58.7%
     3. 12.5%
     4. 130%

b   Find decimal notation.

5. 67%
     6. 17%
     7. 45.6%
     8. 76.3%

9. 59.01%
     10. 30.02%
     11. 10%
     12. 80%

13. 1%
     14. 100%
     15. 200%
     16. 300%

17. 0.1%
     18. 0.4%
     19. 0.09%
     20. 0.12%

21. 0.18%
     22. 5.5%
     23. 23.19%
     24. 87.99%

25. $14\frac{7}{8}\%$
     26. $93\frac{1}{8}\%$
     27. $56\frac{1}{2}\%$
     28. $61\frac{3}{4}\%$

Find decimal notation for the percent notation(s) in each sentence.

29. *Daily Calories.*   In 2006, American adults got about 13% of their daily calories from fast food. This percentage decreased to 11% in 2010.

Source: *Indianapolis Star*, February 21, 2013, Nanci Hellmich

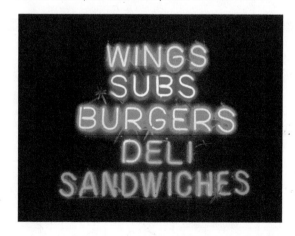

30. *Bachelor's Degrees.*   In 1970, 1% of taxi drivers had a bachelor's degree. By 2010, 15% of taxi drivers had a bachelor's degree.

Source: *USA Today*, January, 28, 2013, Mary Beth Marklein

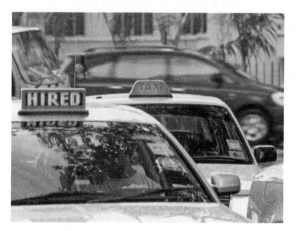

Copyright © 2015 Pearson Education, Inc.

31. *Fuel Efficiency.* Speeding up by only 5 mph on the highway cuts fuel efficiency by approximately 7% to 8%.

Source: *Wall Street Journal,* "Pain Relief," by A. J. Miranda, September 15, 2008

32. *Foreign-Born Population.* In 2010, the U.S. foreign-born population was 12.9%, the highest since 1920.

Source: U.S. Census Bureau

33. *Credit-Card Debt.* In 2012, approximately 13.9% of American households had credit-card debt that exceeded 40% of their income.

Source: statisticbrain.com

34. *Eating Out.* On a given day, 58% of all Americans eat meals and snacks away from home.

Source: U.S. Department of Agriculture

Find percent notation.

35. 0.47   **36.** 0.87   **37.** 0.03   **38.** 0.01   **39.** 8.7

40. 4   **41.** 0.334   **42.** 0.889   **43.** 0.75   **44.** 0.99

45. 0.4   **46.** 0.5   **47.** 0.006   **48.** 0.008   **49.** 0.017

50. 0.024   **51.** 0.2718   **52.** 0.8911   **53.** 0.0239   **54.** 0.00073

Find percent notation for the decimal notation(s) in each sentence.

55. *Recycling Aluminum Cans.* Over 0.651 of all aluminum cans are recycled.

Source: earth911.com

56. *Wasting Food.* Americans waste an estimated 0.27 of the food available for consumption. The waste occurs in restaurants, supermarkets, cafeterias, and household kitchens.

Source: *New York Times,* "One Country's Table Scraps, Another Country's Meal," by Andrew Martin, May 18, 2008

57. *Dining Together.* In 2012, 0.34 of American families dined together four or five times per week.

Source: unitedfamiliesinternational.wordpress.com

58. *Age 65 and Older.* In Alaska, 0.057 of the residents are age 65 and older. In Florida, 0.176 are age 65 and older.

Source: U.S. Census Bureau

59. _Residents Aged 15 or Younger._ In Haiti, 0.359 of the residents are age 15 or younger. In the United States, 0.2 of the residents are age 15 or younger.

Source: _The World Almanac 2012_

60. _Graduation Rates._ In 2010, the high school graduation rate in the United States was 0.742. The dropout rate was 0.034.

Source: National Center for Educational Statistics

Find decimal notation for each percent notation in the graph.

61.

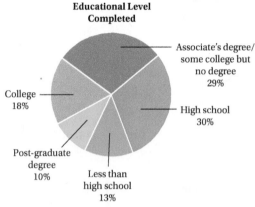

Educational Level Completed

Associate's degree/ some college but no degree 29%

High school 30%

College 18%

Post-graduate degree 10%

Less than high school 13%

SOURCE: U.S. Census Bureau

62.

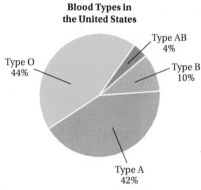

Blood Types in the United States

Type AB 4%

Type O 44%

Type B 10%

Type A 42%

SOURCE: bloodcenter.stanford.edu/ about_blood/blood_types.html

Skill Maintenance

Find all the factors of each number.   [3.1a]

63. 84

64. 620

65. Find the LCM of 18 and 60.   [4.1a]

66. Find the prime factorization of 90.   [3.1d]

67. Solve: $\dfrac{5}{8} + y = -\dfrac{13}{16}$.   [4.3c]

68. Simplify: $(12 - 3)^2 - 9 + 5^2$.   [1.9c]

Synthesis

Find percent notation. (_Hint:_ Multiply by a form of 1 and obtain a denominator of 100.)

69. $\dfrac{1}{2}$

70. $\dfrac{3}{4}$

71. $\dfrac{7}{10}$

72. $\dfrac{2}{5}$

Find percent notation for each shaded area.

73.

74.

Copyright © 2015 Pearson Education, Inc.

Percent Notation and Fraction Notation

a CONVERTING FROM FRACTION NOTATION TO PERCENT NOTATION

Consider the fraction notation $\frac{7}{8}$. To convert to percent notation, we use two skills that we already have. We first find decimal notation by dividing: $7 \div 8$.

$$
\begin{array}{r}
0.8\,7\,5 \\
8 \overline{)\,7.0\,0\,0} \\
\underline{6\,4} \\
6\,0 \\
\underline{5\,6} \\
4\,0 \\
\underline{4\,0} \\
0
\end{array}
\qquad \frac{7}{8} = 0.875
$$

Then we convert the decimal notation to percent notation. We move the decimal point two places to the right

$$0\underset{\curvearrowright}{.8\,7}.5$$

and write a % symbol:

$$\frac{7}{8} = 87.5\%, \text{ or } 87\tfrac{1}{2}\%. \qquad 0.5 = \tfrac{1}{2}$$

To convert from fraction notation to percent notation,

$\dfrac{3}{5}$ Fraction notation

a) find decimal notation by division, and

$$
\begin{array}{r}
0.6 \\
5 \overline{)\,3.0} \\
\underline{3\,0} \\
0
\end{array}
$$

b) convert the decimal notation to percent notation.

$0.6 = 0.60 = 60\%$ Percent notation

$\dfrac{3}{5} = 60\%$

EXAMPLE 1   Find percent notation for $\dfrac{1}{6}$.

a) We first find decimal notation by division.

$$
\begin{array}{r}
0.1\,6\,6 \\
6 \overline{)\,1.0\,0\,0} \\
\underline{6} \\
4\,0 \\
\underline{3\,6} \\
4\,0 \\
\underline{3\,6} \\
4
\end{array}
$$

We get a repeating decimal; $0.16\overline{6}$.

OBJECTIVES

a Convert from fraction notation to percent notation.

b Convert from percent notation to fraction notation.

SKILL TO REVIEW

Objective 5.5a: Convert from fraction notation to decimal notation.

Find decimal notation.

1. $\dfrac{11}{16}$ **2.** $\dfrac{5}{9}$

CALCULATOR CORNER

Converting from Fraction Notation to Percent Notation   A calculator can be used to convert from fraction notation to percent notation. We simply perform the division on the calculator and then use the percent key. To convert $\frac{17}{40}$ to percent notation, for example, we press

$\boxed{1}\,\boxed{7}\,\boxed{\div}\,\boxed{4}\,\boxed{0}\,\boxed{\text{2nd}}\,\boxed{\%}$, or

$\boxed{1}\,\boxed{7}\,\boxed{\div}\,\boxed{4}\,\boxed{0}\,\boxed{\text{SHIFT}}\,\boxed{\%}$.

The display reads $\boxed{\quad 42.5\quad}$, so $\frac{17}{40} = 42.5\%$.

EXERCISES   Use a calculator to find percent notation. Round to the nearest hundredth of a percent.

1. $\dfrac{13}{25}$ **2.** $\dfrac{5}{13}$

3. $\dfrac{43}{39}$ **4.** $\dfrac{12}{7}$

5. $\dfrac{217}{364}$ **6.** $\dfrac{2378}{8401}$

Answers

Skill to Review:
1. 0.6875 2. $0.\overline{5}$

b) Next, we convert the decimal notation to percent notation. We move the decimal point two places to the right and write a % symbol.

$$0.16.\overline{6}$$

$$\frac{1}{6} = 16.\overline{6}\%, \text{ or } 16\frac{2}{3}\% \qquad 0.\overline{6} = \frac{2}{3}$$

Don't forget the % symbol.

◀ **Do Exercises 1 and 2.**

Find percent notation.

1. $\dfrac{5}{6}$

2. $\dfrac{1}{4}$

EXAMPLE 2 *First Language.* The first language of approximately $\frac{3}{16}$ of the world's population is Chinese. Find percent notation for $\frac{3}{16}$.

Sources: *National Geographic,* "Languages at Risk," Virginia W. Mason, July 2012; U.S. Census Bureau; *The CIA World Factbook 2012*

a) Find decimal notation by division.

$$\begin{array}{r} 0.1\ 8\ 7\ 5 \\ 16\overline{)3.0\ 0\ 0\ 0} \\ \underline{1\ 6} \\ 1\ 4\ 0 \\ \underline{1\ 2\ 8} \\ 1\ 2\ 0 \\ \underline{1\ 1\ 2} \\ 8\ 0 \\ \underline{8\ 0} \\ 0 \end{array}$$

$$\frac{3}{16} = 0.1875$$

3. Water is the single most abundant chemical in the human body. The body is about $\frac{2}{3}$ water. Find percent notation for $\frac{2}{3}$.

4. Find percent notation: $\dfrac{5}{8}$.

b) Convert the answer to percent notation.

$$0.18.75$$

$$\frac{3}{16} = 18.75\%, \text{ or } 18\frac{3}{4}\%$$

◀ **Do Exercises 3 and 4.**

Answers

1. $83.\overline{3}\%$, or $83\frac{1}{3}\%$ 2. 25%
3. $66.\overline{6}\%$, or $66\frac{2}{3}\%$ 4. 62.5%

In some cases, division is not the fastest way to convert a fraction to percent notation. The following are some optional ways in which the conversion might be done.

EXAMPLE 3   Find percent notation for $\frac{69}{100}$.

We use the definition of percent as a ratio.

$$\frac{69}{100} = 69\%$$

EXAMPLE 4   Find percent notation for $\frac{17}{20}$.

We want to multiply by 1 to get 100 in the denominator. We think of what we must multiply 20 by in order to get 100. That number is 5, so we multiply by 1 using $\frac{5}{5}$.

$$\frac{17}{20} \cdot \frac{5}{5} = \frac{85}{100} = 85\%$$

Note that this shortcut works only when the denominator is a factor of 100.

EXAMPLE 5   Find percent notation for $\frac{18}{25}$.

$$\frac{18}{25} = \frac{18}{25} \cdot \frac{4}{4} = \frac{72}{100} = 72\%$$

Do Exercises 5–8. ▶

Find percent notation.

5. $\dfrac{57}{100}$

GS 6. $\dfrac{19}{25} = \dfrac{19}{25} \cdot \dfrac{4}{\boxed{}}$

$= \dfrac{76}{\boxed{}} = \boxed{}\%$

7. $\dfrac{7}{10}$ 8. $\dfrac{1}{4}$

b CONVERTING FROM PERCENT NOTATION TO FRACTION NOTATION

To convert from percent notation to fraction notation,	30%	Percent notation
a) use the definition of percent as a ratio, and	$\dfrac{30}{100}$	
b) simplify, if possible.	$\dfrac{3}{10}$	Fraction notation

EXAMPLE 6   Find fraction notation for 75%.

$$75\% = \frac{75}{100} \qquad \text{Using the definition of percent}$$

$$\left.\begin{array}{l} = \dfrac{3 \cdot 25}{4 \cdot 25} = \dfrac{3}{4} \cdot \dfrac{25}{25} \\[2ex] = \dfrac{3}{4} \end{array}\right\} \quad \text{Simplifying}$$

Answers

5. 57%   **6.** 76%   **7.** 70%
8. 25%

Guided Solution:
6. 4, 100, 76

EXAMPLE 7 Find fraction notation for 62.5%.

$$62.5\% = \frac{62.5}{100}$$ Using the definition of percent

$$= \frac{62.5}{100} \times \frac{10}{10}$$ Multiplying by 1 to eliminate the decimal point in the numerator

$$= \frac{625}{1000}$$

$$\left. \begin{array}{l} = \dfrac{5 \cdot 125}{8 \cdot 125} = \dfrac{5}{8} \cdot \dfrac{125}{125} \\[2mm] = \dfrac{5}{8} \end{array} \right\}$$ Simplifying

Find fraction notation.

9. 60%

10. 3.25%

$$= \frac{3.25}{\boxed{}} = \frac{3.25}{100} \times \frac{\boxed{}}{100}$$

$$= \frac{325}{\boxed{}} = \frac{13 \times \boxed{}}{400 \times 25}$$

$$= \frac{13}{400} \times \frac{25}{25} = \frac{\boxed{}}{400}$$

11. $66\frac{2}{3}\%$ **12.** $12\frac{1}{2}\%$

EXAMPLE 8 Find fraction notation for $16\frac{2}{3}\%$.

$$16\frac{2}{3}\% = \frac{50}{3}\%$$ Converting from the mixed numeral to fraction notation

$$= \frac{50}{3} \times \frac{1}{100}$$ Using the definition of percent

$$\left. \begin{array}{l} = \dfrac{50 \cdot 1}{3 \cdot 50 \cdot 2} = \dfrac{1}{3 \cdot 2} \cdot \dfrac{50}{50} \\[2mm] = \dfrac{1}{6} \end{array} \right\}$$ Simplifying

◀ Do Exercises 9–12.

The table below lists fraction, decimal, and percent equivalents that are used so often it would speed up your work if you memorized them. For example, $\frac{1}{3} = 0.\overline{3}$, so we say that the **decimal equivalent** of $\frac{1}{3}$ is $0.\overline{3}$, or that $0.\overline{3}$ has the **fraction equivalent** $\frac{1}{3}$. This table also appears on the inside back cover of the book.

FRACTION, DECIMAL, AND PERCENT EQUIVALENTS

FRACTION NOTATION	$\frac{1}{10}$	$\frac{1}{8}$	$\frac{1}{6}$	$\frac{1}{5}$	$\frac{1}{4}$	$\frac{3}{10}$	$\frac{1}{3}$	$\frac{3}{8}$	$\frac{2}{5}$	$\frac{1}{2}$	$\frac{3}{5}$	$\frac{5}{8}$	$\frac{2}{3}$	$\frac{7}{10}$	$\frac{3}{4}$	$\frac{4}{5}$	$\frac{5}{6}$	$\frac{7}{8}$	$\frac{9}{10}$	$\frac{1}{1}$
DECIMAL NOTATION	0.1	0.125	$0.16\overline{6}$	0.2	0.25	0.3	$0.33\overline{3}$	0.375	0.4	0.5	0.6	0.625	$0.66\overline{6}$	0.7	0.75	0.8	$0.83\overline{3}$	0.875	0.9	1
PERCENT NOTATION	10%	12.5%, or $12\frac{1}{2}\%$	$16.\overline{6}\%$, or $16\frac{2}{3}\%$	20%	25%	30%	$33.\overline{3}\%$, or $33\frac{1}{3}\%$	37.5%, or $37\frac{1}{2}\%$	40%	50%	60%	62.5%, or $62\frac{1}{2}\%$	$66.\overline{6}\%$, or $66\frac{2}{3}\%$	70%	75%	80%	$83.\overline{3}\%$, or $83\frac{1}{3}\%$	87.5%, or $87\frac{1}{2}\%$	90%	100%

Find fraction notation.

13. $33.\overline{3}\%$ **14.** $83.\overline{3}\%$

EXAMPLE 9 Find fraction notation for $16.\overline{6}\%$.

We can use the table above or recall that $16.\overline{6}\% = 16\frac{2}{3}\% = \frac{1}{6}$. We can also recall from our work with repeating decimals in Chapter 5 that $0.\overline{6} = \frac{2}{3}$. Then we have $16.\overline{6}\% = 16\frac{2}{3}\%$ and can proceed as in Example 8.

◀ Do Exercises 13 and 14.

Answers

9. $\frac{3}{5}$ **10.** $\frac{13}{400}$ **11.** $\frac{2}{3}$

12. $\frac{1}{8}$ **13.** $\frac{1}{3}$ **14.** $\frac{5}{6}$

Guided Solution:
10. 100, 100, 10,000, 25, 13

☑ Reading Check

Match each fraction with the equivalent decimal notation from the list at the right. Some choices will not be used.

RC1. $\frac{1}{8}$ _____   **RC2.** $\frac{3}{8}$ _____

RC3. $\frac{5}{8}$ _____   **RC4.** $\frac{7}{8}$ _____

RC5. $\frac{1}{5}$ _____   **RC6.** $\frac{2}{5}$ _____

RC7. $\frac{3}{5}$ _____   **RC8.** $\frac{4}{5}$ _____

a) 0.875
b) 0.2
c) 0.125
d) 0.4
e) 0.375
f) 0.1
g) 0.625
h) 0.6
i) 0.8
j) 0.675

a Find percent notation.

1. $\frac{41}{100}$ **2.** $\frac{36}{100}$ **3.** $\frac{5}{100}$ **4.** $\frac{1}{100}$ **5.** $\frac{2}{10}$ **6.** $\frac{7}{10}$

7. $\frac{3}{10}$ **8.** $\frac{9}{10}$ **9.** $\frac{1}{2}$ **10.** $\frac{3}{4}$ **11.** $\frac{7}{8}$ **12.** $\frac{1}{8}$

13. $\frac{4}{5}$ **14.** $\frac{2}{5}$ **15.** $\frac{2}{3}$ **16.** $\frac{1}{3}$ **17.** $\frac{1}{6}$ **18.** $\frac{5}{6}$

19. $\frac{3}{16}$ **20.** $\frac{11}{16}$ **21.** $\frac{13}{16}$ **22.** $\frac{7}{16}$ **23.** $\frac{4}{25}$ **24.** $\frac{17}{25}$

25. $\frac{1}{20}$ **26.** $\frac{31}{50}$ **27.** $\frac{17}{50}$ **28.** $\frac{3}{20}$

Find percent notation for the fraction notation in each sentence.

29. *Heart Transplants.* In the United States in 2006, $\frac{2}{25}$ of the organ transplants were heart transplants and $\frac{59}{100}$ were kidney transplants.

Source: 2007 OPTN/SRTR Annual Report, Table 1.7

30. *Car Colors.* The four most popular colors for 2006 compact/sports cars were silver, gray, black, and red. Of all cars in this category, $\frac{9}{50}$ were silver, $\frac{3}{20}$ gray, $\frac{3}{20}$ black, and $\frac{3}{20}$ red.

Sources: Ward's Automotive Group; DuPont Automotive Products

In Exercises 31–36, write percent notation for the fractions in the pie chart below.

How Food Dollars Are Spent

Beverages (nonalcoholic) $\frac{3}{25}$

Dairy $\frac{3}{25}$

Sugar $\frac{1}{25}$

Cereal and baked goods $\frac{13}{100}$

Fats and oils $\frac{3}{100}$

Fruits and vegetables $\frac{3}{20}$

Other $\frac{9}{50}$

Eggs $\frac{1}{50}$

Meat, poultry, and fish $\frac{11}{50}$

SOURCES: U.S. Bureau of Labor Statistics; Consumer Price Index; *The Hoosier Farmer*, Summer 2008

31. $\frac{11}{50}$

32. $\frac{9}{50}$

33. $\frac{3}{25}$

34. $\frac{1}{25}$

35. $\frac{3}{20}$

36. $\frac{13}{100}$

b Find fraction notation. Simplify.

37. 85%

38. 55%

39. 62.5%

40. 12.5%

41. $33\frac{1}{3}\%$

42. $83\frac{1}{3}\%$

43. $16.\overline{6}\%$

44. $66.\overline{6}\%$

45. 7.25%

46. 4.85%

47. 0.8%

48. 0.2%

49. $25\frac{3}{8}\%$

50. $48\frac{7}{8}\%$

51. $78\frac{2}{9}\%$

52. $16\frac{5}{9}\%$

53. $64\frac{7}{11}\%$

54. $73\frac{3}{11}\%$

55. 150%

56. 110%

57. 0.0325%

58. 0.419%

59. $33.\overline{3}\%$

60. $83.\overline{3}\%$

Copyright © 2015 Pearson Education, Inc.

In Exercises 61–66, find fraction notation for the percent notations in the table below.

U.S. POPULATION BY SELECTED AGE CATEGORIES
(Data have been rounded to the nearest percent.)

AGE CATEGORY	PERCENT OF POPULATION
5–17 years	18%
18–24 years	10
15–44 years	41
18 years and older	76
65 years and older	13
75 years and older	6

SOURCES: U.S. Census Bureau; 2010 American Community Survey

61. 6%

62. 18%

63. 13%

64. 41%

65. 76%

66. 10%

Find fraction notation for the percent notation in each sentence.

67. A $\frac{3}{4}$-cup serving of Post Selects Great Grains cereal with $\frac{1}{2}$ cup of fat-free milk satisfies 15% of the minimum daily requirement for calcium.

Source: Kraft Foods Global, Inc.

68. A 1.8-oz serving of Frosted Mini-Wheats®, Blueberry Muffin, with $\frac{1}{2}$ cup of fat-free milk satisfies 35% of the minimum daily requirement for Vitamin B_{12}.

Source: Kellogg, Inc.

69. In 2006, 20.9% of Americans age 18 and older smoked cigarettes.

Sources: *Washington Post*, March 9, 2006; U.S. Centers for Disease Control and Prevention

70. In 2010, 11.9% of Californians age 18 and older smoked cigarettes.

Source: California Department of Public Health

Complete each table.

71.

Fraction Notation	Decimal Notation	Percent Notation
$\frac{1}{8}$		12.5%, or $12\frac{1}{2}\%$
$\frac{1}{6}$		
		20%
	0.25	
		$33.\overline{3}\%$, or $33\frac{1}{3}\%$
		37.5%, or $37\frac{1}{2}\%$
		40%
$\frac{1}{2}$		

72.

Fraction Notation	Decimal Notation	Percent Notation
$\frac{3}{5}$		
	0.625	
$\frac{2}{3}$		
	0.75	75%
$\frac{4}{5}$		
$\frac{5}{6}$		$83.\overline{3}\%$, or $83\frac{1}{3}\%$
$\frac{7}{8}$		87.5%, or $87\frac{1}{2}\%$
		100%

73.

Fraction Notation	Decimal Notation	Percent Notation
	0.5	
$\frac{1}{3}$		
		25%
		$16.\overline{6}\%$, or $16\frac{2}{3}\%$
	0.125	
$\frac{3}{4}$		
	$0.8\overline{3}$	
$\frac{3}{8}$		

74.

Fraction Notation	Decimal Notation	Percent Notation
		40%
		62.5%, or $62\frac{1}{2}\%$
	0.875	
$\frac{1}{1}$		
	0.6	
	$0.\overline{6}$	
$\frac{1}{5}$		

Skill Maintenance

Solve.

75. $13 \cdot x = 910$ [1.7b]

76. $15 \cdot y = 75$ [1.7b]

77. $0.05 \times b = -20$ [5.4b]

78. $3 = 0.16 \times b$ [5.4b]

79. $\frac{24}{37} = \frac{15}{x}$ [6.3b]

80. $\frac{17}{18} = \frac{x}{27}$ [6.3b]

81. $\frac{9}{10} = \frac{x}{5}$ [6.3b]

82. $\frac{7}{x} = \frac{4}{5}$ [6.3b]

Convert to a mixed numeral.   [4.4a]

83. $\frac{75}{4}$

84. $-\frac{67}{9}$

Convert from a mixed numeral to fraction notation.   [4.4a]

85. $-101\frac{1}{2}$

86. $20\frac{9}{10}$

Synthesis

Write percent notation.

87. $2.5\overline{74631}$

88. $\frac{54}{999}$

Write decimal notation.

89. $\frac{729}{7}\%$

90. $\frac{19}{12}\%$

91. Arrange the following numbers from smallest to largest.

$$16\frac{1}{6}\%, \ 1.6, \ \frac{1}{6}\%, \ \frac{1}{2}, \ 0.2, \ 1.6\%, \ 1\frac{1}{6}\%, \ 0.5\%, \ \frac{2}{7}\%, \ 0.\overline{54}$$

Copyright © 2015 Pearson Education, Inc.

Solving Percent Problems Using Percent Equations

a TRANSLATING TO EQUATIONS

To solve a problem involving percents, it is helpful to translate first to an equation. To distinguish the method discussed in this section from that of Section 7.4, we will call these *percent equations*.

OBJECTIVES

a Translate percent problems to percent equations.

b Solve basic percent problems.

KEY WORDS IN PERCENT TRANSLATIONS

"**Of**" translates to "·" or "×".

"**What**" translates to any letter.

"**Is**" translates to "=".

"**%**" translates to "$\times \frac{1}{100}$" or "$\times 0.01$".

SKILL TO REVIEW

Objective 5.4b: Solve equations of the type $a \cdot x = b$, where a and b may be in decimal notation.

Solve.

1. $0.05 \cdot x = 830$
2. $8 \cdot y = 40.648$

EXAMPLES Translate each of the following.

1. 23% of 5 is what?

$23\% \cdot 5 = a$ This is a *percent equation*.

2. What is 11% of 49?

$a = 11\% \cdot 49$ Any letter can be used.

Do Margin Exercises 1 and 2. ▶

EXAMPLES Translate each of the following.

3. 3 is 10% of what?

$3 = 10\% \cdot b$

4. 45% of what is 23?

$45\% \times b = 23$

Do Exercises 3 and 4. ▶

EXAMPLES Translate each of the following.

5. 10 is what percent of 20?

$10 = p \times 20$

6. What percent of 50 is 7?

$p \cdot 50 = 7$

Do Exercises 5 and 6. ▶

Translate to an equation. Do not solve.

1. 12% of 50 is what?

2. What is 40% of 60?

Translate to an equation. Do not solve.

3. 45 is 20% of what?

4. 120% of what is 60?

Translate to an equation. Do not solve.

5. 16 is what percent of 40?

6. What percent of 84 is 10.5?

Answers

Skill to Review:
1. 16,600 2. 5.081

Margin Exercises:
1. $12\% \times 50 = a$ 2. $a = 40\% \times 60$
3. $45 = 20\% \times b$ 4. $120\% \times b = 60$
5. $16 = p \times 40$ 6. $p \times 84 = 10.5$

The U.S. gross domestic product for 2010 was approximately $14.66 trillion. Of that amount, Americans spent 17.9% on health care. What was spent on health care? (See Example 7.)

Sources: *EconPost*, April 25, 2011; kaiseredu.org

b SOLVING PERCENT PROBLEMS

In solving percent problems, we use the *Translate* and *Solve* steps in the problem-solving strategy used throughout this text.

Percent problems are actually of three different types. Although the method we present does *not* require that you be able to identify which type you are solving, it is helpful to know them. Each of the three types of percent problems depends on which of the three pieces of information is missing.

1. **Finding the** *amount* **(the result of taking the percent)**

   Example: What is 25% of 60?

   Translation: a = 25% · 60

2. **Finding the** *base* **(the number you are taking the percent of)**

   Example: 15 is 25% of what?

   Translation: 15 = 25% · b

3. **Finding the** *percent number* **(the percent itself)**

   Example: 15 is what percent of 60?

   Translation: 15 = p · 60

Finding the Amount

EXAMPLE 7   What is 17.9% of $14,660,000,000,000?

Translate: $a = 17.9\% \times 14{,}660{,}000{,}000{,}000$.

Solve: The letter is by itself. To solve the equation, we convert 17.9% to decimal notation and multiply:

$$a = 17.9\% \times 14{,}660{,}000{,}000{,}000$$
$$= 0.179 \times 14{,}660{,}000{,}000{,}000 = 2{,}624{,}140{,}000{,}000.$$

Thus, $2,624,140,000,000 is 17.9% of $14,660,000,000,000. The answer is $2,624,140,000,000, or about $2.6 trillion.

◀ **Do Exercise 7.**

EXAMPLE 8   120% of 42 is what?

Translate: $120\% \times 42 = a$.

Solve: The letter is by itself. To solve the equation, we carry out the calculation:

$$a = 120\% \times 42$$
$$a = 1.2 \times 42 \qquad 120\% = 1.2$$
$$a = 50.4.$$

Thus, 120% of 42 is 50.4. The answer is 50.4.

◀ **Do Exercise 8.**

7. Solve:

What is 12% of $50?

8. Solve:

64% of 55 is what?

Answers

7. $6   **8.** 35.2

Finding the Base

EXAMPLE 9 8% of what is 32?

Translate: 8% × b = 32.

Solve: This time the letter is *not* by itself. To solve the equation, we divide by 8% on both sides:

$$\frac{8\% \times b}{8\%} = \frac{32}{8\%} \quad \text{Dividing by 8\% on both sides}$$

$$b = \frac{32}{0.08} \quad 8\% = 0.08$$

$$b = 400.$$

Thus, 8% of 400 is 32. The answer is 400.

A survey of a group of people found that 8% of the group, or 32 people, chose cookies and cream as their favorite ice cream flavor. How many people were surveyed? (See Example 9.)
Source: Rasmussen Reports Survey

EXAMPLE 10 $3 is 16% of what?

Translate:

$$\begin{array}{ccccc} \$3 & \text{is} & 16\% & \text{of} & \text{what?} \\ \downarrow & \downarrow & \downarrow & \downarrow & \downarrow \\ 3 & = & 16\% & \times & b \end{array}$$

Solve: To solve the equation, we divide by 16% on both sides:

$$\frac{3}{16\%} = \frac{16\% \times b}{16\%} \quad \text{Dividing by 16\% on both sides}$$

$$\frac{3}{0.16} = b \quad 16\% = 0.16$$

$$18.75 = b.$$

Thus, $3 is 16% of $18.75. The answer is $18.75.

Do Exercises 9 and 10. ▶

Solve.

GS 9. 20% of what is 45?

$$\begin{array}{ccccc} 20\% & \text{of} & \text{what} & \text{is} & 45? \\ \downarrow & \downarrow & \downarrow & \downarrow & \downarrow \\ \boxed{}\% & \cdot & b & = & \boxed{} \end{array}$$

$$\frac{20\% \cdot b}{20\%} = \frac{45}{\boxed{}\%}$$

$$\boxed{} = \frac{45}{0.2}$$

$$b = \boxed{}$$

10. $60 is 120% of what?

Finding the Percent Number

In solving these problems, you *must* remember to convert to percent notation after you have solved the equation.

EXAMPLE 11 414,000 is what percent of 621,000?

Translate:

$$\begin{array}{ccccc} 414{,}000 & \text{is} & \text{what percent} & \text{of} & 621{,}000? \\ \downarrow & \downarrow & \downarrow & \downarrow & \downarrow \\ 414{,}000 & = & p & \times & 621{,}000 \end{array}$$

Solve: To solve the equation, we divide by 621,000 on both sides and convert the result to percent notation:

$$p \times 621{,}000 = 414{,}000$$

$$\frac{p \times 621{,}000}{621{,}000} = \frac{414{,}000}{621{,}000} \quad \text{Dividing by 621,000 on both sides}$$

$$p = 0.666\ldots \quad \text{Converting to decimal notation}$$

$$p = 66.\overline{6}\%, \text{ or } 66\tfrac{2}{3}\%. \quad \text{Converting to percent notation}$$

Thus, 414,000 is $66\tfrac{2}{3}\%$ of 621,000. The answer is $66\tfrac{2}{3}\%$.

In 2011, 621,000 new housing permits were issued in the United States. Of those new houses, 414,000 have porches. What percent of the houses have porches? (See Example 11.)
Source: U.S. Census Bureau

Answers
9. 225   10. $50
Guided Solution:
9. 20, 45, 20, *b*, 225

Solve.

11. 16 is what percent of 40?

16 is what percent of 40?

$$16 = p \cdot \boxed{}$$

$$\frac{16}{\boxed{}} = \frac{p \cdot \boxed{}}{40}$$

$$\frac{16}{40} = p$$

$$0.4 = p$$

$$\boxed{}\% = p$$

12. What percent of $84 is $10.50?

EXAMPLE 12 What percent of $50 is $16?

Translate: What percent of $50 is $16?

$$p \quad\quad \times \quad 50 \quad = \quad 16$$

Solve: To solve the equation, we divide by 50 on both sides and convert the answer to percent notation:

$$\frac{p \times 50}{50} = \frac{16}{50} \qquad \text{Dividing by 50 on both sides}$$

$$p = \frac{16}{50}$$

$$p = 0.32$$

$$p = 32\%. \qquad \text{Converting to percent notation}$$

Thus, 32% of $50 is $16. The answer is 32%.

◀ **Do Exercises 11 and 12.**

.... **Caution!** ....

When a question asks "what percent?", be sure to give the answer in percent notation.

....

CALCULATOR CORNER

Using Percents in Computations   Many calculators have a $\boxed{\%}$ key that can be used in computations. (See the Calculator Corner on page 384.) For example, to find 11% of 49, we press $\boxed{1}\,\boxed{1}\,\boxed{2\text{nd}}\,\boxed{\%}\,\boxed{\times}\,\boxed{4}\,\boxed{9}\,\boxed{=}$, or $\boxed{4}\,\boxed{9}\,\boxed{\times}\,\boxed{1}\,\boxed{1}\,\boxed{\text{SHIFT}}\,\boxed{\%}$. The display reads $\boxed{5.39}$, so 11% of 49 is 5.39.

In Example 9, we performed the computation 32/8%. To use the $\boxed{\%}$ key in this computation, we press $\boxed{3}\,\boxed{2}\,\boxed{\div}\,\boxed{8}\,\boxed{2\text{nd}}$ $\boxed{\%}\,\boxed{=}$, or $\boxed{3}\,\boxed{2}\,\boxed{\div}\,\boxed{8}\,\boxed{\text{SHIFT}}\,\boxed{\%}$. The result is 400.

We can also use the $\boxed{\%}$ key to find the percent number in a problem. In Example 11, for instance, we answered the question "414,000 is what percent of 621,000?" On a calculator, we press $\boxed{4}\,\boxed{1}\,\boxed{4}\,\boxed{0}\,\boxed{0}\,\boxed{0}\,\boxed{\div}\,\boxed{6}\,\boxed{2}\,\boxed{1}\,\boxed{0}\,\boxed{0}\,\boxed{0}\,\boxed{2\text{nd}}\,\boxed{\%}\,\boxed{=}$, or $\boxed{4}\,\boxed{1}\,\boxed{4}\,\boxed{0}\,\boxed{0}\,\boxed{0}\,\boxed{\div}\,\boxed{6}\,\boxed{2}\,\boxed{1}\,\boxed{0}\,\boxed{0}\,\boxed{0}\,\boxed{\text{SHIFT}}\,\boxed{\%}$. The result is 66.$\overline{6}$, so 414,000 is 66.$\overline{6}$% of 621,000.

EXERCISES   Use a calculator to find each of the following.

1. What is 12.6% of $40?

2. 0.04% of 28 is what?

3. 8% of what is 36?

4. $45 is 4.5% of what?

5. 23 is what percent of 920?

6. What percent of $442 is $53.04?

Answers

11. 40%   **12.** 12.5%

Guided Solution:

11. =, 40; 40, 40, 40

✓ Reading Check

Match each question with the correct translation from the list at the right.

RC1. 18 is 40% of what? _____

RC2. What percent of 45 is 18? _____

RC3. What is 40% of 45? _____

RC4. 0.5% of 1200 is what? _____

RC5. 6 is what percent of 1200? _____

RC6. 6 is 0.5% of what? _____

a) $6 = 0.5\% \cdot b$

b) $6 = p \cdot 1200$

c) $18 = 40\% \cdot b$

d) $0.5\% \cdot 1200 = a$

e) $p \cdot 45 = 18$

f) $a = 40\% \cdot 45$

a Translate to an equation. Do not solve.

1. What is 32% of 78?

2. 98% of 57 is what?

3. 89 is what percent of 99?

4. What percent of 25 is 8?

5. 13 is 25% of what?

6. 21.4% of what is 20?

b Translate to an equation and solve.

7. What is 85% of 276?

8. What is 74% of 53?

9. 150% of 30 is what?

10. 100% of 13 is what?

11. What is 6% of $300?

12. What is 4% of $45?

13. 3.8% of 50 is what?

14. $33\frac{1}{3}\%$ of 480 is what?
(*Hint*: $33\frac{1}{3}\% = \frac{1}{3}$.)

15. $39 is what percent of $50?

16. $16 is what percent of $90?

17. 20 is what percent of 10?

18. 60 is what percent of 20?

19. What percent of $300 is $150?

20. What percent of $50 is $40?

21. What percent of 80 is 100?

22. What percent of 60 is 15?

23. 20 is 50% of what?

24. 57 is 20% of what?

25. 40% of what is $16?

26. 100% of what is $74?

27. 56.32 is 64% of what?

28. 71.04 is 96% of what?

29. 70% of what is 14?

30. 70% of what is 35?

31. What is $62\frac{1}{2}$% of 10?

32. What is $35\frac{1}{4}$% of 1200?

33. What is 8.3% of $10,200?

34. What is 9.2% of $5600?

35. 2.5% of what is 30.4?

36. 8.2% of what is 328?

Skill Maintenance

Write fraction notation.   [5.1b]

37. −0.9375

38. 0.125

Write decimal notation.   [5.1b]

39. $\frac{3}{10}$

40. $-\frac{17}{1000}$

Simplify.   [1.9c]

41. $3 + (8 - 6) \cdot 2$

42. $2 \cdot 7 - (5 + 1)$

Synthesis

▦ Solve.

43. $2496 is 24% of what amount?

Estimate _____

Calculate _____

44. What is 38.2% of $52,345.79?

Estimate _____

Calculate _____

45. 40% of $18\frac{3}{4}$% of $25,000 is what?

Copyright © 2015 Pearson Education, Inc.

Solving Percent Problems Using Proportions*

a TRANSLATING TO PROPORTIONS

A percent is a ratio of some number to 100. For example, 5% is the ratio $\frac{5}{100}$. The numbers 7,700,000 and 154,000,000 have the same ratio as 5 and 100.

$$\frac{5}{100} = \frac{7,700,000}{154,000,000}$$

To solve a percent problem using a proportion, we translate as follows:

$$\text{Number} \longrightarrow \frac{N}{100} = \frac{a}{b} \longleftarrow \text{Amount} \atop \text{Base}$$
$$100 \longrightarrow$$

You might find it helpful to read this as "part is to whole as part is to whole."

For example, 60% of 25 is 15 translates to

$$\frac{60}{100} = \frac{15}{25} \begin{array}{l} \longleftarrow \text{Amount} \\ \longleftarrow \text{Base} \end{array}$$

A clue for translating is that the base, b, corresponds to 100 and usually follows the wording "percent of." Also, $N\%$ always translates to $N/100$. Another aid in translating is to make a comparison drawing. To do this, we start with the percent side and list 0% at the top and 100% near the bottom. Then we estimate where the specified percent—in this case, 60%—is located. The corresponding quantities are then filled in. The base—in this case, 25—always corresponds to 100%, and the amount—in this case, 15—corresponds to the specified percent.

The proportion can then be read easily from the drawing: $\frac{60}{100} = \frac{15}{25}$.

---

*Note: This section presents an alternative method for solving basic percent problems. You can use either equations or proportions to solve percent problems, but you might prefer one method over the other, or your instructor may direct you to use one method rather than the other.

OBJECTIVES

a Translate percent problems to proportions.

b Solve basic percent problems.

SKILL TO REVIEW

Objective 6.3b: Solve proportions.

Solve.

1. $\dfrac{3}{100} = \dfrac{27}{b}$

2. $\dfrac{4.3}{20} = \dfrac{N}{100}$

In the United States, 5% of the labor force is age 65 or older. In 2012, there were approximately 154,000,000 people in the labor force. This means that about 7,700,000 workers were age 65 or older.

Sources: U.S. Department of Labor; U.S. Bureau of Labor Statistics

Answers

Skill to Review:
1. 900 **2.** 21.5

EXAMPLE 1 Translate to a proportion.

23% of 5 is what?

$$\frac{23}{100} = \frac{a}{5}$$

EXAMPLE 2 Translate to a proportion.

What is 124% of 49?

$$\frac{124}{100} = \frac{a}{49}$$

Translate to a proportion. Do not solve.

1. 12% of 50 is what?

2. What is 40% of 60?

3. 130% of 72 is what?

◀ Do Exercises 1–3.

EXAMPLE 3 Translate to a proportion.

3 is 10% of what?

$$\frac{10}{100} = \frac{3}{b}$$

EXAMPLE 4 Translate to a proportion.

45% of what is 23?

$$\frac{45}{100} = \frac{23}{b}$$

Translate to a proportion. Do not solve.

4. 45 is 20% of what?

5. 120% of what is 60?

◀ Do Exercises 4 and 5.

EXAMPLE 5 Translate to a proportion.

10 is what percent of 20?

$$\frac{N}{100} = \frac{10}{20}$$

Answers

1. $\frac{12}{100} = \frac{a}{50}$ 2. $\frac{40}{100} = \frac{a}{60}$ 3. $\frac{130}{100} = \frac{a}{72}$

4. $\frac{20}{100} = \frac{45}{b}$ 5. $\frac{120}{100} = \frac{60}{b}$

EXAMPLE 6 Translate to a proportion.

What percent of 50 is 7?

$$\frac{N}{100} = \frac{7}{50}$$

Do Exercises 6 and 7. ▶

Translate to a proportion. Do not solve.

6. 16 is what percent of 40?

7. What percent of 84 is 10.5?

b SOLVING PERCENT PROBLEMS

After a percent problem has been translated to a proportion, we solve as in Section 6.3.

EXAMPLE 7 5% of what is $20?

Translate: $\dfrac{5}{100} = \dfrac{20}{b}$

Solve: $5 \cdot b = 100 \cdot 20$ Equating cross products

$\dfrac{5 \cdot b}{5} = \dfrac{100 \cdot 20}{5}$ Dividing by 5

$b = \dfrac{2000}{5}$

$b = 400$ Simplifying

Thus, 5% of $400 is $20. The answer is $400.

Do Exercise 8. ▶

 8. Solve: 20% of what is $45?

$$\frac{20}{\boxed{}} = \frac{\boxed{}}{b}$$

$$20 \cdot b = 100 \cdot \boxed{}$$

$$\frac{20 \cdot b}{20} = \frac{100 \cdot 45}{20}$$

$$b = \frac{4500}{20}$$

$$b = \boxed{}$$

EXAMPLE 8 120% of 42 is what?

Translate: $\dfrac{120}{100} = \dfrac{a}{42}$

Solve: $120 \cdot 42 = 100 \cdot a$ Equating cross products

$\dfrac{120 \cdot 42}{100} = \dfrac{100 \cdot a}{100}$ Dividing by 100

$\dfrac{5040}{100} = a$

$50.4 = a$ Simplifying

Thus, 120% of 42 is 50.4. The answer is 50.4.

Do Exercises 9 and 10. ▶

Solve.

9. 64% of 55 is what?

$$\frac{64}{100} = \frac{a}{\boxed{}}$$

$$\boxed{} \cdot 55 = 100 \cdot a$$

$$\frac{64 \cdot 55}{100} = \frac{100 \cdot a}{\boxed{}}$$

$$\frac{\boxed{}}{100} = a$$

$$\boxed{} = a$$

10. What is 12% of 50?

Answers

6. $\dfrac{N}{100} = \dfrac{16}{40}$ **7.** $\dfrac{N}{100} = \dfrac{10.5}{84}$ **8.** $225

9. 35.2   **10.** 6

Guided Solutions:

8. 100, 45, 45, 20, 225

9. 55, 64, 100, 3520, 35.2

EXAMPLE 9 210 is $10\frac{1}{2}$% of what?

Translate: $\dfrac{210}{b} = \dfrac{10.5}{100}$ $10\frac{1}{2}\% = 10.5\%$

Solve: $210 \cdot 100 = b \cdot 10.5$ Equating cross products

$\dfrac{210 \cdot 100}{10.5} = \dfrac{b \cdot 10.5}{10.5}$ Dividing by 10.5

$\dfrac{21{,}000}{10.5} = b$ Multiplying and simplifying

$2000 = b$ Dividing

Thus, 210 is $10\frac{1}{2}$% of 2000. The answer is 2000.

◀ **Do Exercise 11.**

11. Solve:

60 is 120% of what?

EXAMPLE 10 $10 is what percent of $20?

Translate: $\dfrac{10}{20} = \dfrac{N}{100}$

Solve: $10 \cdot 100 = 20 \cdot N$ Equating cross products

$\dfrac{10 \cdot 100}{20} = \dfrac{20 \cdot N}{20}$ Dividing by 20

$\dfrac{1000}{20} = N$ Multiplying and simplifying

$50 = N$ Dividing

Thus, $10 is 50% of $20. The answer is 50%.

> Note when solving percent problems using proportions that *N* is a percent and need not be converted.

12. Solve: **GS**

$12 is what percent of $40?

$\dfrac{12}{40} = \dfrac{N}{\boxed{}}$

$\boxed{} \cdot 100 = 40 \cdot N$

$\dfrac{12 \cdot 100}{\boxed{}} = \dfrac{40 \cdot N}{40}$

$\dfrac{\boxed{}}{40} = N$

$30 = N$

Thus, $12 is 30 $\boxed{}$ of $40.

◀ **Do Exercise 12.**

EXAMPLE 11 What percent of 50 is 16?

Translate: $\dfrac{N}{100} = \dfrac{16}{50}$

Solve: $50 \cdot N = 100 \cdot 16$ Equating cross products

$\dfrac{50 \cdot N}{50} = \dfrac{100 \cdot 16}{50}$ Dividing by 50

$N = \dfrac{1600}{50}$ Multiplying and simplifying

$N = 32$ Dividing

Thus, 32% of 50 is 16. The answer is 32%.

13. Solve:

What percent of 84 is 10.5?

◀ **Do Exercise 13.**

Answers

11. 50   **12.** 30%   **13.** 12.5%

Guided Solution:
12. 100, 12, 40, 1200; %

✓ Reading Check

Match each question with the correct translation from the list at the right.

RC1. 70 is 35% of what? _____

RC2. 70 is what percent of 200? _____

RC3. What is 35% of 200? _____

RC4. 74.8 is 110% of what? _____

RC5. What percent of 68 is 74.8? _____

RC6. 110% of 68 is what? _____

a) $\dfrac{110}{100} = \dfrac{a}{68}$

b) $\dfrac{70}{b} = \dfrac{35}{100}$

c) $\dfrac{a}{200} = \dfrac{35}{100}$

d) $\dfrac{74.8}{68} = \dfrac{N}{100}$

e) $\dfrac{70}{200} = \dfrac{N}{100}$

f) $\dfrac{74.8}{b} = \dfrac{110}{100}$

---

a Translate to a proportion. Do not solve.

1. What is 37% of 74?

2. 66% of 74 is what?

3. 4.3 is what percent of 5.9?

4. What percent of 6.8 is 5.3?

5. 14 is 25% of what?

6. 133% of what is 40?

---

b Translate to a proportion and solve.

7. What is 76% of 90?

8. What is 32% of 70?

9. 70% of 660 is what?

10. 80% of 920 is what?

11. What is 4% of 1000?

12. What is 6% of 2000?

13. 4.8% of 60 is what?

14. 63.1% of 80 is what?

15. $24 is what percent of $96?

16. $14 is what percent of $70?

17. 102 is what percent of 100?

18. 103 is what percent of 100?

19. What percent of $480 is $120?

20. What percent of $80 is $60?

21. What percent of 160 is 150?

22. What percent of 33 is 11?

23. $18 is 25% of what?

24. $75 is 20% of what?

25. 60% of what is 54?

26. 80% of what is 96?

27. 65.12 is 74% of what?

28. 63.7 is 65% of what?

29. 80% of what is 16?

30. 80% of what is 10?

31. What is $62\frac{1}{2}$% of 40?

32. What is $43\frac{1}{4}$% of 2600?

33. What is 9.4% of $8300?

34. What is 8.7% of $76,000?

35. 80.8 is $40\frac{2}{5}$% of what?

36. 66.3 is $10\frac{1}{5}$% of what?

Skill Maintenance

Solve. [6.3b]

37. $\dfrac{x}{188} = \dfrac{2}{47}$

38. $\dfrac{15}{x} = \dfrac{3}{800}$

39. $\dfrac{75}{100} = \dfrac{n}{20}$

40. $\dfrac{612}{t} = \dfrac{72}{244}$

Solve.

41. A recipe for muffins calls for $\frac{1}{2}$ qt of buttermilk, $\frac{1}{3}$ qt of skim milk, and $\frac{1}{16}$ qt of oil. How many quarts of liquid ingredients does the recipe call for? [4.2b]

42. The Ferristown School District purchased $\frac{3}{4}$ ton (T) of clay. If the clay is to be shared equally among the district's 6 art departments, how much will each art department receive? [3.7d]

Synthesis

Solve.

43. ▦ What is 8.85% of $12,640?

Estimate _____

Calculate _____

44. ▦ 78.8% of what is 9809.024?

Estimate _____

Calculate _____

Copyright © 2015 Pearson Education, Inc.

Mid-Chapter Review

Concept Reinforcement

Determine whether each statement is true or false.

_____ **1.** When converting decimal notation to percent notation, move the decimal point two places to the right and write a percent symbol.   [7.1b]

_____ **2.** The symbol % is equivalent to $\times$ 0.10.   [7.1a]

_____ **3.** Of the numbers $\frac{1}{10}$, 1%, 0.1%, and $\frac{1}{100}$ the smallest number is 0.1%.   [7.1b], [7.2a, b]

Guided Solutions

 Fill in each blank with the number that creates a correct statement or solution.   [7.1b], [7.2a,b]

4. $\frac{1}{2}\% = \frac{1}{2} \cdot \frac{1}{\square} = \frac{1}{\square}$

5. $\frac{80}{1000} = \frac{\square}{100} = \square\,\%$

6. $5.5\% = \frac{\square}{100} = \frac{\square}{1000} = \frac{11}{\square}$

7. $0.375 = \frac{\square}{1000} = \frac{\square}{100} = \square\,\%$

8. Solve: 15 is what percent of 80?   [7.3b]

$15 = p \times \square$ Translating

$\dfrac{15}{\square} = \dfrac{p \times \square}{\square}$ Dividing on both sides

$\dfrac{15}{\square} = p$ Simplifying

$\square = p$ Dividing

$\square\,\% = p$ Converting to percent notation

Mixed Review

Find decimal notation.   [7.1b]

9. 28%

10. 0.15%

.0015

11. $5\frac{3}{8}\%$

12. 240%

Find percent notation.   [7.1b], [7.2a]

13. 0.71

14. $\frac{9}{100}$

15. 0.3891

16. $\frac{3}{16}$

17. 0.005

18. $\frac{37}{50}$

19. 6

20. $\frac{5}{6}$

Find fraction notation. Simplify.   [7.2b]

21. 85%

22. 0.048%

23. $22\frac{3}{4}$%

24. $16.\overline{6}$%

Write percent notation for the shaded area.   [7.2a]

25.

Solve.   [7.3b], [7.4b]

27. 25% of what is 14.5?

26.

28. 220 is what percent of 1320?

29. What is 3.2% of 80,000?

30. $17.50 is 35% of what?

31. What percent of $800 is $160?

32. 130% of $350 is what?

33. Arrange the following numbers from smallest to largest.   [7.1b], [7.2a, b]

$$\frac{1}{2}\%, \ 5\%, \ 0.275, \ \frac{13}{100}, \ 1\%, \ 0.1\%, \ 0.05\%, \ \frac{3}{10}, \ \frac{7}{20}, \ 10\%$$

34. Solve: 8.5 is $2\frac{1}{2}$% of what?   [7.3b], [7.4b]

  A. 3.4   **B.** 21.25

  C. 0.2125   **D.** 340

35. Solve: $102,000 is what percent of $3.6 million?   [7.3b], [7.4b]

  A. $2.8\overline{3}$ million   **B.** $2\frac{5}{6}$%

  C. $0.028\overline{3}$%   **D.** $28.\overline{3}$%

Understanding Through Discussion and Writing

36. Is it always best to convert from fraction notation to percent notation by first finding decimal notation? Why or why not?   [7.2a]

37. Suppose we know that 40% of 92 is 36.8. What is a quick way to find 4% of 92? 400% of 92? Explain.   [7.3b]

38. In solving Example 10 in Section 7.4 a student simplifies $\frac{10}{20}$ before solving. Is this a good idea? Why or why not?   [7.4b]

39. What do the following have in common? Explain.   [7.1b], [7.2a, b]

$$\frac{23}{16}, \ 1\frac{875}{2000}, \ 1.4375, \ \frac{207}{144}, \ 1\frac{7}{16}, \ 143.75\%, \ 1\frac{4375}{10,000}$$

Copyright © 2015 Pearson Education, Inc.

STUDYING FOR SUCCESS *Make the Most of Your Time in Class*

☐ Before each class, try to at least glance at the section in your text that will be covered, so you can concentrate on the instruction in class.

☐ Get a great seat! Sitting near the front will help you hear instruction more clearly and avoid distractions.

☐ Let your instructor know in advance if you must miss class, and do your best to keep up with any work that you miss.

Applications of Percent

7.5

a APPLIED PROBLEMS INVOLVING PERCENT

Applied problems involving percent are not always stated in a manner easily translated to an equation. In such cases, it is helpful to rephrase the problem before translating. Sometimes it also helps to make a drawing.

EXAMPLE 1 *Transportation to Work.* In the United States, there are about 154,000,000 workers who are 16 years old or older. Approximately 76.1% of these workers drive to work alone. How many workers drive to work alone?

Transportation to Work in the United States

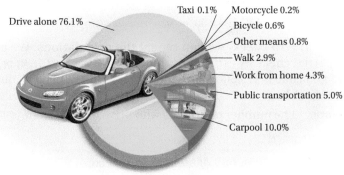

Drive alone 76.1%
Taxi 0.1%
Motorcycle 0.2%
Bicycle 0.6%
Other means 0.8%
Walk 2.9%
Work from home 4.3%
Public transportation 5.0%
Carpool 10.0%

SOURCE: U.S. Bureau of Labor Statistics

OBJECTIVES

a Solve applied problems involving percent.

b Solve applied problems involving percent increase or percent decrease.

SKILL TO REVIEW

Objective 5.4a: Divide using decimal notation.

Divide.
1. $345 \div 57.5$
2. $111.87 \div 9.9$

1. **Familiarize.** We can simplify the pie chart shown above to help familiarize ourselves with the problem. We let a = the total number of workers who drive to work alone.

Transportation to Work in the United States

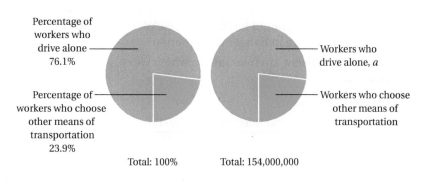

Percentage of workers who drive alone 76.1%

Percentage of workers who choose other means of transportation 23.9%

Total: 100%

Workers who drive alone, a

Workers who choose other means of transportation

Total: 154,000,000

Answers
Skill to Review:
1. 6   **2.** 11.3

2. Translate. There are two ways in which we can translate this problem.

Percent equation (see Section 7.3):

$$\underbrace{\text{What number}}_{a} \ \underset{=}{\text{is}} \ \underbrace{\overset{\downarrow}{76.1\%}}_{76.1\%} \ \underset{\cdot}{\text{of}} \ \underbrace{154{,}000{,}000?}_{154{,}000{,}000}$$

Proportion (see Section 7.4):

$$\frac{76.1}{100} = \frac{a}{154{,}000{,}000}$$

3. Solve. We now have two ways in which to solve the problem.

Percent equation (see Section 7.3):

$$a = 76.1\% \cdot 154{,}000{,}000$$

We convert 76.1% to decimal notation and multiply:

$$a = 0.761 \times 154{,}000{,}000 = 117{,}194{,}000.$$

Proportion (see Section 7.4):

$$\frac{76.1}{100} = \frac{a}{154{,}000{,}000}$$

$$76.1 \times 154{,}000{,}000 = 100 \cdot a \qquad \text{\small Equating cross products}$$

$$\frac{76.1 \cdot 154{,}000{,}000}{100} = \frac{100 \cdot a}{100} \qquad \text{\small Dividing by 100}$$

$$\frac{11{,}719{,}400{,}000}{100} = a$$

$$117{,}194{,}000 = a \qquad \text{\small Simplifying}$$

4. Check. To check, we can repeat the calculations. We also can do a partial check by estimating. Since 76.1% is about 75%, or $\frac{3}{4}$, and $\frac{3}{4}$ of 154,000,000 is 115,500,000, which is close to 117,194,000, our answer is reasonable.

5. State. The number of workers who drive to work alone is 117,194,000.

◀ **Do Exercise 1.**

EXAMPLE 2 *Extinction of Mammals.* According to a study conducted for the International Union for the Conservation of Nature (IUCN), the world's mammals are in danger of an extinction crisis. Of the 5501 species of mammals on Earth, 1139 are on IUCN "vulnerable," "endangered," or "critically endangered" lists. What percent of all mammals are threatened with extinction?

1. Familiarize. The question asks for a percent of the world's mammals that are in danger of extinction. We note that 5501 is approximately 5500 and 1139 is approximately 1100. Since 1100 is $\frac{1100}{5500}$, or $\frac{1}{5}$, or 20% of 5500, our answer should be close to 20%. We let $p = $ the percent of mammals that are in danger of extinction.

2. Translate. There are two ways in which we can translate this problem.

Percent equation:

$$\underbrace{1139}_{1139} \ \underset{=}{\text{is}} \ \underbrace{\overset{\downarrow}{\text{what percent}}}_{p} \ \underset{\cdot}{\text{of}} \ \underbrace{5501}_{5501}$$

---

1. *Transportation to Work.* There are about 154,000,000 workers 16 years old or older in the United States. Approximately 10.0% of them carpool to work. How many workers carpool to work?

Sources: U.S. Census Bureau; American Community Survey

Answer

1. 15,400,000

Mammals that are in danger of extinction include those shown here: Barbary macaque, black rhino, Galápagos seal, Malayan tapir, Cuvier's gazelle, Darwin's fox, and indri (a lemur).

Proportion:

$$\frac{N}{100} = \frac{1139}{5501}$$

For proportions, $N\% = p$.

3. Solve.   We now have two ways in which to solve the problem.

Percent equation:

$$1139 = p \cdot 5501$$

$$\frac{1139}{5501} = \frac{p \cdot 5501}{5501} \quad \text{Dividing by 5501 on both sides}$$

$$\frac{1139}{5501} = p$$

$$0.207 \approx p \qquad \text{Finding decimal notation and rounding to the nearest thousandth}$$

$$20.7\% = p \qquad \text{Remember to find percent notation.}$$

Note here that the solution, p, includes the % symbol.

Proportion:

$$\frac{N}{100} = \frac{1139}{5501}$$

$$N \cdot 5501 = 100 \cdot 1139 \qquad \text{Equating cross products}$$

$$\frac{N \cdot 5501}{5501} = \frac{113{,}900}{5501} \qquad \text{Dividing by 5501 on both sides}$$

$$N = \frac{113{,}900}{5501}$$

$$N \approx 20.7 \qquad \text{Dividing and rounding to the nearest tenth}$$

We use the solution of the proportion to express the answer to the problem as 20.7%. Note that in the proportion method, $N\% = p$.

4. Check.   To check, we note that the answer 20.7% is close to 20%, as estimated in the *Familiarize* step.

5. State.   About 20.7% of the world's mammals are threatened with extinction.

Do Exercise 2. ▶

The percent-quantity scale:

Percents	Quantities
0%	0
$N\%$	1139
100%	5501

2. Presidential Assassinations in Office.   Of the 43 different U.S. presidents, 4 have been assassinated while in office. These were James A. Garfield, William McKinley, Abraham Lincoln, and John F. Kennedy. What percent have been assassinated in office?

Answer

2. About 9.3%

b PERCENT INCREASE OR DECREASE

Percent is often used to state an increase or a decrease. Let's consider an example of each, using the price of a car as the original number.

Percent Increase

One year a car sold for $20,455. The manufacturer decides to raise the price of the following year's model by 6%. The increase is 0.06 × $20,455, or $1227.30. The new price is $20,455 + $1227.30, or $21,682.30. Note that the *new* price is 106% of the *former* price.

The increase, $1227.30, is 6% of the *former* price, $20,455. The *percent increase* is 6%.

Percent Decrease

Abigail buys the car listed above for $20,455. After one year, the car depreciates in value by 25%. The decrease is 0.25 × $20,455, or $5113.75. This lowers the value of the car to $20,455 − $5113.75, or $15,341.25. Note that the new value is 75% of the original price. If Abigail decides to sell the car after one year, $15,341.25 might be the most she could expect to get for it.

The decrease, $5113.75, is 25% of the *original* price, $20,455. The *percent decrease* is 25%.

◀ **Do Exercises 3 and 4.**

When a quantity is decreased by a certain percent, we say that this is a **percent decrease**.

EXAMPLE 3 *Dow Jones Industrial Average.* The Dow Jones Industrial Average (DJIA) plunged from 11,143 to 10,365 on September 29, 2008. This was the largest one-day drop in its history. What was the percent decrease?
Sources: *Nightly Business Reports*, September 29, 2008; DJIA

New price: $21,682.30

Increase ↑

Former price: $20,455

Original price: $20,455

Decrease ↓

New value: $15,341.25

3. *Percent Increase.* The price of a car is $36,875. The price is increased by 4%.

   a) How much is the increase?

   b) What is the new price?

4. *Percent Decrease.* The value of a car is $36,875. The car depreciates in value by 25% after one year.

   a) How much is the decrease?

   b) What is the depreciated value of the car?

Answers

3. (a) $1475; (b) $38,350
4. (a) $9218.75; (b) $27,656.25

1. Familiarize. We first determine the amount of decrease and then make a drawing.

11,143	Opening average
−10,365	Closing average
778	Decrease

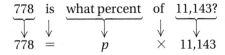

We are asking this question: The decrease is what percent of the opening average? We let p = the percent decrease.

2. Translate. There are two ways in which we can translate this problem.

Percent equation:

$$\underbrace{778}_{} \quad \underbrace{\text{is}}_{} \quad \underbrace{\text{what percent}}_{} \quad \underbrace{\text{of}}_{} \quad \underbrace{11{,}143?}_{}$$
$$778 \quad = \quad\quad p \quad\quad \times \quad 11{,}143$$

Proportion:

$$\frac{N}{100} = \frac{778}{11{,}143}$$

For proportion, $N\% = p$.

3. Solve. We have two ways in which to solve the problem.

Percent equation:

$$778 = p \times 11{,}143$$

$$\frac{778}{11{,}143} = \frac{p \times 11{,}143}{11{,}143} \qquad \text{Dividing by 11,143 on both sides}$$

$$\frac{778}{11{,}143} = p$$

$$0.07 \approx p$$

$$7\% = p \qquad \text{Converting to percent notation}$$

Proportion:

$$\frac{N}{100} = \frac{778}{11{,}143}$$

$$11{,}143 \times N = 100 \times 778 \qquad \text{Equating cross products}$$

$$\frac{11{,}143 \times N}{11{,}143} = \frac{100 \times 778}{11{,}143} \qquad \text{Dividing by 11,143 on both sides}$$

$$N = \frac{77{,}800}{11{,}143}$$

$$N \approx 7$$

We use the solution of the proportion to express the answer to the problem as 7%.

5. _Volume of Mail._ The volume of U.S mail decreased from about 102,379 million pieces of mail in 2002 to 68,696 million pieces in 2012. What was the percent decrease?

Source: U.S. Postal Service

4. Check. To check, we note that, with a 7% decrease, the closing Dow average should be 93% of the opening average. Since

$$93\% \times 11{,}143 = 0.93 \times 11{,}143 \approx 10{,}363,$$

and 10,363 is close to 10,365, our answer checks. (Remember that we rounded to get 7%.)

5. State. The percent decrease in the DJIA was approximately 7%.

◀ **Do Exercise 5.**

When a quantity is increased by a certain percent, we say that this is a **percent increase**.

EXAMPLE 4 _Costs for Moviegoers._ The average cost of a movie ticket was $5.80 in 2002. The cost rose to $8.12 in 2012. What was the percent increase in the cost of a movie ticket?

Sources: National Association of Theatre Owners; theaterseatstore.com

1. **Familiarize.** We first determine the increase in the cost and then make a drawing.

$$
\begin{array}{rl}
\$8.12 & \text{Cost in 2012} \\
-\ 5.80 & \text{Cost in 2002} \\
\hline
\$2.32 & \text{Increase}
\end{array}
$$

We are asking this question: The increase is what percent of the _original_ cost? We let p = the percent increase.

2. **Translate.** There are two ways in which we can translate this problem.

Percent equation:

$$
\underbrace{2.32}_{2.32} \quad \underbrace{\text{is}}_{=} \quad \underbrace{\text{what percent}}_{p} \quad \underbrace{\text{of}}_{\cdot} \quad \underbrace{5.80?}_{5.80}
$$

Proportion:

$$\frac{N}{100} = \frac{2.32}{5.80}$$

For proportions, $N\% = p$.

Answer

5. About 32.9%

3. Solve. We have two ways in which to solve the problem.

Percent equation:

$$2.32 = p \times 5.80$$

$$\frac{2.32}{5.80} = \frac{p \times 5.80}{5.80} \qquad \text{Dividing by 5.80 on both sides}$$

$$\frac{2.32}{5.80} = p$$

$$0.4 = p$$

$$40\% = p \qquad \text{Converting to percent notation}$$

Proportion:

$$\frac{N}{100} = \frac{2.32}{5.80}$$

$$5.80 \times N = 100 \times 2.32 \qquad \text{Equating cross products}$$

$$\frac{5.80 \times N}{5.80} = \frac{100 \times 2.32}{5.80} \qquad \text{Dividing by 5.80 on both sides}$$

$$N = \frac{232}{5.80}$$

$$N = 40$$

We use the solution of the proportion to express the answer to the problem as 40%.

4. Check. To check, we take 40% of 5.80:

$$40\% \times 5.80 = 0.40 \times 5.80 = 2.32.$$

This is the amount of the increase in the price of a movie ticket, so the answer checks.

5. State. The percent increase in the cost of a movie ticket was 40%.

Do Exercise 6. ▶

6. *Centenarians.* As of April 1, 2010, the number of centenarians in the United States was 53,364. It is projected that this number will increase to 601,000 by 2050. What is the projected percent increase?

Sources: *National Geographic,* November 2011; Population Reference Bureau, U.S. Census Bureau

Answer

6. About 1026%

Translating
for Success

1. *Distance Walked.* After a knee replacement, Alex walked $\frac{1}{8}$ mi each morning and $\frac{1}{5}$ mi each afternoon. How much farther did he walk in the afternoon?

2. *Stock Prices.* A stock sold for $5 per share on Monday and only $2.125 per share on Friday. What was the percent decrease from Monday to Friday?

3. *SAT Score.* After attending a class titled *Improving Your SAT Scores,* Jacob raised his total score from 884 to 1040. What was the percent increase?

4. *Change in Population.* The population of a small farming community decreased from 1040 to 884. What was the percent decrease?

5. *Lawn Mowing.* During the summer, brothers Steve and Rob earned money for college by mowing lawns. The largest lawn that they mowed was $2\frac{1}{8}$ acres. Steve can mow $\frac{1}{5}$ acre per hour, and Rob can mow only $\frac{1}{8}$ acre per hour. Working together, how many acres did they mow per hour?

The goal of these matching questions is to practice step (2), *Translate, of* the five-step problem-solving process. Translate each word problem to an equation and select a correct translation from equations A–O.

A. $x + \dfrac{1}{5} = \dfrac{1}{8}$

B. $250 = x \cdot 1040$

C. $884 = x \cdot 1040$

D. $\dfrac{250}{16.25} = \dfrac{1000}{x}$

E. $156 = x \cdot 1040$

F. $16.25 = 250 \cdot x$

G. $\dfrac{1}{5} + \dfrac{1}{8} = x$

H. $2\dfrac{1}{8} = x \cdot 5$

I. $5 = 2.875 \cdot x$

J. $\dfrac{1}{8} + x = \dfrac{1}{5}$

K. $1040 = x \cdot 884$

L. $\dfrac{250}{16.25} = \dfrac{x}{1000}$

M. $2.875 = x \cdot 5$

N. $x \cdot 884 = 156$

O. $x = 16.25 \cdot 250$

Answers on page A-12

6. *Land Sale.* Cole sold $2\frac{1}{8}$ acres of the 5 acres he inherited from his uncle. What percent of his land did he sell?

7. *Travel Expenses.* A magazine photographer is reimbursed 16.25¢ per mile for business travel, up to 1000 mi per week. In a recent week, he traveled 250 mi. What was the total reimbursement for travel?

8. *Trip Expenses.* The total expenses for Claire's recent business trip were $1040. She put $884 on her credit card and paid the balance in cash. What percent did she place on her credit card?

9. *Cost of Copies.* During the first summer session at a community college, the campus copy center advertised 250 copies for $16.25. At this rate, what is the cost of 1000 copies?

10. *Cost of Insurance.* Following a rise in the cost of health insurance, 250 of a company's 1040 employees canceled their insurance. What percent of the employees canceled their insurance?

✓ Reading Check

Complete the table by filling in the missing numbers.

	Original Price	New Price	Change	Percent Increase or Decrease
RC1.	$50	$40	$ _____	$\dfrac{\text{Change}}{\text{Original}} = \dfrac{\$}{\$} = \_\_\_\_ \%$
RC2.	$60	$75	$ _____	$\dfrac{\text{Change}}{\text{Original}} = \dfrac{\$}{\$} = \_\_\_\_ \%$
RC3.	$360	$480	$ _____	$\dfrac{\text{Change}}{\text{Original}} = \dfrac{\$}{\$} = \_\_\_\_ \%$
RC4.	$4000	$2400	$ _____	$\dfrac{\text{Change}}{\text{Original}} = \dfrac{\$}{\$} = \_\_\_\_ \%$

a   Solve.

1. *Winnings from Gambling.* Pre-tax gambling winnings were $417 billion worldwide in 2012. Approximately 25.1% of the winnings were in the United States and 5.9% were in Italy. About how much, in dollars, were the gambling winnings in each country?

Source: H2 Gambling Capital (h2gc.com)

2. *Mississippi River.* The Mississippi River, which extends from its source, at Lake Itasca in Minnesota, to the Gulf of Mexico, is 2348 mi long. Approximately 77% of the river is navigable. How many miles of the river are navigable?

Source: National Oceanic and Atmospheric Administration

Mississippi River

3. A person earns $43,200 one year and receives an 8% raise in salary. What is the new salary?

4. A person earns $28,600 one year and receives a 5% raise in salary. What is the new salary?

5. *Test Results.* On a test, Juan got 85%, or 119, of the items correct. How many items were on the test?

6. *Test Results.* On a test, Maj Ling got 86%, or 43, of the items correct. How many items were on the test?

7. *Farmland.* In Kansas, 47,000,000 acres are farmland. About 5% of all the farm acreage in the United States is in Kansas. What is the total number of acres of farmland in the United States?

Sources: U.S. Department of Agriculture; National Agricultural Statistics Service

8. 🖩 *World Population.* World population is increasing by 1.2% each year. In 2008, it was 6.68 billion. What will the population be in 2015?

Sources: U.S. Census Bureau; International Data Base

9. *Car Depreciation.* A car generally depreciates 25% of its original value in the first year. A car is worth $27,300 after the first year. What was its original cost?

10. *Car Depreciation.* Given normal use, an American-made car will depreciate 25% of its original cost the first year and 14% of its remaining value in the second year. What is the value of a car at the end of the second year if its original cost was $36,400? $28,400? $26,800?

11. *Test Results.* On a test of 80 items, Pedro got 95% correct. How many items did he get correct? incorrect?

12. *Test Results.* On a test of 40 items, Christina got 80% correct. How many items did she get correct? incorrect?

13. *Olympic Team.* The 2012 U.S. Summer Olympics team consisted of 529 members. Approximately 49.3% of the athletes were men. How many men were on the team?

Source: United States Olympic Committee

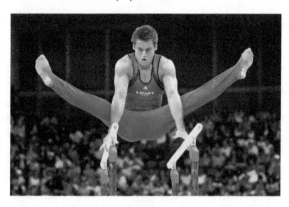

14. *Murder Case Costs.* The cost (for both trial and incarceration) of a life-without-parole case is about 30% of the cost of a death-penalty case. The average cost of a death-penalty case is $505,773. What is the average cost of a life-without-parole case?

Source: Indiana Legislative Services Agency, *2010 Study of Murder Trials*

15. *Spending on Pets.* In 2011, Americans spent approximately $50.8 billion on their pets. Of this amount, $14.1 billion was for veterinarian bills. What percent of the total was spent on veterinary care?

Source: American Pet Products Association

16. *Health Workers' Salaries.* In 2010, the median annual salary of registered nurses was $64,690. The median annual salary of physicians and surgeons was $111,570. What percent of the physician and surgeon's median annual salary is the nurses' median annual salary?

Source: Bureau of Labor Statistics

17. *Tipping.* For a party of 8 or more, some restaurants add an 18% tip to the bill. What is the total amount charged for a party of 10 if the cost of the meal, without tip, is $195?

18. *Tipping.* Diners frequently add a 15% tip when charging a meal to a credit card. What is the total amount charged to a card if the cost of the meal, without tip, is $18? $34? $49?

Copyright © 2015 Pearson Education, Inc.

19. *Wasting Food.* As world population increases and the number of acres of farmland decreases, improvements in food production and packaging must be implemented. Also, wealthy countries need to waste less food. In the United States, consumers waste 39 lb of every 131 lb of fruit purchased. What percent is wasted?

Sources: United States Department of Agriculture; *National Geographic*, July 2011

21. A lab technician has 540 mL of a solution of alcohol and water; 8% is alcohol. How many milliliters are alcohol? water?

23. *U.S. Armed Forces.* There were 1,384,000 people in the United States in active military service in 2006. The numbers in the four armed services are listed in the table below. What percent of the total does each branch represent? Round the answers to the nearest tenth of a percent.

U.S. ARMED FORCES: 2006

TOTAL	1,384,000*
AIR FORCE	349,000
ARMY	505,000
NAVY	350,000
MARINES	180,000

*Includes National Guard, Reserve, and retired regular personnel on extended or continuous active duty. Excludes Coast Guard.

SOURCES: U.S. Department of Defense; U.S. Census Bureau

20. *Credit-Card Debt.* Michael has disposable monthly income of $3400. Each month, he pays $470 toward his credit-card debt. What percent of his disposable income is allotted to paying off credit-card debt?

Monthly Disposable Income: $3400

Credit-card payments: $470

22. A lab technician has 680 mL of a solution of water and acid; 3% is acid. How many milliliters are acid? water?

24. *Living Veterans.* There were 23,977,000 living veterans in the United States in 2006. Numbers in various age groups are listed in the table below. What percent of the total does each age group represent? Round the answers to the nearest tenth of a percent.

LIVING VETERANS BY AGE: 2006

TOTAL	23,977,000
UNDER 35 YEARS OLD	1,949,000
35–44 YEARS OLD	2,901,000
45–54 YEARS OLD	3,846,000
55–64 YEARS OLD	6,081,000
65 YEARS OLD AND OLDER	9,200,000

SOURCES: U.S. Department of Defense; U.S. Census Bureau

b Solve.

25. *Mortgage Payment Increase.* A monthly mortgage payment increases from $840 to $882. What is the percent increase?

26. *Savings Increase.* The amount in a savings account increased from $200 to $216. What was the percent increase?

27. A person on a diet goes from a weight of 160 lb to a weight of 136 lb. What is the percent decrease?

28. During a sale, a dress decreased in price from $90 to $72. What was the percent decrease?

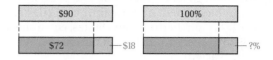

29. *Insulation.* A roll of unfaced fiberglass insulation has a retail price of $23.43. For two weeks, it is on sale for $15.31. What is the percent decrease?

30. *Set of Weights.* A 300-lb weight set retails for $199.95. For its grand opening, a sporting goods store reduced the price to $154.95. What is the percent decrease?

31. *Birds Killed.* In 2009, approximately 440,000 birds were killed by wind turbines in the United States. It is estimated that this number will increase to 1,000,000 per year by 2020. What would the percent increase be?

Sources: National Wind Coordinating Collaborative; American Bird Conservancy; U.S. Fish and Wildlife Service

32. *Miles of Railroad Track.* The greatest combined length of U.S.-owned operating railroad track was 254,037 mi in 1916, when industrial activity increased during World War I. The total length has decreased ever since. By 2006, the number of miles of track had decreased to 140,490 mi. What was the percent decrease from 1916 to 2006?

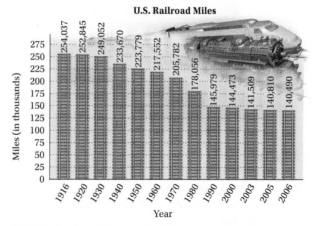

U.S. Railroad Miles

NOTE: The lengths exclude yard tracks, sidings, and parallel tracks.
SOURCE: Association of American Railroads

Copyright © 2015 Pearson Education, Inc.

33. *Overdraft Fees.* Consumers are paying record amounts of fees for overdrawing their bank accounts. In 2007, banks, thrift institutions, and credit unions collected $45.6 billion in overdraft fees, which is $15.1 billion more than in 2001. What was the percent increase?

Source: Moebs Services

34. *Credit-Card Debt.* In 2013, the average credit-card debt per household in the United States was $15,162. In 1990, the average credit-card debt was $2966. What was the percent increase?

Sources: nerdwallet.com

35. *Population over 1 Million.* In 1950, 74 cities in the world had populations of 1 million or more. In 2010, 442 cities had populations of 1 million or more. What was the percent increase?

Sources: *World Cities*, George Modelski; United Nations

36. *Prescription Drug Sales.* Total spending on prescription drugs in the United States was $329.2 billion in 2011. This amount dropped to $325.8 billion in 2012. What was the percent decrease?

Source: IMS Institute for Healthcare Informatics

37. *Patents Issued.* The U.S. Patent and Trademark Office (USPTO) issued a total of 157,284 utility patents in 2007. This number of patents was down from 173,794 in 2006. What was the percent decrease?

Source: IFI Patent Intelligence

38. *Highway Fatalities.* In 2007, there were 41,059 highway fatalities in the United States, which was 1649 fewer than the number in 2006. What was in the percent decrease?

Source: National Highway Traffic Safety Administration

39. *Two-by-Four.* A cross-section of a standard, or nominal, "two-by-four" actually measures $1\frac{1}{2}$ in. by $3\frac{1}{2}$ in. The rough board is 2 in. by 4 in. but is planed and dried to the finished size. What percent of the wood is removed in planing and drying?

40. *Strike Zone.* In baseball, the *strike zone* is normally a 17-in. by 30-in. rectangle. Some batters give the pitcher an advantage by swinging at pitches thrown out of the strike zone. By what percent is the area of the strike zone increased if a 2-in. border is added to the outside?

Source: Major League Baseball

Population Increase. The table below provides data showing how the populations of various states increased from 2000 to 2010. Complete the table by filling in the missing numbers. Round percents to the nearest tenth of a percent.

	State	Population in 2000	Population in 2010	Change	Percent Change
41.	Vermont	608,827	625,741		
42.	Wisconsin	5,363,675		323,311	
43.	Arizona		6,392,017	1,261,385	
44.	Virginia		8,001,024	922,509	
45.	Idaho	1,293,953		273,629	
46.	Georgia	8,186,453	9,535,483		

SOURCE: U.S. Census Bureau

47. *Increase in Population.* Between 2000 and 2010, the population of Utah increased from 2,233,169 to 2,763,885. What was the percent increase?

Sources: U.S. Census Bureau; U.S. Department of Commerce

48. *Decrease in Population.* Between 2000 and 2010, the population of Michigan decreased from 9,938,444 to 9,883,640. What was the percent decrease?

Sources: U.S. Census Bureau; U.S. Department of Commerce

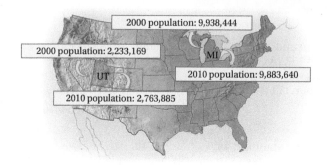

2000 population: 9,938,444
2000 population: 2,233,169
2010 population: 9,883,640
UT
MI
2010 population: 2,763,885

Skill Maintenance

Convert to decimal notation.   [5.1b], [5.5a]

49. $\dfrac{25}{11}$

50. $\dfrac{11}{25}$

51. $-\dfrac{27}{8}$

52. $\dfrac{43}{9}$

Simplify.   [3.5b]

53. $\dfrac{18}{102}$

54. $-\dfrac{135}{510}$

55. $\dfrac{192}{1000}$

56. $\dfrac{70}{406}$

Synthesis

57. A coupon allows a couple to have $10 subtracted from their dinner bill. Before subtracting $10, however, the restaurant adds a tip of 20%. If the couple is presented with a bill for $40.40, how much would the dinner (without tip) have cost without the coupon?

58. If p is 120% of q, then q is what percent of p?

Copyright © 2015 Pearson Education, Inc.

Sales Tax, Commission, and Discount

a SALES TAX

Sales tax computations represent a special type of percent increase problem. The sales tax rate in Colorado is 2.9%. This means that the tax is 2.9% of the purchase price. Suppose the purchase price of a canoe is $749.95. The sales tax is then 2.9% of $749.95, or $0.029 \times \$749.95$, or $21.74855, which is about $21.75.

COLORADO

$749.95
+2.9% sales tax

BILL:

Purchase price	= $749.95
Sales tax (2.9% of $749.95)	= + 21.75
Total price	$771.70

The total that you would pay for the canoe is the purchase price plus the sales tax:

$$\$749.95 + \$21.75, \text{ or } \$771.70.$$

SALES TAX

Sales tax = Sales tax rate $\times$ Purchase price

Total price = Purchase price + Sales tax

EXAMPLE 1 *Maine Sales Tax.* The sales tax rate in Maine is 5%. How much tax is charged on the purchase of 3 shrubs at $42.99 each? What is the total price?

a) We first find the purchase price of the 3 shrubs. It is

$$3 \times \$42.99 = \$128.97.$$

b) The sales tax on items costing $128.97 is

$$\underbrace{\text{Sales tax rate}}_{5\%} \times \underbrace{\text{Purchase price}}_{128.97},$$

or 0.05×128.97, or 6.4485. Thus the tax is $6.45 (rounded to the nearest cent).

Maine

$42.99 each
plus 5% sales tax

c) The total price is given by the purchase price plus the sales tax:

$$\$128.97 + \$6.45, \text{ or } \$135.42.$$

To check, note that the total price is the purchase price plus 5% of the purchase price. Thus the total price is 105% of the purchase price. Since $1.05 \times 128.97 \approx 135.42$, we have a check. The sales tax is $6.45, and the total price is $135.42.

1. *Texas Sales Tax.* The sales tax rate in Texas is 6.25%. In Texas, how much tax is charged on the purchase of an ultrasound toothbrush that sells for $139.95? What is the total price?

2. **Wyoming Sales Tax.** In her hometown, Laramie, Wyoming, Samantha buys 4 copies of *It's All Good* by Gwyneth Paltrow for $18.95 each. The sales tax rate in Wyoming is 4%. How much sales tax will Samantha be charged? What is the total price?

 GS

Sales tax = ☐ % × 4 × $ ☐

= 0.04 × $ ☐

= $3.032

≈ $ ☐

Total price = $75.80 + $ ☐

= $ ☐

3. The sales tax on the purchase of a set of holiday dishes that costs $449 is $26.94. What is the sales tax rate?

4. The sales tax on the purchase of a pair of designer jeans is $4.84 and the sales tax rate is 5.5%. Find the purchase price (the price before the tax is added).

Answers

1. $8.75; $148.70   2. $3.03, $78.83
3. 6%   4. $88

Guided Solution:
2. 4, 18.95, 75.80, 3.03; 3.03, 78.83

◀ **Do Exercises 1 and 2.**

EXAMPLE 2 The sales tax on the purchase of an eReader that costs $199 is $13.93. What is the sales tax rate?

$199.00
plus $13.93
sales tax

We rephrase and translate as follows:

Rephrase: Sales tax is what percent of purchase price?

Translate: $13.93 = r × 199.

To solve the equation, we divide by 199 on both sides:

$$\frac{13.93}{199} = \frac{r \times 199}{199}$$

$$\frac{13.93}{199} = r$$

$$0.07 = r$$

$$7\% = r.$$

The sales tax rate is 7%.

◀ **Do Exercise 3.**

EXAMPLE 3 The sales tax on the purchase of a stone-top firepit is $12.74 and the sales tax rate is 8%. Find the purchase price (the price before the tax is added).

We rephrase and translate as follows:

Rephrase: Sales tax is 8% of what?

Translate: 12.74 = 8% × b,

or $12.74 = 0.08 \times b.$

To solve, we divide by 0.08 on both sides:

$$\frac{12.74}{0.08} = \frac{0.08 \times b}{0.08}$$

$$\frac{12.74}{0.08} = b$$

$$159.25 = b.$$

The purchase price is $159.25.

Price: ?
$12.74 tax @ 8%

◀ **Do Exercise 4.**

b COMMISSION

When you work for a **salary**, you receive the same amount of money each week or month. When you work for a **commission**, you are paid a percentage of the total sales for which you are responsible.

> ### COMMISSION
>
> **Commission** = Commission rate × Sales

EXAMPLE 4 *Membership Sales.* A membership salesperson at a fitness club has a commission rate of 3%. What is the commission on the sale of $8300 worth of memberships?

Commission rate **3%**

WHOLE FITNESS

$$Commission = Commission\ rate \times Sales$$
$$C = 3\% \times 8300$$
$$C = 0.03 \times 8300$$
$$C = 249$$

The commission is $249.

Do Exercise 5. ▶

5. Aniyah's commission rate is 15%. What commission does she earn on the sale of $9260 worth of exercise equipment?

EXAMPLE 5 *Earth-Moving Equipment Sales.* Gavin earns a commission of $20,800 for selling $320,000 worth of earth-moving equipment. What is the commission rate?

Commission
$20,800
Total sales
$320,000

$$Commission = Commission\ rate \times Sales$$
$$20{,}800 = r \times 320{,}000$$

Answer

5. $1389

To solve this equation, we divide by 320,000 on both sides:

$$\frac{20{,}800}{320{,}000} = \frac{r \times 320{,}000}{320{,}000}$$

$$0.065 = r$$

$$6.5\% = r.$$

The commission rate is 6.5%.

6. Zion earns a commission of $2040 for selling $17,000 worth of concert tickets. What is the commission rate?

◀ Do Exercise 6.

EXAMPLE 6 *Cruise Vacations.* Valentina's commission rate on cruise vacation packages is 5.6%. She received a commission of $2457 on packages that she sold in November. How many dollars worth of packages did she sell?

$$Commission = Commission\ rate \times Sales$$
$$2457 \qquad = \qquad 5.6\% \quad \times \quad S, \quad or$$
$$2457 = 0.056 \times S$$

To solve this equation, we divide by 0.056 on both sides:

$$\frac{2457}{0.056} = \frac{0.056 \times S}{0.056}$$

$$\frac{2457}{0.056} = S$$

$$43{,}875 = S.$$

Valentina sold $43,875 worth of cruise vacation packages.

◀ Do Exercise 7.

7. Nathan's commission rate on ski passes is 7.5%. He receives a commission of $2970 from the sale of passes in January. How many dollars worth of ski passes did he sell?

$$\$2970 = \boxed{}\ \% \times S$$
$$\$2970 = 0.075 \times S$$
$$\frac{\$2970}{\boxed{}} = \frac{0.075 \times S}{0.075}$$
$$\$\boxed{} = S$$

c DISCOUNT

Suppose that the regular price of a rug is $60, and the rug is on sale at 25% off. Since 25% of $60 is $15, the sale price is $60 − $15, or $45. We call $60 the **original**, or **marked**, **price**, 25% the **rate of discount**, $15 the **discount**, and $45 the **sale price**. Note that discount problems are a type of percent decrease problem.

DISCOUNT AND SALE PRICE
Discount = Rate of discount × Original price
Sale price = Original price − Discount

Answers
6. 12%   **7.** $39,600
Guided Solution:
7. 7.5, 0.075, 39,600

EXAMPLE 7 A leather sofa marked $2379 is on sale at $33\frac{1}{3}$% off. What is the discount? the sale price?

Leather sofa
$2379 original price
Save $33\frac{1}{3}$%

a) *Discount* = *Rate of discount* × *Original price*

$$D = 33\frac{1}{3}\% \times 2379$$

$$D = \frac{1}{3} \times 2379$$

$$D = \frac{2379}{3} = 793$$

b) *Sale price* = *Original price* − *Discount*

$$S = 2379 - 793$$

$$S = 1586$$

The discount is $793, and the sale price is $1586.

Do Exercise 8. ▶

EXAMPLE 8 The price of a snowblower is marked down from $950 to $779. What is the rate of discount?

We first find the discount by subtracting the sale price from the original price:

$$950 - 779 = 171.$$

The discount is $171.

Next, we use the equation for discount:

Discount = *Rate of discount* × *Original price*

$$171 = r \times 950.$$

To solve, we divide by 950 on both sides:

$$\frac{171}{950} = \frac{r \times 950}{950}$$

$$\frac{171}{950} = r$$

$$0.18 = r$$

$$18\% = r.$$

The rate of discount is 18%.

> To check, note that an 18% rate of discount means that the buyer pays 82% of the original price:
>
> $$0.82 \times \$950 = \$779.$$

Do Exercise 9. ▶

8. A computer marked $660 is on sale at $16\frac{2}{3}$% off. What is the discount? the sale price?

9. The price of a winter coat is reduced from $75 to $60. Find the rate of discount.

Answers

8. $110; $550   **9.** 20%

☑ **Reading Check**

Complete each definition with the word *price*, *rate*, or *tax*.

RC1. Commission = Commission _____ × Sales

RC2. Discount = _____ of discount × Original price

RC3. Sale price = Original _____ − Discount

RC4. Sales tax = Sales _____ rate × Purchase price

RC5. Total price = Purchase price + Sales _____

a   Solve.

1. *Wyoming Sales Tax.*   The sales tax rate in Wyoming is 4%. How much sales tax would be charged on a fireplace screen with doors that costs $239?

2. *Kansas Sales Tax.*   The sales tax rate in Kansas is 6.3%. How much sales tax would be charged on a fireplace screen with doors that costs $239?

3. *New Mexico Sales Tax.*   The sales tax rate in New Mexico is 5.125%. How much sales tax is charged on a camp stove that sells for $129.95?

4. *Ohio Sales Tax.*   The sales tax rate in Ohio is 5.5%. How much sales tax is charged on a pet carrier that sells for $39.99?

5. *California Sales Tax.*   The sales tax rate in California is 7.5%. How much sales tax is charged on a purchase of 4 contour foam travel pillows at $39.95 each? What is the total price?

6. *Illinois Sales Tax.*   The sales tax rate in Illinois is 6.25%. How much sales tax is charged on a purchase of 3 wet-dry vacs at $60.99 each? What is the total price?

7. The sales tax is $30 on the purchase of a diamond ring that sells for $750. What is the sales tax rate?

8. The sales tax is $48 on the purchase of a dining room set that sells for $960. What is the sales tax rate?

9. The sales tax is $9.12 on the purchase of a patio set that sells for $456. What is the sales tax rate?

10. The sales tax is $35.80 on the purchase of a refrigerator-freezer that sells for $895. What is the sales tax rate?

Copyright © 2015 Pearson Education, Inc.

11. The sales tax on the purchase of a new fishing boat is $112 and the sales tax rate is 2%. What is the purchase price (the price before tax is added)?

12. The sales tax on the purchase of a used car is $100 and the sales tax rate is 5%. What is the purchase price?

13. The sales tax rate in New York City is 4.375% for the city plus 4% for the state. Find the total amount paid for 6 boxes of chocolates at $17.95 each.

14. The sales tax rate in Nashville, Tennessee, is 2.25% for Davidson County plus 7% for the state. Find the total amount paid for 2 ladders at $39 each.

15. The sales tax rate in Seattle, Washington, is 2.5% for King County plus 6.5% for the state. Find the total amount paid for 3 ceiling fans at $84.49 each.

16. The sales tax rate in Miami, Florida, is 1% for Dade County plus 6% for the state. Find the total amount paid for 2 tires at $49.95 each.

17. The sales tax rate in Atlanta, Georgia, is 1% for the city, 3% for Fulton County, and 4% for the state. Find the total amount paid for 6 basketballs at $29.95 each.

18. The sales tax rate in Dallas, Texas, is 1% for the city, 1% for Dallas County, and 6.25% for the state. Find the total amount paid for 5 flash drives at $19.95 each.

b Solve.

19. Benjamin's commission rate is 21%. What commission does he earn on the sale of $12,500 worth of windows?

20. Olivia's commission rate is 6%. What commission does she earn on the sale of $45,000 worth of lawn irrigation systems?

21. Alyssa earns $408 for selling $3400 worth of shoes. What is the commission rate?

22. Joshua earns $120 for selling $2400 worth of television sets. What is the commission rate?

23. *Real Estate Commission.* A real estate agent's commission rate is 7%. She receives a commission of $12,950 from the sale of a home. How much did the home sell for?

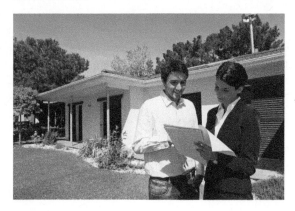

24. *Clothing Consignment Commission.* A clothing consignment shop's commission rate is 40%. The shop receives a commission of $552. How many dollars worth of clothing were sold?

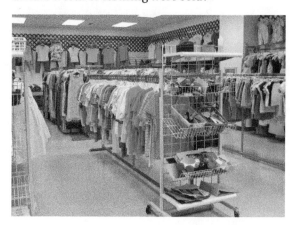

25. A real estate commission rate is 8%. What is the commission from the sale of a piece of land for $68,000?

26. A real estate commission rate is 6%. What is the commission from the sale of a $98,000 home?

27. David earns $1147.50 for selling $7650 worth of car parts. What is the commission rate?

28. Jayla earns $280.80 for selling $2340 worth of tee shirts. What is the commission rate?

29. Laila's commission is increased according to how much she sells. She receives a commission of 4% for the first $1000 of sales and 7% for the amount over $1000. What is her total commission on sales of $5500?

30. Malik's commission is increased according to how much he sells. He receives a commission of 5% for the first $2000 of sales and 8% for the amount over $2000. What is his total commission on sales of $6200?

C Complete the table below by filling in the missing numbers.

	Marked Price	Rate of Discount	Discount	Sale Price
31.	$300	10%		
32.	$2000	40%		
33.	$17	15%		
34.	$20	25%		
35.		10%	$12.50	
36.		15%	$65.70	
37.	$600		$240	
38.	$12,800		$1920	

Copyright © 2015 Pearson Education, Inc.

39. Find the marked price and the rate of discount for the surfboard in this ad.

Save
$120.00
Surfboard Now
$180.00

40. Find the marked price and the rate of discount for the steel log rack in this ad.

Closeout
$35
Save
$15

41. Find the discount and the rate of discount for the pinball machine in this ad.

Best price of the year!
Now only
$3150
Was $3999

PINBALL

42. Find the discount and the rate of discount for the amaryllis in this ad.

Sale
3-in-1 Amaryllis
$37.95
Was $42.95

Skill Maintenance

Solve. [6.3b]

43. $\dfrac{x}{12} = \dfrac{24}{16}$

44. $\dfrac{7}{2} = \dfrac{11}{x}$

Solve. [5.4b]

45. $0.64 \cdot x = 170$

46. $-29.44 = 25.6 \times y$

Convert to standard notation. [5.3b]

47. 4.03 trillion

48. 5.8 million

49. 42.7 million

50. 6.09 trillion

Synthesis

51. 🖩 Sara receives a 10% commission on the first $5000 in sales and 15% on all sales beyond $5000. If Sara receives a commission of $2405, how much did she sell? Use a calculator and trial and error if you wish.

52. Elijah collects baseball memorabilia. He bought two autographed plaques, but then became short of funds and had to sell them quickly for $200 each. On one, he made a 20% profit, and on the other, he lost 20%. Did he make or lose money on the sale?

OBJECTIVES

a Solve applied problems involving simple interest.

b Solve applied problems involving compound interest.

c Solve applied problems involving interest rates on credit cards.

SKILL TO REVIEW

Objective 7.1b: Convert between percent notation and decimal notation.

Find decimal notation.

1. $34\frac{5}{8}\%$ **2.** $5\frac{1}{4}\%$

---

1. What is the simple interest on $4300 invested at an interest rate of 4% for 1 year?

$$I = P \cdot r \cdot t$$
$$= \$4300 \times \boxed{}\% \times 1$$
$$= \$\boxed{} \times 0.04 \times 1$$
$$= \$\boxed{}$$

2. What is the simple interest on a principal of $4300 invested at an interest rate of 4% for 9 months?

Answers

Skill to Review:
1. 0.34625   **2.** 0.0525

Margin Exercises:
1. $172   **2.** $129

Guided Solution:
1. 4, 4300, 172

---

a   SIMPLE INTEREST

Suppose you put $1000 into an investment for 1 year. The $1000 is called the **principal**. If the **interest rate** is 5%, in addition to the principal, you get back 5% of the principal, which is

5% of $1000,   or   0.05 × $1000,   or $50.00.

The $50.00 is called **simple interest**. It is, in effect, the price that a financial institution pays for the use of the money over time.

> ### SIMPLE INTEREST FORMULA
>
> The **simple interest** I on principal P, invested for t years at interest rate r, is given by
>
> $$I = P \cdot r \cdot t.$$

EXAMPLE 1   What is the simple interest on $2500 invested at an interest rate of 6% for 1 year?

We use the formula $I = P \cdot r \cdot t$:

$$I = P \cdot r \cdot t = \$2500 \times 6\% \times 1$$
$$= \$2500 \times 0.06$$
$$= \$150.$$

The simple interest for 1 year is $150.

◀ **Do Margin Exercise 1.**

EXAMPLE 2   What is the simple interest on a principal of $2500 invested at an interest rate of 6% for 3 months?

We use the formula $I = P \cdot r \cdot t$ and express 3 months as a fraction of a year:

$$I = P \cdot r \cdot t = \$2500 \times 6\% \times \frac{3}{12} = \$2500 \times 6\% \times \frac{1}{4}$$

$$= \frac{\$2500 \times 0.06}{4} = \$37.50.$$

The simple interest for 3 months is $37.50.

◀ **Do Margin Exercise 2.**

When time is given in days, we generally divide it by 365 to express the time as a fractional part of a year.

EXAMPLE 3   To pay for a shipment of lawn furniture, Patio by Design borrows $8000 at $9\frac{3}{4}\%$ for 60 days. Find **(a)** the amount of simple interest that is due and **(b)** the total amount that must be paid after 60 days.

a) We express 60 days as a fractional part of a year:

$$I = P \cdot r \cdot t = \$8000 \times 9\frac{3}{4}\% \times \frac{60}{365}$$

$$= \$8000 \times 0.0975 \times \frac{60}{365}$$

$$\approx \$128.22.$$

The interest due for 60 days is $128.22.

b) The total amount to be paid after 60 days is the principal plus the interest:

$$\$8000 + \$128.22 = \$8128.22.$$

The total amount due is $8128.22.

Do Exercise 3. ▶

 3. The Glass Nook borrows $4800 at $5\frac{1}{2}\%$ for 30 days. Find **(a)** the amount of simple interest due and **(b)** the total amount that must be paid after 30 days.

a) $I = P \cdot r \cdot t$

$$= \$4800 \times 5\frac{1}{2}\% \times \frac{\boxed{}}{365}$$

$$= \$4800 \times 0.055 \times \frac{30}{365}$$

$$\approx \$\boxed{}$$

b) Total amount

$$= \$4800 + \boxed{}$$

$$= \boxed{}$$

b COMPOUND INTEREST

When interest is paid *on interest*, we call it **compound interest**. This is the type of interest usually paid on investments. Suppose you have $5000 in a savings account at 6%. In 1 year, the account will contain the original $5000 plus 6% of $5000. Thus the total in the account after 1 year will be

106% of $5000,   or   1.06 × $5000,   or $5300.

Now suppose that the total of $5300 remains in the account for another year. At the end of this second year, the account will contain the $5300 plus 6% of $5300. The total in the account would thus be

106% of $5300,   or   1.06 × $5300,   or $5618.

Note that in the second year, interest is also earned on the first year's interest. When this happens, we say that interest is **compounded annually**.

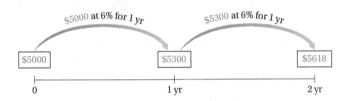

EXAMPLE 4   Find the amount in an account if $2000 is invested at 8%, compounded annually, for 2 years.

a) After 1 year, the account will contain 108% of $2000:

1.08 × $2000 = $2160.

b) At the end of the second year, the account will contain 108% of $2160:

1.08 × $2160 = $2332.80.

The amount in the account after 2 years is $2332.80.

Do Exercise 4. ▶

4. Find the amount in an account if $2000 is invested at 2%, compounded annually, for 2 years.

Answers

3. (a) $21.70; (b) $4821.70   **4.** $2080.80

Guided Solution:

3. (a) 30, 21.70; (b) $21.70, $4821.70

Suppose that the interest in Example 4 were **compounded semi-annually**—that is, every half year. Interest would then be calculated twice a year at a rate of 8% ÷ 2, or 4% each time. The approach used in Example 4 can then be adapted, as follows.

After the first $\frac{1}{2}$ year, the account will contain 104% of $2000:

$$1.04 \times \$2000 = \$2080.$$

After a second $\frac{1}{2}$ year (1 full year), the account will contain 104% of $2080:

$$1.04 \times \$2080 = \$2163.20.$$

After a third $\frac{1}{2}$ year ($1\frac{1}{2}$ full years), the account will contain 104% of $2163.20:

$$1.04 \times \$2163.20 = \$2249.728$$
$$\approx \$2249.73. \qquad \text{Rounding to the nearest cent}$$

Finally, after a fourth $\frac{1}{2}$ year (2 full years), the account will contain 104% of $2249.73:

$$1.04 \times \$2249.73 = \$2339.7192$$
$$\approx \$2339.72. \qquad \text{Rounding to the nearest cent}$$

Let's summarize our results and look at them another way:

End of 1st $\frac{1}{2}$ year $\;\to\; 1.04 \times 2000 = 2000 \times (1.04)^1$;

End of 2nd $\frac{1}{2}$ year $\;\to\; 1.04 \times (1.04 \times 2000) = 2000 \times (1.04)^2$;

End of 3rd $\frac{1}{2}$ year $\;\to\; 1.04 \times (1.04 \times 1.04 \times 2000) = 2000 \times (1.04)^3$;

End of 4th $\frac{1}{2}$ year $\;\to\; 1.04 \times (1.04 \times 1.04 \times 1.04 \times 2000) = 2000 \times (1.04)^4$.

Note that each multiplication was by 1.04 and that

$$\$2000 \times 1.04^4 \approx \$2339.72. \qquad \text{Using a calculator and rounding to the nearest cent}$$

We have illustrated the following result.

COMPOUND INTEREST FORMULA

If a principal P has been invested at interest rate r, compounded n times a year, in t years it will grow to an amount A given by

$$A = P \cdot \left(1 + \frac{r}{n}\right)^{n \cdot t}.$$

Let's apply this formula to confirm our preceding discussion, where the amount invested is $P = \$2000$, the number of years is $t = 2$, and the number of compounding periods each year is $n = 2$. Substituting into the compound interest formula, we have

$$A = P \cdot \left(1 + \frac{r}{n}\right)^{n \cdot t} = 2000 \cdot \left(1 + \frac{8\%}{2}\right)^{2 \cdot 2}$$
$$= \$2000 \cdot \left(1 + \frac{0.08}{2}\right)^4 = \$2000(1.04)^4$$
$$= \$2000 \times 1.16985856 \approx \$2339.72.$$

If you were using a calculator, you could perform this computation in one step.

EXAMPLE 5   The Ibsens invest $4000 in an account paying $3\frac{5}{8}\%$, compounded quarterly. Find the amount in the account after $2\frac{1}{2}$ years.

The compounding is quarterly, so n is 4. We substitute $4000 for P, $3\frac{5}{8}\%$, or 0.03625, for r, 4 for n, and $2\frac{1}{2}$, or $\frac{5}{2}$, for t and compute A:

$$A = P \cdot \left(1 + \frac{r}{n}\right)^{n \cdot t} = \$4000 \cdot \left(1 + \frac{3\frac{5}{8}\%}{4}\right)^{4 \cdot 5/2}$$

$$= \$4000 \cdot \left(1 + \frac{0.03625}{4}\right)^{10}$$

$$= \$4000(1.0090625)^{10}$$

$$\approx \$4377.65.$$

The amount in the account after $2\frac{1}{2}$ years is $4377.65.

Do Exercise 5. ▶

5. A couple invests $7000 in an account paying $6\frac{3}{8}\%$, compounded semiannually. Find the amount in the account after $1\frac{1}{2}$ years.

CALCULATOR CORNER

Compound Interest   A calculator is useful in computing compound interest. Not only does it perform computations quickly but it also eliminates the need to round until the computation is completed. This minimizes round-off errors that occur when rounding is done at each stage of the computation. We must keep order of operations in mind when computing compound interest.

To find the amount due on a $20,000 loan made for 25 days at 11% interest, compounded daily, we compute $20{,}000\left(1 + \frac{0.11}{365}\right)^{25}$. To do this on a calculator, we press 2 0 0 0 0 0 × ((1 + . 1 1 ÷ 3 6 5)) y^x (or ∧) 2 5 = . The result is $20,151.23, rounded to the nearest cent.

Some calculators have business keys that allow such computations to be done more quickly.

EXERCISES

1. Find the amount due on a $16,000 loan made for 62 days at 13% interest, compounded daily.

2. An investment of $12,500 is made for 90 days at 8.5% interest, compounded daily. How much is the investment worth after 90 days?

C CREDIT CARDS

According to nerdwallet.com, the average credit-card debt among U.S. households with such debt was $15,162 per household in 2012. According to the Aggregate Revolving Consumer Debt Survey in 2012, the average credit-card debt carried by undergraduate college students is $3137.

The money you obtain through the use of a credit card is not "free" money. There is a price (interest) to be paid for the convenience of using a credit card. A balance carried on a credit card is a type of loan. Comparing interest rates is essential if one is to become financially responsible. A small change in an interest rate can make a large difference in the cost of a loan. When you make a payment on a credit-card balance, do you know how much of that payment is interest and how much is applied to reducing the principal?

Answer
5. $7690.94

EXAMPLE 6 *Credit Cards.* After the holidays, Addison has a balance of $3216.28 on a credit card with an annual percentage rate (APR) of 19.7%. She decides not to make additional purchases with this card until she has paid off the balance.

a) Many credit cards require a minimum monthly payment of 2% of the balance. At this rate, what is Addison's minimum payment on a balance of $3216.28? Round the answer to the nearest dollar.

b) Find the amount of interest and the amount applied to reduce the principal in the minimum payment found in part (a).

c) If Addison had transferred her balance to a card with an APR of 12.5%, how much of her first payment would be interest and how much would be applied to reduce the principal?

d) Compare the amounts for 12.5% from part (c) with the amounts for 19.7% from part (b).

We solve as follows.

a) We multiply the balance of $3216.28 by 2%:

$$0.02 \times \$3216.28 = \$64.3256. \qquad \text{Addison's minimum payment, rounded to the nearest dollar, is \$64.}$$

b) The amount of interest on $3216.28 at 19.7% for one month* is given by

$$I = P \cdot r \cdot t = \$3216.28 \times 0.197 \times \frac{1}{12} \approx \$52.80.$$

We subtract to find the portion of the first payment applied to reduce the principal:

$$\begin{aligned} \text{Amount applied to reduce the principal} &= \text{Minimum payment} - \text{Interest for the month} \\ &= \$64 - \$52.80 \\ &= \$11.20. \end{aligned}$$

Thus the principal of $3216.28 is decreased by only $11.20 with the first payment. (Addison still owes $3205.08.)

c) The amount of interest on $3216.28 at 12.5% for one month is

$$I = P \cdot r \cdot t = \$3216.28 \times 0.125 \times \frac{1}{12} \approx \$33.50.$$

We subtract to find the amount applied to reduce the principal in the first payment:

$$\begin{aligned} \text{Amount applied to reduce the principal} &= \text{Minimum payment} - \text{Interest for the month} \\ &= \$64 - \$33.50 \\ &= \$30.50. \end{aligned}$$

Thus the principal of $3216.28 would have decreased by $30.50 with the first payment. (Addison would still owe $3185.78.)

---

*Actually, the interest on a credit card is computed daily with a rate called a daily percentage rate (DPR). The DPR for Example 6 would be 19.7%/365 = 0.054%. When no payments or additional purchases are made during a month, the difference in total interest for the month is minimal and we will not deal with it here.

d) Let's organize the information for both rates in the following table.

BALANCE BEFORE FIRST PAYMENT	FIRST MONTH'S PAYMENT	%APR	AMOUNT OF INTEREST	AMOUNT APPLIED TO PRINCIPAL	BALANCE AFTER FIRST PAYMENT
$3216.28	$64	19.7%	$52.80	$11.20	$3205.08
3216.28	64	12.5	33.50	30.50	3185.78

Difference in balance after first payment ⟶ $19.30

At 19.7%, the interest is $52.80 and the principal is decreased by $11.20. At 12.5%, the interest is $33.50 and the principal is decreased by $30.50. Thus the interest at 19.7% is $52.80 − $33.50, or $19.30, greater than the interest at 12.5%. Thus the principal is decreased by $30.50 − $11.20, or $19.30, more with the 12.5% rate than with the 19.7% rate.

Do Exercise 6. ▶

Even though the mathematics of the information in the table below is beyond the scope of this text, it is interesting to compare how long it takes to pay off the balance of Example 6 if Addison continues to pay $64 each month, compared to how long it takes if she pays double that amount, or $128, each month. Financial consultants frequently tell clients that if they want to take control of their debt, they should pay double the minimum payment.

RATE	PAYMENT	NUMBER OF PAYMENTS TO PAY OFF DEBT	TOTAL PAID BACK	ADDITIONAL COST OF PURCHASES
19.7%	$64	107, or 8 yr 11 mo	$6848	$3631.72
19.7	128	33, or 2 yr 9 mo	4224	1007.72
12.5	64	72, or 6 yr	4608	1391.72
12.5	128	29, or 2 yr 5 mo	3712	495.72

As with most loans, if you pay an extra amount toward the principal with each payment, the length of the loan can be greatly reduced. Note that at the rate of 19.7%, it will take Addison almost 9 years to pay off her debt if she pays only $64 per month and does not make additional purchases. If she transfers her balance to a card with a 12.5% rate and pays $128 per month, she can eliminate her debt in approximately $2\frac{1}{2}$ years. You can see how debt can get out of control if you continue to make purchases and pay only the minimum payment each month. The debt will never be eliminated.

6. *Credit Card.* After the holidays, Logan has a balance of $4867.59 on a credit card with an annual percentage rate (APR) of 21.3%. He decides not to make additional purchases with this card until he has paid off the balance.

a) Many credit cards require a minimum monthly payment of 2% of the balance. What is Logan's minimum payment on a balance of $4867.59? Round the answer to the nearest dollar.

b) Find the amount of interest and the amount applied to reduce the principal in the minimum payment found in part (a).

c) If Logan had transferred his balance to a card with an APR of 13.6%, how much of his first payment would be interest and how much would be applied to reduce the principal?

d) Compare the amounts for 13.6% from part (c) with the amounts for 21.3% from part (b).

Answers

6. **(a)** $97; **(b)** interest: $86.40; amount applied to principal: $10.60; **(c)** interest: $55.17; amount applied to principal: $41.83; **(d)** At 13.6%, the principal was reduced by $31.23 more than at the 21.3% rate. The interest at 13.6% is $31.23 less than at 21.3%.

✓ Reading Check

In the simple interest formula, $I = P \cdot r \cdot t$, t must be expressed in years. Convert each length of time to years. Use 1 year = 12 months = 365 days.

RC1. 6 months   **RC2.** 40 days   **RC3.** 285 days

RC4. 9 months   **RC5.** 3 months   **RC6.** 4 months

a Find the simple interest.

	Principal	Rate of Interest	Time	Simple Interest
1.	$200	4%	1 year	
2.	$200	7.7%	1 year	
3.	$4300	10.56%	$\frac{1}{4}$ year	
4.	$80,000	$6\frac{3}{4}$%	$\frac{1}{12}$ year	
5.	$20,000	$4\frac{5}{8}$%	6 months	
6.	$8000	9.42%	2 months	
7.	$50,000	$5\frac{3}{8}$%	3 months	
8.	$100,000	$3\frac{1}{4}$%	9 months	

Solve. Assume that simple interest is being calculated in each case.

9. Mia's Boutique borrows $10,000 at 9% for 60 days. Find **(a)** the amount of interest due and **(b)** the total amount that must be paid after 60 days.

10. Mason's Drywall borrows $8000 at 10% for 90 days. Find **(a)** the amount of interest due and **(b)** the total amount that must be paid after 90 days.

11. Animal Instinct, a pet supply shop, borrows $6500 at $5\frac{1}{4}$% for 90 days. Find **(a)** the amount of interest due and **(b)** the total amount that must be paid after 90 days.

12. Andante's Cafe borrows $4500 at $12\frac{1}{2}$% for 60 days. Find **(a)** the amount of interest due and **(b)** the total amount that must be paid after 60 days.

13. Cameron's Garage borrows $5600 at 10% for 30 days. Find **(a)** the amount of interest due and **(b)** the total amount that must be paid after 30 days.

14. Shear Delights Hair Salon borrows $3600 at 4% for 30 days. Find **(a)** the amount of interest due and **(b)** the total amount that must be paid after 30 days.

Copyright © 2015 Pearson Education, Inc.

b Interest is compounded annually. Find the amount in the account after the given length of time. Round to the nearest cent.

	Principal	Rate of Interest	Time	Amount in the Account
15.	$400	5%	2 years	
16.	$450	4%	2 years	
17.	$2000	8.8%	4 years	
18.	$4000	7.7%	4 years	
19.	$4300	10.56%	6 years	
20.	$8000	9.42%	6 years	
21.	$20,000	$6\frac{5}{8}$%	25 years	
22.	$100,000	$5\frac{7}{8}$%	30 years	

Interest is compounded semiannually. Find the amount in the account after the given length of time. Round to the nearest cent.

	Principal	Rate of Interest	Time	Amount in the Account
23.	$4000	6%	1 year	
24.	$1000	5%	1 year	
25.	$20,000	8.8%	4 years	
26.	$40,000	7.7%	4 years	
27.	$5000	10.56%	6 years	
28.	$8000	9.42%	8 years	
29.	$20,000	$7\frac{5}{8}$%	25 years	
30.	$100,000	$4\frac{7}{8}$%	30 years	

Solve.

31. A family invests $4000 in an account paying 6%, compounded monthly. How much is in the account after 5 months?

32. A couple invests $2500 in an account paying 3%, compounded monthly. How much is in the account after 6 months?

33. A couple invests $1200 in an account paying 10%, compounded quarterly. How much is in the account after 1 year?

34. The O'Hares invest $6000 in an account paying 8%, compounded quarterly. How much is in the account after 18 months?

C   Solve.

35. *Credit Cards.*   Amelia has a balance of $1278.56 on a credit card with an annual percentage rate (APR) of 19.6%. The minimum payment required in the current statement is $25.57. Find the amount of interest and the amount applied to reduce the principal in this payment and the balance after this payment.

36. *Credit Cards.*   Lawson has a balance of $1834.90 on a credit card with an annual percentage rate (APR) of 22.4%. The minimum payment required in the current statement is $36.70. Find the amount of interest and the amount applied to reduce the principal in this payment and the balance after this payment.

37. *Credit Cards.*   Antonio has a balance of $4876.54 on a credit card with an annual percentage rate (APR) of 21.3%.

   a) Many credit cards require a minimum monthly payment of 2% of the balance. What is Antonio's minimum payment on a balance of $4876.54? Round the answer to the nearest dollar.

   b) Find the amount of interest and the amount applied to reduce the principal in the minimum payment found in part (a).

   c) If Antonio had transferred his balance to a card with an APR of 12.6%, how much of his payment would be interest and how much would be applied to reduce the principal?

   d) Compare the amounts for 12.6% from part (c) with the amounts for 21.3% from part (b).

38. *Credit Cards.*   Becky has a balance of $5328.88 on a credit card with an annual percentage rate (APR) of 18.7%.

   a) Many credit cards require a minimum monthly payment of 2% of the balance. What is Becky's minimum payment on a balance of $5328.88? Round the answer to the nearest dollar.

   b) Find the amount of interest and the amount applied to reduce the principal in the minimum payment found in part (a).

   c) If Becky had transferred her balance to a card with an APR of 13.2%, how much of her payment would be interest and how much would be applied to reduce the principal?

   d) Compare the amounts for 13.2% from part (c) with the amounts for 18.7% from part (b).

Skill Maintenance

39. Find the LCM of 32 and 50.   [4.1a]

40. Find the prime factorization of 228.   [3.1d]

Divide and simplify.   [3.7b]

41. $\dfrac{6}{125} \div \dfrac{8}{15}$

42. $-\dfrac{16}{105} \div \dfrac{5}{14}$

Multiply and simplify.   [3.6a]

43. $\dfrac{4}{15} \times \dfrac{3}{20}$

44. $\dfrac{8}{21} \times \dfrac{49}{800}$

45. Simplify: $4^3 - 6^2 \div 2^2$.   [1.9c]

46. Solve: $x + \dfrac{2}{5} = -\dfrac{9}{10}$.   [4.3c]

Synthesis

Effective Yield.   The *effective yield* is the yearly rate of simple interest that corresponds to a rate for which interest is compounded two or more times a year. For example, if P is invested at 12%, compounded quarterly, we multiply P by $(1 + 0.12/4)^4$, or 1.03^4. Since $1.03^4 \approx 1.126$, the 12% compounded quarterly corresponds to an effective yield of approximately 12.6%. In Exercises 47 and 48, find the effective yield for the indicated account.

47. ▥ The account pays 9% compounded monthly.

48. ▥ The account pays 10% compounded daily.

Copyright © 2015 Pearson Education, Inc.

Vocabulary Reinforcement

Complete each statement with the appropriate word or phrase from the list at the right. Some of the choices will not be used.

1. When a quantity is decreased by a certain percent, we say that this is a _____ . [7.5b]

2. The _____ interest I on principal P, invested for t years at interest rate r, is given by $I = P \cdot r \cdot t$. [7.7a]

3. Sale price = Original price − _____ . [7.6c]

4. Commission = Commission rate × _____ . [7.6b]

5. Discount = _____ of discount × Original price. [7.6c]

6. When a quantity is increased by a certain percent, we say that this is a _____ . [7.5b]

discount

rate

sales

commission

price

principal

percent increase

percent decrease

simple

compound

Concept Reinforcement

Determine whether each statement is true or false.

_____ 1. A fixed principal invested for 4 years will earn more interest when interest is compounded quarterly than when interest is compounded semiannually. [7.7b]

_____ 2. Of the numbers 0.5%, $\frac{5}{1000}$%, $\frac{1}{2}$%, $\frac{1}{5}$, and $0.\overline{1}$, the largest number is $0.\overline{1}$. [7.1b], [7.2a, b]

_____ 3. If principal A equals principal B and principal A is invested for 2 years at 4%, compounded quarterly, while principal B is invested for 4 years at 2%, compounded semiannually, the interest earned from each investment is the same. [7.7b]

Study Guide

Objective 7.1b Convert between percent notation and decimal notation.

Example Find percent notation for 1.3.

We move the decimal point two places to the right and write a percent symbol:

$1.3 = 130\%$.

Example Find decimal notation for $12\frac{3}{4}$%.

We convert $12\frac{3}{4}$ to a decimal. Then we drop the percent symbol and move the decimal point two places to the left:

$12\frac{3}{4}\% = 12.75\% = 0.1275$.

Practice Exercise

1. Find percent notation for 0.082.

Practice Exercise

2. Find decimal notation for $62\frac{5}{8}$%.

Objective 7.2a Convert from fraction notation to percent notation.

Example Find percent notation for $\dfrac{5}{12}$.

$$
\begin{array}{r}
0.4\ 1\ 6 \\
1\,2\ \overline{)\ 5.0\ 0\ 0} \\
4\ 8 \\
\hline
2\ 0 \\
1\ 2 \\
\hline
8\ 0 \\
7\ 2 \\
\hline
8
\end{array}
$$

$\dfrac{5}{12} = 0.41\overline{6} = 41.\overline{6}\%,\ \text{or}\ 41\dfrac{2}{3}\%$

Practice Exercise

3. Find percent notation for $\dfrac{7}{11}$.

Objective 7.2b Convert from percent notation to fraction notation.

Example Find fraction notation for 9.5%.

$$9.5\% = \frac{9.5}{100} = \frac{95}{1000}.$$

$$= \frac{5 \cdot 19}{5 \cdot 200}$$

$$= \frac{5}{5} \cdot \frac{19}{200}$$

$$= \frac{19}{200}$$

Practice Exercise

4. Find fraction notation for 6.8%.

Objective 7.3b Solve basic percent problems.

Example 165 is what percent of 3300?

We have

$165 = p \cdot 3300$ Translating to a percent equation

$$\frac{165}{3300} = \frac{p \cdot 3300}{3300}$$

$$\frac{165}{3300} = p$$

$$0.05 = p$$

$$5\% = p.$$

Thus, 165 is 5% of 3300.

Practice Exercise

5. 12 is what percent of 288?

Objective 7.4b Solve basic percent problems.

Example 18% of what is 1296?

$$\frac{18}{100} = \frac{1296}{b}$$ Translating to a proportion

$$18 \cdot b = 100 \cdot 1296$$

$$\frac{18 \cdot b}{18} = \frac{129{,}600}{18}$$

$$b = 7200.$$

Thus, 18% of 7200 is 1296.

Practice Exercise

6. 3% of what is 300?

Example The total cost for 16 basic grocery items in the second quarter of 2008 averaged $46.67 nationally. The total cost of these 16 items in the second quarter of 2007 averaged $42.95. What was the percent increase?

Source: American Farm Bureau Federation

We first determine the amount of increase:

$$\$46.67 - \$42.95 = \$3.72.$$

Then we translate to a percent equation or a proportion and solve.

Rewording: $3.72 is what percent of $42.95?

Percent Equation:

$$3.72 = p \cdot 42.95$$

$$\frac{3.72}{42.95} = \frac{p \cdot 42.95}{42.95}$$

$$\frac{3.72}{42.95} = p$$

$$0.087 \approx p$$

$$8.7\% = p$$

Proportion:

$$\frac{N}{100} = \frac{3.72}{42.95}$$

$$42.95 \cdot N = 100 \cdot 3.72$$

$$\frac{42.95 \cdot N}{42.95} = \frac{100 \cdot 3.72}{42.95}$$

$$N = \frac{372}{42.95}$$

$$N \approx 8.7$$

The percent increase was about 8.7%.

Practice Exercise

7. In Indiana, the cost for 16 basic grocery items increased from $40.07 in the second quarter of 2007 to $46.20 in the second quarter of 2008. What was the percent increase from 2007 to 2008?

Example The sales tax is $34.23 on the purchase of a flat-screen high-definition television that costs $489. What is the sales tax rate?

Rephrase: Sales tax is what percent of purchase price?

Translate: $34.23 = r \times 489$

Solve:

$$\frac{34.23}{489} = \frac{r \times 489}{489}$$

$$\frac{34.23}{489} = r$$

$$0.07 = r$$

$$7\% = r$$

The sales tax rate is 7%.

Practice Exercise

8. The sales tax is $1102.20 on the purchase of a new car that costs $18,370. What is the sales tax rate?

Objective 7.6b Solve applied problems involving commission and percent.

Example   A real estate agent's commission rate is $6\frac{1}{2}$%. She received a commission of $17,160 on the sale of a home. For how much did the home sell?

Rephrase: Commission is $6\frac{1}{2}$% of what selling price?

Translate: $17{,}160 = 6\frac{1}{2}\% \times S$

Solve: $17{,}160 = 0.065 \times S$

$$\frac{17{,}160}{0.065} = \frac{0.065 \times S}{0.065}$$

$$264{,}000 = S$$

The home sold for $264,000.

Practice Exercise

9. A real estate agent's commission rate is 7%. He received a commission of $12,950 on the sale of a home. For how much did the home sell?

Objective 7.7a Solve applied problems involving simple interest.

Example   To meet its payroll, a business borrows $5200 at $4\frac{1}{4}$% for 90 days. Find the amount of simple interest that is due and the total amount that must be paid after 90 days.

$$I = P \cdot r \cdot t = \$5200 \times 4\frac{1}{4}\% \times \frac{90}{365}$$

$$= \$5200 \times 0.0425 \times \frac{90}{365}$$

$$\approx \$54.49$$

The interest due for 90 days $= \$54.49$.

The total amount due $= \$5200 + \$54.49 = \$5254.49$.

Practice Exercise

10. A student borrows $2500 for tuition at $5\frac{1}{2}$% for 60 days. Find the amount of simple interest that is due and the total amount that must be paid after 60 days.

Objective 7.7b Solve applied problems involving compound interest.

Example   Find the amount in an account if $3200 is invested at 5%, compounded semiannually, for $1\frac{1}{2}$ years.

$$A = P \cdot \left(1 + \frac{r}{n}\right)^{n \cdot t}$$

$$= \$3200\left(1 + \frac{0.05}{2}\right)^{2 \cdot \frac{3}{2}}$$

$$= \$3200(1.025)^3$$

$$= \$3446.05$$

The amount in the account after $1\frac{1}{2}$ years is $3446.05.

Practice Exercise

11. Find the amount in an account if $6000 is invested at $4\frac{3}{4}$%, compounded quarterly, for 2 years.

Review Exercises

Find percent notation.   [7.1b]

1. 1.7

2. 0.065

Find decimal notation for the percent notations in each sentence.   [7.1b]

3. In the 2006–2007 school year, about 4% of the 15 million college students in the United States were foreign students. Approximately 14.4% of the foreign students were from India.

Source: Institute of International Education

Copyright © 2015 Pearson Education, Inc.

4. Poland is 62.1% urban; Sweden is 84.2% urban.

Source: *The World Almanac*, 2008

Find percent notation. [7.2a]

5. $\frac{3}{8}$

6. $\frac{1}{3}$

Find fraction notation. [7.2b]

7. 24%

8. 6.3%

Translate to a percent equation. Then solve. [7.3a, b]

9. 30.6 is what percent of 90?

10. 63 is 84% of what?

11. What is $38\frac{1}{2}$% of 168?

Translate to a proportion. Then solve. [7.4a, b]

12. 24% of what is 16.8?

13. 42 is what percent of 30?

14. What is 10.5% of 84?

Solve. [7.5a, b]

15. *Favorite Ice Creams.* According to a survey, 8.9% of those interviewed chose chocolate as their favorite ice cream flavor and 4.2% chose butter pecan. At this rate, of the 2000 students in a freshman class, how many would choose chocolate as their favorite ice cream? butter pecan?

Source: International Ice Cream Association

16. *Prescriptions.* Of the 305 million people in the United States in a recent year, 140.3 million took at least one type of prescription drug per day. What percent took at least one type of prescription drug per day?

Source: William N. Kelly, *Pharmacy: What It Is and How It Works*, 2nd ed., CRC Press Pharmaceutical Education, 2006

17. *Water Output.* The average person loses 200 mL of water per day by sweating. This is 8% of the total output of water from the body. How much is the total output of water?

Source: Elaine N. Marieb, *Essentials of Human Anatomy and Physiology*, 6th ed. Boston: Addison Wesley Longman, Inc., 2000

18. *Test Scores.* After Sheila got a 75 on a math test, she was allowed to go to the math lab and take a retest. She increased her score to 84. What was the percent increase?

19. *Test Scores.* James got an 80 on a math test. By taking a retest in the math lab, he increased his score by 15%. What was his new score?

Solve. [7.6a, b, c]

20. A state charges a meals tax of $7\frac{1}{2}$%. What is the meals tax charged on a dinner party costing $320?

21. In a certain state, a sales tax of $453.60 is collected on the purchase of a used car for $7560. What is the sales tax rate?

22. Kim earns $753.50 for selling $6850 worth of televisions. What is the commission rate?

23. What is the rate of discount of this stepladder?

24. An air conditioner has a marked price of $350. It is placed on sale at 12% off. What are the discount and the sale price?

25. The price of a fax machine is marked down from $305 to $262.30. What is the rate of discount?

26. An insurance salesperson receives a 7% commission. If $42,000 worth of life insurance is sold, what is the commission?

Solve.   [7.7a, b, c]

27. What is the simple interest on $1800 at 6% for $\frac{1}{3}$ year?

28. The Dress Shack borrows $24,000 at 10% simple interest for 60 days. Find **(a)** the amount of interest due and **(b)** the total amount that must be paid after 60 days.

29. What is the simple interest on a principal of $2200 at an interest rate of 5.5% for 1 year?

30. The Armstrongs invest $7500 in an investment account paying an annual interest rate of 4%, compounded monthly. How much is in the account after 3 months?

31. Find the amount in an investment account if $8000 is invested at 9%, compounded annually, for 2 years.

32. *Credit Cards.*   At the end of her junior year of college, Kasha has a balance of $6428.74 on a credit card with an annual percentage rate (APR) of 18.7%. She decides not to make additional purchases with this card until she has paid off the balance.

a) Many credit cards require a minimum payment of 2% of the balance. At this rate, what is Kasha's minimum payment on a balance of $6428.74? Round the answer to the nearest dollar.

b) Find the amount of interest and the amount applied to reduce the principal in the minimum payment found in part (a).

c) If Kasha had transferred her balance to a card with an APR of 13.2%, how much of her payment would be interest and how much would be applied to reduce the principal?

d) Compare the amounts for 13.2% from part (c) with the amounts for 18.7% from part (b).

33. A fishing boat listed at $16,500 is on sale at 15% off. What is the sale price?   [7.6c]

   A. $14,025   **B.** $2475

   C. 85%   **D.** $14,225

34. Find the amount in a money market account if $10,500 is invested at 6%, compounded semiannually, for $1\frac{1}{2}$ years.   [7.7b]

   A. $11,139.45   **B.** $12,505.67

   C. $11,473.63   **D.** $10,976.03

Synthesis

35. Mike's Bike Shop reduces the price of a bicycle by 40% during a sale. By what percent must the store increase the sale price, after the sale, to get back to the original price?   [7.6c]

36. A worker receives raises of 3%, 6%, and then 9%. By what percent has the original salary increased?   [7.5a]

Understanding Through Discussion and Writing

1. Which is the better deal for a consumer and why: a discount of 40% or a discount of 20% followed by another of 22%?   [7.6c]

2. Which is better for a wage earner, and why: a 10% raise followed by a 5% raise a year later, or a 5% raise followed by a 10% raise a year later?   [7.5a]

3. Ollie buys a microwave oven during a 10%-off sale. The sale price that Ollie paid was $162. To find the original price, Ollie calculates 10% of $162 and adds that to $162. Is this correct? Why or why not?   [7.6c]

4. You take 40% of 50% of a number. What percent of the number could you take to obtain the same result making only one multiplication? Explain your answer.   [7.5a]

5. A firm must choose between borrowing $5000 at 10% for 30 days and borrowing $10,000 at 8% for 60 days. Give arguments in favor of and against each option.   [7.7a]

6. On the basis of the mathematics presented in Section 7.7, discuss what you have learned about interest rates and credit cards.   [7.7c]

Copyright © 2015 Pearson Education, Inc.

CHAPTER

7   **Test**

For Extra Help   For step-by-step test solutions, access the Chapter Test Prep Videos in MyMathLab® or on You Tube (search "BittingerBasicEI" and click on "Channels").

1. *Households Owning Pets.*   In 2011, about 61.3% of the households in Colorado owned pets. Find decimal notation for 61.3%.

Source: American Veterinary Medical Association

2. *Gravity.*   The gravity of Mars is 0.38 as strong as Earth's. Find percent notation for 0.38.

Source: www.marsinstitute.info/epo/mermarsfacts.html

3. Find percent notation for $\frac{11}{8}$.

4. Find fraction notation for 65%.

5. Translate to a percent equation. Then solve.
   What is 40% of 55?

6. Translate to a proportion. Then solve. What percent of 80 is 65?

Solve.

7. *Organ Transplants.*   In 2011, there were 28,535 organ transplants in the United States. The pie chart below shows the percentages for the main transplants. How many kidney transplants were there in 2011? liver transplants? heart transplants?

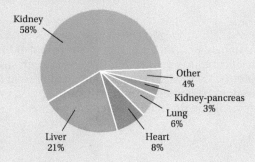

Organ Transplants in the United States, 2011

Kidney 58%
Other 4%
Kidney-pancreas 3%
Lung 6%
Heart 8%
Liver 21%

SOURCE: Milliman Research Report

8. *Batting Average.*   Garrett Atkins, third baseman for the Colorado Rockies, got 175 hits during the 2008 baseball season. This was about 28.64% of his at-bats. How many at-bats did he have?

Source: Major League Baseball

9. *Foreign Adoptions.*   The number of foreign children adopted by Americans declined from 20,679 in 2006 to 19,292 in 2007. Find the percent decrease.

Source: U.S. State Department, *USA TODAY*, August 13, 2008

10. There were about 6,603,000,000 people living in the world in a recent year, and approximately 4,002,000,000 lived in Asia. What percent of people lived in Asia?

Source: Population Division/International Programs Center, U.S. Census Bureau, U.S. Dept. of Commerce

11. *Oklahoma Sales Tax.*   The sales tax rate in Oklahoma is 4.5%. How much tax is charged on a purchase of $560? What is the total price?

12. Noah's commission rate is 15%. What is his commission on the sale of $4200 worth of merchandise?

13. The marked price of a DVD player is $200 and the item is on sale at 20% off. What are the discount and the sale price?

14. What is the simple interest on a principal of $120 at the interest rate of 7.1% for 1 year?

15. A city orchestra invests $5200 at 6% simple interest. How much is in the account after $\frac{1}{2}$ year?

16. Find the amount in an account if $1000 is invested at $5\frac{3}{8}$%, compounded annually, for 2 years.

17. The Suarez family invests $10,000 at an annual interest rate of 4.9%, compounded monthly. How much is in the account after 3 years?

18. *Job Opportunities.* The table below lists job opportunities in 2006 and projected increases for 2016. Complete the table by filling in the missing numbers.

Occupation	Total Employment in 2006	Projected Employment in 2016	Change	Percent of Increase
Dental assistant	280,000	362,000	82,000	29.3%
Plumber	705,000		52,000	
Veterinary assistant	71,000	100,000		
Motorcycle repair technician		24,000	3000	
Fitness professional		298,000		26.8%

SOURCE: EarnMyDegree.com

19. Find the discount and the rate of discount of the television in this ad.

19" LCD HDTV

$299⁹⁹

was $349⁹⁹

20. *Credit Cards.* Jayden has a balance of $2704.27 on a credit card with an annual percentage rate of 16.3%. The minimum payment required on the current statement is $54. Find the amount of interest and the amount applied to reduce the principal in this payment and the balance after this payment.

21. 0.75% of what number is 300?

A. 2.25   **B.** 40,000   **C.** 400   **D.** 225

Synthesis

22. By selling a home without using a realtor, Juan and Marie can avoid paying a 7.5% commission. They receive an offer of $180,000 from a potential buyer. In order to give a comparable offer, for what price would a realtor need to sell the house? Round to the nearest hundred.

23. Karen's commission rate is 16%. She invests her commission from the sale of $15,000 worth of merchandise at an interest rate of 12%, compounded quarterly. How much is Karen's investment worth after 6 months?

Copyright © 2015 Pearson Education, Inc.

1. *Passports.* In 2010, 14,794,604 U.S. passports and passport cards were issued. This number decreased to 12,613,153 in 2011 and then increased to 13,125,829 in 2012. What was the percent decrease from 2010 to 2011? What was the percent increase from 2011 to 2012? Round answers to the nearest tenth of a percent.

Sources: Travel.State.gov; Bureau of Consular Affairs, U.S. Department of State

2. Find percent notation: 0.269.

3. Find percent notation: $\dfrac{9}{8}$.

4. Find decimal notation: $-\dfrac{13}{6}$.

5. Write fraction notation for the ratio 5 to 0.5.

6. Find the rate in kilometers per hour: 350 km, 15 hr.

Use $<$, $>$, or $=$ for $\square$ to write a true sentence.

7. $\dfrac{5}{7}\ \square\ \dfrac{6}{8}$

8. $\dfrac{-15}{25}\ \square\ \dfrac{-6}{14}$

Estimate the sum or the difference by first rounding to the nearest hundred.

9. $263{,}961 + 32{,}090 + 127.89$

10. $73{,}510 - 23{,}450$

Calculate.

11. $46 - [4(6 + 4 \div 2) + 2 \times 3 - 5]$

12. $[-0.8(1.5 - 9.8 \div 49) - (1 + 0.1)^2] \div 1.5$

Compute and simplify.

13. $\dfrac{6}{5} + 1\dfrac{5}{6}$

14. $-46.9 + 2.84$

15. $\begin{array}{r} 4\,8\,7{,}0\,9\,4 \\ 6{,}9\,3\,6 \\ +\ \ 2\,1{,}1\,2\,0 \\ \hline \end{array}$

16. $35 - 34.98$

17. $3\dfrac{1}{3} - 2\dfrac{2}{3}$

18. $-\dfrac{8}{9} - \dfrac{6}{7}$

19. $-\dfrac{7}{9} \cdot \left(-\dfrac{3}{14}\right)$

20. $\begin{array}{r} 2\,3\,6{,}9\,8\,4 \\ \times\ \ \ \ \ 3{,}6\,0\,0 \\ \hline \end{array}$

21. $\begin{array}{r} 4\,6.0\,1\,2 \\ \times\ \ \ \ \ 0.0\,3 \\ \hline \end{array}$

22. $-6\dfrac{3}{5} \div 4\dfrac{2}{5}$

23. $431.2 \div 35.2$

24. $15\,\overline{)\,1\,8\,5\,0\,}$

Solve.

25. $36 \cdot x = 3420$

26. $y + 142.87 = -151$

27. $-\dfrac{2}{15} \cdot t = \dfrac{6}{5}$

28. $\dfrac{3}{4} + x = \dfrac{5}{6}$

29. $\dfrac{y}{25} = \dfrac{24}{15}$

30. $\dfrac{16}{n} = \dfrac{21}{11}$

31. Museum Attendance. Among leading art museums, the Indianapolis Museum of Art ranks sixth in the nation in the number of visitors as a percentage of the metropolitan population. In 2007, the number of visitors was 30.31% of the metropolitan population, which was 1,525,104. What was the total attendance?

Source: dashboard.imamuseum.org/series/2007+MSA+Attendance

32. Salaries of Medical Doctors. In 2007, the starting salary for a doctor in radiology was $172,500 higher than the starting salary of a doctor in neurology. If the starting salary for a radiologist was $350,000, what was the starting salary of a neurologist?

Source: Journal of the American Medical Association

33. At one point during the 2008–2009 NBA season, the Cleveland Cavaliers had won 39 out of 49 games. At this rate, how many games would they win in the entire season of 82 games?

Source: National Basketball Association

34. Shirts. A total of $424.75 was paid for 5 shirts at an upscale men's store. How much did each shirt cost?

35. Unit Price. A 200-oz bottle of liquid laundry detergent costs $14.99. What is the unit price?

36. Patty walked $\frac{7}{10}$ mi to school and then $\frac{8}{10}$ mi to the library. How far did she walk?

37. On a map, 1 in. represents 80 mi. How much does $\frac{3}{4}$ in. represent?

38. Compound Interest. The Bakers invest $8500 in an investment account paying 8%, compounded monthly. How much is in the account after 5 years?

39. Ribbons. How many pieces of ribbon $1\frac{4}{5}$ yd long can be cut from a length of ribbon 9 yd long?

40. Auto Repair Technicians. In 2006, 773,000 people were employed as auto repair technicians. It is projected that by 2016, this number will increase by 110,000. Find the percent increase in the number of auto repair technicians and the number of technicians in 2016.

Source: EarnMyDegree.com

41. Subtract and simplify: $\frac{14}{25} - \frac{3}{20}$.

A. $\frac{11}{500}$

B. $\frac{11}{5}$

C. $\frac{41}{100}$

D. $\frac{205}{500}$

42. The population of the state of Louisiana decreased from 4,468,976 in 2000 to 4,287,768 in 2006. What was the percent decrease?

Source: U.S. Census Bureau

A. 4.1%

B. 4.2%

C. 104%

D. 95.9%

Synthesis

43. If a is 50% of b, then b is what percent of a?

Copyright © 2015 Pearson Education, Inc.

Appendix

Ratio and Proportion

6.1 Introduction to Ratios

6.2 Rates and Unit Prices

6.3 Proportions

Mid-Chapter Review

6.4 Applications of Proportions

Translating for Success

6.5 Geometric Applications

Summary and Review

Test

Cumulative Review

STUDYING FOR SUCCESS   *Working Exercises*

☐   Don't try to solve a homework problem by working backward from the answer given at the back of the text. Remember: quizzes and tests have no answer section!

☐   Check answers to odd-numbered exercises at the back of the book.

☐   Work some even-numbered exercises, whose answers are not provided, as practice. Check your answers later with a friend or your instructor.

6.1   Introduction to Ratios

OBJECTIVES

a   Find fraction notation for ratios.

b   Simplify ratios.

SKILL TO REVIEW

Objective 3.5b: Simplify fraction notation.

Simplify.

1. $\dfrac{16}{64}$ 2. $\dfrac{40}{24}$

a   RATIOS

RATIO

A **ratio** is the quotient of two quantities.

The average wind speed in Chicago is 10.4 mph. The average wind speed in Boston is 12.5 mph. The *ratio* of average wind speed in Chicago to average wind speed in Boston is written using colon notation,

Chicago wind speed → **10.4 : 12.5,** ← Boston wind speed

or fraction notation,

$\dfrac{10.4}{12.5}$.   ← Chicago wind speed
   ← Boston wind speed

We read both forms of notation as "the ratio of 10.4 to 12.5."

RATIO NOTATION

The **ratio** of a to b is expressed by the fraction notation $\dfrac{a}{b}$, where a is the numerator and b is the denominator, or by the colon notation $a : b$.

1. Find the ratio of 5 to 11.

2. Find the ratio of 57.3 to 86.1.

3. Find the ratio of $6\frac{3}{4}$ to $7\frac{2}{5}$.

EXAMPLE 1   Find the ratio of 7 to 8.

The ratio is $\dfrac{7}{8}$,   or $7 : 8$.

EXAMPLE 2   Find the ratio of 31.4 to 100.

The ratio is $\dfrac{31.4}{100}$,   or $31.4 : 100$.

EXAMPLE 3   Find the ratio of $4\frac{2}{3}$ to $5\frac{7}{8}$. You need not simplify.

The ratio is $\dfrac{4\frac{2}{3}}{5\frac{7}{8}}$,   or $4\frac{2}{3} : 5\frac{7}{8}$.

◀ Do Margin Exercises 1–3.

Answers

Skill to Review:

1. $\dfrac{1}{4}$ 2. $\dfrac{5}{3}$

Margin Exercises:

1. $\dfrac{5}{11}$, or 5 : 11   2. $\dfrac{57.3}{86.1}$, or 57.3 : 86.1

3. $\dfrac{6\frac{3}{4}}{7\frac{2}{5}}$, or $6\frac{3}{4} : 7\frac{2}{5}$

In most of our work, we will use fraction notation for ratios.

EXAMPLE 4 *Media Usage.* In 2012, Americans spent an average of 6 hr/month on Facebook and 147 hr/month watching TV. Find the ratio of average time spent on Facebook to average time spent watching TV.

Sources: comScore and Nielsen

The ratio is $\dfrac{6}{147}$.

EXAMPLE 5 *Record Rainfall.*   The greatest rainfall ever recorded in the United States during a 12-month period was 739 in. in Kukui, Maui, Hawaii, from December 1981 to December 1982. What is the ratio of amount of rainfall, in inches, to time, in months? of time, in months, to amount of rainfall, in inches?

Source: *Time Almanac*

The ratio of amount of rainfall, in inches, to time, in months, is

$$\dfrac{739}{12}. \quad \begin{array}{l}\leftarrow \text{Rainfall}\\ \leftarrow \text{Time}\end{array}$$

The ratio of time, in months, to amount of rainfall, in inches, is

$$\dfrac{12}{739}. \quad \begin{array}{l}\leftarrow \text{Time}\\ \leftarrow \text{Rainfall}\end{array}$$

EXAMPLE 6 Refer to the triangle below.

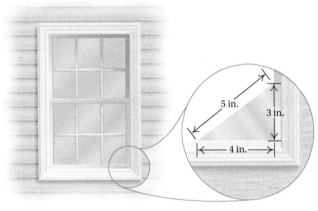

a) What is the ratio of the length of the longest side to the length of the shortest side?

$$\dfrac{5}{3} \quad \begin{array}{l}\leftarrow \text{Longest side}\\ \leftarrow \text{Shortest side}\end{array}$$

b) What is the ratio of the length of the shortest side to the length of the longest side?

$$\dfrac{3}{5} \quad \begin{array}{l}\leftarrow \text{Shortest side}\\ \leftarrow \text{Longest side}\end{array}$$

Do Exercises 4–6. ▶

4. *Record Snowfall.* The greatest snowfall recorded in North America during a 24-hr period was 76 in. in Silver Lake, Colorado, on April 14–15, 1921. What is the ratio of amount of snowfall, in inches, to time, in hours?

Source: U.S. Army Corps of Engineers

5. *Frozen Fruit Drinks.* A Berries & Kreme Chiller from Krispy Kreme contains 960 calories, while Smoothie King's MangoFest drink contains 258 calories. What is the ratio of the number of calories in the Krispy Kreme drink to the number of calories in the Smoothie King drink? of the number of calories in the Smoothie King drink to the number of calories in the Krispy Kreme drink?

Source: Physicians Committee for Responsible Medicine

GS **6.** In the triangle below, what is the ratio of the length of the shortest side to the length of the longest side?

Length of ____ side = ____
Length of ____ side   ____

Answers

4. $\dfrac{76}{24}$ 5. $\dfrac{960}{258}, \dfrac{258}{960}$ 6. $\dfrac{38.2}{55.5}$

Guided Solution:
6. $\dfrac{\text{shortest}}{\text{longest}}, \dfrac{38.2}{55.5}$

EXAMPLE 7 *Grammy Awards.* From 1959 to 2011, a total of 798 musical artists won Grammy awards for Record of the Year, Album of the Year, and Best New Artist. The bar graph below shows the numbers of award winners from four music genres.

Grammy Award Winners

SOURCES: *LA Times*; cbsnews.com

a) What is the ratio of the number of country winners to the number of rock winners?

b) What is the ratio of the number of pop, R&B, and country winners to the number of rock winners?

c) What is the ratio of the number of Grammy winners from genres other than rock, pop, R&B, and country to the total number of Grammy winners?

a) The ratio of the number of country winners to the number of rock winners is

$$\frac{57}{286}. \quad \begin{array}{l}\leftarrow \text{Country winners}\\ \leftarrow \text{Rock winners}\end{array}$$

b) The total number of pop, R&B, and country winners is

$$151 + 135 + 57 = 343.$$

The ratio of the number of these winners to the number of rock winners is

$$\frac{343}{286}. \quad \begin{array}{l}\leftarrow \text{Pop, R\&B, and country winners}\\ \leftarrow \text{Rock winners}\end{array}$$

c) The total number of rock, pop, R&B, and country Grammy winners is

$$286 + 151 + 135 + 57 = 629.$$

Thus the number of Grammy winners from other genres is

$$798 - 629 = 169.$$

The ratio of the number of Grammy winners from other genres to the total number of Grammy winners is

$$\frac{169}{798}. \quad \begin{array}{l}\leftarrow \text{Winners from other genres}\\ \leftarrow \text{Total number of winners}\end{array}$$

◀ **Do Exercise 7.**

---

7. *NBA Playoffs.* In the final game of the 2012 NBA Playoffs, the Miami Heat made a total of 67 baskets. Of these, 27 were free throws, 26 were two-point field goals, and the remainder were three-point field goals.

Source: nba.com

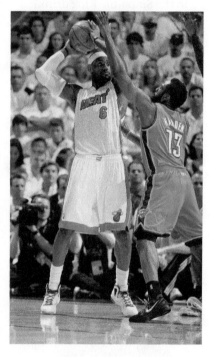

a) What was the ratio of the number of two-point field goals to the number of free throws?

b) What was the ratio of the number of three-point field goals to the total number of baskets?

Answers

7. (a) $\frac{26}{27}$ (b) $\frac{14}{67}$

b SIMPLIFYING NOTATION FOR RATIOS

Sometimes a ratio can be simplified. Simplifying provides a means of finding other numbers with the same ratio.

EXAMPLE 8 Find the ratio of 6 to 8. Then simplify to find two other numbers in the same ratio.

We write the ratio in fraction notation and then simplify:

$$\frac{6}{8} = \frac{2 \cdot 3}{2 \cdot 4} = \frac{2}{2} \cdot \frac{3}{4} = 1 \cdot \frac{3}{4} = \frac{3}{4}.$$

Thus, 3 and 4 have the same ratio as 6 and 8. We can express this by saying "6 is to 8 as 3 is to 4."

Do Exercise 8. ▷

EXAMPLE 9 Find the ratio of 2.4 to 10. Then simplify to find two other numbers in the same ratio.

We first write the ratio in fraction notation. Next, we multiply by 1 to clear the decimal from the numerator. Then we simplify.

$$\frac{2.4}{10} = \frac{2.4}{10} \cdot \frac{10}{10} = \frac{24}{100} = \frac{4 \cdot 6}{4 \cdot 25} = \frac{4}{4} \cdot \frac{6}{25} = \frac{6}{25}$$

Thus, 2.4 is to 10 as 6 is to 25.

Do Exercises 9 and 10. ▷

EXAMPLE 10 An HDTV screen that measures approximately 46 in. diagonally has a width of 40 in. and a height of $22\frac{1}{2}$ in. Find the ratio of width to height and simplify.

The ratio is $\dfrac{40}{22\frac{1}{2}} = \dfrac{40}{22.5} = \dfrac{40}{22.5} \cdot \dfrac{10}{10} = \dfrac{400}{225}$

$$= \frac{25 \cdot 16}{25 \cdot 9} = \frac{25}{25} \cdot \frac{16}{9}$$

$$= \frac{16}{9}.$$

Thus we can say that the ratio of width to height is 16 to 9, which can also be expressed as 16 : 9.

Do Exercise 11. ▷

8. Find the ratio of 18 to 27. Then simplify to find two other numbers in the same ratio.

GS 9. Find the ratio of 3.6 to 12. Then simplify to find two other numbers in the same ratio.

Ratio of 3.6 to 12: $\dfrac{\boxed{}}{\boxed{}}$

Simplifying:

$$\frac{3.6}{12} \cdot \frac{10}{\boxed{}} = \frac{\boxed{}}{120} = \frac{\boxed{} \cdot 3}{12 \cdot 10}$$

$$= \frac{\boxed{}}{12} \cdot \frac{3}{10} = \frac{\boxed{}}{10}$$

10. Find the ratio of 1.2 to 1.5. Then simplify to find two other numbers in the same ratio.

11. An HDTV screen that measures 44 in. diagonally has a width of 38.4 in. and a height of 21.6 in. Find the ratio of height to width and simplify.

Answers

8. 18 is to 27 as 2 is to 3.
9. 3.6 is to 12 as 3 is to 10.
10. 1.2 is to 1.5 as 4 is to 5. 11. $\frac{9}{16}$

Guided Solution:
9. $\frac{3.6}{12}$; 10, 36, 12, 12, 3

✓ Reading Check

Determine whether each statement is true or false.

_____ **RC1.** A ratio is a quotient.

_____ **RC2.** If there are 2 teachers and 27 students in a classroom, the ratio of students to teachers is 27 : 2.

_____ **RC3.** The ratio 6 : 7 can also be written $\dfrac{7}{6}$.

_____ **RC4.** The numbers 2 and 3 are in the same ratio as the numbers 4 and 9.

---

a   Find fraction notation for each ratio. You need not simplify.

1. 4 to 5

2. 3 to 2

3. 178 to 572

4. 329 to 967

5. 0.4 to 12

6. 2.3 to 22

7. 3.8 to 7.4

8. 0.6 to 0.7

9. 56.78 to 98.35

10. 456.2 to 333.1

11. $8\dfrac{3}{4}$ to $9\dfrac{5}{6}$

12. $10\dfrac{1}{2}$ to $43\dfrac{1}{4}$

Shark Attacks.   Of the 75 unprovoked shark attacks recorded worldwide in 2011, 29 occurred in U.S. waters. The bar graph below shows the breakdown by state. Use the graph for Exercises 13–16.

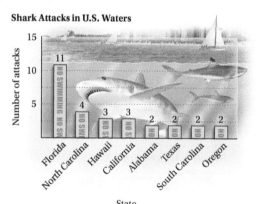

Shark Attacks in U.S. Waters

SOURCE: University of Florida

13. What is the ratio of the number of shark attacks in U.S. waters to the number of shark attacks worldwide?

14. What is the ratio of the number of shark attacks in North Carolina to the number of shark attacks in California?

15. What is the ratio of the number of shark attacks in Florida to the total number of shark attacks in the other seven states?

16. What is the ratio of the total number of shark attacks in states bordering the Pacific Ocean (Hawaii, California, and Oregon) to the total number of shark attacks in the other five states?

Copyright © 2015 Pearson Education, Inc.

17. *Tax Freedom Day.* Of the 366 days in 2012 (a leap year), the average American worked 107 days to pay his or her federal, state, and local taxes. Find the ratio of the number of days worked to pay taxes in 2012 to the number of days in the year.

Source: Tax Foundation

18. *Careers in Medicine.* The number of jobs for nurses is expected to increase by 711,900 between 2010 and 2020. During the same decade, the number of jobs for physicians is expected to increase by 168,300. Find the ratio of the increase in jobs for physicians to the increase in jobs for nurses.

Source: Bureau of Labor Statistics

19. *Music Album Sales.* In 2011, there were 104.8 million albums downloaded digitally and 3100.7 million albums sold on CDs. What is the ratio of downloads to CD sales? of CD sales to downloads?

Source: Recording Industry of America

20. *Silicon in the Earth's Crust.* Every 100 tons of the earth's crust contains about 28 tons of silicon. What is the ratio of the weight of silicon to the weight of crust? of the weight of crust to the weight of silicon?

Source: *The Handy Science Answer Book*

21. *Field Hockey.* A diagram of the playing area for field hockey is shown below. What is the ratio of width to length? of length to width?

Source: *Sports: The Complete Visual Reference*

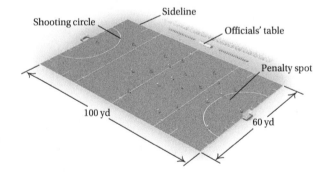

22. *The Leaning Tower of Pisa.* The Leaning Tower of Pisa was reopened to the public in 2001 following a 10-yr stabilization project. The 184.5-ft tower now leans about 13 ft from its base. What is the ratio of the distance that it leans to its height? of its height to the distance that it leans?

Source: CNN

b Find the ratio of the first number to the second and simplify.

23. 4 to 6

24. 6 to 10

25. 18 to 24

26. 28 to 36

27. 4.8 to 10 **28.** 5.6 to 10 **29.** 2.8 to 3.6 **30.** 4.8 to 6.4

31. 20 to 30 **32.** 40 to 60 **33.** 56 to 100 **34.** 42 to 100

35. 128 to 256 **36.** 232 to 116 **37.** 0.48 to 0.64 **38.** 0.32 to 0.96

39. For this rectangle, find the ratios of length to width and of width to length.

478 ft

213 ft

40. For this right triangle, find the ratios of shortest side length to longest side length and of longest length to shortest length.

47.5 m

107.3 m

96.2 m

Skill Maintenance

Add. Simplify if possible.

41. $18{,}468 + 390{,}082$ [1.2a]

42. $24 + 3.006$ [5.2a]

43. $4.2 + 28.07 - 365$ [5.2c]

44. $\dfrac{1}{3} + \dfrac{3}{10}$ [4.2a]

45. $\dfrac{3}{8} + \left(-\dfrac{7}{12}\right)$ [4.2a]

46. $4\dfrac{5}{6} + 9\dfrac{1}{2}$ [4.5a]

Subtract. Simplify if possible.

47. $982{,}001 - 39{,}782$ [1.3a]

48. $12.5 - 9.9$ [5.2b]

49. $-54.1 - 7.29$ [5.2c]

50. $\dfrac{9}{16} - \dfrac{1}{2}$ [4.3a]

51. $8\dfrac{2}{3} - 6\dfrac{4}{5}$ [4.5b]

52. $11 - 6\dfrac{1}{3}$ [4.5b]

Synthesis

53. Find the ratio of $3\frac{3}{4}$ to $5\frac{7}{8}$ and simplify.

Fertilizer.   Exercises 54 and 55 refer to a common lawn fertilizer known as "5, 10, 15." This mixture contains 5 parts of potassium for every 10 parts of phosphorus and 15 parts of nitrogen. (This is often denoted 5 : 10 : 15.)

54. Find and simplify the ratio of potassium to nitrogen and of nitrogen to phosphorus.

55. Simplify the ratio 5 : 10 : 15.

Copyright © 2015 Pearson Education, Inc.

Rates and Unit Prices

a RATES

A 2013 Honda Odyssey can travel 504 mi on 18 gal of gasoline. Let's consider the ratio of miles to gallons:

Source: Kia Motors America, Inc.

$$\frac{504 \text{ mi}}{18 \text{ gal}} = \frac{504}{18} \frac{\text{miles}}{\text{gallon}} = \frac{28}{1} \frac{\text{miles}}{\text{gallon}}$$
$$= 28 \text{ miles per gallon} = 28 \text{ mpg.}$$

> "per" means "division," or "for each."

The ratio

$$\frac{504 \text{ mi}}{18 \text{ gal}}, \quad \text{or} \quad \frac{504}{18} \frac{\text{mi}}{\text{gal}}, \quad \text{or} \quad 28 \text{ mpg,}$$

is called a **rate**.

RATE

When a ratio is used to compare two different kinds of measure, we call it a **rate**.

Suppose David's car travels 475.4 mi on 16.8 gal of gasoline. Is the gas mileage (mpg) of his car better than that of the Honda Odyssey above? To determine this, it helps to convert the ratio to decimal notation and perhaps round. Thus we have

$$\frac{475.4 \text{ miles}}{16.8 \text{ gallons}} = \frac{475.4}{16.8} \text{mpg} \approx 28.298 \text{ mpg.}$$

Since $28.298 > 28$, David's car gets better gas mileage than the Honda Odyssey does.

EXAMPLE 1   It takes 60 oz of grass seed to seed 3000 sq ft of lawn. What is the rate in ounces per square foot?

$$\frac{60 \text{ oz}}{3000 \text{ sq ft}} = \frac{1}{50} \frac{\text{oz}}{\text{sq ft}}, \quad \text{or} \quad 0.02 \frac{\text{oz}}{\text{sq ft}}$$

EXAMPLE 2   Martina bought 5 lb of organic russet potatoes for $4.99. What was the rate in cents per pound?

$$\frac{\$4.99}{5 \text{ lb}} = \frac{499 \text{ cents}}{5 \text{ lb}} = 99.8\text{¢/lb}$$

OBJECTIVES

a   Give the ratio of two different measures as a rate.

b   Find unit prices and use them to compare purchases.

SKILL TO REVIEW

Objective 5.4a: Divide using decimal notation.

Divide.

1. $15\overline{)634.5}$ **2.** $2.4\overline{)6}$

Answers

Skill to Review:
1. 42.3   **2.** 2.5

EXAMPLE 3 *Hourly Wage.* In 2011, Walmart employees earned, on average, $470 for a 40-hr work week. What was the rate of pay per hour?

Source: "Living Wage Policies and Big-Box Retail," UC Berkeley Center for Labor Research and Education, Ken Jacobs, Dave Graham-Squire, and Stephanie Luce, at http://laborcenter.berkeley.edu/retail/bigbox_livingwage_policies11.pdf

The rate of pay is the ratio of money earned to length of time worked, or

$$\frac{\$470}{40 \text{ hr}} = \frac{470}{40} \frac{\text{dollars}}{\text{hr}} = 11.75 \frac{\text{dollars}}{\text{hr}}, \quad \text{or} \quad \$11.75 \text{ per hr.}$$

EXAMPLE 4 *Ratio of Strikeouts to Home Runs.* In the 2012 baseball season, Miguel Cabrera of the Detroit Tigers had 98 strikeouts and 44 home runs. What was his strikeout to home-run rate?

Source: Major League Baseball

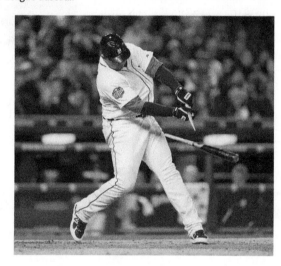

$$\frac{98 \text{ strikeouts}}{44 \text{ home runs}} = \frac{98}{44} \frac{\text{strikeouts}}{\text{home runs}} = \frac{98}{44} \text{ strikeouts per home run}$$
$$\approx 2.227 \text{ strikeouts per home run}$$

◀ Do Exercises 1–5.

b UNIT PRICING

> **UNIT PRICE**
>
> A **unit price**, or **unit rate**, is the ratio of price to the number of units.

EXAMPLE 5 *Unit Price of Pears.* Ruth bought a 15.2-oz can of pears for $1.30. What is the unit price in cents per ounce?

$$\text{Unit price} = \frac{\text{Price}}{\text{Number of units}}$$
$$= \frac{\$1.30}{15.2 \text{ oz}} = \frac{130 \text{ cents}}{15.2 \text{ oz}} = \frac{130}{15.2} \frac{\text{cents}}{\text{oz}}$$
$$\approx 8.553 \text{ cents per ounce}$$

◀ Do Exercise 6.

A ratio of distance traveled to time is called a *speed*. What is the rate, or speed, in miles per hour?

1. 45 mi, 9 hr

2. 120 mi, 10 hr

What is the rate, or speed, in feet per second?

3. 2200 ft, 2 sec

4. 52 ft, 13 sec GS

$$\frac{\boxed{} \text{ ft}}{\boxed{} \text{ sec}} = \boxed{} \text{ ft/sec}$$

5. *Babe Ruth.* In his baseball career, Babe Ruth had 1330 strikeouts and 714 home runs. What was his home-run to strikeout rate?

Source: Major League Baseball

6. Unit Price of Pasta Sauce. GS Gregory bought a 26-oz jar of pasta sauce for $2.79. What is the unit price in cents per ounce?

$$\text{Unit price} = \frac{\text{Price}}{\text{Number of units}}$$
$$= \frac{\$\boxed{}}{26 \text{ oz}} = \frac{\boxed{} \text{ cents}}{26 \text{ oz}}$$
$$= \frac{\boxed{}}{26} \frac{\text{cents}}{\text{oz}} \approx \boxed{} \text{¢/oz}$$

Answers

1. 5 mi/hr, or 5 mph   **2.** 12 mi/hr, or 12 mph
3. 1100 ft/sec   **4.** 4 ft/sec
5. $\frac{714}{1330}$ home run per strikeout ≈ 0.537 home run per strikeout   **6.** 10.731¢/oz
Guided Solutions:
4. $\frac{52}{13}$, 4   **6.** 2.79, 279, 279, 10.731

Unit prices enable us to do comparison shopping and determine the best buy for a product on the basis of price. It is often helpful to change all prices to cents so that we can compare unit prices more easily.

EXAMPLE 6 *Unit Price of Salad Dressing.* At the request of his customers, Angelo started bottling and selling the basil and lemon salad dressing that he serves in his café. The dressing is sold in four sizes of containers as listed in the table below. Compute the unit price of each size of container and determine which size is the best buy on the basis of unit price alone.

Size	Price	Unit Price
10 oz	$2.49	
16 oz	$3.59	
20 oz	$4.09	
32 oz	$6.79	

We compute the unit price of each size and fill in the chart:

10 oz: $\dfrac{\$2.49}{10\,\text{oz}} = \dfrac{249\,\text{cents}}{10\,\text{oz}} = \dfrac{249}{10}\dfrac{\text{cents}}{\text{oz}} = 24.900¢/\text{oz};$

16 oz: $\dfrac{\$3.59}{16\,\text{oz}} = \dfrac{359\,\text{cents}}{16\,\text{oz}} = \dfrac{359}{16}\dfrac{\text{cents}}{\text{oz}} \approx 22.438¢/\text{oz};$

20 oz: $\dfrac{\$4.09}{20\,\text{oz}} = \dfrac{409\,\text{cents}}{20\,\text{oz}} = \dfrac{409}{20}\dfrac{\text{cents}}{\text{oz}} = 20.450¢/\text{oz};$

32 oz: $\dfrac{\$6.79}{32\,\text{oz}} = \dfrac{679\,\text{cents}}{32\,\text{oz}} = \dfrac{679}{32}\dfrac{\text{cents}}{\text{oz}} \approx 21.219¢/\text{oz}.$

Size	Price	Unit Price
10 oz	$2.49	24.900¢/oz
16 oz	$3.59	22.438¢/oz
20 oz	$4.09	20.450¢/oz Lowest unit price
32 oz	$6.79	21.219¢/oz

On the basis of unit price alone, we see that the 20-oz container is the best buy.

Do Exercise 7. ▶

Although we often think that "bigger is cheaper," this is not always the case, as we see in Example 6. In addition, even when a larger package has a lower unit price than a smaller package, it still might not be the best buy for you. For example, some of the food in a large package could spoil before it is used, or you might not have room to store a large package.

7. *Cost of Mayonnaise.*
Complete the following table for Hellmann's mayonnaise sold on an online shopping site. Which size has the lowest unit price?

Source: Peapod.com

Size	Price	Unit Price
8 oz	$2.79	
10 oz	$3.69	
30 oz	$5.39	

Answers

7. 34.875¢/oz; 36.900¢/oz; 17.967¢/oz; the 30-oz size has the lowest unit price.

☑ Reading Check

Complete each sentence with the correct quantity from the list at the right, given the following information.

Jason wrote an 8-page essay in 9 hr.

Keri graded 8 essays in 3 hr.

RC1. Jason wrote at a rate of _____ pages/hr.

RC2. Jason wrote at a rate of _____ hr/page.

RC3. Keri graded at a rate of _____ hr/essay.

RC4. Keri graded at a rate of _____ essays/hr.

a) $\frac{8}{3}$

b) $\frac{8}{9}$

c) $\frac{9}{8}$

d) $\frac{3}{8}$

a In Exercises 1–4, find each rate, or speed, as a ratio of distance to time. Round to the nearest hundredth where appropriate.

1. 120 km, 3 hr

2. 18 mi, 9 hr

3. 217 mi, 29 sec

4. 443 m, 48 sec

5. *Chevrolet Malibu LS—City Driving.* A 2013 Chevrolet Malibu LS will travel 312.5 mi on 12.5 gal of gasoline in city driving. What is the rate in miles per gallon?

Source: Chevrolet

6. *Mazda3—City Driving.* A 2013 Mazda3 i SV will travel 348 mi on 14.5 gal of gasoline in city driving. What is the rate in miles per gallon?

Source: mazdausa.com

7. *Mazda3—Highway Driving.* A 2013 Mazda3 i SV will travel 643.5 mi on 19.5 gal of gasoline in highway driving. What is the rate in miles per gallon?

Source: mazdausa.com

8. *Chevrolet Malibu LS—Highway Driving.* A 2013 Chevrolet Malibu LS will travel 499.5 mi on 13.5 gal of gasoline in highway driving. What is the rate in miles per gallon?

Source: Chevrolet

9. *Population Density of Monaco.* Monaco is a tiny country on the Mediterranean coast of France. It has an area of 0.75 sq mi and a population of 35,427 people. What is the rate of number of people per square mile? The rate of people per square mile is called the *population density.* Monaco has the highest population density of any country in the world.

Source: World Bank

10. *Population Density of Australia.* The continent of Australia, with the island state of Tasmania, has an area of 2,967,893 sq mi and a population of 22,620,600 people. What is the rate of number of people per square mile? The rate of people per square mile is called the *population density.* Australia has one of the lowest population densities in the world.

Source: World Bank

Copyright © 2015 Pearson Education, Inc.

11. A car is driven 500 mi in 20 hr. What is the rate in miles per hour? in hours per mile?

12. A student eats 3 hamburgers in 15 min. What is the rate in hamburgers per minute? in minutes per hamburger?

13. *Broadway Musicals.* In the 17 years from 1987 through 2003, the musical *Les Misérables* was performed on Broadway 6680 times. What was the average rate of performances per year?

Source: broadwaymusicalhome.com

14. *Employment Growth.* In the 10 years from 2010 to 2020, the number of jobs for interpreters and translators is expected to grow by 24,600. What is the expected average rate of growth in jobs per year?

Source: U.S. Bureau of Labor Statistics

15. *Speed of Light.* Light travels 186,000 mi in 1 sec. What is its rate, or speed, in miles per second?

Source: *The Handy Science Answer Book*

16. *Speed of Sound.* Sound travels 1100 ft in 1 sec. What is its rate, or speed, in feet per second?

Source: *The Handy Science Answer Book*

17. Impulses in nerve fibers travel 310 km in 2.5 hr. What is the rate, or speed, in kilometers per hour?

18. A black racer snake can travel 4.6 km in 2 hr. What is its rate, or speed, in kilometers per hour?

19. *Lawn Watering.* Watering a lawn adequately requires 623 gal of water for every 1000 ft². What is the rate in gallons per square foot?

20. A car is driven 200 km on 40 L of gasoline. What is the rate in kilometers per liter?

21. *Elephant Heart Rate.* The heart of an elephant, at rest, beats an average of 1500 beats in 60 min. What is the rate in beats per minute?

Source: *The Handy Science Answer Book*

22. *Human Heart Rate.* The heart of a human, at rest, beats an average of 4200 beats in 60 min. What is the rate in beats per minute?

Source: *The Handy Science Answer Book*

b Find each unit price in Exercises 23–30. Then, in each exercise, determine which size is the better buy based on unit price alone.

23. *Hidden Valley Ranch Dressing.*

Size	Price	Unit Price
16 oz	$4.19	
20 oz	$5.29	

24. *Miracle Whip.*

Size	Price	Unit Price
32 oz	$5.29	
48 oz	$8.29	

25. *Cascade Powder Detergent.*

Size	Price	Unit Price
45 oz	$5.90	
75 oz	$8.59	

26. *Bush's Homestyle Baked Beans.*

Size	Price	Unit Price
16 oz	$2.99	
28 oz	$4.51	

27. *Jif Creamy Peanut Butter.*

Size	Price	Unit Price
18 oz	$3.28	
28 oz	$4.89	

28. *Hills Brothers Coffee.*

Size	Price	Unit Price
26 oz	$9.99	
39 oz	$14.99	

29. *Campbell's Condensed Tomato Soup.*

Size	Price	Unit Price
10.7 oz	$1.09	
26 oz	$2.69	

30. *Nabisco Saltines.*

Size	Price	Unit Price
16 oz	$3.59	
32 oz	$5.19	

Copyright © 2015 Pearson Education, Inc.

Find the unit price of each brand in Exercises 31–34. Then, in each exercise, determine which brand is the better buy based on unit price alone.

31. *Vanilla Ice Cream.*

Brand	Size	Price
B	32 oz	$5.99
E	48 oz	$6.99

32. *Orange Juice.*

Brand	Size	Price
M	54 oz	$4.79
T	59 oz	$5.99

33. *Tomato Ketchup.*

Brand	Size	Price
A	24 oz	$2.49
B	36 oz	$3.29
H	46 oz	$3.69

34. *Yellow Mustard.*

Brand	Size	Price
F	14 oz	$1.29
G	19 oz	$1.99
P	20 oz	$2.49

Skill Maintenance

Multiply. Simplify, if possible.

35. 25×462 [1.4a]

36. 8.4×80.892 [5.3a]

37. 0.01×274.568 [5.3a]

38. $\dfrac{50}{9} \cdot \left(-\dfrac{6}{5}\right)$ [3.6a]

39. $3\dfrac{4}{5} \cdot 2\dfrac{1}{4}$ [4.6a]

40. $-4\dfrac{1}{10} \cdot 3\dfrac{1}{3}$ [4.6a]

Divide. Simplify, if possible.

41. $4000 \div 32$ [1.5a]

42. $95 \div 10$ [5.4a]

43. $-80.892 \div 8.4$ [5.4a]

44. $\dfrac{50}{9} \div \dfrac{6}{5}$ [3.7b]

45. $200 \div 1\dfrac{1}{3}$ [4.6b]

46. $4\dfrac{6}{7} \div \left(-\dfrac{1}{4}\right)$ [4.6b]

Synthesis

47. Manufacturers sometimes change the sizes of their containers in such a way that the consumer thinks the price of a product has been lowered when, in reality, a higher unit price is being charged.

   Some aluminum juice cans are now concave (curved in) on the bottom. Suppose the volume of the can in the figure has been reduced from 6 fl oz to 5.5 fl oz, and the price of each can has been reduced from 65¢ to 60¢. Find the unit price of each container in cents per ounce.

$\frac{5}{16}$ in.

$1\frac{13}{16}$ in.

$2\frac{1}{16}$ in.

6.3

Proportions

OBJECTIVES

a Determine whether two pairs of numbers are proportional.

b Solve proportions.

SKILL TO REVIEW

Objective 3.5c: Use the test for equality to determine whether two fractions name the same number.

Use $=$ or $\neq$ for $\square$ to write a true sentence.

1. $\dfrac{18}{12} \square \dfrac{9}{6}$ **2.** $\dfrac{-4}{7} \square \dfrac{-5}{8}$

Determine whether the two pairs of numbers are proportional.

1. 3, 4 and 6, 8

2. 1, 4 and 10, 39

3. 1, 2 and 20, 39 **GS**

We compare cross products.

$1 \cdot \boxed{} = \boxed{}$ $\dfrac{1}{2} \; ? \; \dfrac{20}{39}$

$2 \cdot \boxed{} = \boxed{}$

Since $39 \neq 40$, the numbers $\underline{}$ proportional.
are/are not

Determine whether the two pairs of numbers are proportional.

4. 6.4, 12.8 and 5.3, 10.6

5. 6.8, 7.4 and 3.4, 4.2

Answers

Skill to Review:
1. $=$ 2. $\neq$

Margin Exercises:
1. Yes   2. No   3. No   4. Yes   5. No

Guided Solution:
3. 39, 39, 20, 40; are not

a PROPORTIONS

When two pairs of numbers, such as 3, 2 and 6, 4, have the same ratio, we say that they are **proportional**. The equation

$$\frac{3}{2} = \frac{6}{4}$$

states that the pairs 3, 2 and 6, 4 are proportional. Such an equation is called a **proportion**. We sometimes read $\frac{3}{2} = \frac{6}{4}$ as "3 is to 2 as 6 is to 4."

Since ratios can be written using fraction notation, we can use the test for equality of fractions to determine whether two ratios are the same.

> ### A TEST FOR EQUALITY OF FRACTIONS
>
> Two fractions are equal if their cross products are equal.

EXAMPLE 1 Determine whether 1, 2 and 3, 6 are proportional.

We can use cross products.

$$1 \cdot 6 = 6 \qquad \frac{1}{2} \overset{?}{=} \frac{3}{6} \qquad 2 \cdot 3 = 6$$

Since the cross products are the same, $6 = 6$, we know that $\frac{1}{2} = \frac{3}{6}$, so the numbers are proportional.

EXAMPLE 2 Determine whether 2, 5 and 4, 7 are proportional.

We can use cross products.

$$2 \cdot 7 = 14 \qquad \frac{2}{5} \overset{?}{=} \frac{4}{7} \qquad 5 \cdot 4 = 20$$

Since the cross products are not the same, $14 \neq 20$, we know that $\frac{2}{5} \neq \frac{4}{7}$, so the numbers are not proportional.

◀ Do Margin Exercises 1–3.

EXAMPLE 3 Determine whether 3.2, 4.8 and 0.16, 0.24 are proportional.

We can use cross products.

$$3.2 \times 0.24 = 0.768 \qquad \frac{3.2}{4.8} \overset{?}{=} \frac{0.16}{0.24} \qquad 4.8 \times 0.16 = 0.768$$

Since the cross products are the same, $0.768 = 0.768$, we know that $\frac{3.2}{4.8} = \frac{0.16}{0.24}$, so the numbers are proportional.

◀ Do Exercises 4 and 5.

EXAMPLE 4 Determine whether $4\frac{2}{3}$, $5\frac{1}{2}$ and $8\frac{7}{8}$, $16\frac{1}{3}$ are proportional.

We can use cross products:

$$4\frac{2}{3} \cdot 16\frac{1}{3} = \frac{14}{3} \cdot \frac{49}{3} \qquad \frac{4\frac{2}{3}}{5\frac{1}{2}} \overset{?}{=} \frac{8\frac{7}{8}}{16\frac{1}{3}} \qquad 5\frac{1}{2} \cdot 8\frac{7}{8} = \frac{11}{2} \cdot \frac{71}{8}$$

$$= \frac{686}{9} \qquad\qquad\qquad\qquad = \frac{781}{16}$$

$$= 76\frac{2}{9}; \qquad\qquad\qquad\qquad = 48\frac{13}{16}.$$

Since the cross products are not the same, $76\frac{2}{9} \neq 48\frac{13}{16}$, we know that the numbers are not proportional.

Do Exercise 6. ▶

6. Determine whether $4\frac{2}{3}$, $5\frac{1}{2}$ and 14, $16\frac{1}{2}$ are proportional.

b SOLVING PROPORTIONS

One way to solve a proportion is to use cross products. Then we can divide on both sides to get the variable alone.

EXAMPLE 5 Solve the proportion $\frac{x}{3} = \frac{4}{6}$.

$$\frac{x}{3} = \frac{4}{6}$$

$x \cdot 6 = 3 \cdot 4$ Equating cross products (finding cross products and setting them equal)

$$\frac{x \cdot 6}{6} = \frac{3 \cdot 4}{6}$$ Dividing by 6 on both sides

$$x = \frac{3 \cdot 4}{6} = \frac{12}{6} = 2$$

We can check that 2 is the solution by replacing x with 2 and finding cross products:

$$2 \cdot 6 = 12 \qquad \frac{2}{3} \overset{?}{=} \frac{4}{6} \qquad 3 \cdot 4 = 12.$$

Since the cross products are the same, it follows that $\frac{2}{3} = \frac{4}{6}$. Thus the pairs of numbers 2, 3 and 4, 6 are proportional, and 2 is the solution of the proportion. ◼

SOLVING PROPORTIONS

To solve $\dfrac{x}{a} = \dfrac{c}{d}$ for x, equate *cross products* and divide on both sides to get x alone.

Do Exercise 7. ▶

7. Solve: $\dfrac{x}{63} = \dfrac{2}{9}$.

Answers
6. Yes   **7.** 14

8. Solve: $\dfrac{x}{9} = \dfrac{5}{4}$. Write a mixed numeral for the answer.

$$\frac{x}{9} = \frac{5}{4}$$

$$x \cdot 4 = 9 \cdot \boxed{}$$

$$\frac{x \cdot 4}{\boxed{}} = \frac{9 \cdot 5}{\boxed{}}$$

$$x = \frac{\boxed{}}{4} = \boxed{}\frac{\boxed{}}{4}$$

EXAMPLE 6 Solve: $\dfrac{x}{7} = \dfrac{5}{3}$. Write a mixed numeral for the answer.

We have

$$\frac{x}{7} = \frac{5}{3}$$

$$x \cdot 3 = 7 \cdot 5 \qquad \text{Equating cross products}$$

$$\frac{x \cdot 3}{3} = \frac{7 \cdot 5}{3} \qquad \text{Dividing by 3}$$

$$x = \frac{7 \cdot 5}{3} = \frac{35}{3}, \text{ or } 11\frac{2}{3}.$$

The solution is $11\frac{2}{3}$.

◀ **Do Exercise 8.**

EXAMPLE 7 Solve: $\dfrac{7.7}{15.4} = \dfrac{y}{2.2}$.

We have

$$\frac{7.7}{15.4} = \frac{y}{2.2}$$

$$7.7 \times 2.2 = 15.4 \times y \qquad \text{Equating cross products}$$

$$\frac{7.7 \times 2.2}{15.4} = \frac{15.4 \times y}{15.4} \qquad \text{Dividing by 15.4}$$

$$\frac{7.7 \times 2.2}{15.4} = y$$

$$\frac{16.94}{15.4} = y \qquad \text{Multiplying}$$

$$1.1 = y. \qquad \text{Dividing: } 15.4\,\overline{)1\,6.9_\wedge 4}$$

$$\begin{array}{r} 1.1 \\ 15.4\,\overline{)16.9_\wedge 4} \\ \underline{15\,4} \\ 1\,5\,4 \\ \underline{1\,5\,4} \\ 0 \end{array}$$

The solution is 1.1.

EXAMPLE 8 Solve: $\dfrac{8}{x} = \dfrac{5}{3}$. Write decimal notation for the answer.

We have

$$\frac{8}{x} = \frac{5}{3}$$

$$8 \cdot 3 = x \cdot 5 \qquad \text{Equating cross products}$$

$$\frac{8 \cdot 3}{5} = x \qquad \text{Dividing by 5}$$

$$\frac{24}{5} = x \qquad \text{Multiplying}$$

$$4.8 = x. \qquad \text{Simplifying}$$

The solution is 4.8.

◀ **Do Exercises 9 and 10.**

9. Solve: $\dfrac{21}{5} = \dfrac{n}{2.5}$.

10. Solve: $\dfrac{6}{x} = \dfrac{25}{11}$. Write decimal notation for the answer.

Answers

8. $11\frac{1}{4}$ **9.** 10.5   **10.** 2.64

Guided Solution:
8. 5, 4, 4, 45, 11, 1

EXAMPLE 9 Solve: $\dfrac{3.4}{4.93} = \dfrac{10}{n}$.

We have

$$\frac{3.4}{4.93} = \frac{10}{n}$$

$$3.4 \times n = 4.93 \times 10 \qquad \text{Equating cross products}$$

$$\frac{3.4 \times n}{3.4} = \frac{4.93 \times 10}{3.4} \qquad \text{Dividing by 3.4}$$

$$n = \frac{4.93 \times 10}{3.4}$$

$$n = \frac{49.3}{3.4} \qquad \text{Multiplying}$$

$$n = 14.5. \qquad \text{Dividing}$$

The solution is 14.5.

Do Exercise 11. ▶

11. Solve: $\dfrac{0.4}{0.9} = \dfrac{4.8}{t}$.

EXAMPLE 10 Solve: $\dfrac{4\frac{2}{3}}{5\frac{1}{2}} = \dfrac{14}{x}$.

We have

$$\frac{4\frac{2}{3}}{5\frac{1}{2}} = \frac{14}{x}$$

$$4\frac{2}{3} \cdot x = 5\frac{1}{2} \cdot 14 \qquad \text{Equating cross products}$$

$$\frac{14}{3} \cdot x = \frac{11}{2} \cdot 14 \qquad \text{Converting to fraction notation}$$

$$\frac{\frac{14}{3} \cdot x}{\frac{14}{3}} = \frac{\frac{11}{2} \cdot 14}{\frac{14}{3}} \qquad \text{Dividing by } \frac{14}{3}$$

$$x = \frac{11}{2} \cdot 14 \div \frac{14}{3}$$

$$x = \frac{11}{2} \cdot 14 \cdot \frac{3}{14} \qquad \text{Multiplying by the reciprocal of the divisor}$$

$$x = \frac{11 \cdot 3}{2} \qquad \begin{array}{l}\text{Simplifying by removing a factor} \\ \text{of 1: } \frac{14}{14} = 1\end{array}$$

$$x = \frac{33}{2}, \text{ or } 16\frac{1}{2}.$$

The solution is $\frac{33}{2}$, or $16\frac{1}{2}$.

Do Exercise 12. ▶

12. Solve:

$$\frac{8\frac{1}{3}}{x} = \frac{10\frac{1}{2}}{3\frac{3}{4}}.$$

Answers

11. 10.8 12. $\dfrac{125}{42}$, or $2\dfrac{41}{42}$

SECTION 6.3 Proportions   **347**

✓ Reading Check

Complete each statement with the appropriate word from the following list.

| cross products | proportion | proportional | ratio |

RC1. The quotient of two quantities is their _____.

RC2. Two pairs of numbers that have the same ratio are _____.

RC3. A _____ states that two pairs of numbers have the same ratio.

RC4. For the equation $\dfrac{2}{x} = \dfrac{3}{y}$, the _____ are $2y$ and $3x$.

a Determine whether the two pairs of numbers are proportional.

1. $5, 6$ and $7, 9$ **2.** $7, 5$ and $6, 4$ **3.** $1, 2$ and $10, 20$ **4.** $7, 3$ and $21, 9$

5. $2.4, 3.6$ and $1.8, 2.7$ **6.** $4.5, 3.8$ and $6.7, 5.2$

7. $5\dfrac{1}{3}, 8\dfrac{1}{4}$ and $2\dfrac{1}{5}, 9\dfrac{1}{2}$ **8.** $2\dfrac{1}{3}, 3\dfrac{1}{2}$ and $14, 21$

b Solve.

9. $\dfrac{18}{4} = \dfrac{x}{10}$ **10.** $\dfrac{x}{45} = \dfrac{20}{25}$ **11.** $\dfrac{x}{8} = \dfrac{9}{6}$ **12.** $\dfrac{8}{10} = \dfrac{n}{5}$

13. $\dfrac{t}{12} = \dfrac{5}{6}$ **14.** $\dfrac{12}{4} = \dfrac{x}{3}$ **15.** $\dfrac{2}{5} = \dfrac{8}{n}$ **16.** $\dfrac{10}{6} = \dfrac{5}{x}$

17. $\dfrac{n}{15} = \dfrac{10}{30}$ **18.** $\dfrac{2}{24} = \dfrac{x}{36}$ **19.** $\dfrac{16}{12} = \dfrac{24}{x}$ **20.** $\dfrac{8}{12} = \dfrac{20}{x}$

21. $\dfrac{6}{11} = \dfrac{12}{x}$ **22.** $\dfrac{8}{9} = \dfrac{32}{n}$ **23.** $\dfrac{20}{7} = \dfrac{80}{x}$ **24.** $\dfrac{36}{x} = \dfrac{9}{5}$

Copyright © 2015 Pearson Education, Inc.

25. $\dfrac{12}{9} = \dfrac{x}{7}$

26. $\dfrac{x}{20} = \dfrac{16}{15}$

27. $\dfrac{x}{13} = \dfrac{2}{9}$

28. $\dfrac{8}{11} = \dfrac{x}{5}$

29. $\dfrac{100}{25} = \dfrac{20}{n}$

30. $\dfrac{35}{125} = \dfrac{7}{m}$

31. $\dfrac{6}{y} = \dfrac{18}{15}$

32. $\dfrac{15}{y} = \dfrac{3}{4}$

33. $\dfrac{x}{3} = \dfrac{0}{9}$

34. $\dfrac{x}{6} = \dfrac{1}{6}$

35. $\dfrac{1}{2} = \dfrac{7}{x}$

36. $\dfrac{2}{5} = \dfrac{12}{x}$

37. $\dfrac{1.2}{4} = \dfrac{x}{9}$

38. $\dfrac{x}{11} = \dfrac{7.1}{2}$

39. $\dfrac{8}{2.4} = \dfrac{6}{y}$

40. $\dfrac{3}{y} = \dfrac{5}{4.5}$

41. $\dfrac{t}{0.16} = \dfrac{0.15}{0.40}$

42. $\dfrac{0.12}{0.04} = \dfrac{t}{0.32}$

43. $\dfrac{0.5}{n} = \dfrac{2.5}{3.5}$

44. $\dfrac{6.3}{0.9} = \dfrac{0.7}{n}$

45. $\dfrac{1.28}{3.76} = \dfrac{4.28}{y}$

46. $\dfrac{10.4}{12.4} = \dfrac{6.76}{t}$

47. $\dfrac{7}{\frac{1}{4}} = \dfrac{28}{x}$

48. $\dfrac{5}{\frac{1}{3}} = \dfrac{3}{x}$

49. $\dfrac{\frac{1}{5}}{\frac{1}{10}} = \dfrac{\frac{1}{10}}{x}$

50. $\dfrac{\frac{1}{4}}{\frac{1}{2}} = \dfrac{\frac{1}{2}}{x}$

51. $\dfrac{y}{\frac{3}{5}} = \dfrac{\frac{7}{12}}{\frac{14}{15}}$

52. $\dfrac{\frac{5}{8}}{\frac{5}{4}} = \dfrac{y}{\frac{3}{2}}$

53. $\dfrac{x}{1\frac{3}{5}} = \dfrac{2}{15}$

54. $\dfrac{1}{7} = \dfrac{x}{4\frac{1}{2}}$

55. $\dfrac{2\frac{1}{2}}{3\frac{1}{3}} = \dfrac{x}{4\frac{1}{4}}$

56. $\dfrac{3\frac{1}{2}}{y} = \dfrac{6\frac{1}{2}}{4\frac{2}{3}}$

57. $\dfrac{5\frac{1}{5}}{6\frac{1}{6}} = \dfrac{y}{3\frac{1}{2}}$

58. $\dfrac{10\frac{3}{8}}{12\frac{2}{3}} = \dfrac{5\frac{3}{4}}{y}$

Skill Maintenance

59. *Drive-in Movie Theaters.* The number of drive-in movie theaters in the United States has declined steadily since the 1950s. In 2012, there were 365 drive-in theaters. This is 3698 fewer than in 1958. How many drive-in movie theaters were there in 1958? [1.8a]

Source: Drive-Ins.com

60. *Bird Feeders.* After Raena poured a 4-lb bag of birdseed into her new bird feeder, the feeder was $\frac{2}{3}$ full. How much seed does the feeder hold when it is full? [3.7d]

61. Mariah bought $\frac{3}{4}$ lb of cheese at the city market and gave $\frac{1}{2}$ lb of it to Lindsay. How much cheese did Mariah have left? [4.3d]

62. David bought $\frac{3}{4}$ lb of fudge and gave $\frac{1}{2}$ of it to Chris. How much fudge did he give to Chris? [3.6b]

63. Rocky is $187\frac{1}{10}$ cm tall and his daughter is $180\frac{3}{4}$ cm tall. How much taller is Rocky? [4.5c]

64. A serving of fish steak (cross section) is generally $\frac{1}{2}$ lb. How many servings can be prepared from a cleaned $18\frac{3}{4}$-lb tuna? [4.6c]

65. *Expense Needs.* Aaron has $34.97 to spend on a book that costs $49.95, a cap that costs $14.88, and a sweatshirt that costs $29.95. How much more money does Aaron need to make these purchases? [5.7a]

66. *Gas Mileage.* Joanna filled her van's gas tank and noted that the odometer read 42,598.2. After the next fill-up, the odometer read 42,912.1. It took 14.6 gal to fill the tank. How many miles per gallon did the van get? [5.7a]

Synthesis

▦ Solve.

67. $\dfrac{1728}{5643} = \dfrac{836.4}{x}$

68. $\dfrac{328.56}{627.48} = \dfrac{y}{127.66}$

69. *Strikeouts per Home Run.* Baseball Hall-of-Famer Babe Ruth had 1330 strikeouts and 714 home runs in his career. Hall-of-Famer Mike Schmidt had 1883 strikeouts and 548 home runs in his career. Find the rate of strikeouts per home run for each player. (These rates were considered among the highest in the history of the game and yet each player was voted into the Hall of Fame.)

Copyright © 2015 Pearson Education, Inc.

Concept Reinforcement

Determine whether each statement is true or false.

_____ **1.** A ratio can be written in fraction notation or in colon notation.   [6.1a]

_____ **2.** A rate is a ratio.   [6.2a]

_____ **3.** The largest size package of an item always has the lowest unit price.   [6.2b]

_____ **4.** If $\dfrac{x}{t} = \dfrac{y}{s}$, then $xy = ts$.   [6.3b]

Guided Solutions

GS   **5.** What is the rate, or speed, in miles per hour?   [6.2a]

120 mi, 2 hr

$$\dfrac{120 \ \boxed{}}{\boxed{} \ \text{hr}} = \dfrac{120}{\boxed{}} \dfrac{\boxed{}}{\text{hr}} = \boxed{} \ \text{mi/hr}$$

6. Solve: $\dfrac{x}{4} = \dfrac{3}{6}$.   [6.3b]

$$\dfrac{x}{4} = \dfrac{3}{6}$$

$$x \cdot \boxed{} = \boxed{} \cdot 3 \qquad \text{Equating cross products}$$

$$\dfrac{x \cdot 6}{\boxed{}} = \dfrac{4 \cdot 3}{\boxed{}} \qquad \text{Dividing on both sides}$$

$$x = \boxed{} \qquad \text{Simplifying}$$

Mixed Review

Find fraction notation for each ratio.   [6.1a]

7. 4 to 7

8. 313 to 199

9. 35 to 17

10. 59 to 101

Find the ratio of the first number to the second and simplify.   [6.1b]

11. 8 to 12

12. 25 to 75

13. 32 to 28

14. 100 to 76

15. 112 to 56

16. 15 to 3

17. 2.4 to 8.4

18. 0.27 to 0.45

Find each rate, or speed, as a ratio of distance to time. Round to the nearest hundredth where appropriate. [6.2a]

19. 243 mi, 4 hr

20. 146 km, 3 hr

21. 65 m, 5 sec

22. 97 ft, 6 sec

23. *Record Snowfall.* The greatest recorded snowfall in a single storm occurred in the Mt. Shasta Ski Bowl in California, when 189 in. fell during a seven-day storm in 1959. What is the rate in inches per day? [6.2a]

Source: U.S. Army Corps of Engineers

24. *Free Throws.* During the 2011–2012 basketball season, Kevin Durant of the Oklahoma City Thunder attempted 501 free throws and made 431 of them. What is the rate in number of free throws made to number of free throws attempted? Round to the nearest thousandth. [6.2a]

Source: National Basketball Association

25. Jerome bought an 18-oz jar of grape jelly for $2.09. What is the unit price in cents per ounce? [6.2b]

26. Martha bought 12 oz of deli honey ham for $5.99. What is the unit price in cents per ounce? [6.2b]

Determine whether the two pairs of numbers are proportional. [6.3a]

27. 3, 7 and 15, 35

28. 9, 7 and 7, 5

29. 2.4, 1.5 and 3.2, 2.1

30. $1\frac{3}{4}, 1\frac{1}{3}$ and $8\frac{3}{4}, 6\frac{2}{3}$

Solve. [6.3b]

31. $\dfrac{9}{15} = \dfrac{x}{20}$

32. $\dfrac{x}{24} = \dfrac{30}{18}$

33. $\dfrac{12}{y} = \dfrac{20}{15}$

34. $\dfrac{2}{7} = \dfrac{10}{y}$

35. $\dfrac{y}{1.2} = \dfrac{1.1}{0.6}$

36. $\dfrac{0.24}{0.02} = \dfrac{y}{0.36}$

37. $\dfrac{\frac{1}{4}}{x} = \dfrac{\frac{1}{8}}{\frac{1}{4}}$

38. $\dfrac{1\frac{1}{2}}{3\frac{1}{4}} = \dfrac{7\frac{1}{2}}{x}$

Understanding Through Discussion and Writing

39. Can every ratio be written as the ratio of some number to 1? Why or why not? [6.1a]

40. What can be concluded about a rectangle's width if the ratio of length to perimeter is 1 to 3? Make some sketches and explain your reasoning. [6.1a, b]

41. Instead of equating cross products, a student solves $\dfrac{x}{7} = \dfrac{5}{3}$ by multiplying on both sides by the least common denominator, 21. Is his approach a good one? Why or why not? [6.3b]

42. An instructor predicts that a student's test grade will be proportional to the amount of time the student spends studying. What is meant by this? Write an example of a proportion that represents the grades of two students and their study times. [6.3b]

Copyright © 2015 Pearson Education, Inc.

STUDYING FOR SUCCESS   *Applications*

☐   If you find applied problems challenging, don't give up! Your skill will improve with each problem you solve.

☐   Make applications real! Look for applications of the math you are studying in newspapers and magazines.

Applications of Proportions

6.4

a APPLICATIONS AND PROBLEM SOLVING

Proportions have applications in such diverse fields as business, chemistry, health sciences, and home economics, as well as in many areas of daily life. Proportions are useful in making predictions.

EXAMPLE 1 *Predicting Total Distance.*   Donna drives her delivery van 800 mi in 3 days. At this rate, how far will she drive in 15 days?

1. **Familiarize.**   We let d = the distance traveled in 15 days.
2. **Translate.**   We translate to a proportion. We make each side the ratio of distance to time, with distance in the numerator and time in the denominator.

$$\text{Distance in 15 days} \rightarrow \frac{d}{15} = \frac{800}{3} \leftarrow \text{Distance in 3 days} \\ \text{Time} \rightarrow \qquad\qquad \leftarrow \text{Time}$$

It may help to verbalize the proportion above as "the unknown distance d is to 15 days as the known distance 800 mi is to 3 days."

3. **Solve.**   Next, we solve the proportion:

$$d \cdot 3 = 15 \cdot 800 \qquad \text{Equating cross products}$$

$$\frac{d \cdot 3}{3} = \frac{15 \cdot 800}{3} \qquad \text{Dividing by 3 on both sides}$$

$$d = \frac{15 \cdot 800}{3}$$

$$d = 4000. \qquad \text{Multiplying and dividing}$$

4. **Check.**   We substitute into the proportion and check cross products:

$$\frac{4000}{15} = \frac{800}{3};$$

$$4000 \cdot 3 = 12{,}000; \quad 15 \cdot 800 = 12{,}000.$$

The cross products are the same.

5. **State.**   Donna will drive 4000 mi in 15 days.

Do Margin Exercise 1. ▶

Problems involving proportions can be translated in more than one way. For Example 1, any one of the following is also a correct translation:

$$\frac{15}{d} = \frac{3}{800}, \quad \frac{15}{3} = \frac{d}{800}, \quad \frac{800}{d} = \frac{3}{15}.$$

Equating the cross products in each proportion gives us the equation $d \cdot 3 = 15 \cdot 800$, which is the equation we obtained in Example 1.

OBJECTIVE

a   Solve applied problems involving proportions.

SKILL TO REVIEW

Objective 5.4b: Solve equations of the type $a \cdot x = b$, where a and b may be in decimal notation.

Solve.

1. $120 \cdot 25 = 100 \cdot n$
2. $-0.3 \times w = 1.68 \times 0.4$

---

1. *Burning Calories.*   The readout on Mary's treadmill indicates that she burns 108 calories when she walks for 24 min. How many calories will she burn if she walks at the same rate for 30 min?

Answers

Skill to Review:
1. 30   **2.** −2.24

Margin Exercise:
1. 135 calories

2. Determining Paint Needs. GS

2. Determining Paint Needs.

Lowell and Chris run a painting company during the summer to pay for their college expenses. They can paint 1600 ft² of clapboard with 4 gal of paint. How much paint would be needed for a building with 6000 ft² of clapboard?

1. Familiarize. Let $p =$ the amount of paint needed, in gallons.

2. Translate.

$$\frac{4}{1600} = \frac{\boxed{}}{\boxed{}}$$

3. Solve.

$$4 \cdot 6000 = 1600 \cdot \boxed{}$$

$$\boxed{} = p$$

4. Check. The cross products are the same.

5. State. For 6000 ft², they would need $\boxed{}$ gal of paint.

EXAMPLE 2 *Recommended Dosage.* To control a fever, a doctor suggests that a child who weighs 28 kg be given 320 mg of a liquid pain reliever. If the dosage is proportional to the child's weight, how much of the medication is recommended for a child who weighs 35 kg?

1. Familiarize. We let $t =$ the number of milligrams of the liquid pain reliever recommended for a child who weighs 35 kg.

2. Translate. We translate to a proportion, keeping the amount of medication in the numerators.

$$\text{Medication suggested} \rightarrow \frac{320}{28} = \frac{t}{35} \leftarrow \text{Medication suggested}$$
$$\text{Child's weight} \rightarrow \qquad\qquad \leftarrow \text{Child's weight}$$

3. Solve. Next, we solve the proportion:

$$320 \cdot 35 = 28 \cdot t \qquad \text{Equating cross products}$$

$$\frac{320 \cdot 35}{28} = \frac{28 \cdot t}{28} \qquad \text{Dividing by 28 on both sides}$$

$$\frac{320 \cdot 35}{28} = t$$

$$400 = t. \qquad \text{Multiplying and dividing}$$

4. Check. We substitute into the proportion and check cross products:

$$\frac{320}{28} = \frac{400}{35};$$

$$320 \cdot 35 = 11{,}200; \qquad 28 \cdot 400 = 11{,}200.$$

The cross products are the same.

5. State. The dosage for a child who weighs 35 kg is 400 mg.

◀ **Do Exercise 2.**

EXAMPLE 3 *Purchasing Tickets.* Carey bought 8 tickets to an international food festival for $52. How many tickets could she purchase with $90?

1. Familiarize. We let $n =$ the number of tickets that can be purchased with $90.

2. Translate. We translate to a proportion, keeping the number of tickets in the numerators.

$$\text{Tickets} \rightarrow \frac{8}{52} = \frac{n}{90} \leftarrow \text{Tickets}$$
$$\text{Cost} \rightarrow \qquad\qquad \leftarrow \text{Cost}$$

Answer

2. 15 gal

Guided Solution:

2. $\dfrac{p}{6000}$; p, 15; 15

3. Solve. Next, we solve the proportion:

$$52 \cdot n = 8 \cdot 90 \qquad \text{Equating cross products}$$

$$\frac{52 \cdot n}{52} = \frac{8 \cdot 90}{52} \qquad \text{Dividing by 52 on both sides}$$

$$n = \frac{8 \cdot 90}{52}$$

$$n \approx 13.8. \qquad \text{Multiplying and dividing}$$

Because it is impossible to buy a fractional part of a ticket, we must round our answer *down* to 13.

4. Check. As a check, we use a different approach: We find the cost per ticket and then divide $90 by that price. Since $52 \div 8 = 6.50$ and $90 \div 6.50 \approx 13.8$, we have a check.

5. State. Carey could purchase 13 tickets with $90.

Do Exercise 3. ▶

3. *Purchasing Shirts.* If 2 shirts can be bought for $47, how many shirts can be bought with $200?

EXAMPLE 4 *Waist-to-Hip Ratio.* To reduce the risk of heart disease, it is recommended that a man's waist-to-hip ratio be 0.9 or lower. Mac's hip measurement is 40 in. To meet the recommendation, what should his waist measurement be?

Source: Mayo Clinic

Waist measurement is the smallest measurement below the ribs but above the navel.

Hip measurement is the largest measurement around the widest part of the buttocks.

1. Familiarize. Note that $0.9 = \dfrac{9}{10}$. We let $w =$ Mac's waist measurement.

2. Translate. We translate to a proportion as follows.

$$\begin{array}{c} \text{Waist measurement} \to \\ \text{Hip measurement} \to \end{array} \frac{w}{40} = \frac{9}{10} \begin{array}{c} \text{Recommended} \\ \text{waist-to-hip ratio} \end{array}$$

3. Solve. Next, we solve the proportion:

$$w \cdot 10 = 40 \cdot 9 \qquad \text{Equating cross products}$$

$$\frac{w \cdot 10}{10} = \frac{40 \cdot 9}{10} \qquad \text{Dividing by 10 on both sides}$$

$$w = \frac{40 \cdot 9}{10}$$

$$w = 36. \qquad \text{Multiplying and dividing}$$

Answer

3. 8 shirts

4. *Waist-to-Hip Ratio.* It is recommended that a woman's waist-to-hip ratio be 0.85 or lower. Martina's hip measurement is 40 in. To meet the recommendation, what should her waist measurement be?

Source: Mayo Clinic

4. Check. As a check, we divide 36 by 40: $36 \div 40 = 0.9$. This is the desired ratio.

5. State. Mac's recommended waist measurement is 36 in. or less.

◀ **Do Exercise 4.**

EXAMPLE 5 *Construction Plans.* Architects make blueprints for construction projects. These are scale drawings in which lengths are in proportion to actual sizes. The Hennesseys are adding a rectangular deck to their house. The architect's blueprint is rendered such that $\frac{3}{4}$ in. on the drawing is actually 2.25 ft on the deck. The width of the deck on the drawing is 4.3 in. How wide is the deck in reality?

1. Familiarize. We let $w = $ the width of the deck.

2. Translate. Then we translate to a proportion, using 0.75 for $\frac{3}{4}$ in.

$$\begin{array}{l} \text{Measure on drawing} \rightarrow \\ \text{Measure on deck} \rightarrow \end{array} \frac{0.75}{2.25} = \frac{4.3}{w} \begin{array}{l} \leftarrow \text{Width on drawing} \\ \leftarrow \text{Width on deck} \end{array}$$

3. Solve. Next, we solve the proportion:

$$0.75 \times w = 2.25 \times 4.3 \qquad \text{Equating cross products}$$

$$\frac{0.75 \times w}{0.75} = \frac{2.25 \times 4.3}{0.75} \qquad \text{Dividing by 0.75 on both sides}$$

$$w = \frac{2.25 \times 4.3}{0.75}$$

$$w = 12.9.$$

4. Check. We substitute into the proportion and check cross products:

$$\frac{0.75}{2.25} = \frac{4.3}{12.9};$$

$$0.75 \times 12.9 = 9.675; \qquad 2.25 \times 4.3 = 9.675.$$

The cross products are the same.

5. State. The width of the deck is 12.9 ft.

◀ **Do Exercise 5.**

5. *Construction Plans.* In Example 5, the length of the actual deck is 28.5 ft. What is the length of the deck on the blueprint?

Answers

4. 34 in. or less   **5.** 9.5 in.

EXAMPLE 6 *Estimating a Wildlife Population.* Scientists often use proportions to estimate the size of a wildlife population. They begin by collecting and marking, or tagging, a portion of the population. This tagged sample is released and mingles with the entire population. At a later date, the scientists collect a second sample from the population. The proportion of tagged individuals in the second sample is estimated to be the same as the proportion of tagged individuals in the entire population.

The marking can be done by using actual tags or by identifying individuals in other ways. For example, marine biologists can identify an individual whale by the patterns on its tail. Recently, scientists have begun using DNA to identify individuals in populations. For example, to identify individual bears in the grizzly bear population of the Northern Continental Divide ecosystem in Montana, geneticists use DNA from fur samples left on branches near the bears' feeding areas.

In one recent large-scale study in this ecosystem, biologists identified 545 individual grizzly bears. If later a sample of 30 bears contained 25 of the previously identified individuals, estimate the total number of bears in the ecosystem.

Source: Based on information from the Northern Divide Grizzly Bear Project

1. **Familiarize.** We let B = the total number of bears in the ecosystem. We assume that the ratio of the number of identified bears to the total number of bears in the ecosystem is the same as the ratio of the number of identified bears in the later sample to the total number of bears in the later sample.

2. **Translate.** We translate to a proportion as follows.

$$\text{Identified bears} \rightarrow \frac{545}{B} = \frac{25}{30} \leftarrow \text{Identified bears in sample}$$
$$\text{Total number of bears} \rightarrow \qquad\qquad \leftarrow \text{Number of bears in sample}$$

3. **Solve.** Next, we solve the proportion:

$$545 \cdot 30 = B \cdot 25 \qquad \text{Equating cross products}$$

$$\frac{545 \cdot 30}{25} = \frac{B \cdot 25}{25} \qquad \text{Dividing by 25 on both sides}$$

$$\frac{545 \cdot 30}{25} = B$$

$$654 = B. \qquad \text{Multiplying and dividing}$$

4. **Check.** We substitute into the proportion and check cross products:

$$\frac{545}{654} = \frac{25}{30};$$

$$545 \cdot 30 = 16{,}350; \qquad 654 \cdot 25 = 16{,}350.$$

The cross products are the same.

5. **State.** We estimate that there are 654 bears in the ecosystem.

Do Exercise 6.

GS 6. **Estimating a Deer Population.** To determine the number of deer in a forest, a conservationist catches 153 deer, tags them, and releases them. Later, 62 deer are caught, and it is found that 18 of them are tagged. Estimate how many deer are in the forest.

1. **Familiarize.** Let D = the number of deer in the forest.

2. **Translate.**
$$\frac{153}{D} = \frac{\boxed{}}{\boxed{}}$$

3. **Solve.**
$$153 \cdot 62 = D \cdot \boxed{}$$
$$\boxed{} = D$$

4. **Check.** The cross products are the same.

5. **State.** There are about _____ deer in the forest.

Answer

6. 527 deer

Guided Solution:

6. $\frac{18}{62}$; 18, 527; 527

Translating for Success

1. Calories in Cereal. There are 140 calories in a $1\frac{1}{2}$-cup serving of Brand A cereal. How many calories are there in 6 cups of the cereal?

2. Calories in Cereal. There are 140 calories in 6 cups of Brand B cereal. How many calories are there in a $1\frac{1}{2}$-cup serving of the cereal?

3. Gallons of Gasoline. Jared's SUV traveled 310 mi on 15.5 gal of gasoline. At this rate, how many gallons would be needed to travel 465 mi?

4. Gallons of Gasoline. Elizabeth's fuel-efficient car traveled 465 mi on 15.5 gal of gasoline. At this rate, how many gallons will be needed to travel 310 mi?

5. Perimeter. What is the perimeter of a rectangular field that measures 83.7 m by 62.4 m?

The goal of these matching questions is to practice step (2), Translate, of the five-step problem-solving process. Translate each word problem to an equation and select a correct translation from equations A–O.

A. $\dfrac{310}{15.5} = \dfrac{465}{x}$

B. $180 = 1\frac{1}{2} \cdot x$

C. $x = 71\frac{1}{8} - 76\frac{1}{2}$

D. $71\frac{1}{8} \cdot x = 74$

E. $74 \cdot 71\frac{1}{8} = x$

F. $x = 83.7 + 62.4$

G. $71\frac{1}{8} + x = 76\frac{1}{2}$

H. $x = 1\frac{2}{3} \cdot 180$

I. $\dfrac{140}{6} = \dfrac{x}{1\frac{1}{2}}$

J. $x = 2(83.7 + 62.4)$

K. $\dfrac{465}{15.5} = \dfrac{310}{x}$

L. $x = 83.7 \cdot 62.4$

M. $x = 180 \div 1\frac{2}{3}$

N. $\dfrac{140}{1\frac{1}{2}} = \dfrac{x}{6}$

O. $x = 1\frac{2}{3} \div 180$

Answers on page A-10

6. Electric Bill. Last month Todd's electric bills for his two rental properties were $83.70 and $62.40. What was the total electric bill for the two properties?

7. Package Tape. A postal service center uses rolls of package tape that each contain 180 ft of tape. If it takes an average of $1\frac{2}{3}$ ft of tape per package, how many packages can be taped with one roll?

8. Online Price. Jane spent $180 for an area rug in a department store. Later, she saw the same rug for sale online and realized she had paid $1\frac{1}{2}$ times the online price. What was the online price?

9. Heights of Sons. Henry's three sons play basketball on three different college teams. Jeff's, Jason's, and Jared's heights are 74 in., $71\frac{1}{8}$ in., and $76\frac{1}{2}$ in., respectively. How much taller is Jared than Jason?

10. Area of a Lot. Bradley bought a lot that measured 74 yd by $71\frac{1}{8}$ yd. What was the area of the lot?

☑ Reading Check

Complete each proportion to form a correct translation of the following problem.

Christy ran 4 marathons in the first 6 months of the year. At this rate, how many marathons will she run in the first 8 months of the year? Let $m =$ the number of marathons she will run in 8 months.

RC1. $\dfrac{4}{6} = \dfrac{\square}{\square}$ **RC2.** $\dfrac{6}{4} = \dfrac{\square}{\square}$ **RC3.** $\dfrac{4}{m} = \dfrac{\square}{\square}$ **RC4.** $\dfrac{m}{4} = \dfrac{\square}{\square}$

a Solve.

1. *Study Time and Test Grades.* An English instructor asserted that students' test grades are directly proportional to the amount of time spent studying. Lisa studies for 9 hr for a particular test and gets a score of 75. At this rate, for how many hours would she have had to study to get a score of 92?

2. *Study Time and Test Grades.* A mathematics instructor asserted that students' test grades are directly proportional to the amount of time spent studying. Brent studies for 15 hr for a final exam and gets a score of 75. At this rate, what score would he have received if he had studied for 18 hr?

3. *Movies.* If *The Hobbit: An Unexpected Journey* is played at the rate preferred by director Peter Jackson, a moviegoer sees 600 frames in $12\frac{1}{2}$ sec. How many frames does a moviegoer see in 160 sec?

4. *Sugaring.* When 20 gal of maple sap are boiled down, the result is $\frac{1}{2}$ gal of maple syrup. How much sap is needed to produce 9 gal of syrup?

Source: University of Maine

5. *Gas Mileage.* A 2013 Ford Mustang GT will travel 403 mi on 15.5 gal of gasoline in highway driving.
   a) How many gallons of gasoline will it take to drive 2690 mi from Boston to Phoenix?
   b) How far can the car be driven on 140 gal of gasoline?

   Source: Ford Motor Company

6. *Gas Mileage.* A 2013 Volkswagen Beetle will travel 495 mi on 16.5 gal of premium gasoline in highway driving.
   a) How many gallons of gasoline will it take to drive 1650 mi from Pittsburgh to Albuquerque?
   b) How far can the car be driven on 130 gal of gasoline?

   Source: Volkswagen of America, Inc.

7. *Overweight Americans.* A recent study determined that of every 100 American adults, 69 are overweight or obese. It is estimated that the U.S. population will be about 337 million in 2020. At the given rate, how many Americans will be considered overweight or obese in 2020?

Source: U.S. Centers for Disease Control and Prevention

8. *Prevalence of Diabetes.* A recent study determined that of every 1000 Americans age 65 or older, 269 have been diagnosed with diabetes. It is estimated that there will be about 55 million Americans in this age group in 2020. At the given rate, how many in this age group will be diagnosed with diabetes in 2020?

Source: American Diabetes Association

9. *Quality Control.* A quality-control inspector examined 100 lightbulbs and found 7 of them to be defective. At this rate, how many defective bulbs will there be in a lot of 2500?

10. *Grading.* A high school math teacher must grade 32 reports on famous mathematicians. She can grade 4 reports in 90 min. At this rate, how long will it take her to grade all 32 reports?

11. *Recommended Dosage.* To control an infection, Dr. Okeke prescribes a dosage of 200 mg of Rocephin every 8 hr for an infant weighing 15.4 lb. At this rate, what would the dosage be for an infant weighing 20.2 lb?

12. *Metallurgy.* In Ethan's white gold ring, the ratio of nickel to gold is 3 to 13. If the ring contains 4.16 oz of gold, how much nickel does it contain?

13. *Painting.* Fred uses 3 gal of paint to cover 1275 ft^2 of siding. How much siding can Fred paint with 7 gal of paint?

14. *Waterproofing.* Bonnie can waterproof 450 ft^2 of decking with 2 gal of sealant. How many gallons of the sealant should Bonnie buy for a 1200-ft^2 deck?

15. *Publishing.* Every 6 pages of an author's manuscript correspond to 5 published pages. How many published pages will a 540-page manuscript become?

16. *Turkey Servings.* An 8-lb turkey breast contains 36 servings of meat. How many pounds of turkey breast would be needed for 54 servings?

Copyright © 2015 Pearson Education, Inc.

17. *Mileage.*   Jean bought a new car. In the first 8 months, it was driven 9000 mi. At this rate, how many miles will the car be driven in 1 year?

18. *Coffee Production.*   Coffee beans from 18 trees are required to produce enough coffee each year for a person who drinks 2 cups of coffee per day. Jared brews 15 cups of coffee each day for himself and his coworkers. How many coffee trees are required for this?

19. *Cap'n Crunch's Peanut Butter Crunch® Cereal.*   The nutritional chart on the side of a box of Quaker Cap'n Crunch's Peanut Butter Crunch® cereal states that there are 110 calories in a $\frac{3}{4}$-cup serving. How many calories are there in 6 cups of the cereal?

20. *Rice Krispies® Cereal.*   The nutritional chart on the side of a box of Kellogg's Rice Krispies® cereal states that there are 130 calories in a $1\frac{1}{4}$-cup serving. How many calories are there in 5 cups of the cereal?

21. *Lefties.*   In a class of 40 students, on average, 6 will be left-handed. If a class includes 9 "lefties," how many students would you estimate are in the class?

22. *Class Size.*   A college advertises that its student-to-faculty ratio is 27 to 2. If 81 students register for Introductory Spanish, how many sections of the course would you expect to see offered?

23. *Painting.*   Helen can paint 950 ft² with 2 gal of paint. How many 1-gal cans does she need in order to paint a 30,000-ft² wall?

24. *Snow to Water.*   Under typical conditions, $1\frac{1}{2}$ ft of snow will melt to 2 in. of water. How many inches of water will result when $5\frac{1}{2}$ ft of snow melts?

25. *Gasoline Mileage.*   Nancy's van traveled 84 mi on 6.5 gal of gasoline. At this rate, how many gallons would be needed to travel 126 mi?

26. *Bicycling.*   Roy bicycled 234 mi in 14 days. At this rate, how far would Roy bicycle in 42 days?

27. *Grass-Seed Coverage.* It takes 60 oz of grass seed to seed 3000 ft² of lawn. At this rate, how much would be needed for 5000 ft² of lawn?

28. *Grass-Seed Coverage.* In Exercise 27, how much seed would be needed for 7000 ft² of lawn?

29. *Estimating a Whale Population.* To determine the number of humpback whales in a population, a marine biologist, using tail markings, identifies 27 individual whales. Several weeks later, 40 whales from the population are randomly sighted. Of the 40 sighted, 12 are among the 27 originally identified. Estimate the number of whales in the population.

30. *Estimating a Trout Population.* To determine the number of trout in a lake, a conservationist catches 112 trout, tags them, and throws them back into the lake. Later, 82 trout are caught, and it is found that 32 of them are tagged. Estimate how many trout there are in the lake.

31. *Map Scaling.* On a road atlas map, 1 in. represents 16.6 mi. If two cities are 3.5 in. apart on the map, how far apart are they in reality?

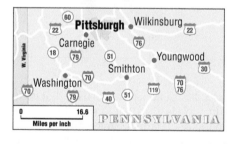

32. *Map Scaling.* On a map, $\frac{1}{4}$ in. represents 50 mi. If two cities are $3\frac{1}{4}$ in. apart on the map, how far apart are they in reality?

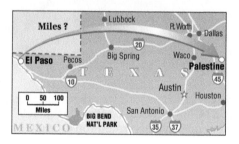

33. *Currency Exchange.* On January 7, 2013, 1 U.S. dollar was worth about 0.76 euro.

  a) How much were 50 U.S. dollars worth in euros on that day?

  b) How much would a car that costs 8640 euros cost in U.S. dollars?

34. *Currency Exchange.* On January 7, 2013, 1 U.S. dollar was worth about 12.74 Mexican pesos.

  a) How much were 150 U.S. dollars worth in Mexican pesos on that day?

  b) While traveling in Mexico at that time, Jake bought a watch that cost 3600 Mexican pesos. How much did it cost in U.S. dollars?

Copyright © 2015 Pearson Education, Inc.

35. *Basketball.* After playing 32 games in the 2012–2013 National Basketball Association season, Kobe Bryant of the Los Angeles Lakers had scored 977 points.

   a) At this rate, how many games would it take him to score 2000 points?

   b) At this rate, how many points would Bryant score in the whole 82-game season?

Source: National Basketball Association

36. *Home Runs.* After playing 118 games in the 2012 Major League Baseball season, Andrew McCutchen of the Pittsburgh Pirates had 24 home runs.

   a) At this rate, how many games would it take him to hit 30 home runs?

   b) At this rate, how many home runs would McCutchen hit in the entire 162-game season?

Source: Major League Baseball

Skill Maintenance

Solve.

37. $12 \cdot x = 1944$ [1.7b]

38. $6807 = m + 2793$ [1.7b]

39. $t + 4.25 = 8.7$ [5.2d]

40. $-112.5 \cdot p = 45$ [5.4b]

41. $3.7 + y = -18$ [5.2d]

42. $0.078 = 0.3 \cdot t$ [5.4b]

43. $c + \dfrac{4}{5} = \dfrac{9}{10}$ [4.3c]

44. $-\dfrac{5}{6} = \dfrac{2}{3} \cdot x$ [3.7c]

Synthesis

45. 🖩 Carney College is expanding from 850 to 1050 students. To avoid any rise in the student-to-faculty ratio, the faculty of 69 professors must also increase. How many new faculty positions should be created?

46. 🖩 In recognition of her outstanding work, Sheri's salary has been increased from $26,000 to $29,380. Tim is earning $23,000 and is requesting a proportional raise. How much more should he ask for?

47. *Baseball Statistics.* Cy Young, one of the greatest baseball pitchers of all time, gave up an average of 2.63 earned runs every 9 innings. Young pitched 7356 innings, more than anyone else in the history of baseball. How many earned runs did he give up?

48. 🖩 *Real-Estate Values.* According to Coldwell Banker Real Estate Corporation, a home selling for $189,000 in Austin, Texas, would sell for $437,850 in Denver, Colorado. How much would a $350,000 home in Denver sell for in Austin? Round to the nearest $1000.

Source: Coldwell Banker Real Estate Corporation

49. 🖩 The ratio 1 : 3 : 2 is used to estimate the relative costs of a CD player, receiver, and speakers when shopping for a sound system. That is, the receiver should cost three times the amount spent on the CD player and the speakers should cost twice the amount spent on the CD player. If you had $900 to spend, how would you allocate the money, using this ratio?

6.5 Geometric Applications

OBJECTIVES

a Find lengths of sides of similar triangles using proportions.

b Use proportions to find lengths in pairs of figures that differ only in size.

SKILL TO REVIEW

Objective 6.3b: Solve proportions.

Solve.

1. $\dfrac{7}{x} = \dfrac{8}{3}$ **2.** $\dfrac{2}{1\frac{1}{2}} = \dfrac{p}{\frac{1}{4}}$

---

a PROPORTIONS AND SIMILAR TRIANGLES

Look at the pair of triangles below. Note that they appear to have the same shape, but their sizes are different. These are examples of **similar triangles**. You can imagine using a magnifying glass to enlarge the smaller triangle so that it looks the same as the larger one. This process works because the corresponding sides of each triangle have the same ratio. That is, the following proportion is true.

$$\frac{a}{d} = \frac{b}{e} = \frac{c}{f}$$

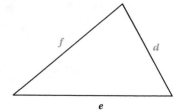

> **SIMILAR TRIANGLES**
>
> **Similar triangles** have the same shape. The lengths of their corresponding sides have the same ratio—that is, they are proportional.

---

1. This pair of triangles is similar. **GS** Find the missing length x.

The ratio of x to 20 is the same as the ratio of 9 to ☐.

$$\frac{x}{20} = \frac{9}{\boxed{}}$$

$$x \cdot \boxed{} = 20 \cdot 9$$

$$\frac{x \cdot 12}{\boxed{}} = \frac{20 \cdot 9}{\boxed{}}$$

$$x = \frac{\boxed{}}{12} = \boxed{}$$

EXAMPLE 1   The triangles below are similar triangles. Find the missing length x.

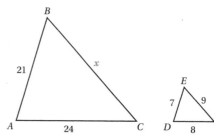

The ratio of x to 9 is the same as the ratio of 24 to 8 or 21 to 7. We get the proportions

$$\frac{x}{9} = \frac{24}{8} \quad \text{and} \quad \frac{x}{9} = \frac{21}{7}.$$

We can solve either one of these proportions. We use the first one:

$$\frac{x}{9} = \frac{24}{8}$$

$x \cdot 8 = 9 \cdot 24$ Equating cross products

$\dfrac{x \cdot 8}{8} = \dfrac{9 \cdot 24}{8}$ Dividing by 8 on both sides

$x = 27.$ Simplifying

The missing length x is 27. Other proportions could also be used.

◀ Do Margin Exercise 1.

Answers

Skill to Review:

1. 2.625   **2.** $\dfrac{1}{3}$

Margin Exercise:

1. 15

Guided Solution:

1. 12; 12, 12, 12, 12, 180, 15

Similar triangles and proportions can often be used to find lengths that would ordinarily be difficult to measure. For example, we could find the height of a flagpole without climbing it or the distance across a river without crossing it.

EXAMPLE 2 How high is a flagpole that casts a 56-ft shadow at the same time that a 6-ft man casts a 5-ft shadow?

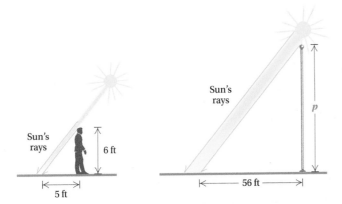

If we use the sun's rays to represent the third side of the triangle in our drawing of the situation, we see that we have similar triangles. Let p = the height of the flagpole. The ratio of 6 to p is the same as the ratio of 5 to 56. Thus we have the proportion

$$\begin{array}{rl} \text{Height of man} \rightarrow & \dfrac{6}{p} = \dfrac{5}{56}. \quad \begin{array}{l} \leftarrow \text{Length of shadow of man} \\ \leftarrow \text{Length of shadow of pole} \end{array} \\ \text{Height of pole} \rightarrow & \end{array}$$

Solve: $6 \cdot 56 = p \cdot 5$ Equating cross products

$$\frac{6 \cdot 56}{5} = \frac{p \cdot 5}{5} \quad \text{Dividing by 5 on both sides}$$

$$\frac{6 \cdot 56}{5} = p \quad \text{Simplifying}$$

$$67.2 = p.$$

The height of the flagpole is 67.2 ft.

Do Exercise 2. ▶

2. How high is a flagpole that casts a 45-ft shadow at the same time that a 5.5-ft woman casts a 10-ft shadow?

EXAMPLE 3 *Rafters of a House.* Carpenters use similar triangles to determine the length of rafters for a house. They first choose the pitch of the roof, or the ratio of the rise over the run. Then using a triangle with that ratio, they calculate the length of the rafters needed for the house. Loren is making rafters for a roof with a 6/12 pitch on a house that is 30 ft wide. Using a rafter guide, Loren knows that the rafter length corresponding to the 6/12 pitch is 13.4. Find the length x of the rafters for this house to the nearest tenth of a foot.

Answer

2. 24.75 ft

We have the proportion

Length of rafter in 6/12 triangle → $\dfrac{13.4}{x} = \dfrac{12}{15}$ ← Run in 6/12 triangle

Length of rafter on the house ↗   ↖ Run in similar triangle on the house

Solve: $13.4 \cdot 15 = x \cdot 12$ Equating cross products

$$\frac{13.4 \cdot 15}{12} = \frac{x \cdot 12}{12}$$ Dividing by 12 on both sides

$$\frac{13.4 \cdot 15}{12} = x$$

$16.8\,\text{ft} \approx x.$ Rounding to the nearest tenth of a foot

The length x of the rafters for the house is about 16.8 ft.

◀ Do Exercise 3.

3. *Rafters of a House.* Referring to Example 3, find the length y of the rise of the rafters of the house to the nearest tenth of a foot.

b PROPORTIONS AND OTHER GEOMETRIC SHAPES

When one geometric figure is a magnification of another, the figures are similar. Thus the corresponding lengths are proportional.

EXAMPLE 4 The sides in the photographs below are proportional. Find the width of the larger photograph.

2.5 cm   ⊢— 3.5 cm —⊣   ⊢———— 10.5 cm ————⊣

We let $x =$ the width of the photograph. Then we translate to a proportion.

Larger width → $\dfrac{x}{2.5} = \dfrac{10.5}{3.5}$ ← Larger length
Smaller width →   ← Smaller length

Solve: $x \times 3.5 = 2.5 \times 10.5$ Equating cross products

$$\frac{x \times 3.5}{3.5} = \frac{2.5 \times 10.5}{3.5}$$ Dividing by 3.5 on both sides

$$x = \frac{2.5 \times 10.5}{3.5}$$ Simplifying

$$x = 7.5.$$

Thus the width of the larger photograph is 7.5 cm.

◀ Do Exercise 4.

4. The sides in the photographs below are proportional. Find the width of the larger photograph.

6 cm   ⊢— 10 cm —⊣

x ⊢———— 35 cm ————⊣

Answers

3. 7.5 ft   **4.** 21 cm

EXAMPLE 5 A scale model of an addition to an athletic facility is 12 cm wide at the base and rises to a height of 15 cm. If the actual base is to be 52 ft, what will the actual height of the addition be?

15 cm

12 cm

h

52 ft

We let $h =$ the height of the addition. Then we translate to a proportion.

Width in model $\rightarrow$ $\dfrac{12}{52} = \dfrac{15}{h}$ $\leftarrow$ Height in model
Actual width $\rightarrow$ $\hphantom{\dfrac{12}{52}}$ $\leftarrow$ Actual height

Solve: $12 \cdot h = 52 \cdot 15$ Equating cross products

$\dfrac{12 \cdot h}{12} = \dfrac{52 \cdot 15}{12}$ Dividing by 12 on both sides

$h = \dfrac{52 \cdot 15}{12} = 65.$

Thus the height of the addition will be 65 ft.

Do Exercise 5. ▶

GS **5.** Refer to the figure in Example 5. If a skylight on the model is 3 cm wide, how wide will an actual skylight be?

Let $w =$ the width of an actual skylight.

$$\dfrac{12}{52} = \dfrac{\boxed{}}{w}$$

$$12 \cdot w = 52 \cdot \boxed{}$$

$$w = \boxed{}$$

The width of an actual skylight will be 13 $\boxed{}$.

EXAMPLE 6 *Bicycle Design.* Two important dimensions to consider when buying a bicycle are *stack* and *reach*, as illustrated in the diagram at the right. The Country Racer bicycle comes in six different frame sizes, each proportional to the others. In the smallest frame size, the stack is 50 cm and the reach is 37.5 cm. In the largest size, the stack is 60 cm. What is the reach in the largest frame size of the Country Racer?

Stack

Reach

We let $r =$ the reach in the largest frame size. Then we translate to a proportion.

Stack in smaller frame $\rightarrow$ $\dfrac{50}{37.5} = \dfrac{60}{r}$ $\leftarrow$ Stack in larger frame
Reach in smaller frame $\rightarrow$ $\hphantom{\dfrac{50}{37.5}}$ $\leftarrow$ Reach in larger frame

Solve:

$50 \cdot r = 37.5 \cdot 60$ Equating cross products

$\dfrac{50 \cdot r}{50} = \dfrac{37.5 \cdot 60}{50}$ Dividing by 50 on both sides

$r = \dfrac{37.5 \cdot 60}{50} = 45.$

Thus the reach in the largest frame size is 45 cm.

Do Exercise 6. ▶

6. Refer to Example 6. In another frame size of the Country Racer, the reach is 42 cm. What is the stack?

Answers

5. 13 ft **6.** 56 cm

Guided Solution:
5. 3, 3, 13; ft

✓ Reading Check

Complete each proportion based on the following similar triangles.

RC1. $\dfrac{a}{3} = \dfrac{c}{\square}$

RC2. $\dfrac{\square}{4} = \dfrac{c}{5}$

RC3. $\dfrac{3}{\square} = \dfrac{5}{c}$

RC4. $\dfrac{8}{4} = \dfrac{a}{\square}$

a The triangles in each exercise are similar. Find the missing lengths.

1.

2.

3.

4.

5.

6.

7.

8.

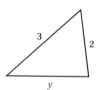

9. When a tree 8 m high casts a shadow 5 m long, how long a shadow is cast by a person 2 m tall?

10. How high is a flagpole that casts a 42-ft shadow at the same time that a $5\frac{1}{2}$-ft woman casts a 7-ft shadow?

11. How high is a tree that casts a 27-ft shadow at the same time that a 4-ft fence post casts a 3-ft shadow?

12. How high is a tree that casts a 32-ft shadow at the same time that an 8-ft light pole casts a 9-ft shadow?

Copyright © 2015 Pearson Education, Inc.

13. Find the height h of the wall.

6 ft

6 ft

7 ft

14. Find the length L of the lake. Assume that the ratio of L to 120 yd is the same as the ratio of 720 yd to 30 yd.

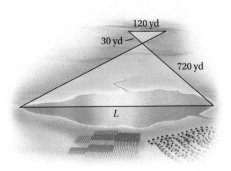

120 yd

30 yd

720 yd

L

15. Find the distance across the river. Assume that the ratio of d to 25 ft is the same as the ratio of 40 ft to 10 ft.

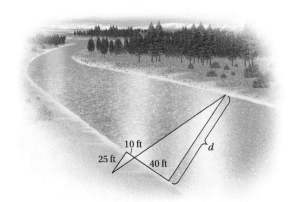

10 ft

25 ft

40 ft

d

16. To measure the height of a hill, a string is stretched from level ground to the top of the hill. A 3-ft stick is placed under the string, touching it at point P, a distance of 5 ft from point G, where the string touches the ground. The string is then detached and found to be 120 ft long. How high is the hill?

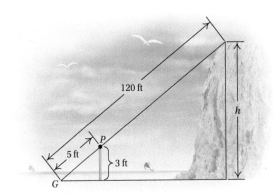

120 ft

h

P

5 ft

3 ft

G

b In each of Exercises 17–26, the sides in each pair of figures are proportional. Find the missing lengths.

17.

6

9

x

6

18.

5

7

x

14

19.

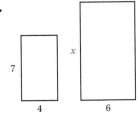

7

x

4

6

20.

7

x

11

4

x

3

21.

22.

23.

24.

25.

26.

27. A scale model of an addition to a medical clinic is 15 cm wide at the base and rises to a height of 19 cm. If the actual base is to be 120 ft, what will the actual height of the addition be?

28. Refer to the figure in Exercise 27. If a large window on the model is 3 cm wide, how wide will the actual window be?

Copyright © 2015 Pearson Education, Inc.

Skill Maintenance

Determine whether each number is prime, composite, or neither.   [3.1c]

29. 83

30. 28

Find the prime factorization of each number.   [3.1d]

31. 808

32. 93

Use = or ≠ for ☐ to write a true sentence.   [3.5c]

33. $\dfrac{12}{8}$ ☐ $\dfrac{6}{4}$

34. $\dfrac{-4}{7}$ ☐ $\dfrac{-5}{9}$

Use < or > for ☐ to write a true sentence.   [4.3b]

35. $\dfrac{7}{12}$ ☐ $\dfrac{11}{15}$

36. $\dfrac{-1}{6}$ ☐ $\dfrac{-2}{11}$

Simplify.

37. $\left(\dfrac{1}{2}\right)^2 + \dfrac{2}{3} \cdot 4\dfrac{1}{2}$ [4.7a]

38. $18.3 + 2.5 \times (-4.2) - (2.6 - 0.3^2)$ [5.4c]

39. $9 \times 15 - [2^3 \cdot 6 - (2 \cdot 5 + 3 \cdot 10)]$ [1.9d]

40. $2600 \div 13 - 5^3$ [1.9c]

Synthesis

Hockey Goals.   An official hockey goal is 6 ft wide. To make scoring more difficult, goalies often position themselves far in front of the goal to "cut down the angle." In Exercises 41 and 42, suppose that a slapshot is attempted from point *A* and that the goalie is 2.7 ft wide. Determine how far from the goal the goalie should be located if point *A* is the given distance from the goal. (*Hint*: First find how far the goalie should be from point *A*.)

41. 25 ft

42. 35 ft

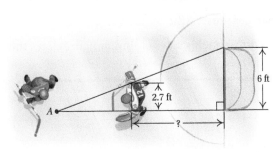

43. A miniature air conditioning unit is built for the model referred to in Exercise 27. An actual unit is 10 ft high. How high should the model unit be?

Solve.   Round the answer to the nearest thousandth.

44. $\dfrac{8664.3}{10{,}344.8} = \dfrac{x}{9776.2}$

45. $\dfrac{12.0078}{56.0115} = \dfrac{789.23}{y}$

The triangles in each exercise are similar triangles. Find the lengths not given.

46.

47.

Vocabulary Reinforcement

Complete each statement with the correct term from the list at the right.
Some of the choices may not be used.

1. A ratio is the _____ of two quantities. [6.1a]

2. Similar triangles have the same _____ . [6.5a]

3. To solve $\dfrac{x}{a} = \dfrac{c}{d}$ for x, equate the _____ and divide on both sides to get x alone on one side. [6.3b]

4. A(n) _____ is a ratio used to compare two different kinds of measure. [6.2a]

5. A(n) _____ states that two pairs of numbers have the same ratio. [6.3a]

6. A unit price is the ratio of _____ to the number of units. [6.2b]

cross products
price
product
proportion
quantity
quotient
rate
shape

Concept Reinforcement

Determine whether each statement is true or false.

_____ 1. When we simplify a ratio like $\frac{8}{12}$, we find two other numbers in the same ratio. [6.1b]

_____ 2. The proportion $\dfrac{a}{b} = \dfrac{c}{d}$ can also be written as $\dfrac{c}{a} = \dfrac{d}{b}$. [6.3a]

_____ 3. Similar triangles must be the same size. [6.5a]

_____ 4. Lengths of corresponding sides of similar figures have the same ratio. [6.5b]

Study Guide

Objective 6.1a Find fraction notation for ratios.

Example Find the ratio of 7 to 18.

Write a fraction with a numerator of 7 and a denominator of 18: $\dfrac{7}{18}$.

Practice Exercise

1. Find the ratio of 17 to 3.

Objective 6.1b Simplify ratios.

Example Simplify the ratio 8 to 2.5.

$$\frac{8}{2.5} = \frac{8}{2.5} \cdot \frac{10}{10} = \frac{80}{25} = \frac{5 \cdot 16}{5 \cdot 5}$$

$$= \frac{5}{5} \cdot \frac{16}{5} = \frac{16}{5}$$

Practice Exercise

2. Simplify the ratio 3.2 to 2.8.

Objective 6.2a Give the ratio of two different measures as a rate.

Example A driver travels 156 mi on 6.5 gal of gas. What is the rate in miles per gallon?

$$\frac{156 \text{ mi}}{6.5 \text{ gal}} = \frac{156}{6.5} \frac{\text{mi}}{\text{gal}} = 24 \frac{\text{mi}}{\text{gal}}, \text{ or } 24 \text{ mpg}$$

Practice Exercise

3. A student earned $120 for working 16 hr. What was the rate of pay per hour?

Objective 6.2b Find unit prices and use them to compare purchases.

Example A 16-oz can of tomatoes costs $1.00. A 20-oz can costs $1.23. Which has the lower unit price?

$$16 \text{ oz}: \frac{\$1.00}{16 \text{ oz}} = \frac{100 \text{ cents}}{16 \text{ oz}} = 6.25¢/\text{oz}$$

$$20 \text{ oz}: \frac{\$1.23}{20 \text{ oz}} = \frac{123 \text{ cents}}{20 \text{ oz}} = 6.15¢/\text{oz}$$

Thus the 20-oz can has the lower unit price.

Practice Exercise

4. A 28-oz jar of Brand A spaghetti sauce costs $2.79. A 32-oz jar of Brand B spaghetti sauce costs $3.29. Find the unit price of each brand and determine which is a better buy based on unit price alone.

Objective 6.3a Determine whether two pairs of numbers are proportional.

Example Determine whether 3, 4 and 7, 9 are proportional.

$$3 \cdot 9 = 27 \qquad \frac{3}{4} \overset{?}{=} \frac{7}{9} \qquad 4 \cdot 7 = 28$$

Since the cross products are not the same ($27 \neq 28$), $\frac{3}{4} \neq \frac{7}{9}$ and the numbers are not proportional.

Practice Exercise

5. Determine whether 7, 9 and 21, 27 are proportional.

Objective 6.3b Solve proportions.

Example Solve: $\frac{3}{4} = \frac{y}{7}$.

$$3 \cdot 7 = 4 \cdot y \qquad \text{Equating cross products}$$

$$\frac{3 \cdot 7}{4} = \frac{4 \cdot y}{4} \qquad \text{Dividing by 4 on both sides}$$

$$\frac{21}{4} = y$$

The solution is $\frac{21}{4}$.

Practice Exercise

6. Solve: $\frac{9}{x} = \frac{8}{3}$.

Objective 6.4a Solve applied problems involving proportions.

Example Martina bought 3 tickets to a campus theater production for $16.50. How much would 8 tickets cost?

We translate to a proportion.

$$\text{Tickets} \rightarrow \frac{3}{16.50} = \frac{8}{c} \leftarrow \text{Tickets}$$
$$\text{Cost} \rightarrow \qquad\qquad \leftarrow \text{Cost}$$

$$3 \cdot c = 16.50 \cdot 8 \qquad \text{Equating cross products}$$

$$c = \frac{16.50 \cdot 8}{3}$$

$$c = 44$$

Eight tickets would cost $44.

Practice Exercise

7. On a map, $\frac{1}{2}$ in. represents 50 mi. If two cities are $1\frac{3}{4}$ in. apart on the map, how far apart are they in reality?

Objective 6.5a Find lengths of sides of similar triangles using proportions.

Example The triangles below are similar. Find the missing length x.

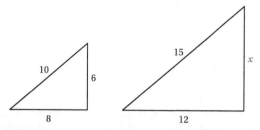

The ratio of 6 to x is the same as the ratio of 8 to 12 (and also as the ratio of 10 to 15). We write and solve a proportion:

$$\frac{6}{x} = \frac{8}{12}$$

$$6 \cdot 12 = x \cdot 8$$

$$\frac{6 \cdot 12}{8} = \frac{x \cdot 8}{8}$$

$$9 = x.$$

The missing length is 9. (We could also have used other proportions, including $\frac{6}{x} = \frac{10}{15}$, to find x.)

Practice Exercise

8. The triangles below are similar. Find the missing length y.

Review Exercises

Write fraction notation for each ratio. Do not simplify. [6.1a]

1. 47 to 84

2. 46 to 1.27

3. 83 to 100

4. 0.72 to 197

5. At Preston Seafood Market, 12,480 lb of tuna and 16,640 lb of salmon were sold one year. [6.1a, b]

 a) Write fraction notation for the ratio of tuna sold to salmon sold.
 b) Write fraction notation for the ratio of salmon sold to the total number of pounds of both kinds of fish sold.

Find the ratio of the first number to the second number and simplify. [6.1b]

6. 9 to 12

7. 3.6 to 6.4

8. *Gas Mileage.* The Chrysler 200 will travel 406 mi on 14.5 gal of gasoline in highway driving. What is the rate in miles per gallon? [6.2a]

 Source: Chrysler Motor Corporation

9. *Flywheel Revolutions.* A certain flywheel makes 472,500 revolutions in 75 min. What is the rate of spin in revolutions per minute? [6.2a]

10. A lawn requires 319 gal of water for every 500 ft^2. What is the rate in gallons per square foot? [6.2a]

11. *Calcium Supplement.* The price for a particular calcium supplement is $18.99 for 300 tablets. Find the unit price in cents per tablet. [6.2b]

12. Raquel bought a 24-oz loaf of 12-grain bread for $4.69. Find the unit price in cents per ounce. [6.2b]

Copyright © 2015 Pearson Education, Inc.

13. *Vegetable Oil.* Find the unit price. Then determine which size has the lowest unit price. [6.2b]

Package	Price	Unit Price
32 oz	$4.79	
48 oz	$5.99	
64 oz	$9.99	

Determine whether the two pairs of numbers are proportional. [6.3a]

14. $9, 15$ and $36, 60$

15. $24, 37$ and $40, 46.25$

Solve. [6.3b]

16. $\dfrac{8}{9} = \dfrac{x}{36}$

17. $\dfrac{6}{x} = \dfrac{48}{56}$

18. $\dfrac{120}{\frac{3}{7}} = \dfrac{7}{x}$

19. $\dfrac{4.5}{120} = \dfrac{0.9}{x}$

Solve. [6.4a]

20. *Quality Control.* A factory manufacturing computer circuits found 3 defective circuits in a lot of 65 circuits. At this rate, how many defective circuits can be expected in a lot of 585 circuits?

21. *Exchanging Money.* On January 7, 2013, 1 U.S. dollar was worth about 0.99 Canadian dollar.

a) How much were 250 U.S. dollars worth in Canada on that day?
b) While traveling in Canada that day, Jamal saw a sweatshirt that cost 50 Canadian dollars. How much would it cost in U.S. dollars?

22. A train travels 448 mi in 7 hr. At this rate, how far will it travel in 13 hr?

23. *Gasoline Consumption.* The United States consumed about 89 billion gallons of gasoline in the first 8 months of 2011. At this rate, how much was consumed in 12 months?

24. *Trash Production.* A study shows that 5 people generate 23 lb of trash each day. The population of Austin, Texas, is 820,611. How many pounds of trash are produced in Austin in one day?

Sources: U.S. Environmental Protection Agency; U.S. Census Bureau

25. *Calories Burned.* Kevin burned 200 calories while playing ultimate frisbee for $\frac{3}{4}$ hr. How many calories would he burn if he played for $1\frac{1}{5}$ hr?

26. *Lawyers in Chicago.* In Illinois, there are about 4.6 lawyers for every 1000 people. The population of Chicago is 2,707,120. How many lawyers would you expect there to be in Chicago?

Sources: American Bar Association; U.S. Census Bureau

Each pair of triangles in Exercises 27 and 28 is similar. Find the missing length(s). [6.5a]

27.

28.

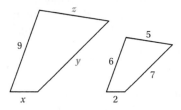

29. How high is a billboard that casts a 25-ft shadow at the same time that an 8-ft sapling casts a 5-ft shadow? [6.5a]

30. The lengths in the figures below are proportional. Find the missing lengths. [6.5b]

31. *Turkey Servings.* A 25-lb turkey serves 18 people. Find the rate in servings per pound. [6.2a]

    A. 0.36 serving/lb   **B.** 0.72 serving/lb
    C. 0.98 serving/lb   **D.** 1.39 servings/lb

32. If 3 dozen eggs cost $5.04, how much will 5 dozen eggs cost? [6.4a]

    A. $6.72   **B.** $6.96
    C. $8.40   **D.** $10.08

Synthesis

33. *Paper Towels.* Find the unit price and determine which item would be the best buy based on unit price alone. [6.2b]

PACKAGE	PRICE	UNIT PRICE PER SHEET
8 rolls, 60 (2 ply) sheets per roll	$8.67	
15 rolls, 60 (2 ply) sheets per roll	$14.92	
6 big rolls, 165 (2 ply) sheets per roll	$13.95	

34. ▦ The following triangles are similar. Find the missing lengths. [6.5a]

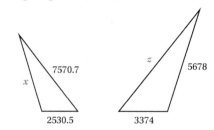

35. Shine-and-Glo Painters uses 2 gal of finishing paint for every 3 gal of primer. Each gallon of finishing paint covers 450 ft^2. If a surface of 4950 ft^2 needs both primer and finishing paint, how many gallons of each should be purchased? [6.4a]

Understanding Through Discussion and Writing

1. If you were a college president, which would you prefer: a low or high faculty-to-student ratio? Why? [6.1a]

2. Can unit prices be used to solve proportions that involve money? Explain why or why not. [6.2b], [6.4a]

3. Write a proportion problem for a classmate to solve. Design the problem so that the solution is "Leslie would need 16 gal of gasoline in order to travel 368 mi." [6.4a]

4. Is it possible for two triangles to have two pairs of sides that are proportional without the triangles being similar? Why or why not? [6.5a]

Copyright © 2015 Pearson Education, Inc.

CHAPTER

6 **Test**

For Extra Help For step-by-step test solutions, access the Chapter Test Prep Videos in MyMathLab® or on YouTube (search "BittingerBasicEI" and click on "Channels").

Write fraction notation for each ratio. Do not simplify.

1. 85 to 97

2. 0.34 to 124

Find the ratio of the first number to the second number and simplify.

3. 18 to 20

4. 0.75 to 0.96

5. What is the rate in feet per second?

10 feet, 16 seconds

6. *Ham Servings.* A 12-lb shankless ham contains 16 servings. What is the rate in servings per pound?

7. *Gas Mileage.* Jeff's convertible will travel 464 mi on 14.5 gal of gasoline in highway driving. What is the rate in miles per gallon?

8. *Bagged Salad Greens.* Ron bought a 16-oz bag of salad greens for $2.49. Find the unit price in cents per ounce.

9. The table below lists prices for concentrated liquid laundry detergent. Find the unit price of each size in cents per ounce. Then determine which has the lowest unit price.

Size	Price	Unit Price
40 oz	$6.59	
50 oz	$6.99	
100 oz	$11.49	
150 oz	$24.99	

Determine whether the two pairs of numbers are proportional.

10. 7, 8 and 63, 72

11. 1.3, 3.4 and 5.6, 15.2

Solve.

12. $\dfrac{9}{4} = \dfrac{27}{x}$

13. $\dfrac{150}{2.5} = \dfrac{x}{6}$

14. $\dfrac{x}{100} = \dfrac{27}{64}$

15. $\dfrac{68}{y} = \dfrac{17}{25}$

Solve.

16. *Distance Traveled.* An ocean liner traveled 432 km in 12 hr. At this rate, how far would the boat travel in 42 hr?

17. *Time Loss.* A watch loses 2 min in 10 hr. At this rate, how much will it lose in 24 hr?

18. *Map Scaling.* On a map, 3 in. represents 225 mi. If two cities are 7 in. apart on the map, how far are they apart in reality?

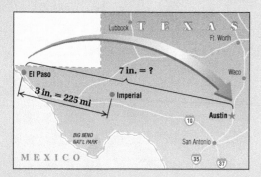

19. *Tower Height.* A birdhouse on a pole that is 3 m high casts a shadow 5 m long. At the same time, the shadow of a tower is 110 m long. How high is the tower?

20. *Charity Work.* Kayla is crocheting hats for a charity. She can make 8 hats from 12 packages of yarn.
  a) How many hats can she make from 20 packages of yarn?
  b) How many packages of yarn does she need to make 20 hats?

21. *Thanksgiving Dinner.* A traditional turkey dinner for 8 people cost about $33.81 in a recent year. How much would it cost to serve a turkey dinner for 14 people?

Source: American Farm Bureau Federation

The sides in each pair of figures are proportional. Find the missing lengths.

22.

23.

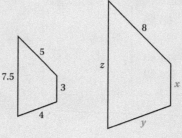

24. Lucita walks $4\frac{1}{2}$ mi in $1\frac{1}{2}$ hr. What is her rate in miles per hour?
  A. $\frac{1}{3}$ mph   **B.** $1\frac{1}{2}$ mph
  C. 3 mph   **D.** $4\frac{1}{2}$ mph

Synthesis

25. Nancy wants to win a gift card from the campus bookstore by guessing the number of marbles in an 8-gal jar. She knows that there are 128 oz in a gallon. She goes home and fills an 8-oz jar with 46 marbles. How many marbles should she guess are in the 8-gal jar?

Copyright © 2015 Pearson Education, Inc.

Calculate and simplify.

1.
```
    2 7.6 8
      3.0 1 9
+ 4 8 3.2 9 7
```

2. $2\frac{1}{3}$
$+ 4\frac{5}{12}$

3. $-\dfrac{6}{35} + \left(-\dfrac{5}{28}\right)$

4.
```
    4 0.2
−    9.7 0 9
```

5. $73.82 - 0.908$

6. $-\dfrac{4}{15} - \dfrac{3}{20}$

7.
```
  3 7.6 4
×     5.9
```

8. 5.678×100

9. $2\dfrac{1}{3} \cdot \left(-1\dfrac{2}{7}\right)$

10. $2.3 \overline{)\, 9\,8.9}$

11. $5\,4 \overline{)\, 4\,8{,}5\,4\,6}$

12. $-\dfrac{7}{11} \div \dfrac{14}{33}$

13. Write expanded notation: 30,074.

14. Write a word name for 120.07.

Which number is larger?

15. 0.7, 0.698

16. −0.8, −0.7999

17. Find the prime factorization of 144.

18. Find the LCM of 18 and 30.

19. What part is shaded?

20. Simplify: $\dfrac{90}{144}$.

Calculate.

21. $\dfrac{3}{5} \times 9.53$

22. $\dfrac{1}{3} \times 0.645 - \dfrac{3}{4} \times 0.048$

23. Write fraction notation for the ratio 0.3 to 15. Do not simplify.

24. Determine whether the pairs 3, 9 and 25, 75 are proportional.

25. What is the rate in meters per second?

　　660 meters, 12 seconds

26. *Unit Prices.*　An 8-oz can of pineapple chunks costs $0.99. A 24.5-oz jar of pineapple chunks costs $3.29. Which has the lower unit price?

Solve.

27. $\dfrac{14}{25} = \dfrac{x}{54}$

28. $423 = 16 \cdot t$

29. $\dfrac{2}{3} \cdot y = \dfrac{16}{27}$

30. $\dfrac{7}{16} = \dfrac{56}{x}$

31. $34.56 + n = -67.9$

32. $t + \dfrac{7}{25} = \dfrac{5}{7}$

33. Ramona's recipe for fettuccini alfredo has 520 calories in 1 cup. How many calories are there in $\frac{3}{4}$ cup?

34. A machine can stamp out 925 washers in 5 min. An order is placed for 1295 washers. How long will it take to stamp them out?

35. A 46-oz juice can contains $5\frac{3}{4}$ cups of juice. A recipe calls for $3\frac{1}{2}$ cups of juice. How many cups are left over?

36. It takes a carpenter $\frac{2}{3}$ hr to hang a door. How many doors can the carpenter hang in 8 hr?

37. *Car Travel.*　A car travels 337.62 mi in 8 hr. How far does it travel in 1 hr?

38. *Shuttle Orbits.*　A space shuttle made 16 orbits a day during an 8.25-day mission. How many orbits were made during the entire mission?

39. How many even prime numbers are there?
　A. 5　　　　　　**B.** 3　　　　　　**C.** 2
　D. 1　　　　　　**E.** None

40. The gas mileage of a car is 28.16 mpg. How many gallons per mile is this?
　A. $\dfrac{704}{25}$　　　　**B.** $\dfrac{25}{704}$　　　　**C.** $\dfrac{2816}{100}$
　D. $\dfrac{250}{704}$　　　　**E.** None

Synthesis

41. A soccer goalie wishing to block an opponent's shot moves toward the shooter to reduce the shooter's view of the goal. If the goalie can only defend a region 10 ft wide, how far in front of the goal should the goalie be? (See the figure at right.)

Copyright © 2015 Pearson Education, Inc.

Answers

Exercise Set 1.1, p. 6

RC1. digit   RC2. period   RC3. expanded   RC4. standard
1. 5 thousands   3. 5 hundreds   5. 1   7. 2
9. 2 thousands + 0 hundreds + 5 tens + 8 ones, or 2 thousands + 5 tens + 8 ones   11. 1 thousand + 5 hundreds + 7 tens + 6 ones   13. 5 thousands + 7 hundreds + 0 tens + 2 ones, or 5 thousands + 7 hundreds + 2 ones   15. 9 ten thousands + 3 thousands + 9 hundreds + 8 tens + 6 ones
17. 1 billion + 3 hundred millions + 4 ten millions + 3 millions + 2 hundred thousands + 3 ten thousands + 9 thousands + 9 hundreds + 2 tens + 3 ones   19. 2 hundred millions + 4 ten millions + 8 millions + 6 hundred thousands + 4 ten thousands + 5 thousands + 0 hundreds + 0 tens + 8 ones, or 2 hundred millions + 4 ten millions + 8 millions + 6 hundred thousands + 4 ten thousands + 5 thousands + 8 ones   21. Eighty-five   23. Eighty-eight thousand   25. One hundred twenty-three thousand, seven hundred sixty-five   27. Seven billion, seven hundred eleven million, two hundred eleven thousand, five hundred seventy-seven
29. Seven hundred one thousand, seven hundred ninety-nine
31. Two million, four hundred seventy-four thousand, two hundred eighty   33. 632,896   35. 50,324   37. 2,233,812
39. 8,000,000,000   41. 40,000,000   43. 30,000,103
45. 64,186,000   47. 138

Calculator Corner, p. 10

1. 121   2. 1602   3. 1932   4. 864

Exercise Set 1.2, p. 12

RC1. addends   RC2. sum   RC3. 0   RC4. perimeter
1. 387   3. 164   5. 5198   7. 100   9. 8503   11. 5266
13. 4466   15. 6608   17. 34,432   19. 101,310   21. 230
23. 18,424   25. 31,685   27. 132 yd   29. 1661 ft   31. 570 ft
33. 8 ten thousands   34. Nine billion, three hundred forty-six million, three hundred ninety-nine thousand, four hundred sixty-eight   35. $1 + 99 = 100, 2 + 98 = 100, \ldots, 49 + 51 = 100$. Then 49 100's = 4900 and 4900 + 50 + 100 = 5050.

Calculator Corner, p. 15

1. 28   2. 47   3. 67   4. 119   5. 2128   6. 2593

Exercise Set 1.3, p. 17

RC1. minuend   RC2. subtraction symbol   RC3. subtrahend
RC4. difference
1. 44   3. 533   5. 39   7. 14   9. 369   11. 26   13. 234
15. 417   17. 5382   19. 2778   21. 3069   23. 1089
25. 7748   27. 4144   29. 56   31. 454   33. 3749
35. 2191   37. 43,028   39. 95,974   41. 4418   43. 1305
45. 9989   47. 48,017   49. 1345   50. 924   51. 22,692

52. 10,920   53. Six million, three hundred seventy-five thousand, six hundred two   54. 9 thousands + 1 hundred + 0 tens + 3 ones, or 9 thousands + 1 hundred + 3 ones   55. 3; 4

Calculator Corner, p. 21

1. 448   2. 21,970   3. 6380   4. 39,564   5. 180,480
6. 2,363,754

Exercise Set 1.4, p. 23

RC1. factors   RC2. product   RC3. 0   RC4. 1
1. 520   3. 564   5. 1527   7. 64,603   9. 4770   11. 3995
13. 870   15. 1920   17. 46,296   19. 14,652   21. 258,312
23. 798,408   25. 20,723,872   27. 362,128   29. 302,220
31. 49,101,136   33. 25,236,000   35. 20,064,048
37. 529,984 sq mi   39. 8100 sq ft   41. 12,685   42. 10,834
43. 8889   44. 254,119   45. 4 hundred thousands   46. 0
47. 1 ten thousand + 2 thousands + 8 hundreds + 4 tens + 7 ones
48. Seven million, four hundred thirty-two thousand
49. 247,464 sq ft

Calculator Corner, p. 30

1. 28   2. 123   3. 323   4. 36

Exercise Set 1.5, p. 32

RC1. quotient   RC2. dividend   RC3. remainder
RC4. divisor
1. 12   3. 1   5. 22   7. 0   9. Not defined   11. 6
13. 55 R 2   15. 108   17. 307   19. 753 R 3   21. 74 R 1
23. 92 R 2   25. 1703   27. 987 R 5   29. 12,700   31. 127
33. 52 R 52   35. 29 R 5   37. 40 R 12   39. 90 R 22   41. 29
43. 105 R 3   45. 1609 R 2   47. 1007 R 1   49. 23
51. 107 R 1   53. 370   55. 609 R 15   57. 304
59. 3508 R 219   61. 8070   63. 1241   64. 66,444
65. 19,800   66. 9380   67. 40 ft   68. 99 sq ft
69. 54, 122; 33, 2772; 4, 8   71. 30 buses

Mid-Chapter Review: Chapter 1, p. 35

1. False   2. True   3. True   4. False   5. True
6. False   7. Ninety-five million, four hundred six thousand, two hundred thirty-seven

8.
$$\begin{array}{r} \overset{5\ 9\ 14}{6\,0\,4} \\ -\ 4\,9\,7 \\ \hline 1\,0\,7 \end{array}$$
9. 6 hundreds   10. 6 ten thousands
11. 6 thousands   12. 6 ones   13. 2   14. 6   15. 5   16. 1
17. 5 thousands + 6 hundreds + 0 tens + 2 ones, or 5 thousands + 6 hundreds + 2 ones   18. 6 ten thousands + 9 thousands + 3 hundreds + 4 tens + 5 ones   19. One hundred thirty-six
20. Sixty-four thousand, three hundred twenty-five   21. 308,716
22. 4,567,216   23. 798   24. 1030   25. 7922   26. 7534
27. 465   28. 339   29. 1854   30. 4328   31. 216
32. 15,876   33. 132,275   34. 5,679,870   35. 253

36. 112 R 5   **37.** 23 R 19   **38.** 144 R 31   **39.** 25 m
40. 8 sq in.   **41.** When numbers are being added, it does
not matter how they are grouped.   **42.** Subtraction is not
commutative. For example, $5 - 2 = 3$, but $2 - 5 \neq 3$.
43. Answers will vary. Suppose one coat costs $150. Then the
multiplication $4 \cdot \$150$ gives the cost of four coats. Or, suppose
one ream of copy paper costs $4. Then the multiplication $\$4 \cdot 150$
gives the cost of 150 reams.   **44.** If we use the definition of
division, $0 \div 0 = a$ such that $a \cdot 0 = 0$. We see that a could be *any*
number since $a \cdot 0 = 0$ for any number a. Thus we cannot say
that $0 \div 0 = 0$. This is why we agree not to allow division by 0.

Exercise Set 1.6, p. 43

RC1. True   **RC2.** False   **RC3.** False   **RC4.** True
1. 50   **3.** 460   **5.** 730   **7.** 900   **9.** 100   **11.** 1000
13. 9100   **15.** 32,800   **17.** 6000   **19.** 8000   **21.** 45,000
23. 373,000   **25.** $80 + 90 = 170$ **27.** $8070 - 2350 = 5720$
29. 220; incorrect   **31.** 890; incorrect
33. $7300 + 9200 = 16,500$ **35.** $6900 - 1700 = 5200$
37. 1600; correct   **39.** 1500; correct
41. $10,000 + 5000 + 9000 + 7000 = 31,000$
43. $92,000 - 23,000 = 69,000$ **45.** $50 \cdot 70 = 3500$
47. $30 \cdot 30 = 900$ **49.** $900 \cdot 300 = 270,000$
51. $400 \cdot 200 = 80,000$ **53.** $350 \div 70 = 5$
55. $8450 \div 50 = 169$ **57.** $1200 \div 200 = 6$
59. $8400 \div 300 = 28$ **61.** $800   **63.** $1200; no
65. Answers will vary depending on the options chosen.
67. (a) $309,600;   **(b)** $360,000   **69.** 90 people   **71.** <
73. >   **75.** <   **77.** >   **79.** >   **81.** >
83. $1,335,475 < 4,134,519$, or $4,134,519 > 1,335,475$
85. $97,382 < 98,817$, or $98,817 > 97,382$ **87.** 86,754
88. 13,589   **89.** 48,824   **90.** 4415   **91.** 1702   **92.** 17,748
93. 54 R 4   **94.** 208   **95.** Left to the student   **97.** Left to the
student

Exercise Set 1.7, p. 52

RC1. (c)   **RC2.** (a)   **RC3.** (d)   **RC4.** (b)
1. 14   **3.** 0   **5.** 90,900   **7.** 450   **9.** 352   **11.** 25   **13.** 29
15. 0   **17.** 79   **19.** 45   **21.** 8   **23.** 14   **25.** 32   **27.** 143
29. 17,603   **31.** 37   **33.** 1035   **35.** 66   **37.** 324   **39.** 335
41. 18,252   **43.** 104   **45.** 45   **47.** 4056   **49.** 2847   **51.** 15
53. 205   **55.** 457   **57.** 142 R 5   **58.** 142   **59.** 334
60. 334 R 11   **61.** <   **62.** >   **63.** >   **64.** <
65. 6,376,000   **66.** 6,375,600   **67.** 347

Translating for Success, p. 62

1. E   **2.** M   **3.** D   **4.** G   **5.** A   **6.** O   **7.** F   **8.** K
9. J   **10.** H

Exercise Set 1.8, p. 63

RC1. Familiarize.   **RC2.** Translate.   **RC3.** Solve.
RC4. Check.
1. 1962 ft   **3.** 1450 ft   **5.** 95 milligrams   **7.** 18 rows
9. 43 events   **11.** 2054 mi   **13.** 2,073,600 pixels   **15.** 168 hr
17. $273 per month   **19.** $197   **21.** $7092   **23.** 151,500
25. $78   **27.** $40 per month   **29.** $24,456   **31.** 35 weeks;
2 episodes   **33.** 21 columns   **35.** 236 gal   **37. (a)** 4200 sq ft;
(b) 268 ft   **39.** 56 cartons   **41.** 645 mi; 5 in.   **43.** $247
45. 525 min, or 8 hr 45 min   **47.** 168,300 jobs   **49.** 104 seats
51. 32 $10 bills   **53.** $400   **55.** 106 bones   **57.** 8273
58. 7759   **59.** 806,985   **60.** 147 R 4   **61.** 34 m
62. 9706 sq ft   **63.** $200 \times 600 = 120,000$ **64.** 66
65. 792,000 mi; 1,386,000 mi

Calculator Corner, p. 71

1. 243   **2.** 15,625   **3.** 20,736   **4.** 2048

Calculator Corner, p. 73

1. 49   **2.** 85   **3.** 36   **4.** 0   **5.** 73   **6.** 49

Exercise Set 1.9, p. 75

RC1. exponent   **RC2.** squared   **RC3.** multiplication
RC4. 3
1. 3^4 **3.** 5^2 **5.** 7^5 **7.** 10^3 **9.** 49   **11.** 729   **13.** 20,736
15. 243   **17.** 22   **19.** 20   **21.** 100   **23.** 1   **25.** 49   **27.** 5
29. 434   **31.** 41   **33.** 88   **35.** 4   **37.** 303   **39.** 20
41. 70   **43.** 295   **45.** 32   **47.** 906   **49.** 62   **51.** 102
53. 32   **55.** $94   **57.** 401   **59.** 110   **61.** 7   **63.** 544
65. 708   **67.** 27   **69.** 452   **70.** 835   **71.** 13   **72.** 37
73. 4898   **74.** 100   **75.** 104,286 sq mi   **76.** 98 gal
77. $24; 1 + 5 \cdot (4 + 3) = 36$ **79.** $7; 12 \div (4 + 2) \cdot 3 - 2 = 4$

Summary and Review: Chapter 1, p. 78

Vocabulary Reinforcement

1. perimeter   **2.** minuend   **3.** digits; periods   **4.** dividend
5. factors; product   **6.** additive   **7.** associative   **8.** divisor;
remainder; dividend

Concept Reinforcement

1. True   **2.** True   **3.** False   **4.** False   **5.** True   **6.** False

Important Concepts

1. 2 thousands   **2.** 65,302   **3.** 3237   **4.** 225,036
5. 315 R 14   **6.** 36,000   **7.** <   **8.** 36   **9.** 216

Review Exercises

1. 8 thousands   **2.** 3   **3.** 2 thousands + 7 hundreds + 9 tens +
3 ones   **4.** 5 ten thousands + 6 thousands + 0 hundreds +
7 tens + 8 ones, or 5 ten thousands + 6 thousands + 7 tens +
8 ones   **5.** 4 millions + 0 hundred thousands +
0 ten thousands + 7 thousands + 1 hundred + 0 tens +
1 one, or 4 millions + 7 thousands + 1 hundred + 1 one
6. Sixty-seven thousand, eight hundred nineteen   **7.** Two
million, seven hundred eighty-one thousand, four hundred
twenty-seven   **8.** 476,588   **9.** 1,640,000,000   **10.** 14,272
11. 66,024   **12.** 21,788   **13.** 98,921   **14.** 5148   **15.** 1689
16. 2274   **17.** 17,757   **18.** 5,100,000   **19.** 6,276,800
20. 506,748   **21.** 27,589   **22.** 5,331,810   **23.** 12 R 3   **24.** 5
25. 913 R 3   **26.** 384 R 1   **27.** 4 R 46   **28.** 54   **29.** 452
30. 5008   **31.** 4389   **32.** 345,800   **33.** 345,760   **34.** 346,000
35. 300,000   **36.** >   **37.** <   **38.** $41,300 + 19,700 = 61,000$
39. $38,700 - 24,500 = 14,200$ **40.** $400 \cdot 700 = 280,000$
41. 8   **42.** 45   **43.** 58   **44.** 0   **45.** 4^3 **46.** 10,000
47. 36   **48.** 65   **49.** 233   **50.** 260   **51.** 165   **52.** $502
53. $484   **54.** 1982   **55.** 19 cartons   **56.** $13,585
57. 14 beehives   **58.** 98 sq ft; 42 ft   **59.** 137 beakers filled;
13 mL left over   **60.** $27,598   **61.** B   **62.** A   **63.** D   **64.** 8
65. $a = 8, b = 4$ **66.** 6 days

Understanding Through Discussion and Writing

1. No; if subtraction were associative, then $a - (b - c) =$
$(a - b) - c$ for any a, b, and c. But, for example,

$$12 - (8 - 4) = 12 - 4 = 8,$$

whereas

$$(12 - 8) - 4 = 4 - 4 = 0.$$

Since $8 \neq 0$, this example shows that subtraction is not associative.
2. By rounding prices and estimating their sum, a shopper can
estimate the total grocery bill while shopping. This is particularly
useful if the shopper wants to spend no more than a certain amount.

3. Answers will vary. Anthony is driving from Kansas City to Minneapolis, a distance of 512 mi. He stops for gas after driving 183 mi. How much farther must he drive?   **4.** The parentheses are not necessary in the expression $9 - (4 \cdot 2)$. Using the rules for order of operations, the multiplication would be performed before the subtraction even if the parentheses were not present. The parentheses are necessary in the expression $(3 \cdot 4)^2$; $(3 \cdot 4)^2 = 12^2 = 144$, but $3 \cdot 4^2 = 3 \cdot 16 = 48$.

Test: Chapter 1, p. 83

1. [1.1a] 5   **2.** [1.1b] 8 thousands + 8 hundreds + 4 tens + 3 ones   **3.** [1.1c] Thirty-eight million, four hundred three thousand, two hundred seventy-seven   **4.** [1.2a] 9989
5. [1.2a] 63,791   **6.** [1.2a] 3165   **7.** [1.2a] 10,515
8. [1.3a] 3630   **9.** [1.3a] 1039   **10.** [1.3a] 6848
11. [1.3a] 5175   **12.** [1.4a] 41,112   **13.** [1.4a] 5,325,600
14. [1.4a] 2405   **15.** [1.4a] 534,264   **16.** [1.5a] 3 R 3
17. [1.5a] 70   **18.** [1.5a] 97   **19.** [1.5a] 805 R 8
20. [1.6a] 35,000   **21.** [1.6a] 34,530   **22.** [1.6a] 34,500
23. [1.6b] 23,600 + 54,700 = 78,300
24. [1.6b] 54,800 − 23,600 = 31,200
25. [1.6b] 800 · 500 = 400,000   **26.** [1.6c] >   **27.** [1.6c] <
28. [1.7b] 46   **29.** [1.7b] 13   **30.** [1.7b] 14   **31.** [1.7b] 381
32. [1.8a] 83 calories   **33.** [1.8a] 20 staplers
34. [1.8a] 1,256,615 sq mi   **35. (a)** [1.2b], [1.4b] 300 in., 5000 sq in.; 264 in., 3872 sq in.; 228 in., 2888 sq in.;
(b) [1.8a] 2112 sq in.   **36.** [1.8a] 1852 12-packs; 7 cakes left over
37. [1.8a] $95   **38.** [1.9a] 12^4 **39.** [1.9b] 343
40. [1.9b] 100,000   **41.** [1.9c] 31   **42.** [1.9c] 98   **43.** [1.9c] 2
44. [1.9c] 18   **45.** [1.9d] 216   **46.** [1.9c] A
47. [1.4b], [1.8a] 336 sq in.   **48.** [1.9c] 9   **49.** [1.8a] 80 payments

CHAPTER 2

Exercise Set 2.1, p. 90

RC1. *G*   **RC2.** *C*   **RC3.** *B*   **RC4.** *E*   **RC5.** True
RC6. True   **RC7.** False   **RC8.** False
1. 24; −2   **3.** 950,000,000; −460   **5.** 1454; −55
7.   **9.**
11. >   **13.** <   **15.** >   **17.** <   **19.** >   **21.** <   **23.** <
25. >   **27.** 3   **29.** 18   **31.** 325   **33.** 29   **35.** 300
37. 53   **39.** 13,549   **40.** 1107   **41.** 50,609   **42.** 219
43. 259   **44.** 8778   **45.** >   **47.** =

Calculator Corner, p. 95

1. 13   **2.** −8   **3.** −12

Exercise Set 2.2, p. 96

RC1. right, right   **RC2.** left, left   **RC3.** right, left
RC4. left, right   **1.** −2   **3.** −4   **5.** 0   **7.** −8   **9.** −7
11. −27   **13.** 0   **15.** −42   **17.** 0   **19.** 0   **21.** 3   **23.** −9
25. 7   **27.** 0   **29.** 45   **31.** −2   **33.** −7   **35.** −19   **37.** −6
39. −1   **41.** 39   **43.** 43   **45.** −1093   **47.** −24   **49.** 26
51. −9   **53.** 14   **55.** −65   **57.** 5   **59.** 14   **61.** −10
63. 3456   **64.** 137,016   **65.** 4,533,324   **66.** 408 R 3
67. 127 R 46   **68.** 221 R 331   **69.** 641,540   **70.** 641,500
71. 642,000   **73.** All positive   **75.** Negative

Exercise Set 2.3, p. 101

RC1. (c)   **RC2.** (b)   **RC3.** (d)   **RC4.** (a)
1. −4   **3.** −7   **5.** −6   **7.** 0   **9.** −4   **11.** −7   **13.** −6
15. 0   **17.** 11   **19.** −14   **21.** 5   **23.** −7   **25.** −5
27. −3   **29.** −23   **31.** −68   **33.** −73   **35.** 116   **37.** −2
39. −5   **41.** −1   **43.** −5   **45.** 22   **47.** 19   **49.** −20
51. −8   **53.** −10   **55.** −3   **57.** −7   **59.** −30   **61.** 0

63. −1   **65.** 37   **67.** −62   **69.** 6   **71.** 107   **73.** 219
75. Profit of $4300   **77.** 3780 m   **79.** −3°   **81.** $348
83. 13,796 ft above sea level   **85.** 64   **86.** 125   **87.** 29
88. 41   **89.** 66   **90.** 3   **91.** 8 cans   **92.** 288 oz   **93.** True
95. True   **97.** True   **99.** True

Mid-Chapter Review: Chapter 2, p. 104

1. True   **2.** False   **3.** True
4. $-x = -(-4) = 4$; $-(-x) = -(-(-4)) = -(4) = -4$
5. $5 - 13 = 5 + (-13) = -8$ **6.** $-6 - (-7) = -6 + 7 = 1$
7. 450; −79   **8.** 20; −23   **9.**
10.   **11.** <   **12.** <   **13.** >
14. >   **15.** 15   **16.** 18   **17.** 0   **18.** 12   **19.** 5   **20.** −7
21. 0   **22.** 49   **23.** 19   **24.** 2   **25.** −2   **26.** −2   **27.** 0
28. −17   **29.** −10   **30.** −7   **31.** −9   **32.** −2   **33.** −10
34. 16   **35.** 2   **36.** −12   **37.** −4   **38.** −6   **39.** −2   **40.** 13
41. 9   **42.** −23   **43.** 75   **44.** 14   **45.** 33°C   **46.** $48
47. Answers will vary.   **48.** The absolute value of a number is its distance from 0, and distance is always nonnegative.
49. Answers may vary. If we think of the addition on the number line, we start at a negative number and move to the left. This always brings us to a point on the negative portion of the number line.
50. Yes; consider $m - (-n)$, where both m and n are positive. Then, $m - (-n) = m + n$. Now $m + n$, the sum of two positive numbers, is positive.

Exercise Set 2.4, p. 108

RC1. negative   **RC2.** positive   **RC3.** positive   **RC4.** negative
1. −16   **3.** −24   **5.** −72   **7.** 16   **9.** 42   **11.** −120
13. −238   **15.** 1200   **17.** 84   **19.** −12   **21.** 24   **23.** 21
25. −69   **27.** 27   **29.** −18   **31.** −45   **33.** 420   **35.** 36
37. −60   **39.** 150   **41.** −90   **43.** 1911   **45.** 56   **47.** 30
49. −960   **51.** 1764   **53.** −240   **55.** −30,240   **57.** 237,460
58. 237,500   **59.** 237,000   **60.** 13   **61.** 3   **62.** 21
63. (a) One must be negative and one must be positive. **(b)** Either or both must be zero. **(c)** Both must be negative or both must be positive.

Translating for Success, p. 114

1. I   **2.** C   **3.** G   **4.** L   **5.** B   **6.** O   **7.** A   **8.** F
9. D   **10.** M

Exercise Set 2.5, p. 115

RC1. True   **RC2.** True   **RC3.** False   **RC4.** False
1. −6   **3.** −13   **5.** −2   **7.** 4   **9.** −8   **11.** 2   **13.** −12
15. −8   **17.** Not defined   **19.** −9   **21.** 38°F   **23.** $26
25. 32 m below sea level   **27.** −7   **29.** −7   **31.** −334
33. 14   **35.** 1880   **37.** 12   **39.** 8   **41.** −86   **43.** 37
45. −1   **47.** −10   **49.** −67   **51.** −7988   **53.** −3000
55. 60   **57.** 1   **59.** 10   **61.** −2   **63.** −4   **65.** 8 thousands
66. 8 millions   **67.** 8 ones   **68.** 8 hundreds   **69.** 2203
70. 848   **71.** 37,239   **72.** 11,851   **73.** 4992 sq ft; 284 ft
74. $784   **75.** −159   **77.** Negative   **79.** Negative
81. Positive

Summary and Review: Chapter 2, p. 118

Vocabulary Reinforcement
1. integers   **2.** absolute   **3.** opposites, additive
4. difference   **5.** positive   **6.** negative

Concept Reinforcement
1. False   **2.** True   **3.** False   **4.** True

Study Guide

1.   **2.** <   **3. (a)** 17; **(b)** 14
4. -3 **5.** -8 **6.** 14   **7.** 72   **8.** -90 **9.** 4   **10.** -4
11. -12

Review Exercises

1. 620; -125 **2.** 38   **3.** 7   **4.** 0   **5.** -2 **6.** <   **7.** >
8. >   **9.** <   **10.**
11.   **12.** -8 **13.** 14   **14.** 0
15. 23   **16.** 34   **17.** 5   **18.** -3 **19.** -7 **20.** -4 **21.** -5
22. 4   **23.** -14 **24.** -8 **25.** 54   **26.** -39 **27.** -56
28. -210 **29.** -7 **30.** -3 **31.** 6   **32.** -62 **33.** 26
34. -5 **35.** 2   **36.** -180 **37.** $-\$360$ **38.** \$62 per share
39. 8-yd gain   **40.** \$19   **41.** C   **42.** B
43. (a) $-7 + (-6) + (-5) + (-4) + (-3) + (-2) + (-1) +$
$0 + 1 + 2 + 3 + 4 + 5 + 6 + 7 + 8 = 8$; **(b)** 0
44. $9 - (3 - 4) + 5 = 15$ **45.** -5 **46.** -5

Understanding Through Discussion and Writing

1. We know that the product of an even number of negative numbers is positive, and the product of an odd number of negative numbers is negative. Since $(-7)^8$ is equivalent to the product of eight negative numbers, it will be a positive number. Similarly, since $(-7)^{11}$ is equivalent to the product of eleven negative numbers, it will be a negative number.   **2.** If the negative integer has the greater absolute value, the sum is negative.   **3.** Jake is expecting the multiplication to be performed before the division.
4. Answers will vary. At 4 P.M., the temperature in Circle City was 23°F. By 11 P.M., the temperature had dropped 32°F. What was the temperature at 11 P.M.?

Test: Chapter 2, p. 123

1. [2.1c] <   **2.** [2.1c] >   **3.** [2.1c] >   **4.** [2.1c] <   **5.** [2.1d] 7
6. [2.1d] 94   **7.** [2.1d] -27 **8.** [2.2b] -23 **9.** [2.2b] 14
10. [2.2b] 8   **11.** [2.1b]
12. [2.3a] 78   **13.** [2.2a] -8 **14.** [2.2a] 2   **15.** [2.3a] 10
16. [2.3a] -25 **17.** [2.2a] 15   **18.** [2.4a] -48 **19.** [2.4a] 24
20. [2.5a] -9 **21.** [2.5a] 9   **22.** [2.5a] -4 **23.** [2.5c] 109
24. [2.3b] 2244 m   **25.** [2.3b] Up 15 pts
26. [2.3b], [2.5b] 16,080   **27.** [2.5b] -2°C each minute
28. [2.2b] D   **29.** [2.1d], [2.3a] 15   **30.** [2.3b] 2385 m
31. (a) [2.3a] $-4, -9, -15$; **(b)** [2.3a] $-2, -6, -10$;
(c) [2.3a] $-18, -24, -31$; **(d)** [2.5a] $4, -2, 1$

CHAPTER 3

Calculator Corner, p. 129

1. No   **2.** Yes   **3.** Yes   **4.** No

Exercise Set 3.1, p. 131

RC1. True   **RC2.** True   **RC3.** False   **RC4.** True
RC5. False   **RC6.** False
1. No   **3.** Yes   **5.** 1, 2, 3, 6, 9, 18   **7.** 1, 2, 3, 6, 9, 18, 27, 54
9. 1, 2, 4   **11.** 1   **13.** 1, 2, 7, 14, 49, 98   **15.** 1, 3, 5, 15, 17, 51, 85, 255   **17.** 4, 8, 12, 16, 20, 24, 28, 32, 36, 40   **19.** 20, 40, 60, 80, 100, 120, 140, 160, 180, 200   **21.** 3, 6, 9, 12, 15, 18, 21, 24, 27, 30
23. 12, 24, 36, 48, 60, 72, 84, 96, 108, 120   **25.** 10, 20, 30, 40, 50, 60, 70, 80, 90, 100   **27.** 9, 18, 27, 36, 45, 54, 63, 72, 81, 90
29. No   **31.** Yes   **33.** Yes   **35.** No   **37.** Neither
39. Composite   **41.** Prime   **43.** Prime   **45.** $2 \cdot 2 \cdot 2$
47. $2 \cdot 7$ **49.** $2 \cdot 3 \cdot 7$ **51.** $5 \cdot 5$ **53.** $2 \cdot 5 \cdot 5$ **55.** $13 \cdot 13$
57. $2 \cdot 2 \cdot 5 \cdot 5$ **59.** $5 \cdot 7$ **61.** $2 \cdot 2 \cdot 2 \cdot 3 \cdot 3$ **63.** $7 \cdot 11$
65. $2 \cdot 2 \cdot 7 \cdot 103$ **67.** $3 \cdot 17$ **69.** $2 \cdot 2 \cdot 2 \cdot 2 \cdot 3 \cdot 5 \cdot 5$
71. $3 \cdot 7 \cdot 13$ **73.** $2 \cdot 3 \cdot 11 \cdot 17$ **75.** 4 thousands

76. 4 millions   **77.** 4 tens   **78.** 4 ten thousands   **79.** 34,560
80. 34,600   **81.** 2,428,000   **82.** 2,428,500   **83.** Row 1: 48, 90, 432, 63; row 2: 7, 2, 2, 10, 8, 6, 21, 10; row 3: 9, 18, 36, 14, 12, 11, 21; row 4: 29, 19, 42

Exercise Set 3.2, p. 137

RC1. (c)   **RC2.** (a)   **RC3.** (g)   **RC4.** (d)   **RC5.** (f)
RC6. (h)   **RC7.** (b)   **RC8.** (e)
1. Yes; the sum of the digits is 12, which is divisible by 3.   **3.** No; the ones digit is not 0 or 5.   **5.** Yes; the ones digit is 0.   **7.** Yes; the sum of the digits is 18, which is divisible by 9.
9. No; the ones digit is not even.   **11.** No; the ones digit is not even.   **13.** No; 30 is not divisible by 4.   **15.** Yes; 840 is divisible by 8.   **17.** 6825 is divisible by 3 and 5.   **19.** 119,117 is divisible by none of these numbers.   **21.** 127,575 is divisible by 3, 5, and 9.   **23.** 9360 is divisible by 2, 3, 4, 5, 6, 8, 9, and 10.   **25.** 324, 42, 501, 3009, 75, 2001, 402, 111,111, 1005   **27.** 55,555, 200, 75, 2345, 35, 1005   **29.** 56, 784, 200   **31.** 200   **33.** 313,332, 7624, 111,126, 876, 1110, 5128, 64,000, 9990   **35.** 313,332, 111,126, 876, 1110, 9990   **37.** 9990   **39.** 1110, 64,000, 9990   **41.** 138
42. 139   **43.** 874   **44.** 56   **45.** 26   **46.** 13   **47.** 45 gal
48. 4320 min   **49.** $2 \cdot 2 \cdot 2 \cdot 3 \cdot 5 \cdot 5 \cdot 13$
51. $2 \cdot 2 \cdot 3 \cdot 3 \cdot 7 \cdot 11$ **53.** 95,238

Exercise Set 3.3, p. 144

RC1. (b)   **RC2.** (a)   **RC3.** (c)   **RC4.** (e)   **RC5.** (f)
RC6. (d)
1. Numerator: 3; denominator: 4   **3.** Numerator: 11; denominator: 2   **5.** Numerator: 0; denominator: 7   **7.** $\frac{6}{12}$
9. $\frac{1}{8}$ **11.** $\frac{3}{4}$ **13.** $\frac{4}{8}$ **15.** $\frac{12}{12}$ **17.** $\frac{9}{8}$ **19.** $\frac{4}{3}$ **21.** $\frac{4}{3}$ **23.** $\frac{5}{8}$
25. $\frac{4}{7}$ **27.** $-\frac{1}{3}$ **29.** $\frac{12}{16}$ **31.** $\frac{38}{16}$ **33. (a)** $\frac{2}{8}$; **(b)** $\frac{6}{8}$
35. (a) $\frac{3}{8}$; **(b)** $\frac{5}{8}$ **37. (a)** $\frac{5}{7}$; **(b)** $\frac{5}{2}$; **(c)** $\frac{2}{7}$; **(d)** $\frac{2}{5}$ **39. (a)** $\frac{4}{15}$;
(b) $\frac{4}{11}$; **(c)** $\frac{11}{15}$ **41. (a)** $\frac{1060}{100,000}$; **(b)** $\frac{743}{100,000}$; **(c)** $\frac{865}{100,000}$; **(d)** $\frac{1026}{100,000}$;
(e) $\frac{905}{100,000}$; **(f)** $\frac{1728}{100,000}$ **43.** $\frac{4}{7}$ **45.** 0   **47.** 7   **49.** 1   **51.** 1
53. 0   **55.** 1   **57.** 1   **59.** 1   **61.** 1   **63.** -18
65. Not defined   **67.** Not defined   **69.** 90,283   **70.** 29,364
71. 4673   **72.** 5338   **73.** 6510   **74.** 14,526   **75.** -7
76. -15 **77.** $\frac{1}{6}$ **79.** $\frac{2}{16}$, or $\frac{1}{8}$
81.   **83.**

Exercise Set 3.4, p. 153

RC1. True   **RC2.** True   **RC3.** True   **RC4.** True
1. $\frac{4}{15}$ **3.** $\frac{70}{9}$ **5.** $\frac{49}{64}$ **7.** $-\frac{2}{15}$ **9.** $\frac{40}{21}$ **11.** $-\frac{6}{5}$ **13.** $\frac{1}{6}$
15. $\frac{85}{6}$ **17.** $-\frac{7}{100}$ **19.** $\frac{2}{5}$ **21.** $-\frac{14}{39}$ **23.** $\frac{5}{8}$ **25.** $\frac{1}{40}$ **27.** $\frac{160}{27}$
29. $\frac{182}{285}$ **31.** $\frac{9}{16}$ **33.** $-\frac{8}{11}$ **35.** $\frac{40}{3}$ yd   **37.** $\frac{1}{2625}$ **39.** $\frac{1}{16}$
41. $\frac{9}{20}$ **43.** \$946   **44.** 201 min, or 3 hr 21 min   **45.** 4^5
46. 16   **47.** 50   **48.** 6399   **49.** $\frac{71,269}{180,433}$ **51.** $-\frac{56}{1125}$

Calculator Corner, p. 158

1. $\frac{14}{15}$ **2.** $\frac{7}{8}$ **3.** $\frac{138}{167}$ **4.** $\frac{7}{25}$

Exercise Set 3.5, p. 160

RC1. Equivalent   **RC2.** simplify   **RC3.** common
RC4. cross
1. $\frac{5}{10}$ **3.** $\frac{20}{32}$ **5.** $-\frac{27}{30}$ **7.** $\frac{20}{48}$ **9.** $\frac{-51}{-54}$ **11.** $\frac{42}{132}$ **13.** $\frac{1}{2}$
15. $-\frac{3}{4}$ **17.** $\frac{1}{5}$ **19.** -3 **21.** $\frac{3}{4}$ **23.** $\frac{7}{8}$ **25.** $\frac{6}{5}$ **27.** $\frac{1}{3}$
29. -6 **31.** $-\frac{1}{3}$ **33.** $\frac{2}{3}$ **35.** $-\frac{7}{90}$ **37.** =   **39.** ≠
41. =   **43.** ≠   **45.** ≠   **47.** =   **49.** $\frac{2}{5}$ **51.** $\frac{11}{50}$ **53.** <
54. <   **55.** >   **56.** <   **57.** 3520   **58.** 89   **59.** 6498   **60.** 85
61. No; $\frac{63}{82} \neq \frac{77}{100}$ because $63 \cdot 100 \neq 82 \cdot 77$.

Mid-Chapter Review: Chapter 3, p. 162

1. True **2.** False **3.** False **4.** True
5. $\frac{25}{25} = 1$ **6.** $\frac{0}{-9} = 0$ **7.** $\frac{-8}{1} = -8$ **8.** $\frac{6}{13} = \frac{18}{39}$
9. $\frac{70}{225} = \frac{2\cdot5\cdot7}{3\cdot3\cdot5\cdot5} = \frac{5}{5}\cdot\frac{2\cdot7}{3\cdot3\cdot5} = 1\cdot\frac{14}{45} = \frac{14}{45}$
10. 84, 17,576, 224, 132, 594, 504, 1632 **11.** 84, 300, 132, 500, 180
12. 17,576, 224, 500 **13.** 84, 300, 132, 120, 1632
14. 300, 180, 120 **15.** Prime **16.** Prime **17.** Composite
18. Neither **19.** 1, 2, 4, 5, 8, 10, 16, 20, 32, 40, 80, 160;
$2\cdot2\cdot2\cdot2\cdot2\cdot5$ **20.** 1, 2, 3, 6, 37, 74, 111, 222; $2\cdot3\cdot37$
21. 1, 2, 7, 14, 49, 98; $2\cdot7\cdot7$ **22.** 1, 3, 5, 7, 9, 15, 21, 35, 45, 63,
105, 315; $3\cdot3\cdot5\cdot7$ **23.** $\frac{8}{24}$, or $\frac{1}{3}$ **24.** $\frac{8}{6}$, or $\frac{4}{3}$ **25.** $\frac{7}{9}$
26. $\frac{8}{45}$ **27.** $-\frac{40}{11}$ **28.** $\frac{21}{32}$ **29.** $\frac{2}{5}$ **30.** $\frac{11}{3}$ **31.** 1 **32.** 0
33. $-\frac{9}{31}$ **34.** $\frac{9}{5}$ **35.** $\frac{5}{42}$ **36.** $\frac{21}{29}$ **37.** Not defined **38.** =
39. $\neq$ **40.** $\frac{25}{200}$, or $\frac{1}{8}$ **41.** $\frac{21}{10,000}$ mi^2 **42.** Find the product
of two prime numbers. **43.** If we use the divisibility tests, it is
quickly clear that none of the even-numbered years is a prime
number. In addition, the divisibility tests for 5 and 3 show that 2001,
2005, 2007, 2013, 2015, and 2019 are not prime numbers. Then the
years 2003, 2009, 2011, and 2017 can be divided by prime numbers
to determine whether they are prime. When we do this, we find that
2003, 2011, and 2017 are prime numbers. If the divisibility tests are
not used, each of the numbers from 2000 to 2020 can be divided by
prime numbers to determine if it is prime. **44.** It is possible to
cancel only when identical *factors* appear in the numerator and the
denominator of a fraction. Situations in which it is not possible to
cancel include the occurrence of identical *addends* or *digits* in the
numerator and the denominator. **45.** No; since the only factors
of a prime number are the number itself and 1, two different prime
numbers cannot contain a common factor (other than 1).

Exercise Set 3.6, p. 166

RC1. products **RC2.** Factor **RC3.** 1 **RC4.** Carry out
1. $\frac{1}{3}$ **3.** $\frac{1}{8}$ **5.** $-\frac{1}{10}$ **7.** $\frac{1}{6}$ **9.** $\frac{27}{10}$ **11.** $-\frac{14}{9}$ **13.** 1 **15.** 1
17. 1 **19.** 1 **21.** 2 **23.** -4 **25.** 9 **27.** -9 **29.** $\frac{15}{2}$
31. $\frac{98}{5}$ **33.** 60 **35.** -30 **37.** $\frac{1}{5}$ **39.** $-\frac{9}{25}$ **41.** $\frac{11}{40}$ **43.** $\frac{5}{14}$
45. $\frac{5}{8}$ in. **47.** 260 million ounces **49.** 480 addresses
51. $\frac{1}{3}$ cup **53.** \$115,500 **55.** 160 mi **57.** Food: \$8400;
housing: \$10,500; clothing: \$4200; savings: \$3000; taxes: \$8400;
other expenses: \$7500 **59.** 8587 **60.** 2707 **61.** -9
62. -13 **63.** 2203 **64.** 848 **65.** -4 **66.** 0
67. 26 **68.** 256 **69.** -425 **70.** 30 **71.** 0 **72.** 22
73. -204 **74.** 8 **75.** $\frac{129}{485}$ **77.** $\frac{1}{12}$ **79.** $\frac{1}{168}$

Translating for Success, p. 174

1. C **2.** H **3.** A **4.** N **5.** O **6.** F **7.** I **8.** L
9. D **10.** M

Exercise Set 3.7, p. 175

RC1. True **RC2.** False **RC3.** True **RC4.** False
1. $\frac{6}{5}$ **3.** $\frac{1}{6}$ **5.** 6 **7.** $-\frac{3}{5}$ **9.** $\frac{4}{5}$ **11.** $-\frac{4}{15}$ **13.** 4 **15.** 2
17. $\frac{1}{8}$ **19.** $\frac{3}{7}$ **21.** -8 **23.** 35 **25.** -1 **27.** $-\frac{2}{3}$ **29.** $\frac{9}{4}$
31. 144 **33.** 75 **35.** -2 **37.** $\frac{3}{5}$ **39.** -315
41. 960 extension cords **43.** 32 pairs **45.** 24 bowls
47. 16 L **49.** 288 km; 108 km **51.** $\frac{1}{16}$ in.
53. 59,960 members **54.** 71 gal **55.** 209,339 degrees
56. 1,650,014 degrees **57.** 526,761 sq yd; 3020 yd **58.** \$928
59. $\frac{9}{19}$ **61.** 36 **63.** $\frac{3}{8}$

Summary and Review: Chapter 3, p. 178

Vocabulary Reinforcement

1. multiplicative **2.** factors **3.** prime **4.** denominator
5. equivalent **6.** reciprocals **7.** factorization **8.** multiple

Concept Reinforcement

1. True **2.** False **3.** True **4.** True

Study Guide

1. 1, 2, 4, 8, 13, 26, 52, 104 **2.** $2\cdot2\cdot2\cdot13$ **3.** 0, 1, 18 **4.** $\frac{5}{14}$
5. $\neq$ **6.** $-\frac{70}{9}$ **7.** $\frac{7}{10}$ **8.** $\frac{7}{3}$ cups

Review Exercises

1. 1, 2, 3, 4, 5, 6, 10, 12, 15, 20, 30, 60 **2.** 1, 2, 4, 8, 11, 16, 22, 44,
88, 176 **3.** 8, 16, 24, 32, 40, 48, 56, 64, 72, 80 **4.** Yes **5.** No
6. Prime **7.** Neither **8.** Composite **9.** $2\cdot5\cdot7$
10. $2\cdot3\cdot5$ **11.** $3\cdot3\cdot5$ **12.** $2\cdot3\cdot5\cdot5$
13. $2\cdot2\cdot2\cdot3\cdot3\cdot3\cdot3$ **14.** $2\cdot3\cdot5\cdot5\cdot5\cdot7$
15. 4344, 600, 93, 330, 255,555, 780, 2802, 711 **16.** 140, 182, 716,
2432, 4344, 600, 330, 780, 2802 **17.** 140, 716, 2432, 4344, 600, 780
18. 2432, 4344, 600 **19.** 140, 95, 475, 600, 330, 255,555, 780
20. 4344, 600, 330, 780, 2802 **21.** 255,555, 711 **22.** 140, 600,
330, 780 **23.** Numerator: 2; denominator: 7 **24.** $\frac{3}{5}$ **25.** $\frac{7}{6}$
26. $\frac{2}{7}$ **27. (a)** $\frac{3}{5}$; **(b)** $\frac{5}{5}$; **(c)** $\frac{3}{8}$ **28.** $\frac{2}{5}$ **29.** $\frac{1}{4}$ **30.** 1
31. 0 **32.** $\frac{39}{40}$ **33.** 18 **34.** $-\frac{1}{3}$ **35.** $-\frac{11}{15}$ **36.** Not defined
37. 6 **38.** $\frac{2}{7}$ **39.** $-\frac{32}{225}$ **40.** $\frac{15}{100} = \frac{3}{20}$; $\frac{38}{100} = \frac{19}{50}$; $\frac{23}{100}$; $\frac{24}{100} = \frac{6}{25}$
41. $\neq$ **42.** = **43.** $\neq$ **44.** = **45.** $\frac{3}{2}$ **46.** 56 **47.** $-\frac{5}{2}$
48. -24 **49.** $\frac{2}{3}$ **50.** $\frac{1}{14}$ **51.** $-\frac{2}{3}$ **52.** $\frac{1}{22}$ **53.** $\frac{3}{20}$ **54.** $\frac{10}{6}$
55. $\frac{5}{4}$ **56.** $-\frac{1}{3}$ **57.** 9 **58.** $-\frac{36}{47}$ **59.** $\frac{9}{2}$ **60.** -2 **61.** $\frac{11}{6}$
62. $-\frac{1}{4}$ **63.** $\frac{9}{4}$ **64.** 300 **65.** 1 **66.** $\frac{4}{9}$ **67.** $\frac{3}{10}$ **68.** -240
69. 9 days **70.** \$32,085 **71.** 1000 km **72.** $\frac{1}{3}$ cup; 2 cups
73. \$15 **74.** 60 bags **75.** D **76.** B
77. $a = 11,176$; $b = 9887$ **78.** 13, 11, 101, 37

Understanding Through Discussion and Writing

1. The student is probably multiplying the divisor by the reciprocal
of the dividend rather than multiplying the dividend by the
reciprocal of the divisor.
2. $9432 = 9\cdot1000 + 4\cdot100 + 3\cdot10 + 2\cdot1 =$
$9(999 + 1) + 4(99 + 1) + 3(9 + 1) + 2\cdot1 =$
$9\cdot999 + 9\cdot1 + 4\cdot99 + 4\cdot1 + 3\cdot9 + 3\cdot1 + 2\cdot1$. Since
999, 99, and 9 are each a multiple of 9, $9\cdot999$, $4\cdot99$, and $3\cdot9$
are multiples of 9. This leaves $9\cdot1 + 4\cdot1 + 3\cdot1 + 2\cdot1$, or
$9 + 4 + 3 + 2$. If $9 + 4 + 3 + 2$, the sum of the digits, is divisible
by 9, then 9432 is divisible by 9. **3.** Taking $\frac{1}{2}$ of a number
is equivalent to multiplying the number by $\frac{1}{2}$. Dividing by $\frac{1}{2}$ is
equivalent to multiplying by the reciprocal of $\frac{1}{2}$, or 2. Thus taking $\frac{1}{2}$
of a number is not the same as dividing by $\frac{1}{2}$. **4.** We first consider
an object, and take $\frac{4}{7}$ of it. We divide the object into 7 parts and take
4 of them, as shown by the shading below.

Next, we take $\frac{2}{3}$ of the shaded area above. We divide it into 3 parts
and take two of them, as shown below.

The entire object has been divided into 21 parts, 8 of which have
been shaded twice. Thus, $\frac{2}{3}\cdot\frac{4}{7} = \frac{8}{21}$. **5.** Since $\frac{1}{7}$ is a smaller
number than $\frac{2}{3}$, there are more $\frac{1}{7}$'s in 5 than $\frac{2}{3}$'s. Thus, $5 \div \frac{1}{7}$ is a
greater number than $5 \div \frac{2}{3}$. **6.** No; in order to simplify a fraction,
we must be able to remove a factor of the type n/n, $n \neq 0$, where n
is a factor that the numerator and the denominator have in common.

Test: Chapter 3, p. 183

1. [3.1a] 1, 2, 3, 4, 5, 6, 10, 12, 15, 20, 25, 30, 50, 60, 75, 100, 150, 300
2. [3.1c] Prime   **3.** [3.1c] Composite   **4.** [3.1d] $2 \cdot 3 \cdot 3$
5. [3.1d] $2 \cdot 2 \cdot 3 \cdot 5$ **6.** [3.2a] Yes   **7.** [3.2a] No   **8.** [3.2a] No
9. [3.2a] Yes   **10.** [3.3a] Numerator: 4; denominator: 5
11. [3.3a] $\frac{3}{4}$ **12.** [3.3a] $\frac{3}{7}$ **13.** [3.3a] (a) $\frac{259}{365}$; (b) $\frac{106}{365}$
14. [3.3b] 26   **15.** [3.3b] 1   **16.** [3.3b] 0   **17.** [3.5b] $-\frac{1}{2}$
18. [3.5b] 6   **19.** [3.3b] Not defined   **20.** [3.3b] Not defined
21. [3.5b] $-\frac{2}{3}$ **22.** [3.5c] $=$ **23.** [3.5c] $\neq$ **24.** [3.6a] 32
25. [3.6a] $-\frac{3}{2}$ **26.** [3.6a] $\frac{5}{2}$ **27.** [3.6a] $\frac{2}{9}$ **28.** [3.7a] $\frac{8}{5}$
29. [3.7a] -4 **30.** [3.7a] $\frac{1}{18}$ **31.** [3.7b] $\frac{8}{7}$ **32.** [3.7b] -18
33. [3.7b] $\frac{18}{7}$ **34.** [3.7c] -64 **35.** [3.7c] $\frac{7}{4}$
36. [3.6b] 4375 students   **37.** [3.7d] $\frac{3}{40}$ m   **38.** [3.7d] 5 qt
39. [3.6b] $\frac{3}{4}$ in.   **40.** [3.3a] C   **41.** [3.6b] $\frac{7}{48}$ acre
42. [3.6a], [3.7b] $-\frac{7}{960}$

Cumulative Review: Chapters 1–3, p. 185

1. [1.1c] Seven million, four hundred fifty-three thousand, sixty-two   **2.** [1.1a] 4 ten thousands   **3.** [3.3b] 5
4. [3.3b] 1   **5.** [3.5b] $-\frac{4}{3}$ **6.** [3.3b] Not defined
7. [3.7a] $\frac{1}{8}$ **8.** [3.7a] $-\frac{2}{3}$ **9.** [1.2a] 5387   **10.** [2.2a] -12
11. [1.3a] 1384   **12.** [2.3a] -16 **13.** [1.4a] 16,452
14. [2.4a] -96 **15.** [3.6a] $-\frac{25}{2}$ **16.** [3.6a] $-\frac{2}{3}$
17. [1.5a] 451 R 22   **18.** [2.5a] 8   **19.** [3.7b] $-\frac{1}{49}$
20. [3.7b] $\frac{4}{3}$ **21.** [1.9c] 0   **22.** [1.9c] 3   **23.** [2.5c] -14
24. [2.5c] -4 **25.** [1.9c] 86   **26.** [1.6a] 166,000
27. [1.9b] 81   **28.** [1.9b] 125   **29.** [1.9b] 16   **30.** [2.1c] $<$
31. [1.6c] $>$ **32.** [2.1d] 33   **33.** [2.1d] 86   **34.** [2.1d] 0
35. [2.2b] -29 **36.** [2.2b] 144   **37.** [2.2b] -7
38. [2.1b] ⟵+——+——+——+——+——+——+——+——+——+——+——+——+——⟶   **39.** [3.1c] Prime
$\quad$ $-2\ -1\ \ 0\ \ 1\ \ 2\ \ 3\ \ 4\ \ 5\ \ 6\ \ 7\ \ 8\ \ 9\ \ 10$
40. [3.1c] Neither   **41.** [3.1c] Composite
42. [3.1d] $2 \cdot 2 \cdot 3 \cdot 3$ **43.** [3.1d] $3 \cdot 3 \cdot 3 \cdot 3$
44. [3.1d] $2 \cdot 3 \cdot 3 \cdot 3 \cdot 5 \cdot 5$ **45.** [3.2a] Divisible by 2, 3, 5, 6, 10; not divisible by 4, 8, 9   **46.** [3.5c] $\neq$
47. [3.5c] $=$ **48.** [1.7b] 44   **49.** [3.7c] $-\frac{3}{5}$
50. [1.8a] 2062   **51.** [1.8a] $36
52. [2.3b], [2.5b] $-17°$C   **53.** [3.6b] 14 students
54. (a) [1.2a], [1.4a] 5, 20; (b) [2.2a], [2.4a] -4, -25;
(c) [1.3a], [1.4a], [2.3a], [2.4a] 10, 10; -10, -10

CHAPTER 4

Exercise Set 4.1, p. 193

RC1. True   **RC2.** True   **RC3.** True   **RC4.** False
1. 4   **3.** 50   **5.** 40   **7.** 54   **9.** 150   **11.** 120   **13.** 72
15. 420   **17.** 144   **19.** 288   **21.** 30   **23.** 90   **25.** 72
27. 60   **29.** 36   **31.** 900   **33.** 48   **35.** 50   **37.** 143
39. 420   **41.** 378   **43.** 810   **45.** 2160   **47.** 9828
49. 6000   **51.** Every 60 years   **53.** Every 420 years   **55.** -18
56. 59 R 77   **57.** $\frac{8}{7}$ **58.** 33,135   **59.** 6,356,118   **60.** 77,699
61. 5 in. by 24 in.

Exercise Set 4.2, p. 199

RC1. True   **RC2.** False   **RC3.** False   **RC4.** True
1. 1   **3.** $\frac{3}{4}$ **5.** $-\frac{1}{6}$ **7.** $\frac{7}{24}$ **9.** $-\frac{1}{10}$ **11.** $\frac{19}{24}$ **13.** $\frac{9}{10}$ **15.** $\frac{1}{18}$
17. $\frac{31}{100}$ **19.** $\frac{41}{60}$ **21.** $\frac{9}{100}$ **23.** $\frac{7}{8}$ **25.** $\frac{13}{24}$ **27.** $\frac{17}{24}$ **29.** $\frac{3}{7}$
31. $\frac{437}{500}$ **33.** $\frac{13}{40}$ **35.** $\frac{391}{144}$ **37.** $\frac{37}{12}$ mi   **39.** $\frac{13}{16}$ lb   **41.** $\frac{27''}{32}$
43. $\frac{51}{32}$ in.   **45.** $\frac{7}{8}$ in.   **47.** $\frac{33}{20}$ mi   **49.** $\frac{4}{5}$ qt; $\frac{8}{5}$ qt; $\frac{2}{5}$ qt   **51.** $\frac{1}{24}$
52. 286 cartons; 2 oz left over   **53.** 18,940,000 lb   **54.** $\frac{3}{64}$ acre
55. $\frac{4}{15}$; $320

Translating for Success, p. 206

1. J   **2.** E   **3.** D   **4.** B   **5.** I   **6.** N   **7.** A   **8.** C
9. L   **10.** F

Exercise Set 4.3, p. 207

RC1. numerators; denominator   **RC2.** denominators
RC3. denominators   **RC4.** numerators
1. $\frac{2}{3}$ **3.** $\frac{3}{4}$ **5.** $-\frac{5}{8}$ **7.** $\frac{1}{24}$ **9.** $-\frac{1}{2}$ **11.** $\frac{9}{14}$ **13.** $\frac{3}{5}$ **15.** $-\frac{7}{10}$
17. $\frac{17}{60}$ **19.** $\frac{53}{100}$ **21.** $\frac{26}{75}$ **23.** $\frac{9}{100}$ **25.** $-\frac{19}{24}$ **27.** $\frac{1}{10}$ **29.** $-\frac{1}{24}$
31. $\frac{13}{16}$ **33.** $-\frac{31}{75}$ **35.** $\frac{13}{75}$ **37.** $<$ **39.** $>$ **41.** $<$ **43.** $<$
45. $>$ **47.** $>$ **49.** $<$ **51.** $\frac{1}{15}$ **53.** $-\frac{22}{15}$ **55.** $\frac{1}{2}$ **57.** $\frac{5}{12}$ hr
59. $\frac{1}{32}$ in.   **61.** $\frac{11}{20}$ lb   **63.** $\frac{1}{4}$ tub   **65.** 1   **66.** Not defined
67. Not defined   **68.** 4   **69.** $-\frac{4}{21}$ **70.** $\frac{3}{2}$ **71.** 21   **72.** $\frac{1}{32}$
73. 12   **74.** $-\frac{5}{2}$ **75.** $\frac{1}{4}$ **76.** $\frac{2}{5}$ **77.** $\frac{14}{3553}$ **79.** $\frac{21}{10}$ km   **81.** $\frac{19}{24}$
83. $-\frac{17}{144}$ **85.** $>$ **87.** *Day 1:* Cut off $\frac{1}{7}$ of bar and pay him. *Day 2:* Cut off $\frac{2}{7}$ of bar. Trade him for the $\frac{1}{7}$. *Day 3:* Give him back the $\frac{1}{7}$. *Day 4:* Trade him the $\frac{4}{7}$ for his $\frac{3}{7}$. *Day 5:* Give him the $\frac{1}{7}$ again. *Day 6:* Trade him the $\frac{2}{7}$ for the $\frac{1}{7}$. *Day 7:* Give him the $\frac{1}{7}$ again. This assumes that he does not spend parts of the gold bar immediately.

Exercise Set 4.4, p. 213

RC1. True   **RC2.** True   **RC3.** False   **RC4.** True
1. $\frac{5}{4}, \frac{15}{4}, \frac{7}{4}$ **3.** $4\frac{1}{4}, 3\frac{1}{4}, 1\frac{1}{8}$ **5.** $\frac{17}{3}$ **7.** $\frac{13}{4}$ **9.** $-\frac{81}{10}$ **11.** $\frac{51}{10}$
13. $\frac{103}{5}$ **15.** $-\frac{59}{6}$ **17.** $\frac{73}{10}$ **19.** $\frac{13}{4}$ **21.** $-\frac{51}{4}$ **23.** $-\frac{43}{10}$
25. $\frac{203}{100}$ **27.** $\frac{200}{3}$ **29.** $-\frac{279}{50}$ **31.** $\frac{1621}{16}$ **33.** $3\frac{3}{5}$ **35.** $4\frac{2}{3}$
37. $-4\frac{1}{2}$ **39.** $5\frac{7}{10}$ **41.** $-7\frac{4}{7}$ **43.** $7\frac{1}{2}$ **45.** $11\frac{1}{2}$ **47.** $-1\frac{1}{2}$
49. $7\frac{57}{100}$ **51.** $-43\frac{1}{8}$ **53.** $108\frac{5}{8}$ **55.** $618\frac{1}{5}$ **57.** $40\frac{4}{7}$ **59.** $55\frac{1}{51}$
61. $2292\frac{23}{35}$ **63.** 45,800   **64.** 45,770   **65.** $\frac{8}{15}$ **66.** $\frac{21}{25}$
67. $-\frac{16}{27}$ **68.** $-\frac{583}{669}$ **69.** $=$ **70.** $\neq$ **71.** $\frac{7}{9}$ **72.** -8 **73.** 35
74. 6407   **75.** $237\frac{19}{541}$ **77.** $8\frac{2}{3}$ **79.** $52\frac{2}{7}$

Mid-Chapter Review: Chapter 4, p. 216

1. True   **2.** True   **3.** False   **4.** False
5. $\frac{11}{42} - \frac{3}{35} = \frac{11}{2 \cdot 3 \cdot 7} - \frac{3}{5 \cdot 7}$
$\qquad = \frac{11}{2 \cdot 3 \cdot 7} \cdot \left(\frac{5}{5}\right) - \frac{3}{5 \cdot 7} \cdot \left(\frac{2 \cdot 3}{2 \cdot 3}\right)$
$\qquad = \frac{11 \cdot 5}{2 \cdot 3 \cdot 7 \cdot 5} - \frac{3 \cdot 2 \cdot 3}{5 \cdot 7 \cdot 2 \cdot 3}$
$\qquad = \frac{55}{2 \cdot 3 \cdot 5 \cdot 7} - \frac{18}{2 \cdot 3 \cdot 5 \cdot 7}$
$\qquad = \frac{55 - 18}{2 \cdot 3 \cdot 5 \cdot 7} = \frac{37}{210}$

6. $\quad x + \frac{1}{8} = \frac{2}{3}$
$\qquad x + \frac{1}{8} - \frac{1}{8} = \frac{2}{3} - \frac{1}{8}$
$\qquad x + 0 = \frac{2}{3} \cdot \frac{8}{8} - \frac{1}{8} \cdot \frac{3}{3}$
$\qquad x = \frac{16}{24} - \frac{3}{24}$
$\qquad x = \frac{13}{24}$

7.

8. $\frac{16}{3}$ **9.** $\frac{25}{12}$ **10.** $-\frac{1}{18}$ **11.** $-\frac{19}{90}$ **12.** $\frac{7}{240}$ **13.** $\frac{156}{119}$ **14.** $\frac{79}{720}$
15. $-\frac{6}{13}$ **16.** $\frac{22}{15}$ mi   **17.** $\frac{101}{15}$ hr   **18.** $\frac{1}{5}, \frac{3}{7}, \frac{4}{10}$ **19.** $\frac{13}{80}$ **20.** $17\frac{8}{15}$
21. C   **22.** C   **23.** No; if one number is a multiple of the other, for example, the LCM is the larger of the numbers.   **24.** We multiply by 1, using the notation n/n, to express each fraction in terms of the least common denominator.   **25.** Write $\frac{8}{5}$ as $\frac{16}{10}$ and $\frac{8}{2}$ as $\frac{40}{10}$ and since taking 40 tenths away from 16 tenths would give a result less than 0, it cannot possibly be $\frac{8}{3}$. You could also find the sum $\frac{8}{3} + \frac{8}{2}$ and show that it is not $\frac{8}{5}$.   **26.** No; $2\frac{1}{3} = \frac{7}{3}$ but $2 \cdot \frac{1}{3} = \frac{2}{3}$.

Exercise Set 4.5, p. 223

RC1. (d)   **RC2.** (a)   **RC3.** (b)   **RC4.** (c)
1. $28\frac{3}{4}$ **3.** $185\frac{7}{12}$ **5.** $6\frac{1}{2}$ **7.** $2\frac{11}{12}$ **9.** $14\frac{7}{12}$ **11.** $12\frac{1}{10}$
13. $16\frac{5}{24}$ **15.** $21\frac{1}{2}$ **17.** $27\frac{7}{8}$ **19.** $27\frac{13}{24}$ **21.** $1\frac{3}{5}$ **23.** $4\frac{1}{10}$
25. $21\frac{17}{24}$ **27.** $12\frac{1}{4}$ **29.** $15\frac{3}{8}$ **31.** $7\frac{5}{12}$ **33.** $13\frac{3}{8}$ **35.** $11\frac{5}{18}$
37. $14\frac{13}{24}$ flats   **39.** $7\frac{5}{12}$ lb   **41.** $\frac{15}{16}$ in.   **43.** $20\frac{1}{12}$ yd
45. $5\frac{3}{8}$ yd   **47.** $95\frac{1}{5}$ mi   **49.** $134\frac{1}{4}$ in.   **51.** $78\frac{1}{12}$ in.   **53.** $28\frac{3}{4}$ yd

55. $7\frac{3}{8}$ ft **57.** $5\frac{7}{8}$ in. **59.** $20\frac{1}{8}$ in. **61.** $3\frac{4}{5}$ hr **63.** $66\frac{5}{6}$ ft
65. Yes **66.** No **67.** No **68.** Yes **69.** No **70.** Yes
71. Yes **72.** Yes **73.** 3 ten thousands + 8 thousands +
1 hundred + 2 tens + 5 ones **74.** Two million, five thousand,
six hundred eighty-nine **75.** 9^4 **76.** 81 **77.** $-8\frac{5}{8}$
79. $-11\frac{1}{24}$

Calculator Corner, p. 231

1. $\frac{7}{12}$ **2.** $\frac{11}{10}$ **3.** $\frac{35}{16}$ **4.** $\frac{3}{10}$ **5.** $10\frac{2}{15}$ **6.** $1\frac{1}{28}$
7. $10\frac{11}{15}$ **8.** $2\frac{91}{115}$

Translating for Success, p. 232

1. O **2.** K **3.** F **4.** D **5.** H **6.** G **7.** L **8.** E
9. M **10.** J

Exercise Set 4.6, p. 233

RC1. True **RC2.** True **RC3.** True **RC4.** True
1. $22\frac{2}{3}$ **3.** $-2\frac{5}{12}$ **5.** $8\frac{1}{6}$ **7.** $9\frac{31}{40}$ **9.** $-24\frac{91}{100}$ **11.** $975\frac{4}{5}$
13. $6\frac{1}{4}$ **15.** $1\frac{1}{5}$ **17.** $-3\frac{9}{16}$ **19.** $1\frac{1}{8}$ **21.** $1\frac{8}{43}$ **23.** $\frac{9}{40}$
25. About \$24 million **27.** About 4,800,000
29. $62\frac{1}{2}$ sq ft **31.** $12\frac{4}{5}$ tiles **33.** $343\frac{3}{4}$ lb **35.** 68°F
37. About \$42,000,000,000 **39.** 75 mph **41.** $5\frac{1}{2}$ cups of
flour, $2\frac{2}{3}$ cups of sugar **43.** 15 mpg **45.** 400 cu ft
47. $16\frac{1}{2}$ servings **49.** $35\frac{115}{256}$ sq in.
51. $13\frac{1}{4}$ in. × $13\frac{1}{4}$ in.: perimeter = 53 in.,
   area = $175\frac{9}{16}$ sq in.;
   $13\frac{1}{4}$ in. × $3\frac{1}{4}$ in.: perimeter = 33 in.,
   area = $43\frac{1}{16}$ sq in.
53. \$408 **54.** 9 bills **55.** 126 slices **56.** 9 cups
57. \$36,500 a year **58.** 16 packages **59.** 22 m
60. 4500 sq yd **61.** $360\frac{60}{473}$ **63.** $-2\frac{25}{64}$ **65.** $\frac{4}{9}$ **67.** $1\frac{4}{5}$

Exercise Set 4.7, p. 242

RC1. (c) **RC2.** (d) **RC3.** (a) **RC4.** (b)
1. $\frac{59}{30}$, or $1\frac{29}{30}$ **3.** $\frac{3}{20}$ **5.** $\frac{211}{8}$, or $26\frac{3}{8}$ **7.** $\frac{7}{16}$ **9.** $\frac{1}{36}$ **11.** $\frac{3}{8}$
13. $\frac{17}{6}$, or $2\frac{5}{6}$ **15.** $\frac{8395}{84}$, or $99\frac{79}{84}$ **17.** $\frac{3}{11}$ **19.** $-\frac{14}{3}$, or $-4\frac{2}{3}$
21. $\frac{5}{4}$, or $1\frac{1}{4}$ **23.** $\frac{1}{100}$ **25.** $-\frac{1}{6}$ **27.** $\frac{7}{12}$ **29.** $\frac{1}{3}$ **31.** $\frac{37}{48}$
33. $\frac{25}{72}$ **35.** $\frac{103}{16}$, or $6\frac{7}{16}$ **37.** $16\frac{7}{96}$ mi **39.** $9\frac{19}{40}$ lb **41.** 0
43. 1 **45.** $\frac{1}{2}$ **47.** $\frac{1}{2}$ **49.** 0 **51.** 1 **53.** 55. 2
57. 3 **59.** $271\frac{1}{2}$ **61.** $29\frac{1}{2}$ **63.** 20 **64.** 2 **65.** 84
66. 100 **67.** 1, 2, 3, 6, 7, 14, 21, 42 **68.** No
69. Prime: 5, 7, 23, 43; composite: 9, 14; neither: 1 **70.** $2 \cdot 3 \cdot 5 \cdot 5$
71. $a = 2, b = 8$ **73.** The largest is $\frac{4}{3} + \frac{5}{2} = \frac{23}{6}$.

Summary and Review: Chapter 4, p. 245

Vocabulary Reinforcement

1. least common multiple **2.** mixed numeral **3.** fraction
4. complex fraction **5.** denominators **6.** least common
multiple **7.** greatest **8.** numerators

Concept Reinforcement

1. True **2.** True **3.** False **4.** True

Study Guide

1. 156 **2.** $\frac{112}{180}$, or $\frac{28}{45}$ **3.** $\frac{4}{35}$ **4.** < **5.** $-\frac{103}{99}$ **6.** $\frac{26}{3}$ **7.** $-7\frac{5}{6}$
8. $7\frac{27}{28}$ **9.** $-14\frac{14}{25}$ **10.** About 4,500,000 **11.** $\frac{9}{2}$, or $4\frac{1}{2}$ **12.** $4\frac{1}{2}$

Review Exercises

1. 36 **2.** 90 **3.** 30 **4.** 1404 **5.** $\frac{63}{40}$ **6.** $-\frac{11}{48}$ **7.** $\frac{25}{12}$
8. $\frac{891}{1000}$ **9.** $\frac{1}{3}$ **10.** $\frac{1}{8}$ **11.** $-\frac{5}{27}$ **12.** $-\frac{19}{18}$ **13.** > **14.** >

15. $\frac{19}{40}$ **16.** $-\frac{7}{5}$ **17.** $\frac{15}{2}$ **18.** $\frac{67}{8}$ **19.** $\frac{13}{3}$ **20.** $-\frac{75}{7}$ **21.** $2\frac{1}{3}$
22. $6\frac{3}{4}$ **23.** $-12\frac{3}{5}$ **24.** $3\frac{1}{2}$ **25.** $877\frac{1}{3}$ **26.** $456\frac{5}{23}$ **27.** $10\frac{2}{5}$
28. $11\frac{11}{15}$ **29.** $10\frac{2}{3}$ **30.** $8\frac{1}{4}$ **31.** $7\frac{7}{9}$ **32.** $4\frac{11}{15}$ **33.** $4\frac{3}{20}$
34. $13\frac{3}{8}$ **35.** 16 **36.** $-3\frac{1}{2}$ **37.** $2\frac{21}{50}$ **38.** -6 **39.** -12
40. $1\frac{7}{17}$ **41.** $\frac{1}{8}$ **42.** $\frac{9}{10}$ **43.** $4\frac{1}{4}$ yd **44.** $177\frac{3}{4}$ in^2
45. $50\frac{1}{4}$ in^2 **46.** $1\frac{73}{100}$ in. **47.** 24 lb **48.** $8\frac{3}{8}$ cups **49.** \$850
50. $3\frac{3}{4}$ mi **51.** $63\frac{2}{3}$ pies; $19\frac{1}{3}$ pies **52.** 1 **53.** $\frac{7}{40}$ **54.** 3
55. $-\frac{4}{5}$ **56.** 30 **57.** $\frac{77}{240}$ **58.** $\frac{1}{2}$ **59.** 0 **60.** 1 **61.** 7
62. 10 **63.** $5\frac{1}{2}$ **64.** 0 **65.** $2\frac{1}{2}$ **66.** $28\frac{1}{2}$ **67.** A
68. D **69.** 12 min **70.** $\frac{6}{3} + \frac{5}{4} = 3\frac{1}{4}$

Understanding Through Discussion and Writing

1. No; if the sum of the fractional parts of the mixed numerals
is n/n, then the sum of the mixed numerals is an integer. For
example, $1\frac{1}{5} + 6\frac{4}{5} = 7\frac{5}{5} = 8$. **2.** Answers may vary. A wheel
makes $33\frac{1}{3}$ revolutions per minute. It rotates for $4\frac{1}{2}$ min. How
many revolutions does it make? **3.** The student is multiplying
the whole numbers to get the whole-number portion of the
answer and multiplying fractions to get the fraction part of the
answer. The student should have converted each mixed numeral
to fraction notation, multiplied, simplified, and then converted
back to a mixed numeral. The correct answer is $4\frac{6}{7}$. **4.** It
might be necessary to find the least common denominator
before adding or subtracting. The least common denominator is
the least common multiple of the denominators. **5.** Answers
may vary. Suppose that a room has dimensions $15\frac{3}{4}$ ft by $28\frac{5}{8}$ ft.
The equation $2 \cdot 15\frac{3}{4} + 2 \cdot 28\frac{5}{8} = 88\frac{3}{4}$ gives the perimeter of the
room, in feet. **6.** Note that $5 \cdot 3\frac{2}{7} = 5\left(3 + \frac{2}{7}\right) = 5 \cdot 3 + 5 \cdot \frac{2}{7}$.
The products $5 \cdot 3$ and $5 \cdot \frac{2}{7}$ should be added rather than multiplied
together. The student could also have converted $3\frac{2}{7}$ to fraction
notation, multiplied, simplified, and converted back to a mixed
numeral. The correct answer is $16\frac{3}{7}$.

Test: Chapter 4, p. 251

1. [4.1a] 48 **2.** [4.1a] 600 **3.** [4.2a] 3 **4.** [4.2a] $-\frac{5}{24}$
5. [4.2a] $\frac{921}{1000}$ **6.** [4.3a] $\frac{1}{3}$ **7.** [4.3a] $\frac{1}{12}$ **8.** [4.3a] $-\frac{31}{40}$
9. [4.3c] $\frac{15}{4}$ **10.** [4.3c] $\frac{1}{4}$ **11.** [4.3b] > **12.** [4.4a] $\frac{7}{2}$
13. [4.4a] $-\frac{79}{8}$ **14.** [4.4a] $4\frac{1}{2}$ **15.** [4.4a] $-8\frac{2}{9}$ **16.** [4.4b] $162\frac{7}{11}$
17. [4.5a] $14\frac{1}{8}$ **18.** [4.5a] $14\frac{5}{12}$ **19.** [4.5b] $4\frac{7}{24}$ **20.** [4.5b] $6\frac{1}{4}$
21. [4.6a] 39 **22.** [4.6a] $-4\frac{1}{2}$ **23.** [4.6b] 2 **24.** [4.6b] $-\frac{1}{36}$
25. [4.6c] About 105 kg **26.** [4.6c] 80 books
27. [4.5c] **(a)** 3 in.; **(b)** $4\frac{1}{2}$ in. **28.** [4.3d] $\frac{1}{16}$ in.
29. [4.7b] $6\frac{11}{36}$ ft **30.** [4.7a] $3\frac{1}{2}$ **31.** [4.7a] $\frac{3}{4}$ **32.** [4.7b] $\frac{1}{6}$
33. [4.7c] 0 **34.** [4.7c] 1 **35.** [4.7c] 16 **36.** [4.1a] D
37. [4.1a] **(a)** 24, 48, 72; **(b)** 24 **38.** [4.3b], [4.5c] Rebecca
walks $\frac{17}{56}$ mi farther.

Cumulative Review: Chapters 1–4, p. 253

1. **(a)** [4.5c] $14\frac{13}{24}$ mi; **(b)** [4.7b] $4\frac{61}{72}$ mi **2.** [1.8a] 31 people
3. [3.6b] $\frac{2}{3}$ tsp; 4 tsp **4.** [4.6c] 16 pieces **5.** [1.8a] \$108
6. [4.2b] $\frac{33}{20}$ mi **7.** [3.3a] $\frac{5}{16}$ **8.** [3.3a] $\frac{4}{3}$ **9.** [1.2a] 8982
10. [1.3a] 4518 **11.** [2.2a] -15 **12.** [4.2a] $\frac{5}{12}$ **13.** [2.3a] -14
14. [4.3a] $-\frac{13}{12}$ **15.** [4.5a] $8\frac{1}{4}$ **16.** [4.5b] $1\frac{1}{6}$ **17.** [2.4a] -75
18. [3.6a] $\frac{3}{2}$ **19.** [3.6a] 15 **20.** [4.6b] $7\frac{1}{3}$ **21.** [1.5a] 715
22. [1.5a] 56 R 11 **23.** [4.4b] $56\frac{11}{45}$ **24.** [1.1a] 5
25. **(a)** [4.6c] $142\frac{1}{4}$ ft^2; **(b)** [4.5c] 54 ft **26.** [1.6a] 38,500
27. [4.1a] 72 **28.** [4.7a] $\frac{1377}{100}$, or $13\frac{77}{100}$ **29.** [4.3b] >
30. [3.5c] = **31.** [4.3b] < **32.** [4.7c] 1 **33.** [4.7c] $\frac{1}{2}$
34. [4.7c] 0 **35.** [3.5b] $\frac{4}{5}$ **36.** [3.3b] 0 **37.** [3.5b] 32
38. [4.4a] $\frac{37}{9}$ **39.** [4.4a] $5\frac{2}{3}$ **40.** [1.7b] 93 **41.** [4.3c] $\frac{5}{9}$
42. [3.7c] $-\frac{12}{7}$ **43.** [1.7b] 905 **44.** [3.1a, c, d], [3.2a]
Factors of 68: 1, 2, 4, 17, 34, 68. Factorization of 68: $2 \cdot 2 \cdot 17$,
or $2 \cdot 34$. Prime factorization of 68: $2 \cdot 2 \cdot 17$. Numbers divisible

by 6: 12, 54, 72, 300. Numbers divisible by 8: 8, 16, 24, 32, 40, 48, 64, 864. Numbers divisible by 5: 70, 95, 215. Prime numbers: 2, 3, 17, 19, 23, 31, 47, 101.   **45.** [3.1c] 2003

CHAPTER 5

Exercise Set 5.1, p. 263

RC1. 5   **RC2.** 2   **RC3.** 3   **RC4.** 0   **RC5.** 8   **RC6.** 4
RC7. 1   **RC8.** 6
1. One hundred nineteen ten-thousandths
3. One hundred thirty-seven and six tenths
5. Five hundred nineteen and twenty-two hundredths
7. Three and seven hundred eighty-five thousandths   **9.** Negative thirty-four and eight hundred ninety-one thousandths
11. $\frac{83}{10}$ **13.** $\frac{356}{100}$ **15.** $\frac{20,003}{1000}$ **17.** $-\frac{10,008}{10,000}$ **19.** $\frac{372}{10}$ **21.** $-\frac{13}{100,000}$
23. 0.8   **25.** 3.798   **27.** -8.89 **29.** 0.00019   **31.** 0.0078
33. -0.376193 **35.** 2.9   **37.** 3.098   **39.** 99.44   **41.** -2.1739
43. 0.58   **45.** 0.91   **47.** -0.0009 **49.** 235.07   **51.** $\frac{4}{100}$
53. -0.432 **55.** 0.1   **57.** -0.5 **59.** 2.7   **61.** -123.7
63. 0.89   **65.** 0.67   **67.** -1.00 **69.** -0.09 **71.** 0.325
73. -17.001 **75.** 10.101   **77.** -9.999 **79.** 800   **81.** 809.573
83. 810   **85.** 34.5439   **87.** 34.54   **89.** 35   **91.** 6170
92. 6200   **93.** 6000   **94.** $2 \cdot 2 \cdot 2 \cdot 2 \cdot 5 \cdot 5 \cdot 5$, or $2^4 \cdot 5^3$
95. $2 \cdot 3 \cdot 3 \cdot 5 \cdot 17$, or $2 \cdot 3^2 \cdot 5 \cdot 17$ **96.** $\frac{5}{21}$ **97.** $\frac{6}{5}$
99. $-2.109, -2.108, -2.1, -2.0302, -2.018, -2.0119, -2.000001$
101. 6.78346   **103.** 0.03030

Exercise Set 5.2, p. 270

RC1. 21.824; 23.7   **RC2.** 146.723; 40.9
1. 334.37   **3.** 1576.215   **5.** 132.560   **7.** 50.0248   **9.** 40.007
11. 977.955   **13.** 771.967   **15.** 8754.8221   **17.** 49.02
19. 85.921   **21.** 2.4975   **23.** 3.397   **25.** 8.85   **27.** 3.37
29. 1.045   **31.** 3.703   **33.** 0.9902   **35.** 99.66   **37.** 4.88
39. 0.994   **41.** 17.802   **43.** 51.13   **45.** 32.7386   **47.** 4.0622
49. -3.29 **51.** -2.5 **53.** -7.2 **55.** 3.379   **57.** -16.6
59. 2.5   **61.** -3.519 **63.** 9.601   **65.** 75.5   **67.** 3.8
69. -10.292 **71.** -8.8 **73.** 11.65   **75.** 384.68
77. $-20,033.3$ **79.** 582.97   **81.** -533.6 **83.** -6.99
85. 35,000   **86.** 34,000   **87.** $\frac{1}{6}$ **88.** $\frac{34}{45}$ **89.** 6166
90. 5366   **91.** $16\frac{1}{2}$ servings   **92.** $60\frac{1}{5}$ mi   **93.** 345.8

Exercise Set 5.3, p. 279

RC1. (c)   **RC2.** (e)   **RC3.** (f)   **RC4.** (a)
RC5. (d)   **RC6.** (b)
1. 60.2   **3.** 6.72   **5.** 0.252   **7.** 0.522   **9.** 237.6
11. $-583,686.852$ **13.** -780 **15.** 8.923   **17.** 0.09768
19. -0.782 **21.** 521.6   **23.** 3.2472   **25.** -897.6 **27.** 322.07
29. 55.68   **31.** 3487.5   **33.** 50.0004   **35.** 114.42902
37. 13.284   **39.** 90.72   **41.** 0.0028728   **43.** 0.72523
45. -1.872115 **47.** 45,678   **49.** 2888¢   **51.** 66¢
53. $0.34   **55.** $34.45   **57.** 3,480,000
59. 50,960,000,000; 13,410,000,000   **61.** 2,200,000
63. $11\frac{1}{5}$ **64.** $-\frac{35}{72}$ **65.** $2\frac{7}{15}$ **66.** $7\frac{2}{15}$ **67.** 87   **68.** 1176 R 14
69. -7 **70.** -14 **71.** $10^{21} = 1$ sextillion
73. $10^{24} = 1$ septillion

Calculator Corner, p. 283

1. 17.15   **2.** 33.83   **3.** 454.74   **4.** 0.5076   **5.** 2.56   **6.** 0.064

Exercise Set 5.4, p. 289

RC1. Subtract: $2 - 0.04$ **RC2.** Divide: $2.06 \div 0.01$
RC3. Evaluate: 8^3 **RC4.** Add: $4.1 + 6.9$
RC5. Divide: $9 \div 3$ **RC6.** Subtract: $10 - 5$
1. 2.99   **3.** 23.78   **5.** 7.48   **7.** 7.2   **9.** -1.143 **11.** -4.041
13. 56   **15.** 70   **17.** 20   **19.** 0.4   **21.** 0.41   **23.** 8.5

25. 9.3   **27.** -0.625 **29.** 0.26   **31.** 15.625   **33.** 2.34
35. 0.47   **37.** 0.2134567   **39.** -2.359 **41.** 4.26487
43. -169.4 **45.** 1023.7   **47.** -4256.1 **49.** 9.3
51. -0.0090678 **53.** 45.6   **55.** 2107   **57.** -302.997
59. 446.208   **61.** 24.14   **63.** -5.0072 **65.** 19.3204
67. 473.188278   **69.** -9.51 **71.** 911.13   **73.** 205
75. $1288.36   **77.** 13,748.5 ft   **79.** $\frac{19}{73}$ **80.** $-\frac{23}{31}$
81. $2 \cdot 2 \cdot 3 \cdot 3 \cdot 19$, or $2^2 \cdot 3^2 \cdot 19$ **82.** $5 \cdot 401$ **83.** $15\frac{1}{8}$
84. $5\frac{7}{8}$ **85.** 343   **86.** 64   **87.** 47   **88.** 41   **89.** 6.254194585
91. 1000   **93.** 100

Mid-Chapter Review: Chapter 5, p. 293

1. False   **2.** True   **3.** True
4.
$$y + 12.8 = 23.35$$
$$y + 12.8 - 12.8 = 23.35 - 12.8$$
$$y + 0 = 10.55$$
$$y = 10.55$$
5. $5.6 + 4.3 \times (6.5 - 0.25)^2 = 5.6 + 4.3 \times (6.25)^2$
$$= 5.6 + 4.3 \times 39.0625$$
$$= 5.6 + 167.96875$$
$$= 173.56875$$
6. Twenty-nine and forty-three hundredths   **7.** 9,400,000
8. $\frac{453}{100}$ **9.** $-\frac{287}{1000}$ **10.** 0.13   **11.** -5.09 **12.** 0.7   **13.** -6.39
14. 35.67   **15.** 8.002   **16.** 28.462   **17.** 28.46   **18.** 28.5
19. 28   **20.** 50.095   **21.** 1214.862   **22.** -3.772 **23.** 18.24
24. 272.19   **25.** 5.593   **26.** 15.55   **27.** -58.77 **28.** 4.14
29. 92.871   **30.** -8123.6 **31.** 2.937   **32.** 5.06   **33.** -3.2
34. 763.4   **35.** 0.914036   **36.** 2045¢   **37.** $1.47   **38.** -105.3
39. 8.4   **40.** 59.774   **41.** 33.83   **42.** The student probably rounded over successively from the thousandths place as follows: $236.448 \approx 236.45 \approx 236.5 \approx 237$. The student should have considered only the tenths place and rounded down.
43. The decimal points were not lined up before the subtraction was carried out.   **44.** $10 \div 0.2 = \frac{10}{0.2} = \frac{10}{0.2} \cdot \frac{10}{10} = \frac{100}{2} = 100 \div 2$
45. For $0.247 \div 0.1 = 0.0247$, the divisor, 0.1, is smaller than the dividend, 0.247. Thus the answer will be larger than 0.247. The correct answer is 2.47. For $0.247 \div 10 = 2.47$, the divisor, 10, is larger than the dividend, 0.247. Thus the answer will be smaller than 0.247. The correct answer is 0.0247.

Exercise Set 5.5, p. 300

RC1. Repeating   **RC2.** Terminating   **RC3.** Terminating
RC4. Repeating   **RC5.** Repeating   **RC6.** Terminating
1. 0.23   **3.** 0.6   **5.** -0.325 **7.** 0.2   **9.** -0.85 **11.** 0.375
13. -0.975 **15.** 0.52   **17.** -20.016 **19.** 0.25   **21.** -1.16
23. 1.1875   **25.** $0.2\overline{6}$ **27.** $0.\overline{3}$ **29.** $-1.\overline{3}$ **31.** $-1.1\overline{6}$
33. 0.571428 **35.** $-0.91\overline{6}$ **37.** 0.3; 0.27; 0.267
39. 0.3; 0.33; 0.333   **41.** $-1.3; -1.33; -1.333$
43. $-1.2; -1.17; -1.167$ **45.** 0.6; 0.57; 0.571
47. $-0.9; -0.92; -0.917$ **49.** 0.2; 0.18; 0.182
51. $-0.3; -0.28; -0.278$ **53.** (a) 0.571; (b) 1.333; (c) 0.429;
(d) 0.75   **55.** 0.281   **57.** 15.8 mpg   **59.** 17.8 mpg
61. $357.6 billion   **63.** 15.2 mph   **65.** 11.06   **67.** 8.4
69. $-417.51\overline{6}$ **71.** 0   **73.** 2.8125   **75.** -0.07675
77. 317.14   **79.** 0.1825   **81.** 18   **83.** -2.736 **85.** 21
86. $1\frac{1}{2}$ **87.** -10 **88.** $30\frac{7}{10}$ **89.** $1\frac{1}{24}$ cups   **90.** $1\frac{33}{100}$ in.
91. $0.\overline{142857}, 0.\overline{285714}, 0.\overline{428571}, 0.\overline{571428}, 0.\overline{714285}; 0.\overline{857142}$

Exercise Set 5.6, p. 306

RC1. (b)   **RC2.** (d)   **RC3.** (c)
RC4. (e)   **RC5.** (a)   **RC6.** (f)
1. (c)   **3.** (a)   **5.** (c)   **7.** 1.6   **9.** 6   **11.** 60
13. 2.3   **15.** 180   **17.** (a)   **19.** (c)   **21.** (b)
23. (b)   **25.** $1800 \div 9 = 200$ posts; answers may vary
27. $2 \cdot 12 = 24; answers may vary   **29.** 2   **30.** 165

A-8   Answers

31. 210 **32.** 69 **33.** 10 **34.** 530 **35.** No
37. (a) +, ×; **(b)** +, ×, −

Translating for Success, p. 314

1. I **2.** C **3.** N **4.** A **5.** G **6.** B **7.** D **8.** O
9. F **10.** M

Exercise Set 5.7, p. 315

RC1. Familiarize **RC2.** Translate **RC3.** Solve
RC4. Check **RC5.** State
1. 61.6 million citizens **3.** About $7142.86 **5.** 102.8°F
7. 78.1 cm **9.** 22,691.5 mi **11.** 9.58 sec **13.** 11.9752 cu ft
15. $0.51 **17.** $24.33 **19.** 20.2 mpg **21.** 227.75 sq ft
23. Area: 268.96 sq ft; perimeter: 65.6 ft **25.** $19,110.83
27. $316,987.20; $196,987.20 **29.** 876 calories **31.** $906.50
33. 236.2 million metric tons **35.** $1180.15, 500.15, 916.42,
875.47, 764.83 **37.** 1.4°F **39.** $1406.75 **41.** $-\frac{23}{15}$ **42.** $6\frac{5}{6}$
43. $\frac{1}{24}$ **44.** 2803 **45.** $\frac{5}{16}$ **46.** $-\frac{13}{25}$ **47.** $7\frac{1}{5}$ min

Summary and Review: Chapter 5, p. 320

Vocabulary Reinforcement

1. repeating **2.** terminating **3.** billion
4. million **5.** trillion **6.** rational numbers

Concept Reinforcement

1. True **2.** False **3.** True **4.** False

Study Guide

1. $\frac{5093}{100}$ **2.** -81.7 **3.** 42.159 **4.** 153.35 **5.** 38.611
6. 207.848 **7.** 19.11 **8.** -0.176 **9.** 60,437 **10.** 7.4
11. 0.047 **12.** $-15,690$

Review Exercises

1. 6,590,000 **2.** 3,100,000,000 **3.** Three and forty-seven
hundredths **4.** Thirty-one thousandths **5.** Twenty-seven and
one ten-thousandth **6.** Negative nine tenths **7.** $\frac{9}{100}$ **8.** $\frac{4561}{1000}$
9. $-\frac{89}{1000}$ **10.** $-\frac{30,227}{10,000}$ **11.** 0.034 **12.** -4.2603 **13.** 27.91
14. -867.006 **15.** 0.034 **16.** 0.91 **17.** 0.741 **18.** -1.038
19. 17.4 **20.** 17.43 **21.** 17.429 **22.** 17 **23.** 574.519
24. 0.6838 **25.** -209.5 **26.** 45.551 **27.** 29.2092
28. 790.29 **29.** 46.142 **30.** -70.8109 **31.** 12.96
32. 0.14442 **33.** 4.3 **34.** -0.02468 **35.** -7.5 **36.** 0.45
37. 45.2 **38.** 1.022 **39.** 0.2763 **40.** -1389.2
41. 496.2795 **42.** -6.95 **43.** 42.54 **44.** 4.9911
45. $15.52 **46.** 1.9 lb **47.** $784.47 **48.** $55.50 **49.** 14.5 mpg
50. 20.7 million books **51.** 272 **52.** 216 **53.** $125 **54.** 0.52
55. -0.45 **56.** 2.75 **57.** -3.25 **58.** $1.1\overline{6}$ **59.** $1.\overline{54}$
60. 1.5 **61.** 1.55 **62.** 1.545 **63.** $82.73 **64.** $4.87 **65.** 2493¢
66. 986¢ **67.** -1.5805 **68.** 57.1449 **69.** -15.6375 **70.** D
71. B **72. (a)** $2.56 \times 6.4 \div 51.2 - 17.4 + 89.7 = 72.62$;
(b) $(11.12 - 0.29) \times 3^4 = 877.23$
73. $1 = 3 \cdot \frac{1}{3} = 3(0.33333333 \dots) = 0.99999999 \dots$, or $0.\overline{9}$

Understanding Through Discussion and Writing

1. Count the number of decimal places. Move the decimal
point that many places to the right and write the result over a
denominator of 1 followed by that many zeros.
2. $346.708 \times 0.1 = \frac{346,708}{1000} \times \frac{1}{10} = \frac{346,708}{10,000} = 34.6708 \ne 3467.08$
3. When the denominator of a fraction is a multiple of 10, long
division is not the fastest way to convert the fraction to decimal
notation. Many times when the denominator is a factor of some
multiple of 10, this is also the case. The latter situation occurs when
the denominator has only 2's or 5's, or both, as factors.

4. Multiply by 1 to get a denominator that is a power of 10:

$$\frac{44}{125} = \frac{44}{125} \cdot \frac{8}{8} = \frac{352}{1000} = 0.352.$$

We can also divide to find that $\frac{44}{125} = 0.352$.

Test: Chapter 5, p. 325

1. [5.3b] 2,600,000,000 **2.** [5.1a] One hundred twenty-three and
forty-seven ten-thousandths **3.** [5.1b] $\frac{91}{100}$ **4.** [5.1b] $-\frac{2769}{1000}$
5. [5.1c] 0.162 **6.** [5.1c] -0.06 **7.** [5.1b] 0.074
8. [5.1b] -3.7047 **9.** [5.1b] 756.09 **10.** [5.1d] 6
11. [5.1d] 5.678 **12.** [5.1d] 5.7 **13.** [5.2c] -18.3
14. [5.2b] 48.357 **15.** [5.2b] 19.0901 **16.** [5.3a] 0.03
17. [5.3a] -0.21345 **18.** [5.4a] -4.75 **19.** [5.4a] 30.4
20. [5.4a] 0.19 **21.** [5.4a] -0.34689 **22.** [5.4b] -84.26
23. [5.2d] 8.982 **24.** [5.4c] 40.0065 **25.** [5.5c] 302.4
26. [5.5a] 0.35 **27.** [5.5a] 0.88 **28.** [5.5a] $0.8\overline{1}$
29. [5.5a] $-7.41\overline{6}$ **30.** [5.5b] 0.8 **31.** [5.5b] 0.82
32. [5.5b] 0.818 **33.** [5.6a] 198 **34.** [5.6a] 4
35. [5.7a] $46.69 **36.** [5.7a] 28.3 mpg **37.** [5.7a] 68.5 years
38. [5.7a] $293.93 **39.** [5.3b] B **40.** [5.7a] $35
41. [5.1b, c] $-\frac{13}{15}, -\frac{17}{20}, -\frac{11}{13}, -\frac{15}{19}, -\frac{5}{7}, -\frac{2}{3}$

Cumulative Review: Chapters 1–5, p. 327

1. [4.4a] $\frac{20}{9}$ **2.** [5.1b] $-\frac{3051}{1000}$ **3.** [5.5a] -1.4 **4.** [5.5a] $0.\overline{54}$
5. [3.1c] Prime **6.** [3.2a] Yes **7.** [1.9c] 1754 **8.** [5.4c] -0.136
9. [5.1d] 584.97 **10.** [5.5b] 218.56 **11.** [5.6a] 160
12. [5.6a] 4 **13.** [1.6b] 12,800,000 **14.** [5.6a] 6 **15.** [4.5a] $6\frac{1}{20}$
16. [1.2a] 139,116 **17.** [4.2a] $\frac{31}{18}$ **18.** [5.2c] -141.847
19. [1.3a] 710,137 **20.** [5.2b] 13.097 **21.** [4.5b] $\frac{5}{7}$
22. [4.3a] $-\frac{1}{110}$ **23.** [3.6a] $-\frac{1}{6}$ **24.** [1.4a] 5,317,200
25. [5.3a] 4.78 **26.** [5.3a] 0.0279431 **27.** [5.4a] 2.122
28. [1.5a] 1843 **29.** [5.4a] 13,862.1 **30.** [3.7b] $\frac{5}{6}$
31. [5.2d] 0.78 **32.** [1.7b] 28 **33.** [5.4b] -8.62
34. [1.7b] 367,251 **35.** [4.3c] $\frac{1}{18}$ **36.** [3.7c] $-\frac{1}{2}$
37. [1.8a] 732 million **38.** [1.8a] 885 million **39.** [3.7d] $1500
40. [3.6b] $2400 **41.** [5.7a] $258.77 **42.** [4.5c] $6\frac{1}{2}$ lb
43. [4.2b] 2 lb **44.** [5.7a] 467.28 sq ft **45.** [4.7a] $\frac{9}{32}$
46. [5.4c] -527.04 **47.** [5.7a] $2.39 **48.** [4.6c] 144 packages

CHAPTER 7

Calculator Corner, p. 384

1. 0.14 **2.** 0.00069 **3.** 0.438 **4.** 1.25

Exercise Set 7.1, p. 385

RC1. 43% **RC2.** 86% **RC3.** 19% **RC4.** 50%
1. $\frac{90}{100}$; $90 \times \frac{1}{100}$; 90×0.01 **3.** $\frac{12.5}{100}$; $12.5 \times \frac{1}{100}$; 12.5×0.01
5. 0.67 **7.** 0.456 **9.** 0.5901 **11.** 0.1 **13.** 0.01 **15.** 2
17. 0.001 **19.** 0.0009 **21.** 0.0018 **23.** 0.2319 **25.** 0.14875
27. 0.565 **29.** 0.13; 0.11 **31.** 0.07; 0.08 **33.** 0.139; 0.4
35. 47% **37.** 3% **39.** 870% **41.** 33.4% **43.** 75%
45. 40% **47.** 0.6% **49.** 1.7% **51.** 27.18% **53.** 2.39%
55. 65.1% **57.** 34% **59.** 35.9%; 20% **61.** 0.29; 0.3; 0.13;
0.1; 0.18 **63.** 1, 2, 3, 4, 6, 7, 12, 14, 21, 28, 42, 84 **64.** 1, 2, 4, 5,
10, 20, 31, 62, 124, 155, 310, 620 **65.** 180 **66.** $2 \cdot 3 \cdot 3 \cdot 5$
67. $-\frac{23}{16}$ **68.** 97 **69.** 50% **70.** 70% **73.** 20%

Calculator Corner, p. 389

1. 52% **2.** 38.46% **3.** 110.26% **4.** 171.43% **5.** 59.62%
6. 28.31%

Exercise Set 7.2, p. 393

RC1. (c) **RC2.** (e) **RC3.** (g) **RC4.** (a) **RC5.** (b)
RC6. (d) **RC7.** (h) **RC8.** (i)

1. 41% **3.** 5% **5.** 20% **7.** 30% **9.** 50% **11.** 87.5%, or $87\frac{1}{2}$% **13.** 80% **15.** 66.$\overline{6}$%, or $66\frac{2}{3}$% **17.** 16.$\overline{6}$%, or $16\frac{2}{3}$%
19. 18.75%, or $18\frac{3}{4}$% **21.** 81.25%, or $81\frac{1}{4}$% **23.** 16% **25.** 5%
27. 34% **29.** 8%; 59% **31.** 22% **33.** 12% **35.** 15%
37. $\frac{17}{20}$ **39.** $\frac{5}{8}$ **41.** $\frac{1}{3}$ **43.** $\frac{1}{6}$ **45.** $\frac{29}{400}$ **47.** $\frac{1}{125}$ **49.** $\frac{203}{800}$
51. $\frac{176}{225}$ **53.** $\frac{711}{1100}$ **55.** $\frac{3}{2}$ **57.** $\frac{13}{40,000}$ **59.** $\frac{1}{3}$ **61.** $\frac{3}{50}$
63. $\frac{13}{100}$ **65.** $\frac{19}{25}$ **67.** $\frac{3}{20}$ **69.** $\frac{209}{1000}$

71.

Fraction Notation	Decimal Notation	Percent Notation
$\frac{1}{8}$	0.125	12.5%, or $12\frac{1}{2}$%
$\frac{1}{6}$	0.1$\overline{6}$	16.$\overline{6}$%, or $16\frac{2}{3}$%
$\frac{1}{5}$	0.2	20%
$\frac{1}{4}$	0.25	25%
$\frac{1}{3}$	0.$\overline{3}$	33.$\overline{3}$%, or $33\frac{1}{3}$%
$\frac{3}{8}$	0.375	37.5%, or $37\frac{1}{2}$%
$\frac{2}{5}$	0.4	40%
$\frac{1}{2}$	0.5	50%

73.

Fraction Notation	Decimal Notation	Percent Notation
$\frac{1}{2}$	0.5	50%
$\frac{1}{3}$	0.$\overline{3}$	33.$\overline{3}$%, or $33\frac{1}{3}$%
$\frac{1}{4}$	0.25	25%
$\frac{1}{6}$	0.1$\overline{6}$	16.$\overline{6}$%, or $16\frac{2}{3}$%
$\frac{1}{8}$	0.125	12.5%, or $12\frac{1}{2}$%
$\frac{3}{4}$	0.75	75%
$\frac{5}{6}$	0.8$\overline{3}$	83.$\overline{3}$%, or $83\frac{1}{3}$%
$\frac{3}{8}$	0.375	37.5%, or $37\frac{1}{2}$%

75. 70 **76.** 5 **77.** -400 **78.** 18.75 **79.** 23.125 **80.** 25.5
81. 4.5 **82.** 8.75 **83.** $18\frac{3}{4}$ **84.** $-7\frac{4}{9}$ **85.** $-\frac{203}{2}$ **86.** $\frac{209}{10}$
87. 257.$\overline{46317}$% **89.** 1.04$\overline{142857}$
91. $\frac{1}{6}$%, $\frac{2}{7}$%, 0.5%, $1\frac{1}{6}$%, 1.6%, $16\frac{1}{6}$%, 0.2, $\frac{1}{2}$, 0.$\overline{54}$, 1.6

Calculator Corner, p. 400

1. $5.04 **2.** 0.0112 **3.** 450 **4.** $1000 **5.** 2.5% **6.** 12%

Exercise Set 7.3, p. 401

RC1. (c) **RC2.** (e) **RC3.** (f) **RC4.** (d) **RC5.** (b)
RC6. (a)
1. $a = 32\% \times 78$ **3.** $89 = p \times 99$ **5.** $13 = 25\% \times b$
7. 234.6 **9.** 45 **11.** $18 **13.** 1.9 **15.** 78% **17.** 200%
19. 50% **21.** 125% **23.** 40 **25.** $40 **27.** 88 **29.** 20
31. 6.25 **33.** $846.60 **35.** 1216 **37.** $-\frac{9375}{10,000}$, or $-\frac{15}{16}$
38. $\frac{125}{1000}$, or $\frac{1}{8}$ **39.** 0.3 **40.** -0.017 **41.** 7 **42.** 8
43. $10,000 (can vary); $10,400 **45.** $1875

Exercise Set 7.4, p. 407

RC1. (b) **RC2.** (e) **RC3.** (c) **RC4.** (f) **RC5.** (d)
RC6. (a)
1. $\frac{37}{100} = \frac{a}{74}$ **3.** $\frac{N}{100} = \frac{4.3}{5.9}$ **5.** $\frac{25}{100} = \frac{14}{b}$ **7.** 68.4 **9.** 462
11. 40 **13.** 2.88 **15.** 25% **17.** 102% **19.** 25%
21. 93.75%, or $93\frac{3}{4}$% **23.** $72 **25.** 90 **27.** 88 **29.** 20
31. 25 **33.** $780.20 **35.** 200 **37.** 8 **38.** 4000 **39.** 15
40. 2074 **41.** $\frac{43}{48}$ qt **42.** $\frac{1}{8}$ T
43. $1170 (can vary); $1118.64

Mid-Chapter Review: Chapter 7, p. 409

1. True **2.** False **3.** True **4.** $\frac{1}{2}\% = \frac{1}{2} \cdot \frac{1}{100} = \frac{1}{200}$
5. $\frac{80}{1000} = \frac{8}{100} = 8\%$ **6.** 5.5% $= \frac{5.5}{100} = \frac{55}{1000} = \frac{11}{200}$
7. 0.375 $= \frac{375}{1000} = \frac{37.5}{100} = 37.5\%$
8.
$$15 = p \times 80$$
$$\frac{15}{80} = \frac{p \times 80}{80}$$
$$\frac{15}{80} = p$$
$$0.1875 = p$$
$$18.75\% = p$$
9. 0.28 **10.** 0.0015
11. 0.05375 **12.** 2.4 **13.** 71% **14.** 9% **15.** 38.91%
16. 18.75%, or $18\frac{3}{4}$% **17.** 0.5% **18.** 74% **19.** 600%
20. 83.$\overline{3}$%, or $83\frac{1}{3}$% **21.** $\frac{17}{20}$ **22.** $\frac{3}{6250}$ **23.** $\frac{91}{400}$ **24.** $\frac{1}{6}$
25. 62.5%, or $62\frac{1}{2}$% **26.** 45% **27.** 58 **28.** 16.$\overline{6}$%, or $16\frac{2}{3}$%
29. 2560 **30.** $50 **31.** 20% **32.** $455
33. 0.05%, 0.1%, $\frac{1}{2}$%, 1%, 5%, 10%, $\frac{13}{100}$, 0.275, $\frac{3}{10}$, $\frac{7}{20}$ **34.** D **35.** B
36. Some will say that the conversion will be done most accurately by first finding decimal notation. Others will say that it is more efficient to become familiar with some or all of the fraction and percent equivalents that appear inside the back cover and to make the conversion by going directly from fraction notation to percent notation. **37.** Since 40% $\div$ 10 = 4%, we can divide 36.8 by 10, obtaining 3.68. Since 400% = 40% $\times$ 10, we can multiply 36.8 by 10, obtaining 368. **38.** Answers may vary. Some will say this is a good idea since it makes the computations in the solution easier. Others will say it is a poor idea since it adds an extra step to the solution. **39.** They all represent the same number.

Translating for Success, p. 418

1. J **2.** M **3.** N **4.** E **5.** G **6.** H **7.** O **8.** C
9. D **10.** B

Exercise Set 7.5, p. 419

RC1. $10, $\frac{\$10}{\$50}$, 20% **RC2.** $15, $\frac{\$15}{\$60}$, 25% **RC3.** $120, $\frac{\$120}{\$360}$, $33\frac{1}{3}$%
RC4. $1600, $\frac{\$1600}{\$4000}$, 40% **1.** United States: about $104.7 billion; Italy: about $24.6 billion **3.** $46,656 **5.** 140 items
7. About 940,000,000 acres **9.** $36,400 **11.** 76 items correct; 4 items incorrect **13.** 261 men **15.** About 27.8%
17. $230.10 **19.** About 29.8% **21.** Alcohol: 43.2 mL; water: 496.8 mL **23.** Air Force: 25.2%; Army: 36.5%; Navy: 25.3%; Marines: 13.0% **25.** 5 **27.** 15% **29.** About 34.7%
31. About 127% **33.** About 49.5% **35.** About 497%
37. About 9.5% **39.** 34.375%, or $34\frac{3}{8}$% **41.** 16,914; 2.8%
43. 5,130,632; 24.6% **45.** 1,567,582; 21.1% **47.** About 23.8%
49. 2.$\overline{27}$ **50.** 0.44 **51.** -3.375 **52.** 4.$\overline{7}$ **53.** $\frac{3}{17}$ **54.** $-\frac{9}{34}$
55. $\frac{24}{125}$ **56.** $\frac{5}{29}$ **57.** $42

Exercise Set 7.6, p. 430

RC1. rate **RC2.** rate **RC3.** price **RC4.** tax **RC5.** tax
1. $9.56 **3.** $6.66 **5.** $11.99; $171.79 **7.** 4% **9.** 2%
11. $5600 **13.** $116.72 **15.** $276.28 **17.** $194.08
19. $2625 **21.** 12% **23.** $185,000 **25.** $5440 **27.** 15%
29. $355 **31.** $30; $270 **33.** $2.55; $14.45 **35.** $125; $112.50
37. 40%; $360 **39.** $300; 40% **41.** $849; 21.2% **43.** 18
44. $\frac{22}{7}$ **45.** 265.625 **46.** -1.15 **47.** 4,030,000,000,000
48. 5,800,000 **49.** 42,700,000 **50.** 6,090,000,000,000
51. $17,700

Calculator Corner, p. 437

1. $16,357.18 **2.** $12,764.72

Exercise Set 7.7, p. 440

RC1. $\frac{6}{12}$ year **RC2.** $\frac{40}{365}$ year **RC3.** $\frac{285}{365}$ year **RC4.** $\frac{9}{12}$ year
RC5. $\frac{3}{12}$ year **RC6.** $\frac{4}{12}$ year

1. $8 **3.** $113.52 **5.** $462.50 **7.** $671.88 **9. (a)** $147.95;
(b) $10,147.95 **11. (a)** $84.14; **(b)** $6584.14 **13. (a)** $46.03;
(b) $5646.03 **15.** $441 **17.** $2802.50 **19.** $7853.38
21. $99,427.40 **23.** $4243.60 **25.** $28,225.00 **27.** $9270.87
29. $129,871.09 **31.** $4101.01 **33.** $1324.58
35. Interest: $20.88; amount applied to principal: $4.69; balance
after the payment: $1273.87 **37. (a)** $98; **(b)** interest: $86.56;
amount applied to principal: $11.44; **(c)** interest: $51.20; amount
applied to principal: $46.80; **(d)** At 12.6%, the principal is reduced
by $35.36 more than at the 21.3% rate. The interest at 12.6% is
$35.36 less than at 21.3%. **39.** 800 **40.** $2 \cdot 2 \cdot 3 \cdot 19$ **41.** $\frac{9}{100}$
42. $-\frac{32}{75}$ **43.** $\frac{1}{25}$ **44.** $\frac{7}{300}$ **45.** 55 **46.** $-\frac{13}{10}$ **47.** 9.38%

Summary and Review: Chapter 7, p. 443

Vocabulary Reinforcement

1. percent decrease **2.** simple **3.** discount **4.** sales
5. rate **6.** percent increase

Concept Reinforcement

1. True **2.** False **3.** True

Study Guide

1. 8.2% **2.** 0.62625 **3.** $63.\overline{63}$%, or $63\frac{7}{11}$% **4.** $\frac{17}{250}$ **5.** $4.1\overline{6}$%,
or $4\frac{1}{6}$% **6.** 10,000 **7.** About 15.3% **8.** 6% **9.** $185,000
10. Simple interest: $22.60; total amount due: $2522.60
11. $6594.26

Review Exercises

1. 170% **2.** 6.5% **3.** 0.04; 0.144 **4.** 0.621; 0.842
5. 37.5%, or $37\frac{1}{2}$% **6.** $33.\overline{3}$%, or $33\frac{1}{3}$% **7.** $\frac{6}{25}$ **8.** $\frac{63}{1000}$
9. $30.6 = p \times 90$; 34% **10.** $63 = 84\% \times b$; 75
11. $a = 38\frac{1}{2}\% \times 168$; 64.68 **12.** $\frac{24}{100} = \frac{16.8}{b}$; 70
13. $\frac{42}{30} = \frac{N}{100}$; 140% **14.** $\frac{10.5}{100} = \frac{a}{84}$; 8.82 **15.** 178 students;
84 students **16.** 46% **17.** 2500 mL **18.** 12% **19.** 92
20. $24 **21.** 6% **22.** 11% **23.** About 18.3%
24. $42; $308 **25.** 14% **26.** $2940 **27.** $36
28. (a) $394.52; **(b)** $24,394.52 **29.** $121 **30.** $7575.25
31. $9504.80 **32. (a)** $129; **(b)** interest: $100.18; amount
applied to principal: $28.82; **(c)** interest: $70.72; amount
applied to principal: $58.28; **(d)** At 13.2%, the principal is
decreased by $29.46 more than at the 18.7% rate. The interest
at 13.2% is $29.46 less than at 18.7%. **33.** A **34.** C
35. $66.\overline{6}$%, or $66\frac{2}{3}$% **36.** About 19%

Understanding Through Discussion and Writing

1. A 40% discount is better. When successive discounts are taken,
each is based on the previous discounted price rather than on the
original price. A 20% discount followed by a 22% discount is the
same as a 37.6% discount off the original price. **2.** Let $S = $ the
original salary. After both raises have been given, the two situations
yield the same salary: $1.05 \cdot 1.1S = 1.1 \cdot 1.05S$. However, the first
situation is better for the wage earner, because $1.1S$ is earned the
first year when a 10% raise is given while in the second situation
$1.05S$ is earned that year. **3.** No; the 10% discount was based on
the original price rather than on the sale price. **4.** For a number n,
40% of 50% of n is $0.4(0.5n)$, or $0.2n$, or 20% of n. Thus, taking 40% of
50% of a number is the same as taking 20% of the number.
5. The interest due on the 30-day loan will be $41.10 while that due
on 60-day loan will be $131.51. This could be an argument in favor
of the 30-day loan. On the other hand, the 60-day loan puts twice as
much cash at the firm's disposal for twice as long as the 30-day loan
does. This could be an argument in favor of the 60-day loan.
6. Answers will vary.

Test: Chapter 7, p. 449

1. [7.1b] 0.613 **2.** [7.1b] 38% **3.** [7.2a] 137.5% **4.** [7.2b] $\frac{13}{20}$
5. [7.3a, b] $a = 40\% \cdot 55$; 22 **6.** [7.4a, b] $\frac{N}{100} = \frac{65}{80}$; 81.25%
7. [7.5a] 16,550 kidney transplants; 5992 liver transplants; 2283
heart transplants **8.** [7.5a] About 611 at-bats **9.** [7.5b] 6.7%
10. [7.5a] 60.6% **11.** [7.6a] $25.20; $585.20 **12.** [7.6b] $630
13. [7.6c] $40; $160 **14.** [7.7a] $8.52 **15.** [7.7a] $5356
16. [7.7b] $1110.39 **17.** [7.7b] $11,580.07 **18.** [7.5b] Plumber:
757,000, 7.4%; veterinary assistant: 29,000, 40.8%; motorcycle repair
technician: 21,000, 14.3%; fitness professional: 235,000, 63,000
19. [7.6c] $50; about 14.3% **20.** [7.7c] Interest: $36.73; amount
applied to the principal: $17.27; balance after payment: $2687
21. [7.3a, b], [7.4a, b] B **22.** [7.6b] $194,600
23. [7.6b], [7.7b] $2546.16

Cumulative Review: Chapters 1–7, p. 451

1. [7.5b] 14.7%; 4.1% **2.** [7.1b] 26.9% **3.** [7.2a] 112.5%
4. [5.5a] $-2.1\overline{6}$ **5.** [6.1a] $\frac{5}{0.5}$, or $\frac{10}{1}$ **6.** [6.2a] $\frac{70\,\text{km}}{3\,\text{hr}}$, or 23.$\overline{3}$ km/hr,
or $23\frac{1}{3}$ km/hr **7.** [3.5c], [4.3b] < **8.** [3.5c], [4.3b] <
9. [1.6b], [5.6a] 296,200 **10.** [1.6b] 50,000 **11.** [1.9d] 13
12. [5.4c] -1.5 **13.** [4.2a] [4.5a] $\frac{91}{30}$, or $3\frac{1}{30}$ **14.** [5.2c] -44.06
15. [1.2a] 515,150 **16.** [5.2b] 0.02 **17.** [4.5b] $\frac{2}{3}$ **18.** [4.3a] $-\frac{110}{63}$
19. [3.6a] $\frac{1}{6}$ **20.** [1.4a] 853,142,400 **21.** [5.3a] 1.38036
22. [4.6b] $-\frac{3}{2}$, or $-1\frac{1}{2}$ **23.** [5.4a] 12.25 **24.** [1.5a] 123 R 5
25. [1.7b] 95 **26.** [5.2d] -293.87 **27.** [3.7c] -9 **28.** [4.3c] $\frac{1}{12}$
29. [6.3b] 40 **30.** [6.3b] $\frac{176}{21}$ **31.** [7.5a] 462,259 visitors
32. [1.8a] $177,500 **33.** [6.4a] About 65 games
34. [5.7a] $84.95 **35.** [6.2b] 7.495 cents/oz
36. [4.2b], [4.4a] $\frac{3}{2}$ mi, or $1\frac{1}{2}$ mi **37.** [6.4a] 60 mi
38. [7.7b] $12,663.69 **39.** [4.6c] 5 pieces **40.** [7.5b] About
14.2%; 883,000 technicians **41.** [4.3a] C **42.** [7.5b] A
43. [7.3b], [7.4b] 200%

APPENDIX CHAPTER 6

Exercise Set 6.1, p. 334

RC1. True **RC2.** True **RC3.** False **RC4.** False

1. $\frac{4}{5}$ **3.** $\frac{178}{572}$ **5.** $\frac{0.4}{12}$ **7.** $\frac{3.8}{7.4}$ **9.** $\frac{56.78}{98.35}$ **11.** $\frac{8\frac{3}{4}}{9\frac{5}{6}}$ **13.** $\frac{29}{75}$
15. $\frac{11}{18}$ **17.** $\frac{107}{366}$ **19.** $\frac{104.8}{3100.7}$; $\frac{3100.7}{104.8}$ **21.** $\frac{60}{100}$; $\frac{100}{60}$ **23.** $\frac{2}{3}$ **25.** $\frac{3}{4}$
27. $\frac{12}{25}$ **29.** $\frac{7}{9}$ **31.** $\frac{2}{3}$ **33.** $\frac{14}{25}$ **35.** $\frac{1}{2}$ **37.** $\frac{3}{4}$ **39.** $\frac{478}{213}$; $\frac{213}{478}$
41. 408,550 **42.** 27.006 **43.** -332.73 **44.** $\frac{19}{30}$ **45.** $-\frac{5}{24}$
46. $14\frac{1}{3}$ **47.** 942,219 **48.** 2.6 **49.** -61.39 **50.** $\frac{1}{16}$
51. $1\frac{13}{15}$ **52.** $4\frac{2}{3}$ **53.** $\frac{30}{47}$ **55.** $1 : 2 : 3$

Exercise Set 6.2, p. 340

RC1. (b) **RC2.** (c) **RC3.** (d) **RC4.** (a)
1. 40 km/h **3.** 7.48 mi/sec **5.** 25 mpg **7.** 33 mpg
9. 47,236 people/sq mi **11.** 25 mph; 0.04 hr/mi **13.** About
393 performances/year **15.** 186,000 mi/sec **17.** 124 km/h
19. 0.623 gal/ft^2 **21.** 25 beats/min **23.** 26.188¢/oz;
26.450¢/oz; 16 oz **25.** 13.111¢/oz; 11.453¢/oz; 75 oz
27. 18.222¢/oz; 17.464¢/oz; 28 oz **29.** 10.187¢/oz; 10.346¢/oz;
10.7 oz **31.** B: 18.719¢/oz; E: 14.563¢/oz; Brand E
33. A: 10.375¢/oz; B: 9.139¢/oz; H: 8.022¢/oz; Brand H
35. 11,550 **36.** 679.4928 **37.** 2.74568 **38.** $-\frac{20}{3}$ **39.** $8\frac{11}{20}$
40. $-13\frac{2}{3}$ **41.** 125 **42.** 9.5 **43.** -9.63 **44.** $\frac{125}{27}$ **45.** 150
46. $-19\frac{3}{7}$ **47.** 6-oz: 10.833¢/oz; 5.5 oz: 10.909¢/oz

Exercise Set 6.3, p. 348

RC1. ratio **RC2.** proportional **RC3.** proportion
RC4. cross products **1.** No **3.** Yes **5.** Yes **7.** No **9.** 45
11. 12 **13.** 10 **15.** 20 **17.** 5 **19.** 18 **21.** 22 **23.** 28
25. $\frac{28}{3}$, or $9\frac{1}{3}$ **27.** $\frac{26}{9}$, or $2\frac{8}{9}$ **29.** 5 **31.** 5 **33.** 0 **35.** 14
37. 2.7 **39.** 1.8 **41.** 0.06 **43.** 0.7 **45.** 12.5725 **47.** 1
49. $\frac{1}{20}$ **51.** $\frac{3}{8}$ **53.** $\frac{16}{75}$ **55.** $\frac{51}{16}$, or $3\frac{3}{16}$ **57.** $\frac{546}{185}$, or $2\frac{176}{185}$
59. 4063 theaters **60.** 6 lb **61.** $\frac{1}{4}$ lb **62.** $\frac{3}{8}$ lb **63.** $6\frac{7}{20}$ cm
64. $37\frac{1}{2}$ servings **65.** $59.81 **66.** 21.5 mpg
67. Approximately 2731.4 **69.** Ruth: 1.863 strikeouts per home run; Schmidt: 3.436 strikeouts per home run

Mid-Chapter Review: Chapter 6, p. 351

1. True **2.** True **3.** False **4.** False
5. $\frac{120\,\text{mi}}{2\,\text{hr}} = \frac{120}{2}\frac{\text{mi}}{\text{hr}} = 60\,\text{mi/hr}$
6.
$$\frac{x}{4} = \frac{3}{6}$$
$$x \cdot 6 = 4 \cdot 3$$
$$\frac{x \cdot 6}{6} = \frac{4 \cdot 3}{6}$$
$$x = 2$$
7. $\frac{4}{7}$ **8.** $\frac{313}{199}$ **9.** $\frac{35}{17}$ **10.** $\frac{59}{101}$ **11.** $\frac{2}{3}$ **12.** $\frac{1}{3}$ **13.** $\frac{8}{7}$ **14.** $\frac{25}{19}$
15. $\frac{2}{1}$ **16.** $\frac{5}{1}$ **17.** $\frac{2}{7}$ **18.** $\frac{3}{5}$ **19.** 60.75 mi/hr, or 60.75 mph
20. 48.67 km/h **21.** 13 m/sec **22.** 16.17 ft/sec **23.** 27 in./day
24. About 0.860 free throw made/attempt **25.** 11.611¢/oz
26. 49.917¢/oz **27.** Yes **28.** No **29.** No **30.** Yes
31. 12 **32.** 40 **33.** 9 **34.** 35 **35.** 2.2 **36.** 4.32 **37.** $\frac{1}{2}$
38. $\frac{65}{4}$, or $16\frac{1}{4}$ **39.** Yes; every ratio $\frac{a}{b}$ can be written as $\frac{\frac{a}{b}}{1}$.
40. By making some sketches, we see that the rectangle's length must be twice the width. **41.** The student's approach will work. However, when we use the approach of equating cross products, we eliminate the need to find the least common denominator.
42. The instructor thinks that the longer a student studies, the higher his or her grade will be. An example is the situation in which one student gets a test grade of 96 after studying for 8 hr while another student gets a score of 78 after studying for $6\frac{1}{2}$ hr. This is represented by the proportion $\dfrac{96}{8} = \dfrac{78}{6\frac{1}{2}}$.

Translating for Success, p. 358

1. N **2.** I **3.** A **4.** K **5.** J **6.** F **7.** M **8.** B
9. G **10.** E

Exercise Set 6.4, p. 359

RC1. $\frac{m}{8}$ **RC2.** $\frac{8}{m}$ **RC3.** $\frac{6}{8}$ **RC4.** $\frac{8}{6}$ **1.** 11.04 hr
3. 7680 frames **5. (a)** About 103 gal; **(b)** 3640 mi
7. 232.53 million, or 232,530,000 **9.** 175 bulbs
11. About 262 mg every 8 hr **13.** 2975 ft^2 **15.** 450 pages
17. 13,500 mi **19.** 880 calories **21.** 60 students **23.** 64 cans
25. 9.75 gal **27.** 100 oz **29.** 90 whales **31.** 58.1 mi
33. (a) 38 euros; **(b)** $11,368.42 **35. (a)** 66 games;
(b) About 2504 points **37.** 162 **38.** 4014 **39.** 4.45 **40.** −0.4
41. −21.7 **42.** 0.26 **43.** $\frac{1}{10}$ **44.** $-\frac{5}{4}$ **45.** 17 positions
47. 2150 earned runs **49.** CD player: $150; receiver: $450; speakers: $300

Exercise Set 6.5, p. 368

RC1. 5 **RC2.** 8 **RC3.** a **RC4.** 3
1. 25 **3.** $\frac{4}{3}$, or $1\frac{1}{3}$ **5.** $x = \frac{27}{4}$, or $6\frac{3}{4}$; $y = 9$ **7.** $x = 7.5$; $y = 7.2$
9. 1.25 m **11.** 36 ft **13.** 7 ft **15.** 100 ft **17.** 4 **19.** $10\frac{1}{2}$
21. $x = 6$; $y = 5.25$; $z = 3$ **23.** $x = 5\frac{1}{3}$, or $5.\overline{3}$; $y = 4\frac{2}{3}$, or $4.\overline{6}$;
$z = 5\frac{1}{3}$, or $5.\overline{3}$ **25.** 20 ft **27.** 152 ft **29.** Prime
30. Composite **31.** $2 \cdot 2 \cdot 2 \cdot 101$, or $2^3 \cdot 101$ **32.** $3 \cdot 31$

33. = **34.** ≠ **35.** < **36.** > **37.** $\frac{13}{4}$, or $3\frac{1}{4}$ **38.** 5.29 **39.** 127
40. 75 **41.** 13.75 ft **43.** 1.25 cm **45.** 3681.437
47. $x \approx 0.35$; $y = 0.4$

Summary and Review: Chapter 6, p. 372

Vocabulary Reinforcement

1. quotient **2.** shape **3.** cross products **4.** rate
5. proportion **6.** price

Concept Reinforcement

1. True **2.** True **3.** False **4.** True

Study Guide

1. $\frac{17}{3}$ **2.** $\frac{8}{7}$ **3.** $7.50/hr **4.** A: 9.964¢/oz; B: 10.281¢/oz;
Brand A **5.** Yes **6.** $\frac{27}{8}$ **7.** 175 mi **8.** 21

Review Exercises

1. $\frac{47}{84}$ **2.** $\frac{46}{1.27}$ **3.** $\frac{83}{100}$ **4.** $\frac{0.72}{197}$ **5. (a)** $\frac{12,480}{16,640}$, or $\frac{3}{4}$; **(b)** $\frac{16,640}{29,120}$, or $\frac{4}{7}$
6. $\frac{3}{4}$ **7.** $\frac{9}{16}$ **8.** 28 mpg **9.** 6300 revolutions/min
10. 0.638 gal/ft^2 **11.** 6.33¢/tablet **12.** 19.542¢/oz
13. 14.969¢/oz; 12.479¢/oz; 15.609¢/oz; 48 oz **14.** Yes **15.** No
16. 32 **17.** 7 **18.** $\frac{1}{40}$ **19.** 24 **20.** 27 circuits
21. (a) 247.50 Canadian dollars; **(b)** 50.51 U.S. dollars
22. 832 mi **23.** 133.5 billion gallons, or 133,500,000,000 gallons
24. About 3,774,811 lb **25.** 320 calories **26.** About 12,453
lawyers **27.** $x = \frac{14}{3}$, or $4\frac{2}{3}$ **28.** $x = \frac{56}{5}$, or $11\frac{1}{5}$; $y = \frac{63}{5}$, or $12\frac{3}{5}$
29. 40 ft **30.** $x = 3$; $y = \frac{21}{2}$, or $10\frac{1}{2}$; $z = \frac{15}{2}$, or $7\frac{1}{2}$ **31.** B
32. C **33.** 1.806¢/sheet; 1.658¢/sheet; 1.409¢/sheet; 6 big rolls
34. $x = 4258.5$; $z \approx 10,094.3$ **35.** Finishing paint: 11 gal;
primer: 16.5 gal

Understanding Through Discussion and Writing

1. In terms of cost, a low faculty-to-student ratio is less expensive than a high faculty-to-student ratio. In terms of quality of education and student satisfaction, a high faculty-to-student ratio is more desirable. A college president must balance the cost and quality issues. **2.** Yes; unit prices can be used to solve proportions involving money. In Example 3 of Section 6.4, for instance, we could have divided $90 by the unit price, or the price per ticket, to find the number of tickets that could be purchased for $90. **3.** Leslie used 4 gal of gasoline to drive 92 mi. At the same rate, how many gallons would be needed to travel 368 mi? **4.** Yes; consider the following pair of triangles.

Two pairs of sides are proportional, but we can see that x is shorter than y, so the ratio of x to y is clearly not the same as the ratio of 1 to 1 (or 2 to 2).

Test: Chapter 6, p. 377

1. [6.1a] $\frac{85}{97}$ **2.** [6.1a] $\frac{0.34}{124}$ **3.** [6.1b] $\frac{9}{10}$ **4.** [6.1b] $\frac{25}{32}$
5. [6.2a] 0.625 ft/sec **6.** [6.2a] $1\frac{1}{3}$ servings/lb **7.** [6.2a] 32 mpg
8. [6.2b] About 15.563¢/oz **9.** [6.2b] 16.475¢/oz; 13.980¢/oz;
11.490¢/oz; 16.660¢/oz; 100 oz **10.** [6.3a] Yes **11.** [6.3a] No
12. [6.3b] 12 **13.** [6.3b] 360 **14.** [6.3b] 42.1875 **15.** [6.3b] 100
16. [6.4a] 1512 km **17.** [6.4a] 4.8 min **18.** [6.4a] 525 mi
19. [6.5a] 66 m **20.** [6.4a] **(a)** 13 hats; **(b)** 30 packages
21. [6.4a] About $59.17 **22.** [6.5a] $x = 8$; $y = 8.8$
23. [6.5b] $x = \frac{24}{5}$, or 4.8; $y = \frac{32}{5}$, or 6.4; $z = 12$ **24.** [6.2a] C
25. [6.4a] 5888 marbles

Cumulative Review: Chapters 1–6, p. 379

1. [5.2a] 513.996   **2.** [4.5a] $6\frac{3}{4}$ **3.** [4.2a] $-\frac{7}{20}$ **4.** [5.2b] 30.491
5. [5.2b] 72.912   **6.** [4.3a] $-\frac{5}{12}$ **7.** [5.3a] 222.076   **8.** [5.3a] 567.8
9. [4.6a] -3 **10.** [5.4a] 43   **11.** [1.5a] 899   **12.** [3.7b] $-\frac{3}{2}$
13. [1.1b] 3 ten thousands $+$ 0 thousands $+$ 0 hundreds $+$
7 tens $+$ 4 ones, or 3 ten thousands $+$ 7 tens $+$ 4 ones
14. [5.1a] One hundred twenty and seven hundredths   **15.** [5.1c] 0.7
16. [5.1c] -0.799 **17.** [3.1d] $2 \cdot 2 \cdot 2 \cdot 2 \cdot 3 \cdot 3$, or $2^4 \cdot 3^2$
18. [4.1a] 90   **19.** [3.3a] $\frac{5}{8}$ **20.** [3.5b] $\frac{5}{8}$ **21.** [5.5c] 5.718

22. [5.5c] 0.179   **23.** [6.1a] $\frac{0.3}{15}$ **24.** [6.3a] Yes
25. [6.2a] 55 m/sec   **26.** [6.2b] 8-oz can   **27.** [6.3b] 30.24
28. [5.4b] 26.4375   **29.** [3.7c] $\frac{8}{9}$ **30.** [6.3b] 128
31. [5.2d] -102.46 **32.** [4.3c] $\frac{76}{175}$ **33.** [3.6b], [6.4a] 390 cal
34. [6.4a] 7 min   **35.** [4.5c] $2\frac{1}{4}$ cups   **36.** [3.7d], [6.4a] 12 doors
37. [5.7a], [6.4a] 42.2025 mi   **38.** [5.7a] 132 orbits
39. [3.1c] D   **40.** [6.2a] B   **41.** [6.5a] $10\frac{1}{2}$ ft

Guided Solutions

CHAPTER 1

Section 1.1

8. $2718 = 2$ thousands $+ 7$ hundreds $+ 1$ ten $+ 8$ ones

17. One million, eight hundred seventy-nine thousand, two hundred four

Section 1.2

2.
$$\begin{array}{r} {\scriptstyle 1\ \ 1\ \ 1} \\ 7\ 9\ 6\ 8 \\ +\ 5\ 4\ 9\ 7 \\ \hline 1\ 3,4\ 6\ 5 \end{array}$$

5. Perimeter $= 4$ in. $+ 5$ in. $+ 9$ in. $+ 6$ in. $+ 5$ in. $= 29$ in.

Section 1.3

1.
$$\begin{array}{r} 7\ 8\ 9\ 3 \\ -\ 4\ 0\ 9\ 2 \\ \hline 3\ 8\ 0\ 1 \end{array}$$
Check:
$$\begin{array}{r} 3\ 8\ 0\ 1 \\ +\ 4\ 0\ 9\ 2 \\ \hline 7\ 8\ 9\ 3 \end{array}$$

5.
$$\begin{array}{r} {\scriptstyle \cdot\ 4\ \ 9\ 13} \\ 5\ \cancel{0}\ \cancel{3} \\ -\ 2\ 9\ 8 \\ \hline 2\ 0\ 5 \end{array}$$

Section 1.4

4.
$$\begin{array}{r} {\scriptstyle 1\ 2\ 4} \\ 1\ 3\ 4\ 8 \\ \times\ \ \ \ \ \ 5 \\ \hline 6\ 7\ 4\ 0 \end{array}$$

20.
$$\begin{aligned} A &= l \cdot w \\ &= 12\,\text{ft} \cdot 8\,\text{ft} \\ &= 96\,\text{sq ft} \end{aligned}$$

Section 1.5

8. $0 \div 2$ means 0 divided by 2.
Since zero divided by any nonzero number is 0, $0 \div 2 = 0$.

9. $7 \div 0$ means 7 divided by 0.
Since division by 0 is not defined, $7 \div 0$ is not defined.

Section 1.6

26. Nearest ten:
$$\begin{array}{r} 8\ 4\ 0 \\ \times\ 2\ 5\ 0 \\ \hline 4\ 2\ 0\ 0\ 0 \\ 1\ 6\ 8\ 0\ 0\ 0 \\ \hline 2\ 1\ 0,0\ 0\ 0 \end{array}$$

Nearest hundred:
$$\begin{array}{r} 8\ 0\ 0 \\ \cdot\ \times\ 2\ 0\ 0 \\ \hline 1\ 6\ 0,0\ 0\ 0 \end{array}$$

31. Since 8 is to the left of 12 on the number line, $8 < 12$.

Section 1.7

13.
$$\begin{aligned} x + 9 &= 17 \\ x + 9 - 9 &= 17 - 9 \\ x &= 8 \end{aligned}$$
Check:
$$\begin{array}{c} x + 9 = 17 \\ \hline 8 + 9\ \overset{?}{}\ 17 \\ 17 \end{array}$$
Since $17 = 17$ is true, the answer checks. The solution is 8.

19.
$$\begin{aligned} \frac{144}{9} &= \frac{9 \cdot n}{9} \\ 16 &= n \end{aligned}$$
Check:
$$\begin{array}{c} 144 = 9 \cdot n \\ \hline 144\ \overset{?}{}\ 9 \cdot 16 \\ 144 \end{array}$$
Since $144 = 144$ is true, the answer checks. The solution is 16.

Section 1.8

4. 1. Familiarize. Let $p = $ the number of pages William still has to read.
2. Translate.

Pages already read	plus	Number of pages to read	is	Total number of pages
↓	↓	↓	↓	↓
86	+	p	=	234

3. Solve.
$$\begin{aligned} 86 + p &= 234 \\ 86 + p - 86 &= 234 - 86 \\ p &= 148 \end{aligned}$$
4. Check. If William reads 148 more pages, he will have read a total of $86 + 148$ pages, or 234 pages.
5. State. William has 148 more pages to read.

9. 1. Familiarize. Let $x = $ the number of hundreds in 3500. Let $t = $ the time it takes to lose one pound.
2. Translate.
$$\begin{aligned} 100 \cdot x &= 3500 \\ x \cdot 2 &= t \end{aligned}$$
3. Solve. From Example 7, we know that $x = 35$.
$$\begin{aligned} x \cdot 2 &= t \\ 35 \cdot 2 &= t \\ 70 &= t \end{aligned}$$
4. Check. Since $70 \div 2 = 35$, there are 35 groups of 2 min in 70 min. Thus you will burn $35 \times 100 = 3500$ calories.
5. State. You must swim for 70 min, or 1 hr 10 min, in order to lose one pound.

Section 1.9

5. $10^4 = 10 \cdot 10 \cdot 10 \cdot 10 = 10,000$

15.
$$\begin{aligned} 9 \times 4 - (20 + 4) \div 8 - (6 - 2) \\ = 9 \times 4 - 24 \div 8 - 4 \\ = 36 - 24 \div 8 - 4 \\ = 36 - 3 - 4 \\ = 33 - 4 \\ = 29 \end{aligned}$$

25.
$$\begin{aligned} [18 - (2 + 7) \div 3] - (31 - 10 \times 2) \\ = [18 - 9 \div 3] - (31 - 10 \times 2) \\ = [18 - 3] - (31 - 20) \\ = 15 - 11 \\ = 4 \end{aligned}$$

CHAPTER 2

Section 2.2

32. $\quad -x = -(-5) = 5$
$\quad\ -(-x) = -(-(-5))$
$\qquad\qquad = -(5) = -5$

Section 2.3

11. $2 - 8 = 2 + (-8) = -6$
19. $-12 - (-9) = -12 + 9 = -3$

Section 2.4

20. $-2 \cdot (-5) \cdot (-4) \cdot (-3)$
$\quad = 10 \cdot (-4) \cdot (-3)$
$\quad = -40 \cdot (-3)$
$\quad = 120$

Section 2.5

12. $32 \div 8 \cdot 2 \div 4$
$\quad = 4 \cdot 2 \div 4$
$\quad = 8 \div 4$
$\quad = 2$

CHAPTER 3

Section 3.1

4. 45
$\quad 1 \cdot 45$
$\qquad$ 2 is not a factor of 45.
$\quad 3 \cdot 15$
$\qquad$ 4 is not a factor of 45.
$\quad 5 \cdot 9$
$\qquad$ 6, 7, and 8 are not factors of 45.
$\qquad$ 9 is already listed.
$\quad$ The factors of 45 are 1, 3, 5, 9, 15, and 45.

10.
$$\begin{array}{r} 8 \\ 2\overline{)16} \\ \underline{16} \\ 0 \end{array}$$

Since the remainder is 0, 16 is divisible by 2.

Section 3.2

8. Add the digits: $1 + 7 + 2 + 1 + 6 = 17$. Since 17 is not divisible by 3, the number 17,216 is not divisible by 3.

28. The number named by the last two digits is 24. Since 24 is divisible by 4, the number 23,524 is divisible by 4.

Section 3.3

11. Each gallon is divided into 4 equal parts. The unit is $\frac{1}{4}$.

There are 7 equal units shaded. The part that is shaded is $\frac{7}{4}$.

23. $\dfrac{4 - 4}{567} = \dfrac{0}{567} = 0$

Section 3.4

2. $\dfrac{3}{8} \cdot \dfrac{5}{7} = \dfrac{3 \cdot 5}{8 \cdot 7}$
$\qquad = \dfrac{15}{56}$

6. $5 \times \dfrac{2}{3} = \dfrac{5}{1} \times \dfrac{2}{3}$
$\qquad = \dfrac{5 \times 2}{1 \times 3}$
$\qquad = \dfrac{10}{3}$

Section 3.5

5. $\dfrac{4}{3} = \dfrac{4}{3} \cdot \dfrac{5}{5}$
$\quad = \dfrac{4 \cdot 5}{3 \cdot 5}$
$\quad = \dfrac{20}{15}$

15. $\dfrac{75}{30} = \dfrac{3 \cdot 5 \cdot 5}{2 \cdot 3 \cdot 5}$
$\qquad = \dfrac{3 \cdot 5 \cdot 5}{3 \cdot 5 \cdot 2}$
$\qquad = \dfrac{3}{3} \cdot \dfrac{5}{5} \cdot \dfrac{5}{2}$
$\qquad = 1 \cdot 1 \cdot \dfrac{5}{2}$
$\qquad = \dfrac{5}{2}$

20. $2 \cdot 20 = 40 \qquad 3 \cdot 14 = 42$
$$\dfrac{2}{3}\ \square\ \dfrac{14}{20}$$
Since $40 \neq 42$, $\dfrac{2}{3} \neq \dfrac{14}{20}$.

Section 3.6

1. $\dfrac{2}{3} \cdot \dfrac{7}{8} = \dfrac{2 \cdot 7}{3 \cdot 8}$
$\qquad = \dfrac{2 \cdot 7}{3 \cdot 2 \cdot 2 \cdot 2}$
$\qquad = \dfrac{2}{2} \cdot \dfrac{7}{3 \cdot 2 \cdot 2}$
$\qquad = 1 \cdot \dfrac{7}{3 \cdot 2 \cdot 2}$
$\qquad = \dfrac{7}{12}$

Section 3.7

5. $\dfrac{6}{7} \div \dfrac{3}{4} = \dfrac{6}{7} \cdot \dfrac{4}{3}$
$\qquad = \dfrac{6 \cdot 4}{7 \cdot 3}$
$\qquad = \dfrac{2 \cdot 3 \cdot 2 \cdot 2}{7 \cdot 3}$
$\qquad = \dfrac{3}{3} \cdot \dfrac{2 \cdot 2 \cdot 2}{7}$
$\qquad = \dfrac{2 \cdot 2 \cdot 2}{7}$
$\qquad = \dfrac{8}{7}$

10. $\dfrac{5}{6} \cdot y = \dfrac{2}{3}$
$\quad \dfrac{\frac{5}{6} \cdot y}{\frac{5}{6}} = \dfrac{\frac{2}{3}}{\frac{5}{6}}$
$\quad y = \dfrac{2}{3} \cdot \dfrac{6}{5}$
$\qquad = \dfrac{2 \cdot 2 \cdot 3}{3 \cdot 5}$
$\qquad = \dfrac{3}{3} \cdot \dfrac{2 \cdot 2}{5}$
$\qquad = \dfrac{4}{5}$

CHAPTER 4

Section 4.1

7. a) $18 = 2 \cdot 3 \cdot 3$
$\qquad 40 = 2 \cdot 2 \cdot 2 \cdot 5$

b) Consider the factor 2. The greatest number of times that 2 occurs in any one factorization is three times. Write 2 as a factor three times.
$$2 \cdot 2 \cdot 2 \cdot ?$$
Consider the factor 3. The greatest number of times that 3 occurs in any one factorization is two times. Write 3 as a factor two times.
$$2 \cdot 2 \cdot 2 \cdot 3 \cdot 3 \cdot ?$$
Consider the factor 5. The greatest number of times that 5 occurs in any one factorization is one time. Write 5 as a factor one time.
$$2 \cdot 2 \cdot 2 \cdot 3 \cdot 3 \cdot 5$$
$\text{LCM} = 360$

16.
$$\begin{array}{r|rrr} 2 & 81 & 90 & 84 \\ 3 & 81 & 45 & 42 \\ 3 & 27 & 15 & 14 \\ \hline & 9 & 5 & 14 \end{array}$$
The LCM is $2 \cdot 3 \cdot 3 \cdot 9 \cdot 5 \cdot 14$, or 11,340.

Section 4.2

7. The LCD is 24.

$$\frac{3}{8} + \frac{5}{6} = \frac{3}{8} \cdot 1 + \frac{5}{6} \cdot 1$$
$$= \frac{3}{8} \cdot \frac{3}{3} + \frac{5}{6} \cdot \frac{4}{4}$$
$$= \frac{9}{24} + \frac{20}{24}$$
$$= \frac{29}{24}$$

12. 1. Familiarize. Let $T =$ the total amount of berries in the salad.

2. Translate. To find the total amount, we add.

$$\frac{7}{8} + \frac{3}{4} + \frac{5}{16} = T$$

3. Solve. The LCD is 16.

$$\frac{7}{8} \cdot \frac{2}{2} + \frac{3}{4} \cdot \frac{4}{4} + \frac{5}{16} = T$$
$$\frac{14}{16} + \frac{12}{16} + \frac{5}{16} = T$$
$$\frac{31}{16} = T$$

4. Check. The answer is reasonable because it is larger than any of the individual amounts.

5. State. The salad contains a total of $\frac{31}{16}$ qt of berries.

Section 4.3

5. The LCD is 18.

$$\frac{5}{6} - \frac{1}{9} = \frac{5}{6} \cdot \frac{3}{3} - \frac{1}{9} \cdot \frac{2}{2}$$
$$= \frac{15}{18} - \frac{2}{18}$$
$$= \frac{13}{18}$$

12. The LCD is 24.

$$\frac{5}{6} = \frac{20}{24}$$
$$\frac{7}{8} = \frac{21}{24}$$

Since $20 < 21$, it follows that
$$\frac{20}{24} < \frac{21}{24}.$$
Thus, $\frac{5}{6} < \frac{7}{8}.$

Section 4.4

6. $4 \cdot 6 = 24$
$24 + 5 = 29$
$4\frac{5}{6} = \frac{29}{6}$

10. $\begin{array}{r} 2 \\ 3\overline{)7} \\ \underline{6} \\ 1 \end{array}$

$\frac{7}{3} = 2\frac{1}{3}$

Section 4.5

5. $\begin{array}{r} 8\frac{2}{3} = 8\frac{4}{6} \\ -5\frac{1}{2} = -5\frac{3}{6} \\ \hline 3\frac{1}{6} \end{array}$

7. $\begin{array}{r} 5 = 4\frac{3}{3} \\ -1\frac{1}{3} = -1\frac{1}{3} \\ \hline 3\frac{2}{3} \end{array}$

Section 4.6

3. $-2 \cdot 6\frac{2}{5} = -\frac{2}{1} \cdot \frac{32}{5}$
$$= -\frac{64}{5}$$
$$= -12\frac{4}{5}$$

7. $2\frac{1}{4} \div 1\frac{1}{5} = \frac{9}{4} \div \frac{6}{5}$
$$= \frac{9}{4} \cdot \frac{5}{6}$$
$$= \frac{3 \cdot 3 \cdot 5}{2 \cdot 2 \cdot 2 \cdot 3}$$
$$= \frac{3}{3} \cdot \frac{3 \cdot 5}{2 \cdot 2 \cdot 2}$$
$$= \frac{15}{8}$$
$$= 1\frac{7}{8}$$

Section 4.7

2. $\frac{1}{3} \cdot \frac{3}{4} \div \frac{5}{8} - \frac{1}{10} = \frac{3}{12} \div \frac{5}{8} - \frac{1}{10}$
$$= \frac{3}{12} \cdot \frac{8}{5} - \frac{1}{10}$$
$$= \frac{3 \cdot 2 \cdot 2 \cdot 2}{3 \cdot 2 \cdot 2 \cdot 5} - \frac{1}{10}$$
$$= \frac{2}{5} - \frac{1}{10}$$
$$= \frac{4}{10} - \frac{1}{10} = \frac{3}{10}$$

8. $\dfrac{\dfrac{3}{5}}{\dfrac{7}{10} - \dfrac{2}{3}} = \dfrac{\dfrac{3}{5}}{\dfrac{7}{10} \cdot \dfrac{3}{3} - \dfrac{2}{3} \cdot \dfrac{10}{10}}$

$$= \dfrac{\dfrac{3}{5}}{\dfrac{21}{30} - \dfrac{20}{30}}$$

$$= \dfrac{\dfrac{3}{5}}{\dfrac{1}{30}} = \frac{3}{5} \div \frac{1}{30}$$

$$= \frac{3}{5} \cdot \frac{30}{1} = \frac{3 \cdot 6 \cdot 5}{5 \cdot 1} = 18$$

CHAPTER 5

Section 5.1

7. 0.896.   3 places
0.896 $= \dfrac{896}{1000}$

11. $\dfrac{743}{100}$ 7.43.

2 zeros   2 places

$\dfrac{743}{100} = 7.43$

Section 5.2

7. $\begin{array}{r} {\scriptstyle 1\ 1\ 1\ 1} \\ 4\,5.7\,8\,0 \\ 2\,4\,6\,7.0\,0\,0 \\ +\quad 1.9\,9\,3 \\ \hline 2\,5\,1\,4.7\,7\,3 \end{array}$

8. $\begin{array}{r} {\scriptstyle 13} \\ {\scriptstyle 6\ \ 3\ 12} \\ 3\,7.4\,2\,8 \\ -\,2\,6.6\,7\,4 \\ \hline 1\,0.7\,5\,4 \end{array}$

14. $\begin{array}{r} {\scriptstyle 4\ 9\ 9\ 9\ 10} \\ 5.0\,0\,0\,0 \\ -\,0.0\,0\,8\,9 \\ \hline 4.9\,9\,1\,1 \end{array}$

Section 5.3

3. First we multiply the absolute values.

$$
\begin{array}{r}
4\,2.6\,5 \\
\times\ \ 0.8\,0\,4 \\
\hline
1\,7\,0\,6\,0 \\
3\,4\,1\,2\,0\,0\,0 \\
\hline
3\,4.2\,9\,0\,6\,0
\end{array}
$$

Since the product of a negative number and a positive number is negative, the answer is -34.2906.

14. $\$15.69 = 15.69 \times \$1$
$ = 15.69 \times 100¢$
$ = 1569¢$

Section 5.4

6.
$$
\begin{array}{r}
0.0\,2\,5 \\
8\,6\,\overline{)\,2.1\,5\,0} \\
1\,7\,2 \\
\hline
4\,3\,0 \\
4\,3\,0 \\
\hline
0
\end{array}
$$

7. $\dfrac{0.375}{0.25} = \dfrac{0.375}{0.25} \times \dfrac{100}{100}$

$\phantom{\dfrac{0.375}{0.25}} = \dfrac{37.5}{25}$

$$
\begin{array}{r}
1.5 \\
0.2\,5\,\overline{)\,0.3\,7{,}5} \\
2\,5 \\
\hline
1\,2\,5 \\
1\,2\,5 \\
\hline
0
\end{array}
$$

15. $\dfrac{100 \cdot x}{100} = \dfrac{78.314}{100}$

$\phantom{\dfrac{100 \cdot x}{100}} x = 0.78314$

17. $625 \div 62.5 \times 25 \div 6250$
$ = 10 \times 25 \div 6250$
$ = 250 \div 6250$
$ = 0.04$

Section 5.5

2. $\dfrac{9}{20} = \dfrac{9}{20} \cdot \dfrac{5}{5} = \dfrac{45}{100} = 0.45$

6. $\dfrac{1}{6} = 1 \div 6$

$$
\begin{array}{r}
0.1\,6\,6 \\
6\,\overline{)\,1.0\,0\,0} \\
6 \\
\hline
4\,0 \\
3\,6 \\
\hline
4\,0 \\
3\,6 \\
\hline
4
\end{array}
$$

$\dfrac{1}{6} = 0.1666\ldots = 0.1\overline{6}$

17. Method 1:
$\dfrac{3}{4} \times 0.62 = 0.75 \times 0.62$
$\phantom{\dfrac{3}{4} \times 0.62} = 0.465$

Method 2:
$\dfrac{3}{4} \times 0.62 = \dfrac{3}{4} \times \dfrac{62}{100}$
$\phantom{\dfrac{3}{4} \times 0.62} = \dfrac{186}{400}$, or 0.465

Method 3:
$\dfrac{3}{4} \times 0.62 = \dfrac{3}{4} \times \dfrac{0.62}{1}$
$\phantom{\dfrac{3}{4} \times 0.62} = \dfrac{1.86}{4}$, or 0.465

CHAPTER 7

Section 7.2

6. $\dfrac{19}{25} = \dfrac{19}{25} \cdot \dfrac{4}{4}$

$\phantom{\dfrac{19}{25}} = \dfrac{76}{100} = 76\%$

10. $3.25\% = \dfrac{3.25}{100} = \dfrac{3.25}{100} \times \dfrac{100}{100}$

$ = \dfrac{325}{10{,}000} = \dfrac{13 \times 25}{400 \times 25}$

$ = \dfrac{13}{400} \times \dfrac{25}{25} = \dfrac{13}{400}$

Section 7.3

9.
$$
\begin{array}{ccccc}
20\% & \text{of} & \text{what} & \text{is} & 45? \\
\downarrow & \downarrow & \downarrow & \downarrow & \downarrow \\
20\% & \cdot & b & = & 45
\end{array}
$$

$\dfrac{20\% \cdot b}{20\%} = \dfrac{45}{20\%}$

$b = \dfrac{45}{0.2}$

$b = 225$

11.
$$
\begin{array}{cccccc}
16 & \text{is} & \text{what percent} & & \text{of} & 40? \\
\downarrow & \downarrow & \downarrow & & \downarrow & \downarrow \\
16 & = & p & \cdot & & 40
\end{array}
$$

$\dfrac{16}{40} = \dfrac{p \cdot 40}{40}$

$\dfrac{16}{40} = p$

$0.4 = p$

$40\% = p$

Section 7.4

8. $\dfrac{20}{100} = \dfrac{45}{b}$

$20 \cdot b = 100 \cdot 45$

$\dfrac{20 \cdot b}{20} = \dfrac{100 \cdot 45}{20}$

$b = \dfrac{4500}{20}$

$b = 225$

9. $\dfrac{64}{100} = \dfrac{a}{55}$

$64 \cdot 55 = 100 \cdot a$

$\dfrac{64 \cdot 55}{100} = \dfrac{100 \cdot a}{100}$

$\dfrac{3520}{100} = a$

$35.2 = a$

12. $\dfrac{12}{40} = \dfrac{N}{100}$

$12 \cdot 100 = 40 \cdot N$

$\dfrac{12 \cdot 100}{40} = \dfrac{40 \cdot N}{40}$

$\dfrac{1200}{40} = N$

$30 = N$

Thus, 12 is 30% of 40.

Section 7.6

2. Sales tax $= 4\% \times 4 \times \$18.95$
$\phantom{\text{Sales tax}} = 0.04 \times \$75.80$
$\phantom{\text{Sales tax}} = \$3.032$
$\phantom{\text{Sales tax}} \approx \$3.03$
Total price $= \$75.80 + \$3.03$
$\phantom{\text{Total price}} = \$78.83$

7. $\$2970 = 7.5\% \times S$
$\$2970 = 0.075 \times S$
$\dfrac{\$2970}{0.075} = \dfrac{0.075 \times S}{0.075}$
$\$39{,}600 = S$

Section 7.7

1. $I = P \cdot r \cdot t$
$ = \$4300 \times 4\% \times 1$
$ = \$4300 \times 0.04 \times 1$
$ = \$172$

3. a) $I = P \cdot r \cdot t$
$ = \$4800 \times 5\tfrac{1}{2}\% \times \dfrac{30}{365}$
$ = \$4800 \times 0.055 \times \dfrac{30}{365}$
$ \approx \$21.70$

b) Total amount
$\phantom{\text{Total}} = \$4800 + \$21.70$
$\phantom{\text{Total}} = \$4821.70$

APPENDIX CHAPTER 6

Section 6.1

6. $\dfrac{\text{Length of shortest side}}{\text{Length of longest side}} = \dfrac{38.2}{55.5}$

9. Ratio of 3.6 to 12: $\dfrac{3.6}{12}$

Simplifying:

$$\dfrac{3.6}{12} \cdot \dfrac{10}{10} = \dfrac{36}{120} = \dfrac{12 \cdot 3}{12 \cdot 10} = \dfrac{12}{12} \cdot \dfrac{3}{10} = \dfrac{3}{10}$$

Section 6.2

4. $\dfrac{52 \text{ ft}}{13 \text{ sec}} = 4 \text{ ft/sec}$

6. Unit price $= \dfrac{\text{Price}}{\text{Number of units}}$

$$= \dfrac{\$2.79}{26 \text{ oz}} = \dfrac{279 \text{ cents}}{26 \text{ oz}}$$

$$= \dfrac{279}{26} \dfrac{\text{cents}}{\text{oz}} \approx 10.731 \text{¢/oz}$$

Section 6.3

3. We compare cross products.

$$1 \cdot 39 = 39 \qquad \dfrac{1}{2} \; ? \; \dfrac{20}{39} \qquad 2 \cdot 20 = 40$$

Since $39 \neq 40$, the numbers are not proportional.

8.
$$\dfrac{x}{9} = \dfrac{5}{4}$$
$$x \cdot 4 = 9 \cdot 5$$
$$\dfrac{x \cdot 4}{4} = \dfrac{9 \cdot 5}{4}$$
$$x = \dfrac{45}{4} = 11\dfrac{1}{4}$$

Section 6.4

2. 1. Familiarize. Let $p =$ the amount of paint needed, in gallons.

   2. Translate. $\dfrac{4}{1600} = \dfrac{p}{6000}$

   3. Solve.
   $$4 \cdot 6000 = 1600 \cdot p$$
   $$15 = p$$

   4. Check. The cross products are the same.

   5. State. For 6000 ft^2, they would need 15 gal of paint.

6. 1. Familiarize. Let $D =$ the number of deer in the forest.

   2. Translate. $\dfrac{153}{D} = \dfrac{18}{62}$

   3. Solve.
   $$153 \cdot 62 = D \cdot 18$$
   $$527 = D$$

   4. Check. The cross products are the same.

   5. State. There are about 527 deer in the forest.

Section 6.5

1. The ratio of x to 20 is the same as the ratio of 9 to 12.

$$\dfrac{x}{20} = \dfrac{9}{12}$$
$$x \cdot 12 = 20 \cdot 9$$
$$\dfrac{x \cdot 12}{12} = \dfrac{20 \cdot 9}{12}$$
$$x = \dfrac{180}{12} = 15$$

5. Let $w =$ the width of an actual skylight.

$$\dfrac{12}{52} = \dfrac{3}{w}$$
$$12 \cdot w = 52 \cdot 3$$
$$w = 13$$

The width of an actual skylight will be 13 ft.

Glossary

A

Absolute value   The distance that a number is from zero on the number line

Acute angle   An angle whose measure is greater than $0°$ and less than $90°$

Acute triangle   A triangle in which all three angles are acute

Addend   In addition, a number being added

Additive identity   The number 0

Additive inverse   A number's opposite. Two numbers are additive inverses of each other if their sum is 0.

Algebraic expression   An expression consisting of variables, constants, numerals, operation signs, and/or grouping symbols

Angle   A set of points consisting of two rays (half-lines) with a common endpoint (vertex)

Area   The number of square units that fill a plane region

Arithmetic mean   A center point of a set of numbers found by adding the numbers and dividing by the number of items of data; also called mean or average

Arithmetic numbers   The whole numbers and the positive fractions; also called the nonnegative rational numbers

Associative law of addition   The statement that when three numbers are added, regrouping the addends does not affect the sum

Associative law of multiplication   The statement that when three numbers are multiplied, regrouping the factors does not affect the product

Average   A center point of a set of numbers found by adding the numbers and dividing by the number of items of data; also called the arithmetic mean or mean

B

Bar graph   A graphic display of data using bars proportional in length to the numbers represented

Base   In exponential notation, the number being raised to a power

C

Celsius   A temperature scale for metric measure

Circle graph   A graphic means of displaying data using sectors of a circle; often used to show the percent of a quantity in different categories or to show visually the ratio of one category to another; also called a pie chart

Circumference   The distance around a circle

Coefficient   The numerical multiplier of a variable

Commission   A percent of total sales paid to a salesperson

Commutative law of addition   The statement that when two numbers are added, changing the order in which the numbers are added does not affect the sum

Commutative law of multiplication   The statement that when two numbers are multiplied, changing the order in which the numbers are multiplied does not affect the product

Complementary angles   Two angles for which the sum of their measures is $90°$

Composite number   A natural number, other than 1, that is not prime

Compound interest   Interest paid on interest

Constant   A known number

Cross products   Given an equation with a single fraction on each side, the products formed by multiplying the left numerator and the right denominator, and the left denominator and the right numerator

D

Decimal notation   A representation of a number containing a decimal point

Denominator   The bottom number in a fraction

Diameter   A segment that passes through the center of a circle and has its endpoints on the circle

Difference   The result of subtracting one number from another

Digit   A number 0, 1, 2, 3, 4, 5, 6, 7, 8, or 9 that names a place-value location

Discount   The amount subtracted from the original price of an item to find the sale price

Distributive law of multiplication over addition   The statement that multiplying a factor by the sum of two numbers gives the same result as multiplying the factor by each of the two numbers and then adding

Distributive law of multiplication over subtraction   The statement that multiplying a factor by the difference of two numbers gives the same result as multiplying the factor by each of the two numbers and then subtracting

Dividend   In division, the number being divided

Divisible   The number a is divisible by another number b if there exists a number c such that $a = b \cdot c$

Divisor   In division, the number dividing another number

E

Equation   A number sentence that says that the expressions on either side of the equals sign, $=$, represent the same number

Equilateral triangle   A triangle in which all sides are the same length

Equivalent equations   Equations with the same solutions

Equivalent expressions   Expressions that have the same value for all allowable replacements

Equivalent fractions Fractions that represent the same number

Even number A number that is divisible by 2; that is, it has an even ones digit

Exponent In expressions of the form a^n, the number n; for n a natural number, a^n represents n factors of a

Exponential notation A representation of a number using a base raised to a power

F

Factor *Verb:* to write an equivalent expression that is a product. *Noun:* a multiplier

Factorization A number expressed as a product of natural numbers

Fahrenheit A temperature scale for American measure

Fraction notation A number written using a numerator and a denominator

H

Histogram A special kind of graph that shows how often certain numbers appear in a set of data

Hypotenuse In a right triangle, the side opposite the right angle

I

Identity property of 1 The statement that the product of a number and 1 is always the original number

Identity property of 0 The statement that the sum of a number and 0 is always the original number

Inequality A mathematical sentence using $<$, $>$, $\leq$, $\geq$, or $\neq$

Integers The whole numbers and their opposites

Interest A percentage of an amount invested or borrowed

Irrational number A real number that cannot be named as a ratio of two integers

Isosceles triangle A triangle in which two or more sides are the same length

L

Least common denominator (LCD) The least common multiple of the denominators of two or more fractions

Least common multiple (LCM) The smallest number that is a multiple of two or more numbers

Legs In a right triangle, the two sides that form the right angle

Like terms Terms that have exactly the same variable factors

Line graph A graphic means of displaying data by connecting adjacent data points with line segments

M

Marked price The original price of an item

Mean A center point of a set of numbers found by adding the numbers and dividing by the number of items of data; also called the arithmetic mean or average

Median In a set of data listed in order from smallest to largest, the middle number if there are an odd number of data items, or the average of the two middle numbers if there are an even number of data items

Minuend The number from which another number is being subtracted

Mixed numeral A number represented by a whole number and a fraction less than 1

Mode The number or numbers that occur most often in a set of data

Multiple A product of a number and some natural number

Multiplicative identity The number 1

Multiplicative inverses Reciprocals; two numbers whose product is 1

N

Natural numbers The numbers 1, 2, 3, 4, 5, ...

Negative integers The integers to the left of 0 on the number line

Nonnegative rational numbers The whole numbers and the positive fractions; also called the arithmetic numbers

Numerator The top number in a fraction

O

Obtuse angle An angle whose measure is greater than 90° and less than 180°

Obtuse triangle A triangle in which one angle is an obtuse angle

Opposite The opposite, or additive inverse, of a number a can be named $-a$. Opposites are the same distance from 0 on the number line but on different sides of 0.

Original price The price of an item before a discount is deducted

P

Palindrome prime A prime number that remains a prime number when its digits are reversed

Parallelogram A four-sided polygon with two pairs of parallel sides

Percent notation A representation of a number as parts per 100

Perimeter The distance around a polygon, or the sum of the lengths of its sides

Pi (π) The number that results when the circumference of a circle is divided by its diameter; $\pi \approx 3.14$, or $22/7$

Pictograph A graphic means of displaying data using pictorial symbols

Pie chart A graphic means of displaying data using sectors of a circle; often used to show the percent of a quantity used in different categories or to show visually the ratio of one category to another; also called a circle graph

Polygon A closed geometric figure with three or more sides

Positive integers The natural numbers, or the integers to the right of 0 on the number line

Prime factorization A factorization of a composite number as a product of prime numbers

Prime number A natural number that has exactly two *different* factors: only itself and 1

Principal The amount invested

Product The result in multiplication

Proportion An equation that states that two ratios are equal

Protractor A device used to measure angles

Purchase price The price of an item before sales tax is added

Pythagorean equation The equation $a^2 + b^2 = c^2$, where a and b are the lengths of the legs of a right triangle and c is the length of the hypotenuse

Q

Quotient The result when one number is divided by another

R

Radical sign The symbol $\sqrt{}$

Radius A segment with one endpoint on the center of a circle and the other endpoint on the circle

Rate A ratio used to compare two different kinds of measure

Ratio The quotient of two quantities

Rational numbers All numbers that can be named in the form a/b, where a and b are integers and b is not 0

Ray A half-line

Real numbers All rational and irrational numbers

Reciprocal A multiplicative inverse; two numbers are reciprocals if their product is 1

Rectangle A four-sided polygon with four 90° angles

Repeating decimal A decimal that cannot be written using a finite number of decimal places

Right angle An angle whose measure is 90°

Right triangle A triangle that includes a right angle

Rounding Approximating the value of a number; used when estimating

S

Sale price The price of an item after a discount has been deducted

Sales tax A tax added to the purchase price of an item

Scalene triangle A triangle in which each side is a different length

Similar triangles Triangles that have the same shape because the lengths of their corresponding sides have the same ratio—that is, they are proportional

Simple interest A percentage of an amount P invested or borrowed for t years, computed by calculating principal $\times$ interest rate $\times$ time

Solution of an equation A replacement for the variable that makes the equation true

Sphere The set of all points in space that are a given distance from a given point

Square A four-sided polygon with four right angles and all sides of equal length

Square of a number A number multiplied by itself

Square root of a number A number that when multiplied by itself yields the given original number

Statistic A number describing a set of data

Straight angle An angle whose measure is 180°

Substitute To replace a variable with a number

Subtrahend In subtraction, the number being subtracted

Sum The result in addition

Supplementary angles Two angles for which the sum of their measures is 180°

T

Table A means of displaying data in rows and columns

Term A number, a variable, or a product or a quotient of numbers and/or variables

Terminating decimal A decimal that can be written using a finite number of decimal places

Total price The sum of the purchase price of an item and the sales tax on the item

Trapezoid A four-sided polygon with two parallel sides

Triangle A three-sided polygon

U

Unit price The ratio of price to the number of units; also called unit rate

Unit rate The ratio of price to the number of units; also called unit price

V

Variable A letter that represents an unknown number

Vertex The common endpoint of the two rays that form an angle

Volume The number of cubic units that fill a solid region

W

Whole numbers The natural numbers and 0: 0, 1, 2, 3, …

Index

A

Absolute value, 89
Account balance, checking, 318, 319
Acre, 578
Acute angle, 593
Acute triangle, 596
Addends, 9
Addition
    addends, 9
    associative law of, 10
    on a calculator, 10
    and carrying, 9
    commutative law of, 10
    using decimal notation, 266, 268
    using fraction notation, 195–197
    of integers, 92, 93
    using mixed numerals, 218
    on the number line, 92
    and regrouping, 9
    repeated, 19
    sum, 9
        estimating, 39
        of whole numbers, 9
        of zero, 10, 631
Addition principle, 631
Additive identity, 10
Additive inverses, 94, 95. *See also*
    Opposite.
Algebraic expressions, 622
    collecting like terms, 628
    equivalent, 624
    evaluating, 622
    factoring, 29
    multiplying, 625, 626
    terms, 626
    translating to, 653
    value of, 622
American system of measures
    area, 539, 544
    capacity, 527, 544
    changing units, 501, 508, 519, 521,
        527, 533, 539, 544
        to metric, 513, 535, 544
    length, 500, 544
    temperature, 534, 544
    time, 533, 544
    weight, 519, 544
Angle(s), 591
    acute, 593
    complementary, 594

    measuring, 592
    naming, 591
    obtuse, 593
    rays, 591
    right, 593
    side, 591
    straight, 593
    supplementary, 594, 595
    unit, 592
    vertex, 591
Annual compounding of interest,
    435
Annual percentage rate (APR),
    438
Approximately equal to ($\approx$), 40
Approximating, *see* Estimating
Approximating square roots, 601
Area
    American units, 539, 544
    of a circle, 573, 608
    metric units, 539
    of a parallelogram, 561, 608
    of a rectangle, 22, 559, 608
    of a square, 560, 608
    of a trapezoid, 563, 608
    of a triangle, 561, 608
Arithmetic mean, 454
Array, *see* Rectangular array
Associative law
    of addition, 10
    of multiplication, 22
Augustus, 383
Average, 72, 288, 454
    grade point (GPA), 455

B

Balancing a checkbook, 318, 319
Bar graph, 474, 475
Base(s)
    in exponential notation, 70
    of a parallelogram, 560
    of a trapezoid, 562
Billion, 277
Billions period, 2
Borrowing, 15
Braces, 74
Brackets, 74
British-American system of
    measures, *see* American system
    of measures

C

Calculations, fraction and decimal
    notation together, 299
Calculator
    adding whole numbers, 10
    addition with decimal notation, 283
    compound interest, 437
    converting from fraction notation to
        percent notation, 389
    converting from percent notation to
        decimal notation, 384
    dividing whole numbers, 30
    and divisibility, 129
    division with decimal notation, 283
    evaluating algebraic expressions, 624
    exponential notation, 71
    and factors, 129
    fractions, operations on, 231
    mixed numerals, operations on, 231
    multiplication with decimal
        notation, 283
    multiplying whole numbers, 21
    negative numbers, 95
    order of operations, 73
    percents, using in computations, 400
    π key, 572
    simplifying fraction notation, 158
    square roots, 601
    subtracting whole numbers, 15
    subtraction with decimal notation,
        283
    temperature conversion, 535
Calculator Corner, 10, 15, 21, 30, 71,
    73, 95, 129, 158, 283, 384, 389, 400,
    437, 535, 572, 601, 624
Canceling, 158
Capacity, 527, 528, 544
Carat, 526
Carrying, 9
Celsius temperature, 534, 535, 544
Center point, 454
Centigram, 520, 544
Centimeter, 506, 544
    cubic, 528, 544
Central tendency, measure of, 454
Cents, converting from/to dollars, 278
Changing the sign, 95
Changing units, *see* American system
    of measures; Metric system of
    measures

Chart
  pie, 483, 484
  place-value, 2, 256
Checkbook, balancing, 318, 319
Checking
  account balance, 318, 319
  division, 27
  in problem solving, 54, 654
  solutions of equations, 49, 632, 635
  solutions of proportions, 345
  subtraction, 15
Circle
  area, 573, 608
  circumference, 571, 572, 608
  diameter, 570, 608
  radius, 570, 608
Circle graph, 483, 484
Circular cone, volume, 584, 608
Circular cylinder, volume, 582, 583, 608
Circumference of a circle, 571, 572, 608
Clearing decimals, 645, 647
Clearing fractions, 645, 646
Coefficient, 635
Collecting (or combining) like terms, 628
  in equation solving, 644
Commission, 427
Common denominator, 158
  least, 188, 196, 202
Common factor, 627
Common multiple, least, 188, 189, 192
Commutative law
  of addition, 10
  of multiplication, 22
Comparing numbers in decimal notation, 260, 261
Complementary angles, 594
Complex fractions, 239
Composite numbers, 128
Compound interest, 435–437
Cone, circular, volume, 584, 608
Constant, 622
Converse, 601
Converting
  American measures to metric measures, 513, 544
  area units, 539, 540
  capacity units, 527, 528, 544
  cents to dollars, 278
  decimal notation to fraction notation, 258
  decimal notation to percent notation, 385
  decimal notation to a word name, 257
  dollars to cents, 278
  fraction notation to decimal notation, 259, 295
  fraction notation to a mixed numeral, 212
  fraction notation to percent notation, 389

length units, 501, 508, 544
mass units, 521, 544
mentally, in metric system, 509, 521, 540
metric measures to American measures, 513, 535, 544
mixed numerals to decimal notation, 260
mixed numerals to fraction notation, 211
percent notation to decimal notation, 384
percent notation to fraction notation, 391
ratios to decimal notation, 297
standard notation to expanded notation, 4
standard notation to word names, 5
temperature units, 535, 544
time units, 533, 544
weight units, 519, 544
word names to standard notation, 5
Credit cards, 437–439
Cross products, 344, 345
Cube, unit, 581
Cubic centimeter, 528, 544
Cubit, 505
Cup, 527, 544
Cylinder, circular, volume, 582, 583, 608

D
Daily percentage rate (DPR), 438
Day, 533, 544
Decigram, 520, 544
Decima, 256
Decimal equivalent, 392
Decimal notation, 256
  addition with, 266, 268
  and checking account balance, 318, 319
  comparing numbers in, 260, 261
  converting
    from/to fraction notation, 258, 259
    from mixed numerals, 260
    from/to percent notation, 383–385
    ratios to, 297
    to a word name, 257
  division with, 282, 284
  and estimating, 304
  and fraction notation together, 299
  and money conversion, 278
  multiplication with, 274–276
  and naming large numbers, 277
  and order, 260, 261
  order of operations, 287
  and percent notation, 383
  place-value, 256
  repeating, 296
    rounding, 297
  rounding, 261, 262, 265, 297
  subtraction, 267, 268, 269

terminating, 296
  word names, 257
Decimal point, 256
Decimals, clearing, 645, 647
Decimeter, 506, 544
Decrease, percent, 414
Degree measure, 592
Dekagram, 520, 544
Dekameter, 506, 544
Denominators, 139
  common, 158
  least common, 188, 196, 202
  of zero, 143
Diameter, 570, 608
Difference, 14
  estimating, 40
Digits, 2
Discount, 428
Distance and absolute value, 89
Distributive laws, 20, 625
  and factoring, 627
  and multiplying, 20, 625
Dividend, 26
  of zero, 27, 111
Divisibility, 128
  by 2, 133
  by 3, 134
  by 4, 136
  by 5, 135
  by 6, 134
  by 7, 136
  by 8, 136
  by 9, 135
  by 10, 135
  and simplifying fraction notation, 157
Divisible, see Divisibility
Division
  by 0.1, 0.01, 0.001, and so on, 286
  by 10, 100, 1000, and so on, 285
  on a calculator, 30
  checking, 27
  with decimal notation, 282, 284
  definition, 27
  dividend, 26
    of zero, 27, 111
  divisor, 26
  estimating quotients, 40
  with fraction notation, 171
  of integers, 100, 111
  and LCMs, 192
  with mixed numerals, 229
  of a number by itself, 27
  by one, 27
  by a power of ten, 285, 286
  by primes, 192
  quotient, 26
  and reciprocals, 171
  and rectangular arrays, 26
  with remainders, 28
  as repeated subtraction, 26
  of whole numbers, 26

by zero, 28, 110, 111
  of zero by a nonzero number,
    27, 111
  zero in quotients, 31
Divisor, 26
Dollars, converting from/to cents,
  278

E

Effective yield, 442
Eight, divisibility by, 136
English system of measures, *see*
  American system of measures
Equality of fractions, test for,
  159, 344
Equation(s), 42, 48
  checking solutions, 49, 632,
    635
  equivalent, 631
  false, 48
  percent, 397
  Pythagorean, 601
  solution of, 48
  solving, 48–51, 631, 635, 642.
    See also Solving equations.
  translating to, 54, 397, 654
  true, 48
Equilateral triangle, 596
Equivalent, decimal, 392
Equivalent, fraction, 392
Equivalent, percent, 392
Equivalent equations, 631
Equivalent expressions, 624
Equivalent fractions, 155
Estimating. *See also* Rounding.
  with decimal notation, 304
  differences, 39
  with fraction notation, 241
  with mixed numerals, 241
  products, 40
  quotients, 40
  sums, 39
  wildlife populations, 357
Evaluating
  algebraic expressions, 622
  exponential notation, 71
Even number, 133
Expanded notation, 4
Exponent, 70
Exponential notation, 70
  on a calculator, 71
  evaluating, 71
  and LCMs, 191
Expressions
  algebraic, 622
  equivalent, 624
  evaluating, 622
  factoring, 627
  multiplying, 625, 626
  simplifying, 71
  terms, 626
  value of, 622

F

Factor, 19, 126. *See also* Factoring;
  Factorization; Factors.
Factor tree, 130
Factoring, 126
  algebraic expressions, 627
Factorization
  of natural numbers, 127
  prime, 129
    and LCMs, 192
Factorization method, 189
Factors, 19, 126. *See also* Factor.
Fahrenheit temperature, 534, 535,
  544
False equation, 48
False inequality, 42
Familiarize, 54, 654, 655
Feet, 500, 544
Five, divisibility by, 135
Fluid ounce, 527
Foot, 500, 544
Four, divisibility by, 135
Fraction equivalent, 392
Fraction notation, 139. *See also*
  Fractions.
  addition, 195–197
  converting
    from/to decimal notation, 258,
      259, 295
    from/to mixed numerals, 211, 212
    from/to percent notation, 389,
      391
  and decimal notation together, 299
  denominator, 139
    of zero, 143
  in division, 171
  estimation with, 241
  for integers, 143
  multiplication using, 149, 150
  numerator, 139
  for one, 142
  order, 203
  order of operations, 238
  and percent notation, 383
  for ratios, 141, 330
  simplest, 156
  simplifying, 156, 158
  subtraction, 202
  for zero, 143
Fractions, 139. *See also* Fraction
  notation.
  clearing, 645, 646
  complex, 239
  equality, test for, 161, 344
  equivalent, 155
  estimation with, 241
  improper, 141, 212
  multiplication by an integer, 150
  multiplicative identity, 20, 155, 624
  as ratios, 141
  reciprocals, 170
Frequency, 467

G

Gallon, 527, 544
GPA, 455
Grade point average, 455
Gram, 520, 544
Graph
  bar, 474, 475
  circle, 483, 484
  of an integer, 88
  line, 476, 477
  of a number, 88
  picture, 464
Greater than ($>$), 42, 88
Greatest common factor, 627

H

Hectogram, 520, 544
Hectometer, 506, 544
Height of a parallelogram, 560
Histogram, 467
Hour, 533, 544
Hundred, 277
  dividing by, 286
  multiplying by, 276
Hundred-thousandths, 256
Hundredths, 256
  dividing by, 285
  multiplying by, 276
Hypotenuse, 601

I

Identity
  additive, 10
  multiplicative, 20, 155, 624
Identity property
  of one, 624
  of zero, 93
Improper fraction, 141, 212
Inch, 500, 544
Increase, percent, 30
Inequality, 42
Inequality symbols, 42
Integers, 86
  addition of, 92, 93
  division of, 110, 111
  fraction notation for, 143
  graphs of, 88
  multiplication of, 106, 107
  order of, 88
  subtraction of, 98, 99
Interest
  compound, 435–437
  rate, 434
  simple, 434
Inverse
  additive, 94, 95
  multiplicative, 635
Isosceles triangle, 596

K

Karat, 526
Key for a pictograph, 464

Kilogram, 520, 544
Kilometer, 506, 544

L
Large numbers, naming, 277
Laws
  associative, 10, 22
  commutative, 10, 22
  distributive, 20, 625
Leap year, 533
Least common denominators, 188,
  196, 202
Least common multiple (LCM), 188,
  189, 192
  of denominators, 188, 196, 202, 646
Legs of a right triangle, 601
Leibniz, Gottfried Wilhelm von, 19
Length, *see* American system of
  measures; Metric system of
  measures
Less than (<), 42, 88
Like terms, 628
Line graph, 476, 477
Linear measure, *see* American system
  of measures; Metric system of
  measures
List of multiples, 188
Liter, 527, 544

M
Marked price, 428
Mass, 519, 520, 544. *See also* Weight.
Mean, 454
Measures, *see* American system
  of measures; Metric system of
  measures
Measures of central tendency, 454
Measuring angles, 592
Median, 456, 457
Medical applications, 522, 529
Meter, 506, 544
Metric system of measures, 506
  area, 539, 544
  capacity, 508, 528, 533, 539
  converting to American system, 513,
    535, 544
    mentally, 509, 521, 540
  length, 506, 544
  mass, 520, 544
  temperature, 534, 544
  time, 533, 544
Metric ton, 520, 544
Microgram, 522
Mile, 500, 544
Milligram, 520, 544
Milliliter, 528, 544
Millimeter, 506, 544
Million, 277
Millions period, 2
Minimum payment, 438
Minuend, 14
Minute, 533, 544

Mixed numerals, 210
  and addition, 218
  converting from/to fraction
    notation, 211, 212
  converting to decimal notation,
    260
  and division, 229
  estimation with, 241
  and multiplication, 228
  order of operations, 238
  as quotients, 212
  and subtraction, 219
Mode, 458
Money conversion, 278
Multiples, 127
  and divisibility, 127
  least common, 188, 189, 192
  list of, 188
  of natural numbers, 127, 128
Multiples method, 188
Multiplication
  of algebraic expressions, 625,
    626
  associative law of, 22
  on a calculator, 21
  commutative law of, 22
  with decimal notation, 274–276
  using the distributive laws, 20, 625
  estimating products, 40
  factors, 19
  of a fraction by an integer, 150
  using fraction notation, 149, 150
  by a hundred, 276
  by a hundredth, 276
  of integers, 106, 107
  using mixed numerals, 228
  by one, 155
  by a power of ten, 276
  product, 19
  as a rectangular array, 19
  as repeated addition, 19
  and simplifying, 164
  symbols for, 19
  by ten, 276
  by a tenth, 276
  by a thousand, 276
  by a thousandth, 276
  of whole numbers, 19
Multiplication principle, 635
Multiplicative identity, 20, 155, 624
Multiplicative inverse, 635. *See also*
  Reciprocal.
Multiplying, *see* Multiplication

N
Naming angles, 591
Naming large numbers, 277
Natural numbers, 9
  composite, 128
  divisibility, 128. *See also* Divisibility.
  factoring, 126
  factorization, 127

least common multiple,
    188–192
  multiples of, 127, 128
  prime, 128
Negative integers, 86
Nine, divisibility by, 135
Not equal to (≠), 42
Notation
  decimal, 256
  expanded, 4
  exponential, 70
  fraction, 139
  for an opposite, 94
  percent, 382, 383
  ratio, 141, 300
  for rational numbers, 142
  standard, for numbers, 4
Number line, addition on, 92
Numbers
  composite, 128
  digits, 2
  even, 133
  expanded notation, 4
  graphing, 88
  integers, 86
  natural, 9
  palindrome, 182
  periods, 2
  place-value, 2, 256
  prime, 128
  ratio, 141, 330
  rational, 142, 256
  signs of, 95
  standard notation, 4
  whole, 9
  word names, 4
Numerals, mixed, 210. *See also*
  Mixed numerals.
Numerator, 139

O
Obtuse angle, 593
Obtuse triangle, 596
One
  division by, 27
  fraction notation for, 142
  identity property, 624
  multiplying by, 155
Ones period, 2
Operations, order of, 71, 73, 112,
  287
Opposites, 86, 94, 95
  and subtraction, 99
Order
  in decimal notation, 260, 261
  in fraction notation, 203
  of integers, 88
  of operations, 71, 73, 112, 287
  of whole numbers, 42
Original price, 428
Ounce, 519, 544
  fluid, 527, 544

P

Palindrome prime, 182
Parallelogram, 560
    area, 561, 608
Parentheses, 71
    equations containing, 647
    in multiplication, 19
    within parentheses, 74
Payment, minimum, 438
Percent, *see* Percent notation
Percent decrease, 414
Percent equation, 397
Percent equivalent, 392
Percent increase, 414
Percent notation, 382, 383
    in circle graphs, 483, 484
    converting
        from/to decimal notation,
            383–385
        from/to fraction notation, 389, 391
    solving problems involving, 397–400,
        403–406, 411–417
Perimeter, 11, 554
    of a rectangle, 555, 608
    of a square, 555, 608
Periods, 2
Pi (π), 571
Pictographs, 464
Picture graph, 464
Pie chart, 483, 484
Pint, 527, 544
Pitch of a screw, 167
Pixels, 64
Place value, 2, 256
Polygon, 554
Positive integers, 86
Pound, 519, 544
Power, 70
Power of ten
    dividing by, 285, 286
    multiplying by, 276
Price
    marked, 428
    original, 428
    purchase, 425
    sale, 428
    total, 425
    unit, 328
Prime factorization, 129
    in finding LCMs, 189
    in simplifying fractions, 157
Prime numbers, 128
    division by, 192
    palindrome, 182
Principal, 434
Principles
    addition, 631
    multiplication, 635
Problem solving, 54, 61, 654
Products, 19. *See also* Multiplication.
    cross, 344, 345
    estimating, 40

Proportional, 344. *See also*
    Proportions.
Proportions, 344
    and geometric shapes, 364, 366
    and similar triangles, 364
    solving, 345
    used in solving percent problems,
        403–406
Protractor, 592
Purchase price, 425
Pythagoras, 602
Pythagorean equation, 601
Pythagorean theorem, 601

Q

Quadrillion, 281
Quality points, 455
Quart, 527, 544
Quintillion, 281
Quotient, 26
    estimating, 40
    as a mixed numeral, 212
    zeros in, 31

R

Radical sign ($\sqrt{\ }$), 600
Radius, 570, 608
Rate
    commission, 427
    of discount, 428
    interest, 434
    ratio as, 337
    sales tax, 425
    unit, 338
Ratio, 141, 330
    and circle graphs, 483
    converting to decimal notation,
        297
    notation, 141, 330
    percent as, 383
    and proportion, 344
    as a rate, 337
    simplifying, 333
Rational numbers, 142, 256
Rays, 591
Reciprocal, 170
    and division, 171
    of a fraction, 170
    of zero, 170
Rectangle, 554
    area, 22, 559, 608
    perimeter, 555, 608
Rectangular array
    in division, 26
    in multiplication, 19
Rectangular solid, volume, 581, 582,
    608
Regrouping, in addition, 15
Remainder, 28
Removing a factor of 1, 156
Repeated addition, 19
Repeated subtraction, 26

Repeating decimals, 296
    rounding, 297
Right angle, 593
Right triangle, 596, 601
Rounding
    decimal notation, 261, 262, 265, 297
    and estimating
        in addition, 39, 304
        in division, 40, 305
        in multiplication, 40, 305
        in subtraction, 39, 304
    by truncating, 265
    of whole numbers, 37, 38

S

Salary, 427
Sale price, 428
Sales tax, 425
Scalene triangle, 596
Screw, pitch, 167
Second, 533, 544
Segment, unit, 500
Semiannual compounding of interest,
    436
Septillion, 281
Seven, divisibility by, 136
Sextillion, 281
Sides of an angle, 591
Signs of numbers, 95
    changing, 95
Similar geometric shapes, 364, 366
Similar triangles, 364
Simple interest, 434
Simplest fraction notation, 156, 158
Simplifying complex fractions, 240
Simplifying expressions, 71
Simplifying fraction notation, 156, 158
Simplifying ratio notation, 333
Six, divisibility by, 134
Solution of an equation, 48. *See also*
    Solving equations.
Solve, in problem solving, 54, 654
Solving equations, 48–51, 631, 635, 642
    using addition principle, 631
    by carrying out a calculation, 49
    checking solutions, 49, 632, 635
    and clearing fractions or decimals,
        645–647
    and collecting like terms, 644
    by dividing on both sides, 50, 172, 286
    using multiplication principle, 635
    with parentheses, 647
    using the principles together, 642
    procedure, 648
    by subtracting on both sides, 49, 204,
        269
    by trial, 48
Solving percent problems, 398–400,
    405, 406
Solving problems, 54. *See also* Index of
    Applications.
Solving proportions, 345

Span, 505
Sphere, volume, 583, 608
Square, 555
 area, 560, 608
 perimeter, 555, 608
Square of a number, 600
Square roots, 600
 approximating, 601
Standard notation for numbers, 4
State the answer, 54, 654
Statistic, 454
Straight angle, 593
Strike zone, 423
Studying for Success, 2, 37, 86, 106, 126, 164, 188, 218, 256, 295, 330, 353, 382, 411, 454, 474, 500, 519, 554, 581, 622, 642
Substituting for a variable, 622
Subtraction
 and additive inverses, 99
 and borrowing, 15
 on calculator, 15
 checking, 15, 99
 with decimal notation, 267, 268, 269
 definition, 14, 98
 difference, 14
  estimating, 39
 using fraction notation, 202
 of integers, 98, 99
 minuend, 14
 using mixed numerals, 219
 and opposites, 99
 repeated, 26
 subtrahend, 14
 of whole numbers, 14
Subtrahend, 14
Subunits, 500
Sum, 9
 of angle measures in a triangle, 596
 estimating, 39, 304
 of opposites, 95
Supplementary angles, 594, 595
Symbol
 approximately equal to ($\approx$), 40
 greater than ($>$), 42
 less than ($<$), 42
 for multiplication ($\times$ and $\cdot$), 19
 not equal to ($\neq$), 42
 radical ($\sqrt{}$), 600

T
Table of data, 463
Table of prime numbers, 129

Tax, sales, 425
Temperature, 534, 535, 544
Ten
 dividing by, 285
 divisibility by, 135
 multiplying by, 276
Ten-thousandths, 256
Tenths, 256
 dividing by, 286
 multiplying by, 276
Terminating decimal, 296
Terms, 626
 like, 628
Test for equality of fractions, 159, 344
Theorem, Pythagorean, 601
Thousand, 277
 dividing by, 285
 multiplying by, 276
Thousands period, 2
Thousandths, 256
 dividing by, 286
 multiplying by, 276
Three, divisibility by, 134
Time, 533, 544
Ton
 American, 519, 544
 metric, 520, 544
Total price, 425
Translate
 to an algebraic expression, 653
 to an equation, 54, 397, 654
Translating for Success, 62, 114, 174, 232, 314, 358, 418, 485, 541, 604, 654, 662
Trapezoid, 562
 area, 563, 608
Tree, factor, 130
Trial, solving equations by, 48
Triangle(s), 561, 595
 acute, 596
 area, 561, 608
 equilateral, 596
 isosceles, 596
 obtuse, 596
 right, 596, 601
 scalene, 596
 similar, 364
 sum of angle measures, 596
Trillion, 277
Trillions period, 2
True equation, 48
True inequality, 42
Truncating, 265
Two, divisibility by, 133

U
Unit angle, 592
Unit cube, 581
Unit price (or rate), 338
Unit segment, 500

V
Value of an expression, 622
Variable, 48, 622
 substituting for, 622
Vertex, 591
Volume
 of a circular cone, 584, 608
 of a circular cylinder, 582, 583, 608
 of a rectangular solid, 581, 582, 608
 of a sphere, 538, 608

W
Week, 533, 544
Weight, 519, 544. *See also* Mass.
Whole numbers, 9
 addition, 9
 division, 26
 expanded notation, 4
 fraction notation for, 143
 multiplication, 19
  by fractions, 150
 order, 42
 rounding, 37, 38
 standard notation, 4
 subtraction, 14
 word names for, 4
Wildlife population, estimating, 357
Word names
 for decimal notation, 257
 for whole numbers, 4

Y
Yard, 500, 544
Year, 533, 544
Yield, effective, 442

Z
Zero
 addition of, 10, 93
 denominator of, 143
 dividend of, 27, 111
 division by, 28, 110, 111
 fraction notation for, 143
 identity property, 93
 in quotients, 31
 reciprocal of, 143